MTH 1110

FINITE MATHEMATICS

Custom Version for TROY University

Taken from:

A Survey of Mathematics with Applications, Eighth Edition
by Allen R. Angel, Christine D. Abbott, and Dennis C. Runde

Finite Mathematics for Business, Economics, Life Sciences, and Social Sciences, Eleventh Edition
by Raymond A. Barnett, Michael R. Ziegler, and Karl E. Byleen

D1401011

Custom Publishing

New York   Boston   San Francisco
London   Toronto   Sydney   Tokyo   Singapore   Madrid
Mexico City   Munich   Paris   Cape Town   Hong Kong   Montreal

Cover Art: *Feathers*, by Nathan Pullen

Taken from:

A Survey of Mathematics with Applications, Eighth Edition
by Allen R. Angel, Christine D. Abbott, and Dennis C. Runde
Copyright © 2009 by Pearson Education, Inc.
Published by Addison Wesley
Boston, Massachusetts 02116

Finite Mathematics for Business, Economics, Life Sciences, and Social Sciences, Eleventh Edition
by Raymond A. Barnett, Michael R. Ziegler, and Karl E. Byleen
Copyright © 2008, 2005, 2002, 1999, 1996, 1993, 1990, 1987 by Pearson Education, Inc.
Published by Prentice Hall
Upper Saddle River, New Jersey 07458

This special edition published in cooperation with Pearson Custom Publishing.

Printed in the United States of America

10 9 8 7 6 5 4

2008360562

LR

**Pearson
Custom Publishing**
is a division of

www.pearsonhighered.com

ISBN 10: 0-536-25010-3
ISBN 13: 978-0-536-25010-0

CONTENTS

TAKEN FROM: *A SURVEY OF MATHEMATICS WITH APPLICATIONS*, EIGHTH EDITION, BY ALLEN R. ANGEL, CHRISTINE D. ABBOTT, AND DENNIS C. RUNDE.

TAKEN FROM: *FINITE MATHEMATICS FOR BUSINESS, ECONOMICS, LIFE SCIENCES, AND SOCIAL SCIENCES*, ELEVENTH EDITION, BY RAYMOND A. BARNETT, MICHAEL R. ZIEGLER, AND KARL E. BYLEEN.

TO THE STUDENT

Mathematics is an exciting, living study. Its applications shape the world around you and influence your everyday life. We hope that as you read this book you will realize just how important mathematics is and gain an appreciation of both its usefulness and its beauty. We also hope to teach you some practical mathematics that you can use every day and that will prepare you for further mathematics courses.

The primary purpose of this text is to provide material that you can read, understand, and enjoy. To this end, we have used straightforward language and tried to relate the mathematical concepts to everyday experiences. We have also provided many detailed examples for you to follow.

The concepts, definitions, and formulas that deserve special attention are in boxes or are set in boldface type. Within each category, the exercises are graded, with more difficult problems appearing at the end. Exercises with numbers set in color are writing exercises. At the end of most exercise sets are Challenge Problem/Group Activity Exercises that contain challenging or exploratory exercises. At the end of each chapter are Group Projects that reinforce the material learned or provide related material.

Each chapter has a summary, review exercises, and a chapter test. Be sure to read the chapter summary, work the review exercises, and take the chapter test. The answers to the odd-numbered exercises, all review exercises, all chapter test exercises, and selected recreational mathematics exercises appear in the answer section in the back of the text. You should, however, use the answers only to check your work.

It is difficult to learn mathematics without becoming involved. To be successful, we suggest that you read the text carefully *and work each exercise in each assignment in detail*. Check with your instructor to determine which supplements are available for your use.

We welcome your suggestions and your comments. You may contact us at the following address:

Allen Angel
c/o Marketing
Mathematics and Statistics
Addison-Wesley
75 Arlington St., Suite 300
Boston, MA 02116

Or by email at:

math@awl.com
Subject: for Allen Angel

Good luck in your adventure in mathematics!

Allen R. Angel

Christine D. Abbott

Dennis C. Runde

MATH We Use It Every Day!

We present *A Survey of Mathematics with Applications*, eighth edition, with the vision in mind that we use math every day. In this edition, we stress how mathematics is used in our daily lives whenever possible. Our primary goal is to give students a text they can read, understand, and enjoy while learning how mathematics affects the world around them. Numerous real-life applied examples motivate topics. A variety of interesting exercises demonstrate the real-life nature of mathematics and its importance in students' lives.

The text is intended for students who require a broad-based general overview of mathematics, especially those majoring in the liberal arts, elementary education, the social sciences, business, nursing, and allied health fields. It is particularly suitable for those courses that satisfy the minimum competency requirement in mathematics for graduation or transfer.

The expanded version of *A Survey of Mathematics with Applications*, eighth edition, contains all the material covered in the basic text, with additional chapters on graph theory and on voting and apportionment. Although many wished inclusion of these topics, others did not. Therefore, we have two versions of the book.

CONTENT REVISION

In this edition, we have revised and expanded certain topics to introduce new material and to increase understanding.

Chapter 1   "Critical Thinking Skills," has been updated with exciting and current examples and exercises.

Chapter 2   "Sets," now includes new material on the difference of two sets and the Cartesian product of two sets.

Chapter 3   "Logic," has more exercises and a greater variety of exercises, such as in Section 3.1. Certain material has been rewritten for greater clarity. A new section (3.7) on switching circuits has been added.

Chapter 4   "Systems of Numeration," has increased use of the bases 2, 8, and 16, which have applications to modern computers and electronics. See Section 4.3.

Chapter 5   "Number Theory and the Real Number System," has the most current number theory information (largest prime number, most accurate value of pi). Updated examples and exercises include the most current economic numbers, such as federal debt and gross domestic product.

Chapter 6   "Algebra, Graphs, and Functions," has more and a greater variety of examples and exercises dealing with real-life situations. Additional exercises involving exponential equations have been included.

Chapter 7 "Systems of Linear Equations and Inequalities," now includes annotations and more detailed explanations of certain topics.

Chapter 8 "The Metric System," has many examples and interesting photographs of real-life (metric) situations taken from around the world.

Chapter 9 "Geometry," now includes information on finding surface area. Some information on non-Euclidean geometry has been rewritten.

Chapter 10 "Mathematical Systems," has additional exercises and examples. We have tied this material to real-life situations more.

Chapter 11 "Consumer Mathematics," contains current interest rates and updated information on items that may be of interest to students, including material on credit and mutual funds. Additional information on stocks, bonds, and mutual funds is also included. Section 11.6, "Ordinary Annuities, Sinking Funds, and Retirement Investments" has been added.

Chapter 12 "Probability," has a greater variety of examples and exercises, and many that deal with real-life situations have been added. Certain material has been rewritten for greater clarity. Calculator keystrokes for solving permutation and combination exercises are included.

Chapter 13 "Statistics," now includes calculator keystrokes and commands for using Microsoft Excel to determine several statistical measures (see the Technology Tip on page 906). Material related to standard scores has been revised.

NEW AND REVISED FEATURES

Several important improvements in presentation have also been made.

- Each section opening contains interesting and motivational applications to introduce each section and illustrate the real-world nature of the material in that section.
- Technology Tips that explain how a graphing calculator or a computer spreadsheet may be used to work certain problems have been added in selected sections.
- The number of examples has been increased throughout the text to promote student understanding.
- Sources have been added; up-to-date tables, graphs, and charts make the material more relevant and encourage students to read graphs and analyze data.
- The feature previously called Mathematics Everywhere is now called Mathematics Today. Current mathematical topics related to material presented in this book are included in the Mathematics Today boxes. The information provided in these boxes relates mathematics to students' everyday lives. This material will help students see the need for mathematics and gain appreciation for it.
- Additional Did You Know? and Profiles in Mathematics features have been added throughout the book.
- In various exercise sets, the number and variety of exercises has been increased. Approximately 40% of the exercises have been revised or updated to reflect current data, new material in the text, and the needs and interests of today's students.

CONTINUING FEATURES

Several features appear throughout the book, adding interest and provoking thought.

- *Chapter openings* Interesting and motivational applications introduce each chapter and illustrate the real-world nature of the chapter topics.
- *Problem solving* Beginning in Chapter 1, students are introduced to problem solving and critical thinking. The theme of problem solving is then continued throughout the text, and special problem-solving exercises are presented in the exercise sets.
- *Critical thinking skills* In addition to a focus on problem solving, this book also features sections on inductive and deductive reasoning, estimation, and dimensional analysis.
- *Profiles in Mathematics* Brief historical sketches and vignettes present the stories of people who have advanced the discipline of mathematics.
- *Did You Know?* The colorful, engaging, and lively Did You Know? boxes highlight the connection of mathematics to history, the arts and sciences, technology, and a broad variety of disciplines.
- *Group Projects* At the end of each chapter are suggested projects that can be used to have students work together. These projects can also be assigned to individual students if desired.
- *Chapter Summaries, Review Exercises, and Chapter Tests* End-of-chapter summaries, exercises, and tests help students review material and prepare for exams.

TECHNOLOGY RESOURCES

MyMathLab®

MyMathLab is a series of text-specific, easily customizable online courses for Pearson Education textbooks in mathematics and statistics. Powered by CourseCompass™ (Pearson Education's online teaching and learning environment) and MathXL® (our online homework, tutorial, and assessment system), MyMathLab gives you the tools you need to deliver all or a portion of your course online, whether your students are in a lab setting or working from home. MyMathLab provides a rich and flexible set of course materials, featuring free-response exercises that are algorithmically generated for unlimited practice and mastery. Students can also use online tools, such as video lectures, animations, and a multimedia textbook, to improve their understanding and performance independently. Instructors can use MyMathLab's homework and test managers to select and assign online exercises correlated directly to the textbook, and they can also create and assign their own online exercises and import TestGen tests for added flexibility. MyMathLab's online gradebook—designed specifically for mathematics and statistics—automatically tracks students' homework and test results and gives the instructor control over how to calculate final grades. Instructors can also add offline (paper-and-pencil) grades to the gradebook. MyMathLab is available to qualified adopters. For more information, visit our website at www.mymathlab.com or contact your Pearson Education sales representative.

MathXL®, www.mathxl.com

MathXL® is a powerful online homework, tutorial, and assessment system that accompanies Pearson Education textbooks in mathematics or statistics. With MathXL, instructors can create, edit, and assign online homework and tests using algorithmically generated exercises correlated at the objective level to the textbook. They can also create and assign their own online exercises and import TestGen tests for added flexibility. All student work is tracked in MathXL's online gradebook. Students can take chapter tests in MathXL and receive personalized study plans based on their test results. The study plan diagnoses weaknesses and links students directly to tutorial exercises for the objectives they need to study and retest. Students can also access supplemental animations and video clips directly from selected exercises. MathXL is available to qualified adopters. For more information, visit our website at www.mathxl.com or contact your sales representative.

InterAct Math Tutorial Website: www.interactmath.com

Get practice and tutorial help online! The interactive InterAct Math tutorial website provides algorithmically generated practice exercises that correlate directly to the exercises in the book. Students can retry an exercise as many times as they like with new values each time for unlimited practice and mastery. Each exercise is accompanied by an interactive guided solution that provides helpful feedback for incorrect answers. Students can also view a worked-out sample problem that guides them through an exercise similar to the one they're working on.

Video Lectures on CD with Optional Captioning

The video lectures for this text are also available on CD-ROM, making it easy and convenient for students to watch the videos from a computer at home or on campus. The complete digitized video set, affordable and portable for students, is ideal for distance learning or supplemental instruction (ISBN 13: 978-0-321-51091-4; ISBN 10: 0-321-51091-7).

S U P P L E M E N T S for Students

Student's Solutions Manual
ISBN 13: 978-0-321-51089-1; ISBN 10: 0-321-51089-5

This for-sale manual contains solutions to all odd-numbered exercises and to all review and chapter test exercises.

Addison-Wesley Math Tutor Center

The Addison-Wesley Math Tutor Center is staffed by qualified mathematics instructors who provide students with tutoring on examples and odd-numbered exercises from the textbook. Tutoring is available via toll-free telephone, toll-free fax, e-mail, or the Internet. White Board technology allows tutors and students to actually see problems worked while they "talk" in real time over the Internet during tutoring sessions. www.aw-bc/tutorcenter

SUPPLEMENTS for Instructors

Annotated Instructor's Edition
ISBN 13: 978-0-321-50132-5; ISBN 10: 0-321-50132-2

This special edition of the text includes answers next to the exercises, when they fit. Answers that do not fit next to the exercise are placed in a separate section in the back of the book. Answers to all text exercises are included.

Instructor's Solutions Manual
ISBN 13: 978-0-321-51092-1; ISBN 10: 0-321-51092-5

This manual contains solutions to all exercises in the text and answers to Group Projects.

Instructor's Testing Manual
ISBN 13: 978-0-321-51093-8; ISBN 10: 0-321-51093-3

This manual includes three alternate tests per chapter.

New! Insider's Guide
ISBN 13: 978-0-321-52833-9; ISBN 10: 0-321-52833-6

This manual includes resources and helpful teaching tips designed to help both new and adjunct faculty with course preparation and classroom management.

PowerPoint Lecture Presentation

Available through www.aw-bc.com/irc or at MyMathLab. This classroom presentation software covers all-important topics from sections in the text.

TestGen®

TestGen enables instructors to build, edit, print, and administer tests using a computerized bank of questions developed to cover all the objectives of the text. TestGen is algorithmically based, allowing instructors to create multiple but equivalent versions of the same question or test with the click of a button. Instructors can also modify test bank questions or add new questions. Tests can be printed or administered online. The software and testbank are available for download from Pearson Education's online catalog.

ACKNOWLEDGMENTS

We thank our spouses, Kathy Angel, Jason Abbott, and Kris Runde, for their support and encouragement throughout the project. They helped us in a great many ways, including proofreading, typing, and offering valuable suggestions. We are grateful for their wonderful support and understanding while we worked on the book.

We also thank our children: Robert and Steven Angel; Matthew and Jake Abbott; and Alex, Nicholas, and Max Runde. They also gave us support and encouragement and were very understanding when we could not spend as much time with them as we wished because of book deadlines. Without the support and understanding of our families, this book would not be a reality.

We thank Patricia Nelson and Paul Lorczak for their conscientious job of checking the text and answers for accuracy. We also thank Sherry Tornwall of the University of Florida for reading the manuscript and suggesting improvements to its content. And thanks to Becky Troutman for preparing the Index of Applications.

Many people at Addison-Wesley deserve thanks, including all those listed on the copyright page. In particular, we thank Anne Kelly, executive editor; Marnie Greenhut, acquisitions editor; Rachel Reeve, senior project editor; Elizabeth Bernardi, associate project editor; Leah Goldberg, editorial assistant; Peggy McMahon, senior production supervisor; Becky Anderson, executive marketing manager; Bonnie Gill, marketing assistant; Ashley O'Shaughnessy, media producer; Barbara Atkinson, senior designer; Beth Anderson, photo researcher; and Karen Wernholm, managing editor. We also thank Maria McColligan of Nesbitt Graphics, Inc., for her assistance as project manager for this project.

Elka Block and Frank Purcell also deserve our thanks for the excellent work they did on the *Student's Solutions Manual* and the *Instructor's Solutions Manual* and Debra McGivney for her work on the *Instructor's Testing Manual*.

Finally, we thank the reviewers from all editions of the book and all the students who have offered suggestions for improving it. A list of reviewers for all editions of this book follows. Thanks to you all for helping make *A Survey of Mathematics with Applications* the most successful liberal arts mathematics textbook in the country.

Allen R. Angel

Christine D. Abbott

Dennis C. Runde

REVIEWERS FOR THIS AND PREVIOUS EDITIONS

*Mary Anne Anthony-Smith, Santa Ana College

Frank Asta, College of DuPage, IL

Robin L. Ayers, Western Kentucky University

Hughette Bach, California State University–Sacramento

Madeline Bates, Bronx Community College, NY

Rebecca Baum, Lincoln Land Community College, IL

Vivian Baxter, Fort Hays State University, KS

Una Bray, Skidmore College, NY

David H. Buckley, Polk Community College, FL

Robert C. Bueker, Western Kentucky University

Carl Carlson, Moorhead State University, MN

Kent Carlson, St. Cloud State University, MN

Donald Catheart, Salisbury State College, MD

Yungchen Cheng, Southwest Missouri State University

Joseph Cleary, Massasoit Community College, MA

Donald Cohen, SUNY Ag & Tech College at Cobleskill, NY

David Dean, Santa Fe Community College, FL

*John Diamantopoulos, Northeastern State University, OK

*Greg Dietrich, Florida Community College at Jacksonville

Charles Downey, University of Nebraska

Annie Droullard, Polk Community College, FL

Ruth Ediden, Morgan State University, MD

Lee Erker, Tri-County Community College, NC

*Nancy Eschen, Florida Community College at Jacksonville

Karen Estes, St. Petersburg College, FL

Teklay Fessanaye, Santa Fe Community College, FL

Kurtis Fink, Northwest Missouri State University

Raymond Flagg, McPherson College, KS

Penelope Fowler, Tennessee Wesleyan College

Gilberto Garza, El Paso Community College, TX

Judith L. Gersting, Indiana University–Purdue University at Indianapolis

Lucille Groenke, Mesa Community College, AZ

John Hornsby, University of New Orleans, LA

Nancy Johnson, Broward Community College, FL

*Phyllis H. Jore, Valencia Community College, FL

*Heidi Kiley, Suffolk County Community College, NY

Daniel Kimborowicz, Massasoit Community College, MA

Mary Lois King, Tallahassee Community College, FL

David Lehmann, Southwest Missouri State University

Peter Lindstrom, North Lake College, TX

James Magliano, Union College, NJ

Yash Manchanda, East Los Angeles College & Fullerton College, CA

Don Marsian, Hillsborough Community College, FL

Marilyn Mays, North Lake College, TX

Robert McGuigan, Westfield State College, MA

Wallace H. Memmer, Brookdale Community College, NJ

Maurice Monahan, South Dakota State University

Julie Monte, Daytona Beach Community College, FL

ACKNOWLEDGMENTS

Karen Mosely, Alabama Southern Community College
*Kathleen Offenholley, Brookdale Community College, NY
Edwin Owens, Pennsylvania College of Technology
Wing Park, College of Lake County, IL
Bettye Parnham, Daytona Beach Community College, FL
Joanne Peeples, El Paso Community College, TX
Nelson Rich, Nazareth College, NY
Kenneth Ross, University of Oregon
Ronald Ruemmler, Middlesex County College, NJ
Rosa Rusinek, Queensborough Community College, NY
Len Ruth, Sinclair Community College, OH
John Samoylo, Delaware County Community College, PA
Sandra Savage, Orange Coast College, CA
Gerald Schultz, Southern Connecticut State University
Richard Schwartz, College of Staten Island, NY
Kara Shavo, Mercer County Community College, NJ
Minnie Shuler, Chipola Junior College, FL
Paula R. Stickles, University of Southern Indiana
Kristin Stoley, Blinn College–Bryan, TX
Steve Sworder, Saddleback College, CA
Shirley Thompson, Moorhead College, GA
Alvin D. Tinsley, Central Missouri State University
*Sherry Tornwall, University of Florida
William Trotter, University of South Carolina
Zia Uddin, Lock Haven University of Pennsylvania
Sandra Welch, Stephen F. Austin State University, TX
Joyce Wellington, Southeastern Community College, NC
Sue Welsch, Sierra Nevada College
Robert F. Wheeler, Northern Illinois University
Susan Wirth, Indian River Community College, FL
James Wooland, Florida State University
*Judith B. Wood, Central Florida Community College
Jean Woody, Tulsa Community College, OK
Michael A. Zwick, Monroe Community College, NY
*Denotes reviewers for eighth edition.

To my wife, Kathy Angel (photo on page 60)
A.R.A.

To my husband Jason; and children, Matthew and Jake (photo on page 197)
C.D.A.

To my parents, Bud and Tina Runde
D.C.R.

CHAPTER 2

Sets

▲ Children learn how to classify sets, such as shapes and colors, at a very early age.

WHY IT IS IMPORTANT

A basic human impulse is to sort or classify things. As you will see in this chapter, putting elements into sets helps you order and arrange your world. It allows you to deal with large quantities of information. Set building is a learning tool that helps answer the question, What are the characteristics of this group? Studying sets is also important because sets underlie other mathematical topics such as logic and abstract algebra.

2.1 SET CONCEPTS

Can you think of a few different categories or groups to which you belong? One way you could categorize yourself is by your gender. Another way is by your academic major. A third way is by your state of residence. In this section, we will discuss ways to sort or classify objects. We will also discuss different methods that can be used to indicate collections of objects.

▲ Horses may be classified in many ways.

We encounter sets in many different ways every day of our lives. A *set* is a collection of objects, which are called *elements* or *members* of the set. For example, the United States is a collection or set of 50 states plus the District of Columbia. The 50 individual states plus the District of Columbia are the members or elements of the set that is called the United States.

A set is *well defined* if its contents can be clearly determined. The set of U.S. presidents is a well-defined set because its contents, the presidents, can be named. The set of the three best movies is not a well-defined set because the word *best* is interpreted differently by different people. In this text, we use only well-defined sets.

Three methods are commonly used to indicate a set: (1) description, (2) roster form, and (3) set-builder notation.

The method of indicating a set by *description* is illustrated in Example 1.

EXAMPLE ❶ *Description of Sets*

Write a description of the set containing the elements Monday, Tuesday, Wednesday, Thursday, Friday, Saturday, Sunday.

SOLUTION The set is the days of the week. ●

Listing the elements of a set inside a pair of *braces*, { }, is called *roster form*. The braces are an essential part of the notation because they identify the contents as a set. For example, {1, 2, 3} is notation for the set whose elements are 1, 2, and 3, but (1, 2, 3) and [1, 2, 3] are not sets because parentheses and brackets do not indicate a set. For a set written in roster form, commas separate the elements of the set. The order in which the elements are listed is not important.

Sets are generally named with capital letters. For example, the name commonly selected for the set of *natural numbers* or *counting numbers* is N.

NATURAL NUMBERS

$$N = \{1, 2, 3, 4, 5, \dots\}$$

The three dots after the 5, called an *ellipsis,* indicate that the elements in the set continue in the same manner. An ellipsis followed by a last element indicates that the elements continue in the same manner up to and including the last element. This notation is illustrated in Example 2(b).

▲ The planets of Earth's solar system.

EXAMPLE ❷ *Roster Form of Sets*

Express the following in roster form.

a) Set A is the set of natural numbers less than 5.
b) Set B is the set of natural numbers less than or equal to 75.
c) Set P is the set of planets in Earth's solar system.

SOLUTION

a) The natural numbers less than 5 are 1, 2, 3, and 4. Thus, set A in roster form is
$$A = \{1, 2, 3, 4\}.$$
b) $B = \{1, 2, 3, 4, \ldots, 75\}$. The 75 after the ellipsis indicates that the elements continue in the same manner up to and including the number 75.
c) $P = \{$Mercury, Venus, Earth, Mars, Jupiter, Saturn, Uranus, Neptune$\}$* ●

EXAMPLE ❸ *The Word* Inclusive

Express the following in roster form.

a) The set of natural numbers between 4 and 9.
b) The set of natural numbers between 4 and 9, inclusive.

SOLUTION

a) $A = \{5, 6, 7, 8\}$
b) $B = \{4, 5, 6, 7, 8, 9\}$. Note that the word *inclusive* indicates that the values of 4 and 9 are included in the set. ●

The symbol $\in$, read, "is an element of," is used to indicate membership in a set. In Example 3, because 6 is an element of set A, we write $6 \in A$. This may also be written $6 \in \{5, 6, 7, 8\}$. We may also write $9 \notin A$, meaning that 9 is not an element of set A.

Set-builder notation (sometimes called *set-generator notation*) may be used to symbolize a set. Set-builder notation is frequently used in algebra. The following example illustrates its form.

$$
\begin{array}{cccccc}
D & = & \{ & x & | & \text{Condition(s)} \ \} \\
\uparrow & \uparrow & \uparrow & \uparrow & \uparrow & \uparrow \\
\text{Set } D & \text{is} & \text{the} & \text{all} & \text{such} & \text{the condition(s)} \\
 & & \text{set of} & \text{elements} & \text{that} & x \text{ must meet in} \\
 & & & x & & \text{order to be a} \\
 & & & & & \text{member of the set.}
\end{array}
$$

Consider $E = \{x \mid x \in N \text{ and } x > 10\}$. The statement is read: "Set E is the set of all the elements x such that x is a natural number and x is greater than 10." The conditions that x must meet to be a member of the set are $x \in N$, which means that x must be a natural number, and $x > 10$, which means that x must be greater than 10. The numbers that meet both conditions are the set of natural numbers greater than 10. Set E in roster form is

$$E = \{11, 12, 13, 14, \ldots\}$$

*In August 2006, Pluto was reclassified as a dwarf planet.

EXAMPLE ❹ *Using Set-Builder Notation*

a) Write set $B = \{1, 2, 3, 4, 5\}$ in set-builder notation.

b) Write, in words, how you would read set B in set-builder notation.

SOLUTION

a) Because set B consists of the natural numbers less than 6, we write

$$B = \{x \mid x \in N \text{ and } x < 6\}$$

Another acceptable answer is $B = \{x \mid x \in N \text{ and } x \leq 5\}$.

b) Set B is the set of all elements x such that x is a natural number and x is less than 6.

EXAMPLE ❺ *Roster Form to Set-Builder Notation*

a) Write set $C = \{$North America, South America, Europe, Asia, Australia, Africa, Antarctica$\}$ in set-builder notation.

b) Write in words how you would read set C in set-builder notation.

SOLUTION

a) $C = \{x \mid x \text{ is a continent}\}$.

b) Set C is the set of all elements x such that x is a continent.

EXAMPLE ❻ *Set-Builder Notation to Roster Form*

Write set $A = \{x \mid x \in N \text{ and } 2 \leq x < 8\}$ in roster form.

SOLUTION $A = \{2, 3, 4, 5, 6, 7\}$

EXAMPLE ❼ *Largest Cities*

The chart shows the 10 most populated U.S. cities in 2005. Let set C be the set of cities in California that are among the 10 most populated U.S. cities in 2005. Write set C in roster form.

Ten Most Populated Cities in the U.S., 2005	Population
New York, New York	8,143,197
Los Angeles, California	3,844,829
Chicago, Illinois	2,842,518
Houston, Texas	2,016,582
Philadelphia, Pennsylvania	1,463,281
Phoenix, Arizona	1,461,575
San Antonio, Texas	1,256,509
San Diego, California	1,255,540
Dallas, Texas	1,213,825
San Jose, California	912,332

Source: U.S. Census Bureau

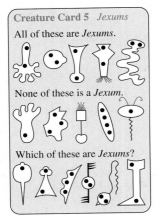
We learn to group objects according to what we see as the relevant distinguishing characteristics. One way used by educators to measure this ability is through visual cues. An example can be seen in this test, called "Creature Cards," offered by the Education Development Center. How would you describe membership in the set of Jexums?

SOLUTION By examining the chart we find that three California cities appear in the chart. They are Los Angeles, San Diego, and San Jose. Thus, set $C = \{$Los Angeles, San Diego, San Jose$\}$.

A set is said to be *finite* if it either contains no elements or the number of elements in the set is a natural number. The set $B = \{2, 4, 6, 8, 10\}$ is a finite set because the number of elements in the set is 5, and 5 is a natural number. A set that is not finite is said to be *infinite*. The set of counting numbers is one example of an infinite set. Infinite sets are discussed in more detail in Section 2.6.

Another important concept is equality of sets.

> Set A is **equal** to set B, symbolized by $A = B$, if and only if set A and set B contain exactly the same elements.

For example, if set $A = \{1, 2, 3\}$ and set $B = \{3, 1, 2\}$, then $A = B$ because they contain exactly the same elements. The order of the elements in the set is not important. If two sets are equal, both must contain the same number of elements. The number of elements in a set is called its *cardinal number*.

> The **cardinal number** of set A, symbolized by $n(A)$, is the number of elements in set A.

Both set $A = \{1, 2, 3\}$ and set $B = \{$England, Brazil, Japan$\}$ have a cardinal number of 3; that is, $n(A) = 3$, and $n(B) = 3$. We can say that set A and set B both have a cardinality of 3.

Two sets are said to be *equivalent* if they contain the same number of elements.

> Set A is **equivalent** to set B if and only if $n(A) = n(B)$.

Any sets that are equal must also be equivalent. Not all sets that are equivalent are equal, however. The sets $D = \{a, b, c\}$ and $E = \{$apple, orange, pear$\}$ are equivalent because both have the same cardinal number, 3. Because the elements differ, however, the sets are not equal.

Two sets that are equivalent or have the same cardinality can be placed in *one-to-one correspondence*. Set A and set B can be placed in one-to-one correspondence if every element of set A can be matched with exactly one element of set B and every element of set B can be matched with exactly one element of set A. For example, there is a one-to-one correspondence between the student names on a class list and the student identification numbers because we can match each student with a student identification number.

Consider set S, states, and set C, state capitals.

$$S = \{\text{North Carolina, Georgia, South Carolina, Florida}\}$$
$$C = \{\text{Columbia, Raleigh, Tallahassee, Atlanta}\}$$

Two different one-to-one correspondences for sets S and C follow.

S = {North Carolina, Georgia, South Carolina, Florida}

C = {Columbia, Raleigh, Tallahassee, Atlanta}

S = {North Carolina, Georgia, South Carolina, Florida}

C = {Columbia, Raleigh, Tallahassee, Atlanta}

Other one-to-one correspondences between sets S and C are possible. Do you know which capital goes with which state?

Null or Empty Set

Some sets do not contain any elements, such as the set of zebras that live in your house.

> The set that contains no elements is called the **empty set** or **null set** and is symbolized by { } or Ø.

Note that {Ø} is not the empty set. This set contains the element Ø and has a cardinality of 1. The set {0} is also not the empty set because it contains the element 0. It also has a cardinality of 1.

EXAMPLE 8 *Natural Number Solutions*

Indicate the set of natural numbers that satisfies the equation $x + 2 = 0$.

SOLUTION The values that satisfy the equation are those that make the equation a true statement. Only the number -2 satisfies this equation. Because -2 is not a natural number, the solution set of this equation is { } or Ø.   ●

Universal Set

Another important set is a *universal set*.

> A **universal set,** symbolized by U, is a set that contains all the elements for any specific discussion.

When a universal set is given, only the elements in the universal set may be considered when working the problem. If, for example, the universal set for a particular problem is defined as $U = \{1, 2, 3, 4, \ldots, 10\}$, then only the natural numbers 1 through 10 may be used in that problem.

SECTION 2.1   EXERCISES

CONCEPT/WRITING EXERCISES

In Exercises 1–12, answer each question with a complete sentence.

1. What is a set?

2. What is an ellipsis, and how is it used?

3. What are the three ways that a set can be written? Give an example of each.

4. What is an infinite set?

5. What is a finite set?

6. What are equal sets?

7. What are equivalent sets?

8. What is the cardinal number of a set?

9. What is the empty set?

10. What are the two ways to indicate the empty set?

11. What is a universal set?

12. What does a one-to-one correspondence of two sets mean?

PRACTICE THE SKILLS

In Exercises 13–18, determine whether each set is well defined.

13. The set of the best books

14. The set of the easiest courses at your school

15. The set of states that have a common border with Kansas

16. The set of the four states in the United States having the largest areas

17. The set of astronauts who walked on the moon

18. The set of the most interesting teachers at your school

In Exercises 19–24, determine whether each set is finite or infinite.

19. $\{2, 4, 6, 8, \dots\}$

20. The set of multiples of 6 between 0 and 90

21. The set of odd numbers greater than 25

22. The set of fractions between 1 and 2

23. The set of odd numbers greater than 15

24. The set of apple trees in Gro-More Farms Orchards

In Exercises 25–34, express each set in roster form. You may need to use a world almanac or some other reference source.

25. The set of states in the United States whose names begin with the letter M

26. The set of oceans in the world

27. The set of natural numbers between 10 and 178

28. $C = \{x \mid x + 6 = 10\}$

29. $B = \{x \mid x \in N \text{ and } x \text{ is even}\}$

30. The set of states west of the Mississippi River that have a common border with the state of Florida

31. The set of football players over the age of 70 who are still playing in the National Football League

32. The set of states in the United States that have no common border with any other state

33. $E = \{x \mid x \in N \text{ and } 14 \le x < 85\}$

34. The set of states in the United States that are not in the contiguous 48 states

In Exercises 35–38, use the following table, which shows the average price for a Big Mac in selected countries as of March 20, 2005. Let the 15 selected countries represent the universal set.

Average Price for a Big Mac

Country	Price
Switzerland	$5.46
Denmark	$4.97
Sweden	$4.46
United Kingdom	$3.61
Germany	$3.58
New Zealand	$3.16
United States*	$3.00
Turkey	$2.80
Peru	$2.74
Canada	$2.60
Chile	$2.56
Japan	$2.50
Australia	$2.46
Czech Republic	$2.45
China	$1.26

*Average price in four selected cities.
Source: *Economist*

Use the list to represent each set in roster form.

35. The set of countries in which the average price for a Big Mac is more than $3.00

36. The set of countries in which the average price for a Big Mac is less than $2.50

37. The set of countries in which the average price for a Big Mac is between $3.25 and $5.50

38. The set of countries in which the average price for a Big Mac is between $2.00 and $2.99

In Exercises 39–42, use the following graph, which shows the digital camera sales, in millions, for the years 1996–2005.

Digital Camera Sales

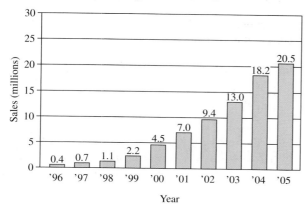

Values: '96 0.4, '97 0.7, '98 1.1, '99 2.2, '00 4.5, '01 7.0, '02 9.4, '03 13.0, '04 18.2, '05 20.5

Year

Source: PMA Marketing Research

Use the graph to represent each set in roster form.

39. The set of years included in the graph in which digital camera sales were more than 13 million

40. The set of years included in the graph in which digital camera sales were less than 6 million

41. The set of years included in the graph in which digital camera sales were between 1 million and 7 million

42. The set of years included in the graph in which digital camera sales were more than 25 million

In Exercises 43–50, express each set in set-builder notation.

43. $B = \{5, 6, 7, 8, 9, 10, 11, 12\}$

44. $A = \{1, 2, 3, 4, 5, 6, 7, 8, 9\}$

45. $C = \{3, 6, 9, 12, \dots\}$

46. $D = \{5, 10, 15, 20, \dots\}$

47. E is the set of odd natural numbers

48. A is the set of national holidays in the United States in July

49. C is the set of months that contain less than 30 days

50. $F = \{15, 16, 17, \dots, 100\}$

In Exercises 51–58, write a description of each set.

51. $A = \{1, 2, 3, 4, 5, 6, 7\}$

52. $D = \{3, 6, 9, 12, 15, 18, \dots\}$

53. $V = \{a, e, i, o, u\}$

54. $S = \{$Bashful, Doc, Dopey, Grumpy, Happy, Sleepy, Sneezy$\}$

55. $T = \{$oak, maple, elm, pine, $\dots\}$

56. $E = \{x \mid x \in N$ and $4 \le x < 11\}$

57. $S = \{$Spring, Summer, Fall, Winter$\}$

58. B = {John Lennon, Ringo Starr, Paul McCartney, George Harrison}

▲ The Beatles

In Exercises 59–62, use the following list, which shows the 10 corporations with the highest favorable consumer opinion ratings as of December 2005. Let the 10 corporations in the list represent the universal set.

Corporation	Percent of Consumers with a Favorable Opinion
1. Johnson & Johnson	91
2. Google	91
3. Home Depot	90
4. Target	85
5. Coca-Cola	85
6. Toyota	84
7. Microsoft	83
8. Southwest Airlines	83
9. United Airlines	78
10. McDonald's	74

Source: Pew Research Center

Use the list to represent each set in roster form.

59. $\{x \mid x$ is a corporation in which at least 90 percent of consumers reported having a favorable opinion$\}$

60. $\{x \mid x$ is a corporation in which fewer than 80 percent of consumers reported having a favorable opinion$\}$

61. $\{x \mid x$ is a corporation in which between 75 and 80 percent of consumers reported having a favorable opinion$\}$

62. $\{x \mid x$ is a corporation in which between 80 and 95 percent of consumers reported having a favorable opinion$\}$

In Exercises 63–66, use the following graph which shows the number of Internal Revenue Service (IRS) audits of individual taxpayers, in millions, for the years 1996–2004.

Audits on the Rise

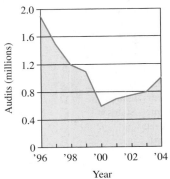

Source: Internal Revenue Service

Use the graph to represent each set in roster form.

63. The set of years in which the number of IRS audits of individual taxpayers exceeded 1 million

64. The set of years in which the number of IRS audits of individual taxpayers were between 0.5 million and 2 million

65. The set of years in which the number of IRS audits of individual taxpayers were fewer than 1.4 million

66. The set of years in which the number of IRS audits of individual taxpayers exceeded 2 million

In Exercises 67–74, state whether each statement is true or false. If false, give the reason.

67. $\{e\} \in \{a, e, i, o, u\}$

68. $b \in \{a, b, c, d, e, f\}$

69. $h \in \{a, b, c, d, e, f\}$

70. Mickey Mouse $\in$ {characters created by Walt Disney}

71. $3 \notin \{x \mid x \in N$ and x is odd$\}$

72. Maui $\in$ {capital cities in the United States}

73. *Titanic* $\in$ {top 10 motion pictures with the greatest revenues}

74. $2 \in \{x \mid x$ is an odd natural number$\}$

In Exercises 75–78, for the sets A = $\{2, 4, 6, 8\}$, B = $\{1, 3, 7, 9, 13, 21\}$, C = $\{\ \}$, and D = $\{\#, \&, \%, \square, *\}$.

75. Determine $n(A)$.

76. Determine $n(B)$.

77. Determine $n(C)$.

78. Determine $n(D)$.

In Exercises 79–84, determine whether the pairs of sets are equal, equivalent, both, or neither.

79. $A = \{$algebra, geometry, trigonometry$\}$,
$B = \{$geometry, trigonometry, algebra$\}$

80. $A = \{7, 9, 10\}$, $B = \{a, b, c\}$

81. $A = \{$grapes, apples, oranges$\}$,
$B = \{$grapes, peaches, apples, oranges$\}$

82. *A* is the set of Siamese cats.
B is the set of cats.

83. *A* is the set of letters in the word *tap*.
B is the set of letters in the word *ant*.

84. *A* is the set of states.
B is the set of state capitals.

PROBLEM SOLVING

85. Set-builder notation is often more versatile and efficient than listing a set in roster form. This versatility is illustrated with the two sets.

$$A = \{x \mid x \in N \text{ and } x > 2\}$$
$$B = \{x \mid x > 2\}$$

a) Write a description of set *A* and set *B*.

b) Explain the difference between set *A* and set *B*. (*Hint:* Is $4\frac{1}{2} \in A$? Is $4\frac{1}{2} \in B$?)

c) Write set *A* in roster form.

d) Can set *B* be written in roster form? Explain your answer.

86. Start with sets

$$A = \{x \mid 2 < x \le 5 \text{ and } x \in N\}$$

and

$$B = \{x \mid 2 < x \le 5\}$$

a) Write a description of set *A* and set *B*.

b) Explain the difference between set *A* and set *B*.

c) Write set *A* in roster form.

d) Can set *B* be written in roster form? Explain your answer.

A cardinal number answers the question "How many?" An **ordinal number** *describes the relative position that an element occupies. For example, Molly's desk is the third desk from the aisle.*

In Exercises 87–90, determine whether the number used is a cardinal number or an ordinal number.

87. J. K. Rowling has written 7 Harry Potter books.

▲ J. K. Rowling

88. Study the chart on page 25 in the book.

89. Lincoln was the sixteenth president of the United States.

90. Emily paid $35 for her new blouse.

91. Describe three sets of which you are a member.

92. Describe three sets that have no members.

93. Write a short paragraph explaining why the universal set and the empty set are necessary in the study of sets.

CHALLENGE PROBLEM/GROUP ACTIVITY

94. a) In a given exercise, a universal set is not specified, but we know that actor Orlando Bloom is a member of the universal set. Describe five different possible universal sets of which Orlando Bloom is a member.

b) Write a description of one set that includes all the universal sets in part (a).

INTERNET/RESEARCH ACTIVITY

95. Georg Cantor is recognized as the founder and a leader in the development of set theory. Do research and write a paper on his life and his contributions to set theory and to the field of mathematics. References include history of mathematics books, encyclopedias, and the Internet.

2.2   SUBSETS

▲ The set of occupations contains firefighters.

Consider the following sets. Set A = {architect, firefighter, mail carrier}. Set B = {architect, engineer, firefighter, mail carrier, teacher}. Note that each element of set A is also an element of set B. In this section, we will discuss how to illustrate the relationship between two sets, A and B, such that each element of set A is also an element of set B.

In our complex world, we often break larger sets into smaller more manageable sets, called *subsets*. For example, consider the set of people in your class. Suppose we categorize the set of people in your class according to the first letter of their last name (the A's, B's, C's, etc.). When we do so, each of these sets may be considered a subset of the original set. Each of these subsets can be separated further. For example, the set of people whose last name begins with the letter A can be categorized as either male or female or by their age. Each of these collections of people is also a subset. A given set may have many different subsets.

> Set A is a **subset** of set B, symbolized by $A \subseteq B$, if and only if all the elements of set A are also elements of set B.

The symbol $A \subseteq B$ indicates that "set A is a subset of set B." The symbol $\not\subseteq$ is used to indicate "is not a subset." Thus, $A \not\subseteq B$ indicates that set A is not a subset of set B. *To show that set A is not a subset of set B, we must find at least one element of set A that is not an element of set B.*

EXAMPLE ❶ A Subset?

Determine whether set A is a subset of set B.
a) A = {marigold, pansy, geranium}
    B = {marigold, pansy, begonia, geranium}
b) A = {2, 3, 4, 5}
    B = {2, 3}
c) A = {$x \mid x$ is a yellow fruit}
    B = {$x \mid x$ is a red fruit}
d) A = {vanilla, chocolate, rocky road}
    B = {chocolate, vanilla, rocky road}

SOLUTION
a) All the elements of set A are contained in set B, so $A \subseteq B$.
b) The elements 4 and 5 are in set A but not in set B, so $A \not\subseteq B$ (A is not a subset of B). In this example, however, all the elements of set B are contained in set A; therefore, $B \subseteq A$.
c) There are fruits, such as bananas, that are in set A that are not in set B, so $A \not\subseteq B$.
d) All the elements of set A are contained in set B, so $A \subseteq B$. Note also that $B \subseteq A$. In fact, set A = set B.   ●

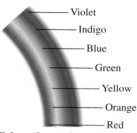
Proper Subsets

> Set *A* is a **proper subset** of set *B*, symbolized by $A \subset B$, if and only if all the elements of set *A* are elements of set *B* and set *A* $\neq$ set *B* (that is, set *B* must contain at least one element not in set *A*).

Consider the sets $A = \{$red, blue, yellow$\}$ and $B = \{$red, orange, yellow, green, blue, violet$\}$. Set *A* is a *subset* of set *B*, $A \subseteq B$, because every element of set *A* is also an element of set *B*. Set *A* is also a *proper subset* of set *B*, $A \subset B$, because set *A* and set *B* are not equal. Now consider $C = \{$car, bus, train$\}$ and $D = \{$train, car, bus$\}$. Set *C* is a subset of set *D*, $C \subseteq D$, because every element of set *C* is also an element of set *D*. Set *C*, however, is not a proper subset of set *D*, $C \not\subset D$, because set *C* and set *D* are equal sets.

EXAMPLE 2   *A Proper Subset?*

Determine whether set *A* is a proper subset of set *B*.
a) $A = \{$jazz, pop, hip hop$\}$
   $B = \{$classical, jazz, pop, rap, hip hop$\}$
b) $A = \{a, b, c, d\}$ $B = \{a, c, b, d\}$

SOLUTION

a) All the elements of set *A* are contained in set *B*, and sets *A* and *B* are not equal; thus, $A \subset B$.
b) Set $A =$ set *B*, so $A \not\subset B$. (However, $A \subseteq B$.) ●

Every set is a subset of itself, but no set is a proper subset of itself. For all sets *A*, $A \subseteq A$, but $A \not\subset A$. For example, if $A = \{1, 2, 3\}$, then $A \subseteq A$ because every element of set *A* is contained in set *A*, but $A \not\subset A$ because set $A =$ set *A*.

Let $A = \{\ \}$ and $B = \{1, 2, 3, 4\}$. Is $A \subseteq B$? To show $A \not\subseteq B$, you must find at least one element of set *A* that is not an element of set *B*. Because this cannot be done, $A \subseteq B$ must be true. Using the same reasoning, we can show that *the empty set is a subset of every set, including itself.*

EXAMPLE 3   *Element or Subset?*

Determine whether the following are true or false.
a) $3 \in \{3, 4, 5\}$
b) $\{3\} \in \{3, 4, 5\}$
c) $\{3\} \in \{\{3\}, \{4\}, \{5\}\}$
d) $\{3\} \subseteq \{3, 4, 5\}$
e) $3 \subseteq \{3, 4, 5\}$
f) $\{\ \} \subseteq \{3, 4, 5\}$

SOLUTION

a) $3 \in \{3, 4, 5\}$ is a true statement because 3 is a member of the set $\{3, 4, 5\}$.
b) $\{3\} \in \{3, 4, 5\}$ is a false statement because $\{3\}$ is a set, and the set $\{3\}$ is not an element of the set $\{3, 4, 5\}$.

c) $\{3\} \in \{\{3\}, \{4\}, \{5\}\}$ is a true statement because $\{3\}$ is an element in the set. The elements of the set $\{\{3\}, \{4\}, \{5\}\}$ are themselves sets.

d) $\{3\} \subseteq \{3, 4, 5\}$ is a true statement because every element of the first set is an element of the second set.

e) $3 \subseteq \{3, 4, 5\}$ is a false statement because the 3 is not in braces, so it is not a set and thus cannot be a subset. The 3 is an element of the set as indicated in part (a).

f) $\{ \ \} \subseteq \{3, 4, 5\}$ is a true statement because the empty set is a subset of every set.   ●

Number of Subsets

How many distinct subsets can be made from a given set? The empty set has no elements and has exactly one subset, the empty set. A set with one element has two subsets. A set with two elements has four subsets. A set with three elements has eight subsets. This information is illustrated in Table 2.1. How many subsets will a set with four elements contain?

> The **number of distinct subsets** of a finite set A is 2^n, where n is the number of elements in set A.

Table 2.1 Number of Subsets

Set	Subsets	Number of Subsets
$\{ \ \}$	$\{ \ \}$	$1 = 2^0$
$\{a\}$	$\{a\}$ $\{ \ \}$	$2 = 2^1$
$\{a, b\}$	$\{a, b\}$ $\{a\}, \{b\}$ $\{ \ \}$	$4 = 2 \times 2 = 2^2$
$\{a, b, c\}$	$\{a, b, c\}$ $\{a, b\}, \{a, c\}, \{b, c\}$ $\{a\}, \{b\}, \{c\}$ $\{ \ \}$	$8 = 2 \times 2 \times 2 = 2^3$

By continuing this table with larger and larger sets, we can develop a general formula for finding the number of distinct subsets that can be made from any given set.

EXAMPLE ❹ *Distinct Subsets*

a) Determine the number of distinct subsets for the set $\{S, L, E, D\}$.

b) List all the distinct subsets for the set $\{S, L, E, D\}$.

c) How many of the distinct subsets are proper subsets?

SOLUTION

a) Since the number of elements in the set is 4, the number of distinct subsets is
$2^4 = 2 \times 2 \times 2 \times 2 = 16$.

b) {S, L, E, D}   {S, L, E}   {S, L}   {S}   { }
    {S, L, D}   {S, E}   {L}
    {S, E, D}   {S, D}   {E}
    {L, E, D}   {L, E}   {D}
    {L, D}
    {E, D}

c) There are 15 proper subsets. Every subset except {S, L, E, D} is a proper subset.

EXAMPLE 5 *Variations of Pizza*

Sharon Bhatt is going to purchase a pizza at Pizza Hut. To her cheese pizza, she can add any of the following toppings: pepperoni, sausage, onions, mushrooms, anchovies, and ham. How many different variations of the pizza and toppings can be made?

SOLUTION Sharon can order the cheese pizza with no extra toppings, any one topping, any two toppings, any three toppings, and so on, up to six toppings. One technique used in problem solving is to consider similar problems that you have solved previously. If you think about this problem, you will realize that it is the same as asking how many distinct subsets can be made from a set with six elements. The number of different variations of the pizza is the same as the number of possible subsets of a set that has six elements. There are 2^6 or 64 possible subsets of a set with six elements. Therefore, there are 64 possible variations of the pizza and toppings.

DID YOU KNOW?

The Ladder of Life

cientists use sets to classify and categorize knowledge. In biology, the science of classifying all living things is called *taxonomy*. More than 2000 years ago, Aristotle formalized animal classification with his "ladder of life": higher animals, lower animals, higher plants, lower plants. Today, living organisms are classified into six kingdoms (or sets) called animalia, plantae, archaea, eubacteria, fungi, and protista. Even more general groupings of living things are made according to shared characteristics. The groupings, from most general to most specific, are kingdom, phylum, class, order, family, genus, and species. For example, a zebra, *Equus burchelli*, is a member of the genus *Equus*, as is the horse, *Equus caballus*. Both the zebra and the horse are members of the universal set called the kingdom of animals and the same family, Equidae; they are members of different species (*E. burchelli* and *E. caballus*), however.

SECTION 2.2   EXERCISES

CONCEPT/WRITING EXERCISES

In Exercises 1–6, answer each question with a complete sentence.

1. What is a subset?

2. What is a proper subset?

3. Explain the difference between a subset and a proper subset.

4. Write the formula for determining the number of distinct subsets for a set with n distinct elements.

5. Write the formula for determining the number of distinct proper subsets for a set with n distinct elements.

6. Can any set be a proper subset of itself? Explain.

PRACTICE THE SKILLS

In Exercises 7–24, answer true or false. If false, give the reason.

7. Spanish $\subseteq$ {Spanish, French, Latin, German, Italian}

8. { } $\in$ {salt, pepper, basil, garlic powder}

9. { } $\subseteq$ {table, chair, sofa}

10. red $\subset$ {red, green, blue}

11. 5 $\notin$ {2, 4, 6}

12. {engineer, social worker} $\subseteq$ {physician, attorney, engineer, teacher}

13. { } = {∅}

14. {motorboat, kayak} $\subseteq$ {kayak, fishing boat, sailboat, motorboat}

15. ∅ = { }

16. 0 = { }

17. {0} = ∅

18. {3, 8, 11} $\subseteq$ {3, 8, 11}

19. {swimming} $\in$ {sailing, waterskiing, swimming}

20. {3, 5, 9} $\not\subset$ {3, 9, 5}

21. { } $\subseteq$ { }

22. {1} $\in$ {{1}, {2}, {3}}

23. {Panasonic, Sharp, Pioneer} $\subset$ {Sharp, Panasonic, Pioneer}

24. {b, a, t} $\subseteq$ {t, a, b}

In Exercises 25–32, determine whether $A = B$, $A \subseteq B$, $B \subseteq A$, $A \subset B$, $B \subset A$ or if none of these answers applies. (There may be more than one answer.)

25. A = {Chevrolet, Pontiac, Honda, Lexus}
    B = {Chevrolet, Lexus}

26. A = {$x \mid x \in N$ and $x < 6$}
    B = {$x \mid x \in N$ and $1 \le x \le 5$}

27. Set A is the set of states that border the Atlantic Ocean. Set B is the set of states east of the Mississippi River.

28. A = {1, 3, 5, 7, 9}
    B = {3, 9, 5, 7, 6}

29. A = {$x \mid x$ is a brand of ice cream}
    B = {Breyers, Ben & Jerry's, Häagen-Dazs}

30. A = {$x \mid x$ is a sport that uses a ball}
    B = {basketball, soccer, tennis}

31. Set A is the set of natural numbers between 2 and 7. Set B is the set of natural numbers greater than 2 and less than 7.

32. Set A is the set of all exercise classes offered at Gold's Gym. Set B is the set of aerobic exercise classes offered at Gold's Gym.

In Exercises 33–38, list all the subsets of the sets given.

33. $D = \varnothing$

34. $A = \{\bigcirc\}$

35. $B = \{\text{pen, pencil}\}$

36. $C = \{\text{steak, pork, chicken}\}$

PROBLEM SOLVING

37. For set $A = \{a, b, c, d\}$,

   a) list all the subsets of set A.

   b) state which of the subsets in part (a) are not proper subsets of set A.

38. A set contains nine elements.

   a) How many subsets does it have?

   b) How many proper subsets does it have?

In Exercises 39–50, if the statement is true for all sets A and B, write "true." If it is not true for all sets A and B, write "false." Assume that $A \neq \varnothing$, $U \neq \varnothing$, and $A \subset U$.

39. If $A \subseteq B$, then $A \subset B$.
40. If $A \subset B$, then $A \subseteq B$.

41. $A \subseteq A$
42. $A \subset A$

43. $\varnothing \subset A$
44. $\varnothing \subseteq A$

45. $A \subseteq U$
46. $\varnothing \subset \varnothing$

47. $\varnothing \subset U$
48. $U \subseteq \varnothing$

49. $\varnothing \subseteq \varnothing$
50. $U \subset \varnothing$

51. *Building a House* The Jacobsens are planning to build a house in a new development. They can either build the base model offered by the builder or add any of the following options: deck, hot tub, security system, hardwood flooring. How many different variations of the house are possible?

52. *Salad Toppings* Donald Wheeler is ordering a salad at a Ruby Tuesday restaurant. He can purchase a salad consisting of just lettuce, or he can add any of the following items: cucumber, onion, tomato, carrot, green pepper, olive, mushroom. How many different variations of a salad are possible?

53. *Telephone Features* A customer with Verizon can order telephone service with some, all, or none of the following features: call waiting, call forwarding, caller identification, three-way calling, voice mail, fax line. How many different variations of the set of features are possible?

54. *Hamburger Variations* Customers ordering hamburgers at Vic and Irv's Hamburger stand are always asked, "What do you want on it?" The choices are ketchup, mustard, relish, hot sauce, onions, lettuce, tomato. How many different variations are there for ordering a hamburger?

55. If $E \subseteq F$ and $F \subseteq E$, what other relationship exists between E and F? Explain.

56. How can you determine whether the set of boys is equivalent to the set of girls at a roller-skating rink?

57. For the set $D = \{a, b, c\}$

   a) is a an element of set D? Explain.

   b) is c a subset of set D? Explain.

   c) is $\{a, b\}$ a subset of set D? Explain.

CHALLENGE PROBLEM/GROUP ACTIVITY

58. *Hospital Expansion* A hospital has four members on the board of directors: Arnold, Benitez, Cathy, and Dominique.

   a) When the members vote on whether to add a wing to the hospital, how many different ways can they vote (abstentions are not allowed)? For example, Arnold—yes, Benitez—no, Cathy—no, and Dominique—yes is one of the many possibilities.

   b) Make a listing of all the possible outcomes of the vote. For example, the vote described in part (a) could be represented as (YNNY).

   c) How many of the outcomes given in part (b) would result in a majority supporting the addition of a wing to the hospital? That is, how many of the outcomes have three or more Y's?

RECREATIONAL MATHEMATICS

59. How many elements must a set have if the number of proper subsets of the set is $\frac{1}{2}$ of the total number of subsets of the set?

60. If $A \subset B$ and $B \subset C$, must $A \subset C$?

61. If $A \subset B$ and $B \subseteq C$, must $A \subset C$?

62. If $A \subseteq B$ and $B \subseteq C$, must $A \subset C$?

INTERNET/RESEARCH ACTIVITY

63. On page 57, we discussed the ladder of life. Do research and indicate all the different classifications in the Linnaean system, from most general to the most specific, in which a koala belongs.

2.3   VENN DIAGRAMS AND SET OPERATIONS

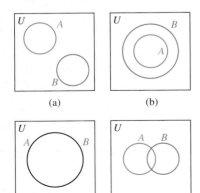

▲ Some soft drinks contain caffeine, some soft drinks contain sugar, and some soft drinks contain caffeine *and* sugar.

Suppose your boss sends you to the store to purchase a soft drink that contains caffeine *and* sugar. You were a bit distracted when he made his request and thought he said to purchase a soft drink that contains caffeine *or* sugar. Which soft drinks are contained in the set of soft drinks that contain caffeine *and* sugar? Which soft drinks are contained in the set of soft drinks that contain caffeine *or* sugar? These two questions are quite different. The first involves soft drinks joined by the word *and*. The second involves soft drinks joined by the word *or*. In this section, you will learn how to illustrate these and other set relationships.

Figure 2.1

A useful technique for illustrating set relationships is the Venn diagram, named for English mathematician John Venn (1834–1923). Venn invented the diagrams and used them to illustrate ideas in his text on symbolic logic, published in 1881.

In a Venn diagram, a rectangle usually represents the universal set, U. The items inside the rectangle may be divided into subsets of the universal set. The subsets are usually represented by circles. In Fig. 2.1, the circle labeled A represents set A, which is a subset of the universal set.

Two sets may be represented in a Venn diagram in any of four different ways, as shown in Fig. 2.2. Two sets A and B are *disjoint* when they have no elements in common. Two disjoint sets A and B are illustrated in Fig. 2.2(a). If set A is a proper subset of set B, $A \subset B$, the two sets may be illustrated as in Fig. 2.2(b). If set A contains exactly the same elements as set B, that is, $A = B$, the two sets may be illustrated as in Fig. 2.2(c). Two sets A and B with some elements in common are shown in Fig. 2.2(d), which is regarded as the most general form of a Venn diagram.

If we label the regions of the diagram in Fig. 2.2(d) using I, II, III, and IV, we can illustrate the four possible cases with this one diagram, Fig. 2.3, on page 61.

CASE 1: DISJOINT SETS When sets A and B are disjoint, they have no elements in common. Therefore, region II of Fig. 2.3 is empty.

CASE 2: SUBSETS When $A \subseteq B$, every element of set A is also an element of set B. Thus, there can be no elements in region I of Fig. 2.3. If $B \subseteq A$, however, then region III of Fig. 2.3 is empty.

(a)   (b)

(c)   (d)

Figure 2.2

Figure 2.3

Figure 2.4

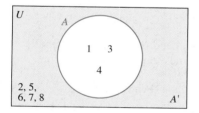

Figure 2.5

Figure 2.6

CASE 3: EQUAL SETS When set A = set B, all the elements of set A are elements of set B and all the elements of set B are elements of set A. Thus, regions I and III of Fig. 2.3 are empty.

CASE 4: OVERLAPPING SETS When sets A and B have elements in common, those elements are in region II of Fig. 2.3. The elements that belong to set A but not to set B are in region I. The elements that belong to set B but not to set A are in region III.

In each of the four cases, any element not belonging to set A or set B is placed in region IV.

Venn diagrams will be helpful in understanding set operations. The basic operations of arithmetic are $+$, $-$, $\times$, and $\div$. When we see these symbols, we know what procedure to follow to determine the answer. Some of the operations in set theory are $'$, $\cap$, and $\cup$. They represent complement, intersection, and union, respectively.

Complement

> The **complement** of set A, symbolized by A', is the set of all the elements in the universal set that are not in set A.

In Fig. 2.4, the shaded region outside of set A within the universal set represents the complement of set A, or A'.

EXAMPLE ❶ *A Set and Its Complement*

Given

$$U = \{1, 2, 3, 4, 5, 6, 7, 8\} \text{ and } A = \{1, 3, 4\}$$

find A' and illustrate the relationship among sets U, A, and A' in a Venn diagram.

SOLUTION The elements in U that are not in set A are 2, 5, 6, 7, 8. Thus, $A' = \{2, 5, 6, 7, 8\}$. The Venn diagram is illustrated in Fig. 2.5. ●

Intersection

The word *intersection* brings to mind the area common to two crossing streets. The red car in the figure is in the intersection of the two streets. The set operation intersection is defined as follows.

> The **intersection** of sets A and B, symbolized by $A \cap B$, is the set containing all the elements that are common to both set A and set B.

The shaded region, region II, in Fig. 2.6 represents the intersection of sets A and B.

EXAMPLE ❷ *Sets with Overlapping Regions*

Let the universal set, *U*, represent the 50 states in the United States. Let set *A* represent the set of states with a population of more than 10 million people as of 2005. Let set *B* represent the set of states that have at least one city with a population of more than 1 million people, as of 2005 (see the table). Draw a Venn diagram illustrating the relationship between set *A* and set *B*.

States With a Population of More Than 10 Million People	States with at Least One City with a Population of More Than 1 Million People
California	California
Texas	Texas
New York	New York
Florida	Illinois
Illinois	Pennsylvania
Pennsylvania	Arizona
Ohio	
Michigan	

Source: Bureau of the U.S. Census, U.S. Dept. of Commerce

SOLUTION First determine the intersection of sets *A* and *B*. The states common to both sets are California, Texas, New York, Illinois, and Pennsylvania. Therefore,

$$A \cap B = \{\text{California, Texas, New York, Illinois, Pennsylvania}\}$$

Place these elements in region II of Fig. 2.7. Complete region I by determining the elements in set *A* that have not been placed in region II. Therefore, Ohio, Michigan, and Florida are placed in region I. Complete region III by determining the elements in set *B* that have not been placed in region II. Thus, Arizona is placed in region III. Finally, place those elements in *U* that are not in either set within the rectangle but are outside both circles. This group includes the remaining 41 states, which are placed in region IV. ●

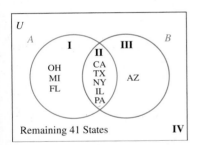

Figure 2.7

EXAMPLE ❸ *The Intersection of Sets*

Given

$$U = \{1, 2, 3, 4, 5, 6, 7, 8, 9, 10\}$$
$$A = \{1, 2, 3, 8\}$$
$$B = \{1, 3, 6, 7, 9\}$$
$$C = \{\ \}$$

find

a) $A \cap B$.   b) $A \cap C$.   c) $A' \cap B$.   d) $(A \cap B)'$.

SOLUTION

a) $A \cap B = \{1, 2, 3, 8\} \cap \{1, 3, 6, 7, 9\} = \{1, 3\}$. The elements common to both set A and set B are 1 and 3.

b) $A \cap C = \{1, 2, 3, 8\} \cap \{\ \} = \{\ \}$. There are no elements common to both set A and set C.

c) $A' = \{4, 5, 6, 7, 9, 10\}$
    $A' \cap B = \{4, 5, 6, 7, 9, 10\} \cap \{1, 3, 6, 7, 9\}$
        $= \{6, 7, 9\}$

d) To find $(A \cap B)'$, first determine $A \cap B$.
    $A \cap B = \{1, 3\}$ from part (a)
    $(A \cap B)' = \{1, 3\}' = \{2, 4, 5, 6, 7, 8, 9, 10\}$

Union

The word *union* means to unite or join together, as in marriage, and that is exactly what is done when we perform the operation of union.

> The **union** of set A and set B, symbolized by $A \cup B$, is the set containing all the elements that are members of set A or of set B (or of both sets).

$A \cup B$

Figure 2.8

The three shaded regions of Fig. 2.8, regions I, II, and III, together represent the union of sets A and B. If an element is common to both sets, it is listed only once in the union of the sets.

EXAMPLE ❹ *Determining Sets from a Venn Diagram*

Use the Venn diagram in Fig. 2.9 to determine the following sets.

a) U b) A c) B' d) $A \cap B$
e) $A \cup B$ f) $(A \cup B)'$ g) $n(A \cup B)$

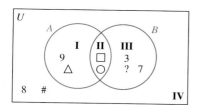

Figure 2.9

SOLUTION

a) The universal set consists of all the elements within the rectangle, that is, the elements in regions I, II, III, and IV. Thus, $U = \{9, \triangle, \square, \bigcirc, 3, 7, ?, \#, 8\}$.

b) Set A consists of the elements in regions I and II. Thus, $A = \{9, \triangle, \square, \bigcirc\}$.

c) B' consists of the elements outside set B, or the elements in regions I and IV. Thus, $B' = \{9, \triangle, \#, 8\}$.

d) $A \cap B$ consists of the elements that belong to both set A and set B (region II). Thus, $A \cap B = \{\square, \bigcirc\}$.

e) $A \cup B$ consists of the elements that belong to set A or set B (regions I, II, or III). Thus, $A \cup B = \{9, \triangle, \square, \bigcirc, 3, 7, ?\}$.

f) $(A \cup B)'$ consists of the elements in U that are not in $A \cup B$. Thus, $(A \cup B)' = \{\#, 8\}$.

g) $n(A \cup B)$ represents the *number of elements* in the union of sets A and B. Thus, $n(A \cup B) = 7$, as there are seven elements in the union of sets A and B.

EXAMPLE ⑤ *The Union of Sets*

Given

$$U = \{1, 2, 3, 4, 5, 6, 7, 8, 9, 10\}$$
$$A = \{1, 2, 4, 6\}$$
$$B = \{1, 3, 6, 7, 9\}$$
$$C = \{\ \}$$

determine each of the following.

a) $A \cup B$ b) $A \cup C$ c) $A' \cup B$ d) $(A \cup B)'$

SOLUTION

a) $A \cup B = \{1, 2, 4, 6\} \cup \{1, 3, 6, 7, 9\} = \{1, 2, 3, 4, 6, 7, 9\}$
b) $A \cup C = \{1, 2, 4, 6\} \cup \{\ \} = \{1, 2, 4, 6\}$. Note that $A \cup C = A$.
c) To determine $A' \cup B$, we must determine A'.

$$A' = \{3, 5, 7, 8, 9, 10\}$$
$$A' \cup B = \{3, 5, 7, 8, 9, 10\} \cup \{1, 3, 6, 7, 9\}$$
$$= \{1, 3, 5, 6, 7, 8, 9, 10\}$$

d) Find $(A \cup B)'$ by first determining $A \cup B$, and then find the complement of $A \cup B$.

$$A \cup B = \{1, 2, 3, 4, 6, 7, 9\} \text{ from part (a)}$$
$$(A \cup B)' = \{1, 2, 3, 4, 6, 7, 9\}' = \{5, 8, 10\}$$

EXAMPLE ⑥ *Union and Intersection*

Given

$$U = \{a, b, c, d, e, f, g\}$$
$$A = \{a, b, e, g\}$$
$$B = \{a, c, d, e\}$$
$$C = \{b, e, f\}$$

determine each of the following.

a) $(A \cup B) \cap (A \cup C)$ b) $(A \cup B) \cap C'$ c) $A' \cap B'$

SOLUTION

a) $(A \cup B) \cap (A \cup C) = \{a, b, c, d, e, g\} \cap \{a, b, e, f, g\}$
$$= \{a, b, e, g\}$$
b) $(A \cup B) \cap C' = \{a, b, c, d, e, g\} \cap \{a, c, d, g\}$
$$= \{a, c, d, g\}$$
c) $A' \cap B' = \{c, d, f\} \cap \{b, f, g\}$
$$= \{f\}$$

The Meaning of *and* and *or*

The words *and* and *or* are very important in many areas of mathematics. We use these words in several chapters in this book, including the probability chapter. The word *and* is generally interpreted to mean *intersection*, whereas *or* is generally interpreted to mean *union*. Suppose $A = \{1, 2, 3, 5, 6, 8\}$ and $B = \{1, 3, 4, 7, 9, 10\}$. The elements that belong to set A *and* set B are 1 and 3. These are the elements in the intersection of the sets. The elements that belong to set A *or* set B are 1, 2, 3, 4, 5, 6, 7, 8, 9, and 10. These are the elements in the union of the sets.

The Relationship Between $n(A \cup B)$, $n(A)$, $n(B)$, and $n(A \cap B)$

Having looked at unions and intersections, we can now determine a relationship between $n(A \cup B)$, $n(A)$, $n(B)$, and $n(A \cap B)$. Suppose set A has eight elements, set B has five elements, and $A \cap B$ has two elements. How many elements are in $A \cup B$? Let's make up some arbitrary sets that meet the criteria specified and draw a Venn diagram. If we let set $A = \{a, b, c, d, e, f, g, h\}$, then set B must contain five elements, two of which are also in set A. Let set $B = \{g, h, i, j, k\}$. We construct a Venn diagram by filling in the intersection first, as shown in Fig. 2.10. The number of elements in $A \cup B$ is 11. The elements g and h are in both sets, and if we add $n(A) + n(B)$, we are counting these elements twice.

To find the number of elements in the union of sets A and B, we can add the number of elements in sets A and B and then subtract the number of elements common to both sets.

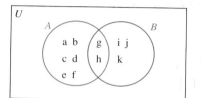

Figure 2.10

> **FOR ANY FINITE SETS A AND B,**
>
> $$n(A \cup B) = n(A) + n(B) - n(A \cap B)$$

EXAMPLE ❼ *How Many Visitors Speak Spanish or French?*

The results of a survey of visitors at the Grand Canyon showed that 25 speak Spanish, 14 speak French, and 4 speak both Spanish and French. How many speak Spanish or French?

SOLUTION If we let set A be the set of visitors who speak Spanish and let set B be the set of visitors who speak French, then we need to determine $n(A \cup B)$. We can use the above formula to find $n(A \cup B)$.

$$n(A \cup B) = n(A) + n(B) - n(A \cap B)$$
$$n(A \cup B) = 25 + 14 - 4$$
$$= 35$$

Thus, 35 of the visitors surveyed speak either Spanish or French. •

EXAMPLE ❽ *The Number of Elements in Set A*

Of the homes listed for sale with RE/MAX, 39 have either a three-car garage or a fireplace, 31 have a fireplace, and 18 have both a three-car garage and a fireplace. How many of these homes have a three-car garage?

SOLUTION If we let set A be the set of homes with a three-car garage and set B be the set of homes with a fireplace, we need to determine $n(A)$. We are given the number of homes with either a three-car garage or a fireplace, which is $n(A \cup B)$. We are also given the number of homes with a fireplace, $n(B)$, and the number of homes that have both a three-car garage and a fireplace, $n(A \cap B)$. We can use the formula $n(A \cup B) = n(A) + n(B) - n(A \cap B)$ to solve for $n(A)$.

$$n(A \cup B) = n(A) + n(B) - n(A \cap B)$$
$$39 = n(A) + 31 - 18$$
$$39 = n(A) + 13$$
$$39 - 13 = n(A) + 13 - 13$$
$$26 = n(A)$$

Thus, the number of homes listed for sale that have a three-car garage is 26.

Two other set operations are the difference of two sets and the Cartesian product. We will first discuss the difference of two sets.

Difference of Two Sets

> The **difference** of two sets A and B, symbolized $A - B$, is the set of elements that belong to set A but not to set B.

$A - B$

Figure 2.11

Using set-builder notation, the difference of two sets A and B is indicated by $A - B = \{x \mid x \in A \text{ and } x \notin B\}$. The shaded region, region I, in Fig. 2.11 represents the difference of two sets A and B, or $A - B$.

EXAMPLE ⑨ *The Difference of Two Sets*

Given

$$U = \{a, b, c, d, e, f, g, h, i, j, k\}$$
$$A = \{b, c, e, f, g, h\}$$
$$B = \{a, b, c, g, i\}$$
$$C = \{b, e, g\}$$

determine

a) $A - B$ b) $A - C$ c) $A' - B$ d) $A - C'$

SOLUTION

a) $A - B$ is the set of elements that are in set A but not set B. The elements that are in set A but not set B are $e, f,$ and h. Therefore, $A - B = \{e, f, h\}$.

b) $A - C$ is the set of elements that are in set A but not set C. The elements that are in set A but not set C are $c, f,$ and h. Therefore, $A - C = \{c, f, h\}$.

c) To determine $A' - B$, we must first determine A'.

$$A' = \{a, d, i, j, k\}$$

$A' - B$ is the set of elements that are in set A' but not set B. The elements that are in set A' but not set B are $d, j,$ and k. Therefore, $A' - B = \{d, j, k\}$.

d) To determine $A - C'$, we must first determine C'.

$$C' = \{a, c, d, f, h, i, j, k\}$$

$A - C'$ is the set of elements that are in set A but not set C'. The elements that are in set A but not set C' are $b, e,$ and g. Therefore, $A - C' = \{b, e, g\}$. •

Next we discuss the Cartesian product.

Cartesian Product

> The **Cartesian product** of set A and set B, symbolized by $A \times B$ and read "A cross B," is the set of all possible *ordered pairs* of the form (a, b), where $a \in A$ and $b \in B$.

To determine the ordered pairs in a Cartesian product, select the first element of set A and form an ordered pair with each element of set B. Then select the second element of set A and form an ordered pair with each element of set B. Continue in this manner until you have used each element of set A.

EXAMPLE ⑩ *The Cartesian Product of Two Sets*

Given $A = \{$orange, banana, apple$\}$ and $B = \{1, 2\}$, determine the following.
a) $A \times B$ b) $B \times A$ c) $A \times A$ d) $B \times B$

SOLUTION

a) $A \times B = \{($orange, 1$), ($orange, 2$) ($banana, 1$), ($banana, 2$), ($apple, 1$), ($apple, 2$)\}$

b) $B \times A = \{(1, $orange$), (1, $banana$), (1, $apple$), (2, $orange$), (2, $banana$), (2, $apple$)\}$

c) $A \times A = \{($orange, orange$), ($orange, banana$), ($orange, apple$), ($banana, orange$), ($banana, banana$), ($banana, apple$), ($apple, orange$), ($apple, banana$), ($apple, apple$)\}$

d) $B \times B = \{(1, 1), (1, 2), (2, 1), (2, 2)\}$ •

We can see from Example 10 that, in general, $A \times B \neq B \times A$. The ordered pairs in $A \times B$ are not the same as the ordered pairs in $B \times A$ because (orange, 1) $\neq$ (1, orange).

In general, if a set A has m elements and a set B has n elements, then the number of ordered pairs in $A \times B$ will be $m \times n$. In Example 10, set A contains 3 elements and set B contains 2 elements. Notice that $A \times B$ contains 3×2 or 6 ordered pairs.

SECTION 2.3   EXERCISES

CONCEPT/WRITING EXERCISES

In Exercises 1–5, use Fig. 2.2 as a guide to draw a Venn diagram that illustrates the situation described.

1. Set A and set B are disjoint sets.

2. $A \subset B$

3. $B \subset A$

4. $A = B$

5. Set A and set B are overlapping sets.

6. How do we obtain the union of two sets A and B, $A \cup B$?

7. If we are given set A, how do we obtain A complement, A'?

8. In a Venn diagram with two overlapping sets, which region(s) represents $A \cup B$?

9. How do we obtain the intersection of two sets A and B, $A \cap B$?

10. In a Venn diagram with two overlapping sets, which region(s) represents $A \cap B$?

11. a) Which set operation is the word *or* generally interpreted to mean?

  b) Which set operation is the word *and* generally interpreted to mean?

12. Give the relationship between $n(A \cup B)$, $n(A)$, $n(B)$, and $n(A \cap B)$.

13. What is the difference of two sets A and B?

14. a) What is the Cartesian product of set A and set B?

  b) If set A has m elements and set B has n elements, how many elements will be in $A \times B$?

PRACTICE THE SKILLS/PROBLEM SOLVING

15. *National Parks* For the sets U, A, and B, construct a Venn diagram and place the elements in the proper regions.

  $U = \{$Badlands, Death Valley, Glacier, Grand Teton, Mammoth Cave, Mount Rainier, North Cascades, Shenandoah, Yellowstone, Yosemite$\}$

  $A = \{$Badlands, Glacier, Grand Teton, Mount Rainier, Yellowstone$\}$

  $B = \{$Death Valley, Glacier, Mammoth Cave, Mount Rainier, Yosemite$\}$

▲ Yosemite National Park

16. *Appliances and Electronics* For the sets U, A, and B, construct a Venn diagram and place the elements in the proper regions.

  $U = \{$microwave oven, washing machine, dryer, refrigerator, dishwasher, compact disc player, videocassette recorder, computer, camcorder, television$\}$

  $A = \{$microwave oven, washing machine, dishwasher, computer, television$\}$

  $B = \{$washing machine, dryer, refrigerator, compact disc player, computer, television$\}$

17. *Occupations* The following table shows the fastest-growing occupations for college graduates based on employment in 2002 and the estimated employment in 2012. Let the occupations in the table represent the universal set.

Fastest-Growing Occupations for College Graduates, 2002–2012

Occupation	Employment (in thousands of jobs) 2002	2012
Systems analysts	186	292
Physician assistants	63	94
Medical records technicians	147	216
Software engineers, applications	394	573
Software engineers, software	281	409
Physical therapist assistants	50	73
Fitness and aerobics instructors	183	264
Database administrators	110	159
Veterinary technicians	53	76
Dental hygienists	148	212

Source: U.S. Bureau of Labor Statistics

Let A = the set of fastest-growing occupations for college graduates whose 2002 employment was at least 150,000.

Let B = the set of fastest-growing occupations for college graduates whose estimated employment in 2012 is at least 400,000.

Construct a Venn diagram illustrating the sets.

18. Golf Statistics The following table shows the number of wins at the Masters Golf Tournament and the U.S. Open for selected golfers as of March 1, 2007. Let these golfers represent the universal set.

Golfer	Masters Golf Tournament	U.S. Open
Tiger Woods	4	2
Phil Mickelson	2	0
Payne Stewart	0	2
Fred Couples	1	0
Ray Floyd	1	1
Jack Nicklaus	6	4
Arnold Palmer	4	1
Ben Hogan	2	4
V. J. Singh	1	0
Retief Goosen	0	2

Let A = the set of golfers who won the Masters Golf Tournament at least two times.

Let B = the set of golfers who won the U.S. Open at least two times.

Construct a Venn diagram illustrating the sets.

19. Let U represent the set of animals in U.S. zoos. Let A represent the set of animals in the San Diego zoo. Describe A'.

▲ San Diego Zoo

20. Let U represent the set of U.S. colleges and universities. Let A represent the set of U.S. colleges and universities in the state of Mississippi. Describe A'.

In Exercises 21–26,

U is the set of insurance companies in the U.S.

A is the set of insurance companies that offer life insurance.

B is the set of insurance companies that offer car insurance.

Describe each of the following sets in words.

21. A'

22. B'

23. $A \cup B$

24. $A \cap B$

25. $A \cap B'$

26. $A \cup B'$

In Exercises 27–32,

U is the set of furniture stores in the U.S.

A is the set of furniture stores that sell mattresses.

B is the set of furniture stores that sell outdoor furniture.

C is the set of furniture stores that sell leather furniture.

Describe the following sets.

27. $A \cap B$

28. $A \cup C$

29. $B' \cap C$

30. $A \cap B \cap C$

31. $A \cup B \cup C$

32. $A' \cup C'$

In Exercises 33–40, use the Venn diagram in Fig. 2.12 to list the set of elements in roster form.

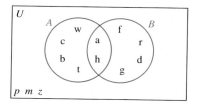

Figure 2.12

33. A

34. B

35. $A \cap B$

36. U

37. $A \cup B$

38. $(A \cup B)'$

39. $A' \cap B'$

40. $(A \cap B)'$

In Exercises 41–48, use the Venn diagram in Fig. 2.13 to list the set of elements in roster form.

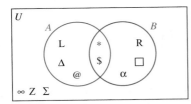

Figure 2.13

41. A

42. B

43. U

44. $A \cap B$

45. $A' \cup B$

46. $A \cup B'$

47. $A' \cap B$

48. $(A \cup B)'$

In Exercises 49–58, let

$$U = \{1, 2, 3, 4, 5, 6, 7, 8\}$$
$$A = \{1, 2, 4, 5, 8\}$$
$$B = \{2, 3, 4, 6\}$$

Determine the following.

49. $A \cup B$

50. $A \cap B$

51. B'

52. $A \cup B'$

53. $(A \cup B)'$

54. $A' \cap B'$

55. $(A \cup B)' \cap B$

56. $(A \cup B) \cap (A \cup B)'$

57. $(B \cup A)' \cap (B' \cup A')$

58. $A' \cup (A \cap B)$

In Exercises 59–68, let

$$U = \{a, b, c, d, e, f, g, h, i, j, k\}$$
$$A = \{a, c, d, f, g, i\}$$
$$B = \{b, c, d, f, g\}$$
$$C = \{a, b, f, i, j\}$$

Determine the following.

59. B'

60. $B \cup C$

61. $A \cap C$

62. $A' \cup B'$

63. $(A \cap C)'$

64. $(A \cap B) \cup C$

65. $A \cup (C \cap B)'$

66. $A \cup (C' \cup B')$

67. $(A' \cup C) \cup (A \cap B)$

68. $(C \cap B) \cap (A' \cap B)$

In Exercises 69–76, let

$$U = \{1, 2, 3, 4, 5, 6, 7, 8, 9, 10\}$$
$$A = \{1, 2, 4, 6, 9\}$$
$$B = \{1, 3, 4, 5, 8\}$$
$$C = \{4, 5, 9\}$$

Determine the following.

69. $A - B$

70. $A - C$

71. $A - B'$

72. $A' - C$

73. $(A - B)'$

74. $(A - B)' - C$

75. $C - A'$

76. $(C - A)' - B$

In Exercises 77–82, let

$$A = \{a, b, c\}$$
$$B = \{1, 2\}$$

77. Determine $A \times B$.

78. Determine $B \times A$.

79. Does $A \times B = B \times A$?

80. Determine $n(A \times B)$.

81. Determine $n(B \times A)$.

82. Does $n(A \times B) = n(B \times A)$?

PROBLEM SOLVING

In Exercises 83–96, let

$$U = \{x \,|\, x \in N \text{ and } x < 10\}$$
$$A = \{x \,|\, x \in N \text{ and } x \text{ is odd and } x < 10\}$$
$$B = \{x \,|\, x \in N \text{ and } x \text{ is even and } x < 10\}$$
$$C = \{x \,|\, x \in N \text{ and } x < 6\}$$

Determine the following.

83. $A \cap B$

84. $A \cup B$

85. $A' \cup B$

86. $(B \cup C)'$

87. $A \cap C'$

88. $A \cap B'$

89. $(B \cap C)'$

90. $(A \cup C) \cap B$

91. $(C' \cup A) \cap B$

92. $(C \cap B) \cup A$

93. $(A \cap B)' \cup C$

94. $(A' \cup C) \cap B$

95. $(A' \cup B') \cap C$

96. $(A' \cap C) \cup (A \cap B)$

97. When will a set and its complement be disjoint? Explain and give an example.

98. When will $n(A \cap B) = 0$? Explain and give an example.

99. *Pet Ownership* The results of a survey of customers at PetSmart showed that 27 owned dogs, 38 owned cats, and 16 owned both dogs and cats. How many people owned either a dog or a cat?

100. *Chorus and Band* At Henniger High School, 46 students sang in the chorus or played in the stage band, 30 students played in the stage band, and 4 students sang in the chorus and played in the stage band. How many students sang in the chorus?

101. Consider the formula

$$n(A \cup B) = n(A) + n(B) - n(A \cap B)$$

a) Show that this relation holds for $A = \{a, b, c, d\}$ and $B = \{b, d, e, f, g, h\}$.

b) Make up your own sets A and B, each consisting of at least six elements. Using these sets, show that the relation holds.

c) Use a Venn diagram and explain why the relation holds for any two sets A and B.

102. The Venn diagram in Fig. 2.14 shows a technique of labeling the regions to indicate membership of elements in a particular region. Define each of the four regions with a set statement. (*Hint:* $A \cap B'$ defines region I.)

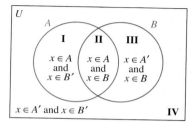

Figure 2.14

In Exercises 103–112, let $U = \{0, 1, 2, 3, 4, 5, \ldots\}$, $A = \{1, 2, 3, 4, \ldots\}$, $B = \{4, 8, 12, 16, \ldots\}$, *and* $C = \{2, 4, 6, 8, \ldots\}$. *Determine the following.*

103. $A \cup B$

104. $A \cap B$

105. $B \cap C$

106. $B \cup C$

107. $A \cap C$

108. $A' \cap C$

109. $B' \cap C$

110. $(B \cup C)' \cup C$

111. $(A \cap C) \cap B'$

112. $U' \cap (A \cup B)$

CHALLENGE EXERCISES/GROUP ACTIVITIES

In Exercises 113–120, determine whether the answer is $\emptyset$, *A, or U. (Assume* $A \neq \emptyset$, $A \neq U$.)

113. $A \cup A'$

114. $A \cap A'$

115. $A \cup \emptyset$

116. $A \cap \emptyset$

117. $A' \cup U$

118. $A \cap U$

119. $A \cup U$

120. $A \cup U'$

In Exercises 121–126, determine the relationship between set A and set B if

121. $A \cap B = B$.

122. $A \cup B = B$.

123. $A \cap B = \emptyset$.

124. $A \cup B = A$.

125. $A \cap B = A$.

126. $A \cup B = \emptyset$.

2.4 VENN DIAGRAMS WITH THREE SETS AND VERIFICATION OF EQUALITY OF SETS

▲ Some of the highest-rated hospitals in the field of neurology are also among the highest-rated hospitals in the field of orthopedics.

Consider the set of the 10 highest-rated hospitals in the field of neurology. Next consider the set of the 10 highest-rated hospitals in the field of cardiology. Also, consider the set of the 10 highest-rated hospitals in the field of orthopedics. Are there any hospitals that are among the 10 highest rated in the fields of neurology, cardiology, and orthopedics? Are there any hospitals that are among the 10 highest rated in the fields of neurology and cardiology, but not orthopedics? In this section, we will learn how to use Venn diagrams to answer questions like these.

In Section 2.3, we learned how to use Venn diagrams to illustrate two sets. Venn diagrams can also be used to illustrate three sets.

For three sets, A, B, and C, the diagram is drawn so the three sets overlap (Fig. 2.15), creating eight regions. The diagrams in Fig. 2.16 emphasize selected regions of three intersecting sets. *When constructing Venn diagrams with three sets, we generally start with region V and work outward* as explained in the following procedure.

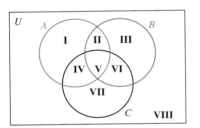

Figure 2.15

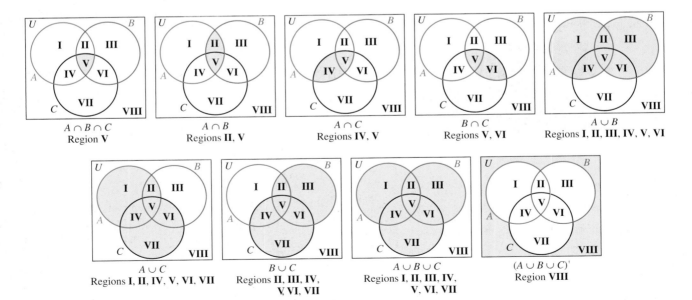

Figure 2.16

> ### GENERAL PROCEDURE FOR CONSTRUCTING VENN DIAGRAMS WITH THREE SETS, *A*, *B*, AND *C*
>
> 1. Determine the elements to be placed in region V by finding the elements that are common to all three sets, $A \cap B \cap C$.
>
> 2. Determine the elements to be placed in region II. Find the elements in $A \cap B$. The elements in this set belong in regions II and V. Place the elements in the set $A \cap B$ that are not listed in region V in region II. The elements in regions IV and VI are found in a similar manner.
>
> 3. Determine the elements to be placed in region I by determining the elements in set *A* that are not in regions II, IV, and V. The elements in regions III and VII are found in a similar manner.
>
> 4. Determine the elements to be placed in region VIII by finding the elements in the universal set that are not in regions I through VII.

Example 1 illustrates the general procedure.

EXAMPLE ❶ *Constructing a Venn Diagram for Three Sets*

Construct a Venn diagram illustrating the following sets.

$$U = \{1, 2, 3, 4, 5, 6, 7, 8, 9, 10, 11, 12, 13, 14\}$$
$$A = \{1, 5, 8, 9, 10, 12\}$$
$$B = \{2, 4, 5, 9, 10, 13\}$$
$$C = \{1, 3, 5, 8, 9, 11\}$$

SOLUTION First find the intersection of all three sets. Because the elements 5 and 9 are in all three sets, $A \cap B \cap C = \{5, 9\}$. The elements 5 and 9 are placed in region V in Fig. 2.17. Next complete region II by determining the intersection of sets *A* and *B*.

$$A \cap B = \{5, 9, 10\}$$

$A \cap B$ consists of regions II and V. The elements 5 and 9 have already been placed in region V, so 10 must be placed in region II.

Now determine what numbers go in region IV.

$$A \cap C = \{1, 5, 8, 9\}$$

Since 5 and 9 have already been placed in region V, place the 1 and 8 in region IV. Now determine the numbers to go in region VI.

$$B \cap C = \{5, 9\}$$

Since both the 5 and 9 have been placed in region V, there are no numbers to be placed in region VI. Now complete set *A*. The only element of set *A* that has not previously been placed in regions II, IV, or V is 12. Therefore, place the element 12 in region I. The element 12 that is placed in region I is only in set *A* and not in set *B* or set *C*. Using set *B*, complete region III using the same general procedure used to determine the numbers in region I. Using set *C*, complete region VII by using the same procedure used to complete regions I and III. To determine the elements in region VIII, find the elements in *U* that have not been placed in regions I–VII. The elements 6, 7, and 14 have not been placed in regions I–VII, so place them in region VIII. ●

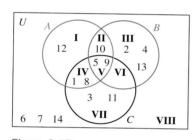

Figure 2.17

Venn diagrams can be used to illustrate and analyze many everyday problems. One example follows.

EXAMPLE ❷ *Blood Types*

Human blood is classified (typed) according to the presence or absence of the specific antigens A, B, and Rh in the red blood cells. Antigens are highly specified proteins and carbohydrates that will trigger the production of antibodies in the blood to fight infection. Blood containing the Rh antigen is labeled positive, $+$, while blood lacking the Rh antigen is labeled negative, $-$. Blood lacking both A and B antigens is called type O. Sketch a Venn diagram with three sets A, B, and Rh and place each type of blood listed in the proper region. A person has only one type of blood.

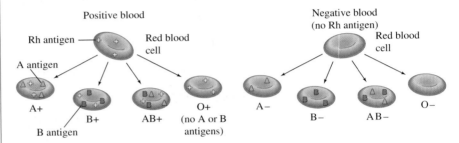

SOLUTION   As illustrated in Chapter 1, the first thing to do is to read the question carefully and make sure you understand what is given and what you are asked to find. There are three antigens A, B, and Rh. Therefore, begin by naming the three circles in a Venn diagram with the three antigens; see Fig. 2.18.

Any blood containing the Rh antigen is positive, and any blood not containing the Rh antigen is negative. Therefore, all blood in the Rh circle is positive, and all blood outside the Rh circle is negative. The intersection of all three sets, region V, is AB+. Region II contains only antigens A and B and is therefore AB−. Region I is A− because it contains only antigen A. Region III is B−, region IV is A+, and region VI is B+. Region VII is O+, containing only the Rh antigen. Region VIII, which lacks all three antigens, is O−.   ●

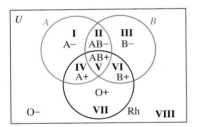

Figure 2.18

Verification of Equality of Sets

In this chapter, for clarity we may refer to operations on sets, such as $A \cup B'$ or $A \cap B \cap C$, as *statements involving sets* or simply as *statements*. Now we discuss how to determine if two statements involving sets are equal.

Consider the question: Is $A' \cup B = A' \cap B$ *for all sets A and B*? For the specific sets $U = \{1, 2, 3, 4, 5\}$, $A = \{1, 3\}$, and $B = \{2, 4, 5\}$, is $A' \cup B = A' \cap B$? To answer the question, we do the following.

Find $A' \cup B$	Find $A' \cap B$
$A' = \{2, 4, 5\}$	$A' = \{2, 4, 5\}$
$A' \cup B = \{2, 4, 5\}$	$A' \cap B = \{2, 4, 5\}$

For these sets, $A' \cup B = A' \cap B$, because both set statements are equal to $\{2, 4, 5\}$. At this point you may believe that $A' \cup B = A' \cap B$ for all sets A and B.

If we select the sets $U = \{1, 2, 3, 4, 5\}$, $A = \{1, 3, 5\}$, and $B = \{2, 3\}$, we see that $A' \cup B = \{2, 3, 4\}$ and $A' \cap B = \{2\}$. For this case, $A' \cup B \neq A' \cap B$. Thus, we have proved that $A' \cup B \neq A' \cap B$ for all sets A and B by using a *counterexample*. A counterexample, as explained in Chapter 1, is an example that shows a statement is not true.

In Chapter 1, we explained that proofs involve the use of deductive reasoning. Recall that deductive reasoning begins with a general statement and works to a specific conclusion. To verify, or determine whether set statements are equal for any two sets selected, we use deductive reasoning with Venn diagrams. Venn diagrams are used because they can illustrate general cases. To determine if statements that contain sets, such as $(A \cup B)'$ and $A' \cap B'$, are equal for all sets A and B, we use the regions of Venn diagrams. If both statements represent the same regions of the Venn diagram, then the statements are equal for all sets A and B. See Example 3.

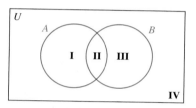

Figure 2.19

EXAMPLE ❸ *Equality of Sets*

Determine whether $(A \cap B)' = A' \cup B'$ for all sets A and B.

SOLUTION Draw a Venn diagram with two sets A and B, as in Fig. 2.19. Label the regions as indicated.

Find $(A \cap B)'$

Set	Corresponding Regions
A	I, II
B	II, III
$A \cap B$	II
$(A \cap B)'$	I, III, IV

Find $A' \cup B'$

Set	Corresponding Regions
A'	III, IV
B'	I, IV
$A' \cup B'$	I, III, IV

Both statements are represented by the same regions, I, III, and IV, of the Venn diagram. Thus, $(A \cap B)' = A' \cup B'$ for all sets A and B.   ●

In Example 3, when we proved that $(A \cap B)' = A' \cup B'$, we started with two general sets and worked to the specific conclusion that both statements represented the same regions of the Venn diagram. We showed that $(A \cap B)' = A' \cup B'$ *for all sets A and B*. No matter what sets we choose for A and B, this statement will be true. For example, let $U = \{1, 2, 3, 4, 5, 6, 7, 8, 9, 10\}$, $A = \{3, 4, 6, 10\}$, and $B = \{1, 2, 4, 5, 6, 8\}$.

$$(A \cap B)' = A' \cup B'$$
$$\{4, 6\}' = \{3, 4, 6, 10\}' \cup \{1, 2, 4, 5, 6, 8\}'$$
$$\{1, 2, 3, 5, 7, 8, 9, 10\} = \{1, 2, 5, 7, 8, 9\} \cup \{3, 7, 9, 10\}$$
$$\{1, 2, 3, 5, 7, 8, 9, 10\} = \{1, 2, 3, 5, 7, 8, 9, 10\}$$

We can also use Venn diagrams to prove statements involving three sets.

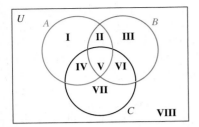

Figure 2.20

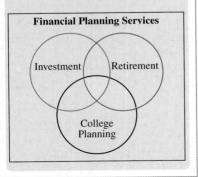
EXAMPLE ❹   *Equality of Sets*

Determine whether $A \cup (B \cap C) = (A \cup B) \cap (A \cup C)$ for all sets, A, B, and C.

SOLUTION Because the statements include three sets, A, B, and C, three circles must be used. The Venn diagram illustrating the eight regions is shown in Fig. 2.20.

First we will find the regions that correspond to $A \cup (B \cap C)$, and then we will find the regions that correspond to $(A \cup B) \cap (A \cup C)$. If both answers are the same, the statements are equal.

Find $A \cup (B \cap C)$

Set	Corresponding Regions
A	I, II, IV, V
$B \cap C$	V, VI
$A \cup (B \cap C)$	I, II, IV, V, VI

Find $(A \cup B) \cap (A \cup C)$

Set	Corresponding Regions
$A \cup B$	I, II, III, IV, V, VI
$A \cup C$	I, II, IV, V, VI, VII
$(A \cup B) \cap (A \cup C)$	I, II, IV, V, VI

The regions that correspond to $A \cup (B \cap C)$ are I, II, IV, V, and VI, and the regions that correspond to $(A \cup B) \cap (A \cup C)$ are also I, II, IV, V, and VI. The results show that both statements are represented by the same regions, namely, I, II, IV, V, and VI, and therefore $A \cup (B \cap C) = (A \cup B) \cap (A \cup C)$ for all sets A, B, and C. ●

In Example 4, we proved that $A \cup (B \cap C) = (A \cup B) \cap (A \cup C)$ for all sets A, B, and C. Show that this statement is true for the specific sets $U = \{1, 2, 3, 4, 5, 6, 7, 8, 9, 10\}$, $A = \{1, 2, 3, 7\}$, $B = \{2, 3, 4, 5, 7, 9\}$, and $C = \{1, 4, 7, 8, 10\}$.

De Morgan's Laws

In set theory, logic, and other branches of mathematics, a pair of related theorems known as De Morgan's laws make it possible to transform statements and formulas into alternative and often more convenient forms. In set theory, *De Morgan's laws* are symbolized as follows.

DE MORGAN'S LAWS
1. $(A \cap B)' = A' \cup B'$
2. $(A \cup B)' = A' \cap B'$

Law 1 was verified in Example 3. We suggest that you verify law 2 at this time. The laws were expressed verbally by William of Ockham in the fourteenth century. In the nineteenth century, Augustus De Morgan expressed them mathematically. De Morgan's laws will be discussed more thoroughly in Chapter 3, Logic.

SECTION 2.4 EXERCISES

CONCEPT/WRITING EXERCISES

1. How many regions are created when constructing a Venn diagram with three overlapping sets?

2. When constructing a Venn diagram with three overlapping sets, which region do you generally complete first?

3. When constructing a Venn diagram with three overlapping sets, after completing region V, which regions do you generally complete next?

4. A Venn diagram contains three sets, A, B, and C, as in Fig. 2.15 on page 72. If region V contains 4 elements and there are 12 elements in $B \cap C$, how many elements belong in region VI? Explain.

5. A Venn diagram contains three sets, A, B, and C, as in Fig. 2.15 on page 72. If region V contains 4 elements and there are 9 elements in $A \cap B$, how many elements belong in region II? Explain.

6. Give De Morgan's laws.

7. a) For $U = \{1, 2, 3, 4, 5\}$, $A = \{1, 4, 5\}$, and $B = \{1, 4, 5\}$, does $A \cup B = A \cap B$?

   b) By observing the answer to part (a), can we conclude that $A \cup B = A \cap B$ for all sets A and B? Explain.

   c) Using a Venn diagram, determine if $A \cup B = A \cap B$ for all sets A and B.

8. What type of reasoning do we use when using Venn diagrams to verify or determine whether set statements are equal?

PRACTICE THE SKILLS

9. Construct a Venn diagram illustrating the following sets.

$$U = \{a, b, c, d, e, f, g, h, i, j\}$$
$$A = \{c, d, e, g, h, i\}$$
$$B = \{a, c, d, g\}$$
$$C = \{c, f, i, j\}$$

10. Construct a Venn diagram illustrating the following sets.

    $U = \{$Delaware, Pennsylvania, New Jersey, Georgia, Connecticut, Massachusetts, Maryland, South Carolina, New Hampshire, Virginia, New York, North Carolina, Rhode Island$\}$

    $A = \{$New York, New Jersey, Pennsylvania, Massachusetts, New Hampshire$\}$

    $B = \{$Delaware, Connecticut, Georgia, Maryland, New York, Rhode Island$\}$

    $C = \{$New York, South Carolina, Rhode Island, Massachusetts$\}$

11. Construct a Venn diagram illustrating the following sets.

    $U = \{$Circuit City, Best Buy, Wal-Mart, Kmart, Target, Sears, JCPenney, Costco, Kohl's, Gap, Gap Kids, Foot Locker, Old Navy, Macy's$\}$

    $A = \{$Circuit City, Wal-Mart, Target, JCPenney, Old Navy$\}$

    $B = \{$Best Buy, Target, Costco, Old Navy, Macy's$\}$

    $C = \{$Target, Sears, Kohl's, Gap, JCPenney$\}$

12. Construct a Venn diagram illustrating the following sets.

    $U = \{$*The Lion King, Aladdin, Cinderella, Beauty and the Beast, Snow White and the Seven Dwarfs, Toy Story, 101 Dalmatians, The Little Mermaid, The Incredibles*$\}$

    $A = \{$*Aladdin, Toy Story, The Lion King, Snow White and the Seven Dwarfs*$\}$

    $B = \{$*Snow White and the Seven Dwarfs, Toy Story, The Lion King, Beauty and the Beast*$\}$

    $C = \{$*Snow White and the Seven Dwarfs, Toy Story, Beauty and the Beast, Cinderella, 101 Dalmatians*$\}$

13. Construct a Venn diagram illustrating the following sets.

    $U = \{$peach, pear, banana, apple, grape, melon, carrot, corn, orange, spinach$\}$

    $A = \{$pear, grape, melon, carrot$\}$

    $B = \{$peach, pear, banana, spinach, corn$\}$

    $C = \{$pear, banana, apple, grape, melon, spinach$\}$

14. Construct a Venn diagram illustrating the following sets.

    $U = \{$Louis Armstrong, Glenn Miller, Stan Kenton, Charlie Parker, Duke Ellington, Benny Goodman, Count Basie, John Coltrane, Dizzy Gillespie, Miles Davis, Thelonius Monk$\}$

    $A = \{$Stan Kenton, Count Basie, Dizzy Gillespie, Duke Ellington, Thelonius Monk$\}$

B = {Louis Armstrong, Glenn Miller, Count Basie, Duke Ellington, Miles Davis}

C = {Count Basie, Miles Davis, Stan Kenton, Charlie Parker, Duke Ellington}

15. *Olympic Medals* Consider the following table, which shows countries that won at least 22 medals in the 2004 Summer Olympics. Let the countries shown in the table represent the universal set.

Country	Gold Medals	Silver Medals	Bronze Medals	Total Medals
United States	35	39	29	103
Russia	27	27	38	92
China	32	17	14	63
Australia	17	16	16	49
Germany	14	16	18	48
Japan	16	9	12	37
France	11	9	13	33
Italy	10	11	11	32
South Korea	9	12	9	30
Great Britain	9	9	12	30
Cuba	9	7	11	27
Ukraine	9	5	9	23
Netherlands	4	9	9	22

Source: *2006 Time Almanac*

Let A = set of teams that won at least 48 medals.

Let B = set of teams that won at least 20 gold medals.

Let C = set of teams that won at least 10 bronze medals.

Construct a Venn diagram that illustrates the sets A, B, and C.

16. *Popular TV Shows* Let U = {*60 Minutes, American Idol–Tues., American Idol–Wed., CSI, CSI:Miami, Desperate Housewives, Friends, Grey's Anatomy, Law & Order, The Apprentice*}. Sets A, B, and C that follow show the five most watched television shows for the years 2004, 2005, and 2006, respectively (according to Nielsen Media Research). Then

A = {*CSI, American Idol–Tues., American Idol–Wed., Friends, The Apprentice*}

B = {*CSI, American Idol–Tues., American Idol–Wed., Desperate Housewives, CSI:Miami*}

C = {*American Idol–Tues., American Idol–Wed., CSI, Desperate Housewives, Grey's Anatomy*}

Construct a Venn diagram illustrating the sets.

Best Hospitals For Exercises 17–22, use the chart below which shows the *U.S. News and World Report* top 10 rankings of hospitals in 2005 in the fields of neurology, cardiology, and orthopedics. The universal set is the set of all U.S. hospitals.

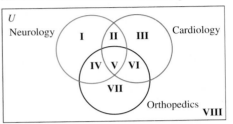

Figure 2.21

Top-Rated Hospitals

Neurology	Cardiology	Orthopedics
1. Mayo Clinic	1. Cleveland Clinic	1. Mayo Clinic
2. Johns Hopkins	2. Mayo Clinic	2. Hospital for Special Surgery
3. New York Presbyterian University Hospital	3. Johns Hopkins	3. Massachusetts General
4. Massachusetts General	4. Duke University Medical Center	4. Johns Hopkins
5. University of California, San Francisco	5. Massachusetts General	5. Cleveland Clinic
6. Cleveland Clinic	6. Brigham and Women's Hospital	6. UCLA Medical Center
7. St. Joseph's Hospital and Medical Center	7. New York–Presbyterian University Hospital	7. University of Iowa Hospitals and Clinics
8. Barnes-Jewish	8. Texas Heart Institute at St. Luke's Episcopal Hospital	8. Rush University Medical Center
9. UCLA Medical Center	9. Barnes-Jewish	9. University of Washington Medical Center
10. Methodist Hospital	10. University of Alabama	10. Duke University Medical Center

Source: *U.S. News and World Report*

Indicate in which region, I–VIII, in Fig. 2.21 each of the following hospitals belongs.

17. Mayo Clinic

18. UCLA Medical Center

19. Methodist Hospital

20. Barnes-Jewish

21. Brigham and Women's Hospital

22. Yale–New Haven Hospital

Rankings of Government Agencies For Exercises 23–28, use the following table, which shows the top 10 government agencies based on employee satisfaction in the areas of effective leadership, family-friendly culture, and pay and benefits. The universal set is the set of all government agencies.

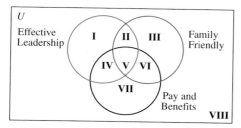

Figure 2.22

Rankings of Government Agencies

Effective Leadership	Family-Friendly Culture	Pay and Benefits
1. National Aeronautics and Space Administration	1. Federal Deposit Insurance Corp.	1. Federal Deposit Insurance Corp.
2. Nuclear Regulatory Commission	2. General Services Administration	2. Office of Management and Budget
3. Office of Management and Budget	3. Environmental Protection Agency	3. Securities and Exchange Commission
4. General Services Administration	4. Nuclear Regulatory Commission	4. National Aeronautics and Space Administration
5. National Science Foundation	5. National Aeronautics and Space Administration	5. Nuclear Regulatory Commission
6. Department of State	6. Office of Personnel Management	6. General Services Administration
7. Department of Energy	7. Department of Energy	7. Department of Commerce
8. Department of Defense	8. Equal Employment Opportunity Commission	8. Agency for International Development
8. Agency for International Development	9. Department of Agriculture	9. Office of Personnel Management
10. Securities and Exchange Commission	9. Department of Education	9. Small Business Administration

Source: Partnership for Public Service

Indicate in which region, I–VIII, in Fig. 2.22 each of the following agencies belongs.

23. Department of Energy

24. National Aeronautics and Space Administration

25. Department of Justice

26. Small Business Administration

27. Department of Agriculture

28. Office of Personnel Management

Figures In Exercises 29–40, indicate in Fig. 2.23 the region in which each of the figures would be placed.

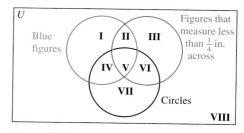

Figure 2.23

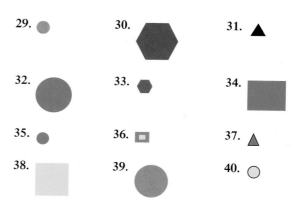

Senate Bills *During a session of the U.S. Senate, three bills were voted on. The votes of six senators are shown below the figure. Determine in which region of Fig. 2.24 each senator would be placed. The set labeled Bill 1 represents the set of senators who voted yes on Bill 1, and so on.*

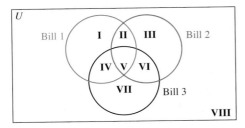

Figure 2.24

SENATOR	BILL 1	BILL 2	BILL 3
41. Feingold	yes	no	no
42. Lott	no	no	yes
43. McCain	no	no	no
44. Mikulski	yes	yes	yes
45. Obama	no	yes	yes
46. Specter	no	yes	no

In Exercises 47–60, use the Venn diagram in Fig. 2.25 to list the sets in roster form.

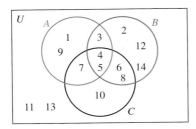

Figure 2.25

47. *A*

48. *U*

49. *B*

50. *C*

51. *A ∩ B*

52. *A ∩ C*

53. *(B ∩ C)'*

54. *A ∩ B ∩ C*

55. *A ∪ B*

56. *B ∪ C*

57. *(A ∪ C)'*

58. *A ∩ (B ∪ C)*

59. *A'*

60. *(A ∪ B ∪ C)'*

In Exercises 61–68, use Venn diagrams to determine whether the following statements are equal for all sets A and B.

61. $(A \cup B)'$, $A' \cap B'$

62. $(A \cap B)'$, $A \cup B'$

63. $A' \cup B'$, $A \cap B$

64. $(A \cup B)'$, $(A \cap B)'$

65. $A' \cap B'$, $(A \cap B)'$

66. $A' \cap B'$, $A \cup B'$

67. $(A' \cap B)'$, $A \cup B'$

68. $A' \cap B'$, $(A' \cap B')'$

In Exercises 69–78, use Venn diagrams to determine whether the following statements are equal for all sets A, B, and C.

69. $A \cap (B \cup C)$, $(A \cap B) \cup C$

70. $A \cup (B \cap C)$, $(B \cap C) \cup A$

71. $A \cap (B \cup C)$, $(B \cup C) \cap A$

72. $A \cup (B \cap C)'$, $A' \cap (B \cup C)$

73. $A \cap (B \cup C)$, $(A \cap B) \cup (A \cap C)$

74. $A \cup (B \cap C)$, $(A \cup B) \cap (A \cup C)$

75. $A \cap (B \cup C)'$, $A \cap (B' \cap C')$

76. $(A \cup B) \cap (B \cup C)$, $B \cup (A \cap C)$

77. $(A \cup B)' \cap C$, $(A' \cup C') \cap (B' \cup C)$

78. $(C \cap B)' \cup (A \cap B)'$, $A \cap (B \cap C)$

In Exercises 79–82, use set statements to write a description of the shaded area. Use union, intersection and complement as necessary. More than one answer may be possible.

79.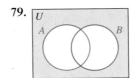

80.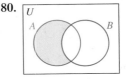

81.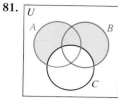

82.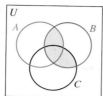

PROBLEM SOLVING

83. Let

$$U = \{1, 2, 3, 4, 5, 6, 7, 8, 9, 10\}$$
$$A = \{1, 2, 3, 4\}$$
$$B = \{3, 6, 7\}$$
$$C = \{6, 7, 9\}$$

a) Show that $(A \cup B) \cap C = (A \cap C) \cup (B \cap C)$ for these sets.

b) Make up your own sets A, B, and C. Verify that $(A \cup B) \cap C = (A \cap C) \cup (B \cap C)$ for your sets A, B, and C.

c) Use Venn diagrams to verify that $(A \cup B) \cap C = (A \cap C) \cup (B \cap C)$ for all sets A, B, and C.

84. Let

$$U = \{a, b, c, d, e, f, g, h, i\}$$
$$A = \{a, c, d, e, f\}$$
$$B = \{c, d\}$$
$$C = \{a, b, c, d, e\}$$

a) Determine whether $(A \cup C)' \cap B = (A \cap C)' \cap B$ for these sets.

b) Make up your own sets, A, B, and C. Determine whether $(A \cup C)' \cap B = (A \cap C)' \cap B$ for your sets.

c) Determine whether $(A \cup C)' \cap B = (A \cap C)' \cap B$ for all sets A, B, and C.

85. *Blood Types* A hematology text gives the following information on percentages of the different types of blood worldwide.

Type	Positive Blood, %	Negative Blood, %
A	37	6
O	32	6.5
B	11	2
AB	5	0.5

Construct a Venn diagram similar to the one in Example 2 and place the correct percent in each of the eight regions.

86. Define each of the eight regions in Fig. 2.26 using sets A, B, and C and a set operation. (*Hint:* $A \cap B' \cap C'$ defines region I.)

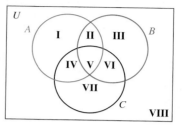

Figure 2.26

87. *Categorizing Contracts* J & C Mechanical Contractors wants to classify its projects. The contractors categorize set A as construction projects, set B as plumbing projects, and set C as projects with a budget greater than $300,000.

a) Draw a Venn diagram that can be used to categorize the company projects according to the listed criteria.

b) Determine the region of the diagram that contains construction projects and plumbing projects with a budget greater than $300,000. Describe the region using sets A, B, and C with set operations. Use union, intersection, and complement as necessary.

c) Determine the region of the diagram that contains plumbing projects with a budget greater than $300,000 that are not construction projects. Describe the region using sets A, B and C with set operations. Use union, intersection, and complement as necessary.

d) Determine the region of the diagram that contains construction projects and nonplumbing projects whose budget is less than or equal to $300,000. Describe the region using sets A, B, and C with set operations. Use union, intersection, and complement as necessary.

CHALLENGE PROBLEM/GROUP ACTIVITY

88. We were able to determine the number of elements in the union of two sets with the formula

$$n(A \cup B) = n(A) + n(B) - n(A \cap B).$$

Can you determine a formula for finding the number of elements in the union of three sets? In other words, write a formula to determine $n(A \cup B \cup C)$. [*Hint:* The formula will contain each of the following: $n(A)$, $n(B)$, $n(C)$, $n(A \cap B \cap C')$, $n(A \cap B' \cap C)$, $n(A' \cap B \cap C)$, and $2n(A \cap B \cap C)$.]

RECREATIONAL MATHEMATICS

89. a) Construct a Venn diagram illustrating four sets, *A*, *B*, *C*, and *D*. (*Hint*: Four circles cannot be used, and you should end up with 16 *distinct* regions.) Have fun!

    b) Label each region with a set statement (see Exercise 86). Check all 16 regions to make sure that *each is distinct*.

INTERNET/RESEARCH ACTIVITY

90. The two Venn diagrams on the right illustrate what happens when colors are added or subtracted. Do research in an art text, an encyclopedia, the Internet, or another source and write a report explaining the creation of the colors in the Venn diagrams, using such terms as union of colors and subtraction (or difference) of colors.

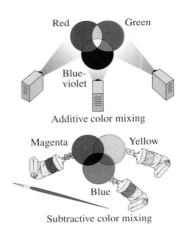

Additive color mixing

Subtractive color mixing

2.5   APPLICATIONS OF SETS

▲ We can use a Venn diagram to determine how many members of a health club use a particular piece of equipment.

The members of a health club were surveyed about their use of the equipment at the club. Suppose the results of the survey show how many members use the treadmill, how many members use the StairMaster, and how many members use both pieces of equipment. How can the manager of the club use this information to determine how many members use only the treadmill? In this section, we will learn how to use Venn diagrams to answer this type of question.

    We can solve practical problems involving sets by using the problem-solving process discussed in Chapter 1: Understand the problem, devise a plan, carry out the plan, and then examine and check the results. First determine: What is the problem? or What am I looking for? To devise the plan, list all the facts that are given and how they are related. *Look for key words or phrases* such as "only set *A*," "set *A* and set *B*," "set *A* or set *B*," "set *A* and set *B* and not set *C*." Remember that *and* means intersection, *or* means union, and *not* means complement. The problems we solve in this section contain two or three sets of elements, which can be represented in a Venn diagram. Our plan will generally include drawing a Venn diagram, labeling the diagram, and filling in the regions of the diagram.

    Whenever possible, follow the procedure in Section 2.4 for completing the Venn diagram and then answer the questions. *Remember, when drawing Venn diagrams, we generally start with the intersection of the sets and work outward.*

EXAMPLE ❶ *Fitness Equipment*

Fitness for Life health club is considering adding additional cardiovascular equipment. It is considering two types of equipment, treadmills (T) and Stair-Masters (S). The health club surveyed a sample of members and asked which equipment they had used in the previous month. Of 150 members surveyed, it was determined that

102 used the treadmills.

71 used the StairMasters.

40 used both types.

Of those surveyed,

a) how many did not use either the treadmill or the StairMaster?
b) how many used the treadmill but not the StairMaster?
c) how many used the StairMaster but not the treadmill?
d) how many used either the treadmill or StairMaster?

SOLUTION The problem provides the following information.

The number of members surveyed is 150: $n(U)$ is 150.

The number of members surveyed who used the treadmill is 102: $n(T) = 102$.

The number of members surveyed who used the StairMaster is 71: $n(S) = 71$.

The number of members surveyed who used both the treadmill and the Stair-Master is 40: $n(T \cap S) = 40$.

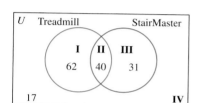

Figure 2.27

We illustrate this information on the Venn diagram shown in Fig. 2.27. We already know that $T \cap S$ corresponds to region II. As $n(T \cap S) = 40$, we write 40 in region II. Set T consists of regions I and II. We know that set T, the members who used the treadmill, contains 102 members. Therefore, region I contains $102 - 40$, or 62 members. We write the number 62 in region I. Set S consists of regions II and III. As $n(S) = 71$, the total in these two regions must be 71. Region II contains 40, leaving $71 - 40$ or 31 for region III. We write 31 in region III.

The total number of members surveyed who used the treadmill or the Stair-Master is found by adding the numbers in regions I, II, and III. Therefore, $n(T \cup S) = 62 + 40 + 31 = 133$. The number in region IV is the difference between $n(U)$ and $n(T \cup S)$. There are $150 - 133$, or 17 members in region IV.

a) The members surveyed who did not use either the treadmill or the StairMaster are those members of the universal set who are not contained in set T or set S. The 17 members in region IV did not use the treadmill or StairMaster.

b) The 62 members in region I are those members surveyed who used the treadmill but not the StairMaster.

c) The 31 members in region III are those members surveyed who used the Stair-Master but not the treadmill.

d) The members in regions I, II, or III are those members surveyed who used either the treadmill or the StairMaster. Thus, $62 + 40 + 31$ or 133 members surveyed used either the treadmill or the StairMaster. Notice that the 40 members in region II who use both types of equipment are included in those members surveyed who used either the treadmill or the StairMaster. ●

Similar problems involving three sets can be solved, as illustrated in Example 2.

EXAMPLE ❷ *Software Purchases*

CompUSA has recorded recent sales for three types of computer software: games, educational software, and utility programs. The following information regarding software purchases was obtained from a survey of 893 customers.

> 545 purchased games.
>
> 497 purchased educational software.
>
> 290 purchased utility programs.
>
> 297 purchased games and educational software.
>
> 196 purchased educational software and utility programs.
>
> 205 purchased games and utility programs.
>
> 157 purchased all three types of software.

Use a Venn diagram to answer the following questions. How many customers purchased

a) none of these types of software?

b) only games?

c) at least one of these types of software?

d) exactly two of these types of software?

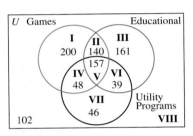

Figure 2.28

SOLUTION Begin by constructing a Venn diagram with three overlapping circles. One circle represents games, another educational software, and the third utilities. See Fig 2.28. Label the eight regions.

Whenever possible, work from the center of the diagram outwards. First fill in region V. Since 157 customers purchased all three types of software, we place 157 in region V. Next determine the number to be placed in region II. Regions II and V together represent the customers who purchased both games and educational software. Since 297 customers purchased both of these types of software, the sum of the numbers in these regions must be 297. Since 157 have already been placed in region V, $297 - 157 = 140$ must be placed in region II. Now we determine the number to be placed in region IV. Since 205 customers purchased both games and utility programs, the sum of the numbers in regions IV and V must be 205. Since 157 have already been placed in region V, $205 - 157 = 48$ must be placed in region IV. Now determine the number to be placed in region VI. A total of 196 customers purchased educational software and utility programs. The numbers in regions V and VI must total 196. Since 157 have already been placed in region V, the number to be placed in region VI is $196 - 157 = 39$.

Now that we have determined the numbers for regions V, II, IV, and VI, we can determine the numbers to be placed in regions I, III, and VII. We are given that 545 customers purchased games. The sum of the numbers in regions I, II, IV, and V must be 545. To determine the number to be placed in region I, subtract the amounts in regions II, IV, and V from 545. There must be $545 - 140 - 48 - 157 = 200$ in region I. Determine the numbers to be placed in regions III and VII in a similar manner.

$$\text{Region III} = 497 - 140 - 157 - 39 = 161$$
$$\text{Region VII} = 290 - 48 - 157 - 39 = 46$$

Now that we have determined the numbers in regions I through VII, we can determine the number to be placed in region VIII. Adding the numbers in regions I through VII yields a sum of 791. The difference between the total number of customers surveyed, 893, and the sum of the numbers in regions I through VII must be placed in region VIII.

$$\text{Region VIII} = 893 - 791 = 102$$

Now that we have completed the Venn diagram, we can answer the questions.

a) One hundred two customers did not purchase any of these types of software. These customers are indicated in region VIII.

b) Region I represents those customers who purchased only games. Thus, 200 customers purchased only games.

c) The words *at least one* mean "one or more." All those in regions I through VII purchased at least one of the types of software. The sum of the numbers in regions I through VII is 791, so 791 customers purchased at least one of the types of software.

d) The customers in regions II, IV, and VI purchased exactly two of the types of software. Summing the numbers in these regions $140 + 48 + 39$ we find that 227 customers purchased exactly two of these types of software. Notice that we did not include the customers in region V. Those customers purchased all three types of software.

The procedure to work problems like those given in Example 2 is generally the same. Start by completing region V. Next complete regions II, IV, and VI. Then complete regions I, III, and VII. Finally, complete region VIII. When you are constructing Venn diagrams, be sure to check your work carefully.

> **TIMELY TIP** When constructing a Venn diagram, the most common mistake made by students is forgetting to subtract the number in region V from the respective values in determining the numbers to be placed in regions II, IV, and VI.

EXAMPLE ❸ *Travel Packages*

Liberty Travel surveyed 125 potential customers. The following information was obtained.

68 wished to travel to Hawaii.

53 wished to travel to Las Vegas.

47 wished to travel to Disney World.

34 wished to travel to Hawaii and Las Vegas.

26 wished to travel to Las Vegas and Disney World.

23 wished to travel to Hawaii and Disney World.

18 wished to travel to all three destinations.

Use a Venn diagram to answer the following questions. How many of those surveyed

a) did not wish to travel to any of these destinations?

b) wished to travel only to Hawaii?

c) wished to travel to Disney World *and* Las Vegas, but not to Hawaii?

d) wished to travel to Disney World *or* Las Vegas, but not to Hawaii?

e) wished to travel to exactly one of these destinations?

▲ Hawaii

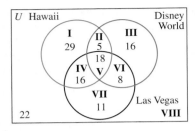

Figure 2.29

SOLUTION The Venn diagram is constructed using the procedures we outlined in Example 2. The diagram is illustrated in Fig. 2.29. We suggest you construct the diagram by yourself now and check your diagram with Fig. 2.29.

a) Twenty-two potential customers did not wish to travel to any of these destinations (see region VIII).

b) Twenty-nine potential customers wished to travel only to Hawaii (see region I).

c) Those potential customers in region VI wished to travel to Disney World *and* Las Vegas, but not to Hawaii. Therefore, eight customers satisfied the criteria.

d) The word *or* in this type of problem means one or the other or both. All the potential customers in regions II, III, IV, V, VI, and VII wished to travel to Disney World or Las Vegas. Those in regions II, IV, and V also wished to travel to Hawaii. The potential customers that wished to travel to Disney World or Las Vegas, but not to Hawaii, are found by adding the numbers in regions III, VI, and VII. There are $16 + 8 + 11 = 35$ potential customers who satisfy the criteria.

e) Those potential customers in regions I, III, and VII wished to travel to exactly one of the destinations. Therefore, $29 + 16 + 11 = 56$ customers wished to travel to exactly one of these destinations.

SECTION 2.5   EXERCISES

PRACTICE THE SKILLS/PROBLEM SOLVING

In Exercises 1–15, draw a Venn diagram to obtain the answers.

1. **Campus Activities** At a local college, a survey was taken to determine participation in different campus activities. Of 150 students surveyed, it was determined that
   32 participated in clubs
   27 participated in intramural sports
   18 participated in both clubs and intramural sports

   Of those surveyed,

   a) how many participated only in clubs?

   b) how many participated only in intramural sports?

   c) how many did not participate in either clubs or intramural sports?

2. **Landscape Purchases** Agway Lawn and Garden collected the following information regarding purchases from 130 of its customers.
   74 purchased shrubs.
   70 purchased trees.
   41 purchased both shrubs and trees.

   Of those surveyed,

   a) how many purchased only shrubs?

   b) how many purchased only trees?

   c) how many did not purchase either of these items?

3. **Real Estate** The Maiello's are moving to Wilmington, Delaware. Their real estate agent located 83 houses listed for sale, in the Wilmington area, in their price range. Of these houses listed for sale,
   47 had a family room.
   42 had a deck.
   30 had a family room and a deck.

   How many had

   a) a family room but not a deck?

   b) a deck but not a family room?

   c) either a family room or a deck?

4. **Soft Drink Taste Test** A soft drink company wishes to introduce a new soft drink. The company is considering two flavors, lemon lime and cherry cola. In a sample of 125 people, it was found that

80 liked lemon lime.
68 liked cherry cola.
42 liked both types.

a) How many liked only lemon lime?

b) How many liked only cherry cola?

c) How many liked either one or the other or both?

d) How many did not like either flavor?

5. *Cultural Activities* Thirty-three U.S. cities were researched to determine whether they had a professional sports team, a symphony, or a children's museum. The following information was determined.

16 had a professional sports team.
17 had a symphony.
15 had a children's museum.
11 had a professional sports team and a symphony.
7 had a professional sports team and a children's museum.
9 had a symphony and children's museum.
5 had all three activities.

How many of the cities surveyed had

a) only a professional sports team?

b) a professional sports team and a symphony, but not a children's museum?

c) a professional sports team or a symphony?

d) a professional sports team or a symphony, but not a children's museum?

e) exactly two of the activities?

6. *Amusement Parks* In a survey of 85 amusement parks, it was found that

24 had a hotel on site.
55 had water slides.
38 had a wave pool.
13 had a hotel on site and water slides.
10 had a hotel on site and a wave pool.
19 had water slides and a wave pool.
7 had all three features.

How many of the amusement parks surveyed had

a) only water slides?

b) exactly one of these features?

c) at least one of these features?

d) exactly two of these features?

e) none of these features?

▲ See Exercise 6

7. *Book Purchases* A survey of 85 customers was taken at Barnes & Noble regarding the types of books purchased. The survey found that

44 purchased mysteries.
33 purchased science fiction.
29 purchased romance novels.
13 purchased mysteries and science fiction.
5 purchased science fiction and romance novels.
11 purchased mysteries and romance novels.
2 purchased all three types of books.

How many of the customers surveyed purchased

a) only mysteries?

b) mysteries and science fiction, but not romance novels?

c) mysteries or science fiction?

d) mysteries or science fiction, but not romance novels?

e) exactly two types?

8. *Movies* A survey of 350 customers was taken at Regal Cinemas in Austin, Texas, regarding the type of movies customers liked. The following information was determined.

196 liked dramas.
153 liked comedies.
88 liked science fiction.
59 liked dramas and comedies.
37 liked dramas and science fiction.
32 liked comedies and science fiction.
21 liked all three types of movies.

Of the customers surveyed, how many liked

a) none of these types of movies?

b) only dramas?

c) exactly one of these types of movies?

d) exactly two of these types of movies?

e) dramas or comedies?

9. *Transportation* Seventy businesspeople in Sacramento, California, were asked how they traveled to work during the previous month. The following information was determined.
   28 used public transportation.
   18 rode in a car pool.
   37 drove alone.
    5 used public transportation and rode in a car pool.
    9 used public transportation and drove alone.
    4 rode in a car pool and drove alone.
    3 used all three forms of transportation.

How many of those surveyed

a) only used public transportation?

b) only drove alone?

c) used public transportation and rode in a car pool, but did not drive alone?

d) used public transportation or rode in a car pool, but did not drive alone?

e) used none of these forms of transportation?

10. *Colleges and Universities* In a survey of four-year colleges and universities, it was found that
    356 offered a liberal arts degree.
    293 offered a computer engineering degree.
    285 offered a nursing degree.
    193 offered a liberal arts degree and a computer engineering degree.
    200 offered a liberal arts degree and a nursing degree.
    139 offered a computer engineering degree and a nursing degree.
     68 offered a liberal arts degree, a computer engineering degree, and a nursing degree.
     26 offered none of these degrees.

a) How many four-year colleges and universities were surveyed?

Of the four-year colleges and universities surveyed, how many offered

b) a liberal arts degree and a nursing degree, but not a computer engineering degree?

c) a computer engineering degree, but neither a liberal arts degree nor a nursing degree?

d) exactly two of these degrees?

e) at least one of these degrees?

11. *Homeowners' Insurance Policies* A committee of the Florida legislature decided to analyze 350 homeowners' insurance policies to determine if the consumers' homes were covered for damage due to sinkholes, mold, and floods. The following results of the analysis were determined.
    170 homes were covered for damage due to sinkholes.
    172 homes were covered for damage due to mold.
    234 homes were covered for damage due to floods.
    105 homes were covered for damage due to sinkholes and mold.
    115 homes were covered for damage due to mold and floods.
    109 homes were covered for damage due to sinkholes and floods.
     78 homes were covered for damage due to all three conditions.

How many of the homes

a) were covered for damage due to mold but were not covered for damage due to sinkholes?

b) were covered for damage due to sinkholes or mold?

c) were covered for damage due to mold and floods, but were not covered for damage due to sinkholes?

d) were not covered for damage due to any of the three conditions?

12. *Appetizers Survey* Da Tulio's Restaurant hired Dennis Goldstein to determine what kind of appetizers customers liked. He surveyed 100 people, with the following results: 78 liked shrimp cocktail, 56 liked mozzarella sticks, and 35 liked both shrimp cocktail and mozzarella sticks. Every person interviewed liked one or the other or both kinds of appetizers. Does this result seem correct? Explain your answer.

13. *Discovering an Error* An immigration agent sampled cars going from the United States into Canada. In his report, he indicated that of the 85 cars sampled,

35 cars were driven by women.
53 cars were driven by U.S. citizens.
43 cars had two or more passengers.
27 cars were driven by women who are U.S. citizens.
25 cars were driven by women and had two or more passengers.
20 cars were driven by U.S. citizens and had two or more passengers.
15 cars were driven by women who are U.S. citizens and had two or more passengers.

After his supervisor reads the report, she explains to the agent that he made a mistake. Explain how his supervisor knew that the agent's report contained an error.

CHALLENGE PROBLEMS/GROUP ACTIVITIES

14. *Parks* A survey of 300 parks showed the following.

15 had only camping.
20 had only hiking trails.
35 had only picnicking.
185 had camping.
140 had camping and hiking trails.
125 had camping and picnicking.
210 had hiking trails.

Find the number of parks that

a) had at least one of these features.

b) had all three features.

c) did not have any of these features.

d) had exactly two of these features.

15. *Surveying Farmers* A survey of 500 farmers in a midwestern state showed the following.

125 grew only wheat.
110 grew only corn.
90 grew only oats.
200 grew wheat.
60 grew wheat and corn.
50 grew wheat and oats.
180 grew corn.

Find the number of farmers who

a) grew at least one of the three.

b) grew all three.

c) did not grow any of the three.

d) grew exactly two of the three.

RECREATIONAL MATHEMATICS

16. *Number of Elements* A universal set U consists of 12 elements. If sets A, B, and C are proper subsets of U and $n(U) = 12$, $n(A \cap B) = n(A \cap C) = n(B \cap C) = 6$, $n(A \cap B \cap C) = 4$, and $n(A \cup B \cup C) = 10$, determine

a) $n(A \cup B)$ **b)** $n(A' \cup C)$ **c)** $n(A \cap B)'$

2.6   INFINITE SETS

▲ Georg Cantor, founder of set theory

Which set is larger, the set of integers or the set of even integers? One might argue that because the set of even integers is a subset of the set of integers, the set of integers must be larger than the set of even integers. Yet both sets are infinite sets, so how can we determine which set is larger? This question puzzled mathematicians for centuries until 1874, when Georg Cantor developed a method of determining the cardinal number of an infinite set. In this section, we will discuss infinite sets and how to determine the number of elements in an infinite set.

On page 48, we state that a finite set is a set in which the number of elements is zero or the number of elements can be expressed as a natural number. On page 48, we define a one-to-one correspondence. To determine the number of elements in a finite set, we can place the set in a one-to-one correspondence with a subset of the set of counting numbers. For example, the set $A = \{\#, ?, \$\}$ can be placed in one-to-one correspondence with set $B = \{1, 2, 3\}$, a subset of the set of counting numbers.

$$A = \{\#, ?, \$\}$$
$$\downarrow \downarrow \downarrow$$
$$B = \{1, 2, 3\}$$

Because the cardinal number of set B is 3, the cardinal number of set A is also 3. Any two sets such as set A and set B that can be placed in a one-to-one correspondence must have the same number of elements (therefore the same cardinality) and must be equivalent sets. Note that $n(A)$ and $n(B)$ both equal 3.

German mathematician Georg Cantor (1845–1918), known as the father of set theory, thought about sets that were not bounded. He called an unbounded set an *infinite set* and provided the following definition.

> An **infinite set** is a set that can be placed in a one-to-one correspondence with a proper subset of itself.

In Example 1, we use Cantor's definition of an infinite set to show that the set of counting numbers is infinite.

EXAMPLE ❶ *The Set of Natural Numbers*

Show that $N = \{1, 2, 3, 4, 5, \ldots, n, \ldots\}$ is an infinite set.

SOLUTION To show that the set N is infinite, we establish a one-to-one correspondence between the counting numbers and a proper subset of itself. By removing the first element from the set of counting numbers, we get the set $\{2, 3, 4, 5, \ldots\}$, which is a proper subset of the set of counting numbers. Now we establish the one-to-one correspondence.

$$\text{Counting numbers} = \{1, 2, 3, 4, 5, \ldots, \quad n \quad, \ldots\}$$
$$\downarrow \downarrow \downarrow \downarrow \downarrow \qquad \downarrow$$
$$\text{Proper subset} \quad = \{2, 3, 4, 5, 6, \ldots, n + 1, \ldots\}$$

Note that for any number, n, in the set of counting numbers, its corresponding number in the proper subset is one greater, or $n + 1$. We have now shown the desired one-to-one correspondence, and thus the set of counting numbers is infinite. ●

Note in Example 1 that we showed the pairing of the general terms $n \rightarrow (n + 1)$. Showing a one-to-one correspondence of infinite sets requires showing the pairing of the general terms in the two infinite sets.

In the set of counting numbers, n represents the general term. For any other set of numbers, the general term will be different. The general term in any set should be written in terms of n such that when 1 is substituted for n in the general term, we get the first number in the set; when 2 is substituted for n in the general term, we get the

second number in the set; when 6 is substituted for n in the general term, we get the sixth number in the set; and so on.

Consider the set $\{4, 9, 14, 19, \dots\}$. Suppose we want to write the general term for this set (or sequence) of numbers. What would the general term be? The numbers differ by 5, so the general term will be of the form $5n$ plus or minus some number. Substituting 1 for n yields $5(1)$, or 5. Because the first number in the set is 4, we need to subtract 1 from the 5. Thus, the general term is $5n - 1$. Note that when $n = 1$, the value is $5(1) - 1$ or 4; when $n = 2$, the value is $5(2) - 1$ or 9; when $n = 3$, the value is $5(3) - 1$ or 14; and so on. Therefore, we write the set of numbers with the general term as

$$\{4, 9, 14, 19, \dots, 5n - 1, \dots\}$$

Now that you are aware of how to determine the general term of a set of numbers, we can do some more problems involving sets.

EXAMPLE ❷ *The Set of Even Numbers*

Show that the set of even counting numbers $\{2, 4, 6, 8, \dots, 2n, \dots\}$ is an infinite set.

SOLUTION First create a proper subset of the set of even counting numbers by re-moving the first number from the set. Then establish a one-to-one correspondence.

Even counting numbers: $\{2, 4, 6, 8, \quad \dots, \quad 2n \quad, \dots\}$

Proper subset: $\{4, 6, 8, 10, \dots, 2n + 2, \dots\}$

A one-to-one correspondence exists between the two sets, so the set of even count-ing numbers is infinite. ●

EXAMPLE ❸ *The Set of Multiples of Four*

Show that the set $\{4, 8, 12, 16, \dots, 4n, \dots\}$ is an infinite set.

SOLUTION

Given set: $\{4, 8, 12, 16, 20, \dots, \quad 4n \quad, \dots\}$

Proper subset: $\{8, 12, 16, 20, 24, \dots, 4n + 4, \dots\}$

Therefore, the given set is an infinite set. ●

Countable Sets

In his work with infinite sets, Cantor developed ideas on how to determine the cardi-nal number of an infinite set. He called the cardinal number of infinite sets "transfinite cardinal numbers" or "transfinite powers." He defined a set as *countable* if it is finite or if it can be placed in a one-to-one correspondence with the set of counting num-bers. All infinite sets that can be placed in a one-to-one correspondence with the set of counting numbers have cardinal number *aleph-null*, symbolized $\aleph_0$ (the first Hebrew letter, aleph, with a zero subscript, read "null").

EXAMPLE ❹   *The Cardinal Number of the Set of Even Numbers*

Show that the set of even counting numbers has cardinal number $\aleph_0$.

SOLUTION   In Example 2, we showed that a set of even counting numbers is infinite by setting up a one-to-one correspondence between the set and a proper subset of itself.

Now we will show that it is countable and has cardinality $\aleph_0$ by setting up a one-to-one correspondence between the set of counting numbers and the set of even counting numbers.

Counting numbers: $N = \{1, 2, 3, 4, \ldots, n, \ldots\}$

$$\downarrow \downarrow \downarrow \downarrow \qquad \downarrow$$

Even counting numbers: $E = \{2, 4, 6, 8, \ldots, 2n, \ldots\}$

For each number n in the set of counting numbers, its corresponding number is $2n$. Since we found a one-to-one correspondence between the set of counting numbers and the set of even counting numbers, the set of even counting numbers is countable. Thus, the cardinal number of the set of even counting numbers is $\aleph_0$; that is, $n(E) = \aleph_0$. As we mentioned earlier, the set of even counting numbers is an infinite set since it can be placed in a one-to-one correspondence with a proper subset of itself. Therefore, the set of even counting numbers is both infinite and countable.   ●

Any set that can be placed in a one-to-one correspondence with the set of counting numbers has cardinality $\aleph_0$ and is infinite and is countable.

EXAMPLE ❺   *The Cardinal Number of the Set of Odd Numbers*

Show that the set of odd counting numbers has cardinality $\aleph_0$.

SOLUTION   To show that the set of odd counting numbers has cardinality $\aleph_0$, we need to show a one-to-one correspondence between the set of counting numbers and the set of odd counting numbers.

Counting numbers: $N = \{1, 2, 3, 4, 5, \ldots, \quad n, \ldots\}$

$$\downarrow \downarrow \downarrow \downarrow \downarrow \qquad \downarrow$$

Odd counting numbers: $O = \{1, 3, 5, 7, 9, \ldots, 2n - 1, \ldots\}$

Since there is a one-to-one correspondence, the odd counting numbers have cardinality $\aleph_0$; that is, $n(O) = \aleph_0$.   ●

We have shown that both the odd and even counting numbers have cardinality $\aleph_0$. Merging the odd counting numbers with the even counting numbers gives the set of counting numbers, and we may reason that

$$\aleph_0 + \aleph_0 = \aleph_0$$

This result may seem strange, but it is true. What could such a statement mean? Well, consider a hotel with infinitely many rooms. If all the rooms are occupied, the hotel is, of course, full. If more guests appear wanting accommodations, will they be turned away? The answer is *no*, for if the room clerk were to reassign each guest to a new room

Welcome to
HOTEL INFINITY

▲ . . . where there's always room
for one more. . .

with a room number twice that of the present room, all the odd-numbered rooms would become unoccupied and there would be space for more guests!

Cantor showed that there are different orders of infinity. Sets that are countable and have cardinal number $\aleph_0$ are the lowest order of infinity. Cantor showed that the set of integers and the set of rational numbers (fractions of the form p/q, where $q \neq 0$) are infinite sets with cardinality $\aleph_0$. He also showed that the set of real numbers (discussed in Chapter 5) could not be placed in a one-to-one correspondence with the set of counting numbers and that they have a higher order of infinity.

SECTION 2.6 EXERCISES

CONCEPT/WRITING EXERCISES

1. What is an infinite set as defined in this section?

2. **a)** What is a countable set?

   b) How can we determine if a given set has cardinality $\aleph_0$?

PRACTICE THE SKILLS

In Exercises 3–12, show that the set is infinite by placing it in a one-to-one correspondence with a proper subset of itself. Be sure to show the pairing of the general terms in the sets.

3. $\{5, 6, 7, 8, 9, \dots\}$

4. $\{20, 21, 22, 23, 24, \dots\}$

5. $\{3, 5, 7, 9, 11, \dots\}$

6. $\{20, 22, 24, 26, 28, \dots\}$

7. $\{3, 7, 11, 15, 19, \dots\}$

8. $\{4, 8, 12, 16, 20, \dots\}$

9. $\{6, 11, 16, 21, 26, \dots\}$

10. $\{1, \frac{1}{2}, \frac{1}{3}, \frac{1}{4}, \frac{1}{5}, \dots\}$

11. $\{\frac{1}{2}, \frac{1}{4}, \frac{1}{6}, \frac{1}{8}, \frac{1}{10}, \dots\}$

12. $\{\frac{6}{13}, \frac{7}{13}, \frac{8}{13}, \frac{9}{13}, \frac{10}{13}, \dots\}$

In Exercises 13–22, show that the set has cardinal number $\aleph_0$ by establishing a one-to-one correspondence between the set of counting numbers and the given set. Be sure to show the pairing of the general terms in the sets.

13. $\{3, 6, 9, 12, 15, \dots\}$

14. $\{50, 51, 52, 53, 54, \dots\}$

15. $\{4, 6, 8, 10, 12, \dots\}$

16. $\{0, 2, 4, 6, 8, \dots\}$

17. $\{2, 5, 8, 11, 14, \dots\}$

18. $\{6, 11, 16, 21, 26, \dots\}$

19. $\{5, 9, 13, 17, 21, \dots\}$

20. $\{\frac{1}{2}, \frac{1}{4}, \frac{1}{6}, \frac{1}{8}, \dots\}$

21. $\{\frac{1}{3}, \frac{1}{4}, \frac{1}{5}, \frac{1}{6}, \frac{1}{7}, \dots\}$

22. $\{\frac{1}{2}, \frac{2}{3}, \frac{3}{4}, \frac{4}{5}, \frac{5}{6}, \dots\}$

CHALLENGE PROBLEMS/GROUP ACTIVITIES

In Exercises 23–26, show that the set has cardinality $\aleph_0$ by establishing a one-to-one correspondence between the set of counting numbers and the given set.

23. $\{1, 4, 9, 16, 25, \dots\}$ 24. $\{2, 4, 8, 16, 32, \dots\}$

25. $\{3, 9, 27, 81, 243, \dots\}$ 26. $\{\frac{1}{3}, \frac{1}{6}, \frac{1}{12}, \frac{1}{24}, \frac{1}{48}, \dots\}$

RECREATIONAL MATHEMATICS

In Exercises 27–31, insert the symbol $<$, $>$, or $=$ in the shaded area to make a true statement.

27. $\aleph_0$ ▦ $\aleph_0 + \aleph_0$

28. $2\aleph_0$ ▦ $\aleph_0 + \aleph_0$

29. $2\aleph_0$ ▦ $\aleph_0$

30. $\aleph_0 + 5$ ▪ $\aleph_0 - 3$

31. $n(N)$ ▪ $\aleph_0$

32. There are a number of paradoxes (a statement that appears to be true and false at the same time) associated with infinite sets and the concept of infinity. One of these, called *Zeno's Paradox*, is named after the mathematician Zeno, born about 496 B.C. in Italy. According to Zeno's paradox, suppose Achelles starts out 1 meter behind a tortoise. Also, suppose Achelles walks 10 times as fast as the tortoise crawls. When Achelles reaches the point where the tortoise started, the tortoise is 1/10 of a meter ahead of Achelles; when Achelles reaches the point where the tortoise was 1/10 of a meter ahead, the tortoise is now 1/100 of a meter ahead; and

so on. According to Zeno's Paradox, Achelles gets closer and closer to the tortoise but never catches up to the tortoise.

a) Do you believe the reasoning process is sound? If not, explain why not.

b) In actuality, if this situation were real, would Achelles ever pass the tortoise?

INTERNET/RESEARCH ACTIVITIES

33. Do research to explain how Cantor proved that the set of rational numbers has cardinal number $\aleph_0$.

34. Do research to explain how it can be shown that the real numbers do not have cardinal number $\aleph_0$.

CHAPTER ❷ SUMMARY

IMPORTANT FACTS

And is generally interpreted to mean *intersection*.

Or is generally interpreted to mean *union*.

DE MORGAN'S LAWS

$$(A \cap B)' = A' \cup B'$$
$$(A \cup B)' = A' \cap B'$$

For any sets A and B,

$$n(A \cup B) = n(A) + n(B) - n(A \cap B).$$

Number of distinct subsets of a finite set with n elements is 2^n.

Symbol	Meaning
$\in$	is an element of
$\notin$	is not an element of
$n(A)$	number of elements in set A
$\varnothing$ or $\{\ \}$	the empty set
U	the universal set
$\subseteq$	is a subset of
$\nsubseteq$	is not a subset of
$\subset$	is a proper subset of
$\not\subset$	is not a proper subset of
$'$	complement
$\cap$	intersection
$\cup$	union
$-$	difference of two sets
$\times$	cartesian product
$\aleph_0$	aleph-null

CHAPTER ❷ REVIEW EXERCISES

2.1, 2.2, 2.3, 2.4, 2.6

In Exercises 1–14, state whether each is true or false. If false, give a reason.

1. The set of colleges located in the state of Oregon is a well-defined set.

2. The set of the three best cities in the United States is a well-defined set.

3. maple $\in$ {oak, elm, maple, sycamore}

4. $\{\ \} \subset \varnothing$

5. $\{3, 6, 9, 12, \dots\}$ and $\{2, 4, 6, 8, \dots\}$ are disjoint sets.

6. $\{a, b, c, 1, 2\}$ is an example of a set in roster form.

7. {plane, train, automobile} $=$ {train, plane, motorcycle}

8. {apple, orange, banana, pear} is equivalent to {tomato, corn, spinach, radish}.

9. If $A = \{a, e, i, o, u\}$, then $n(A) = 5$.

10. $A = \{1, 4, 9, 16, \ldots\}$ is a countable set.

11. $A = \{1, 4, 7, 10, \ldots, 31\}$ is a finite set.

12. $\{2, 5, 7\} \subseteq \{2, 5, 7, 10\}$.

13. $\{x \mid x \in N \text{ and } 3 < x \le 9\}$ is a set in set-builder notation.

14. $\{x \mid x \in N \text{ and } 2 < x \le 12\} \subseteq \{1, 2, 3, 4, 5, \ldots, 20\}$

In Exercises 15–18, express each set in roster form.

15. Set A is the set of odd natural numbers between 5 and 16.

16. Set B is the set of states that border Kansas.

17. $C = \{x \mid x \in N \text{ and } x < 162\}$

18. $D = \{x \mid x \in N \text{ and } 8 < x \le 96\}$

In Exercises 19–22, express each set in set-builder notation.

19. Set A is the set of natural numbers between 52 and 100.

20. Set B is the set of natural numbers greater than 42.

21. Set C is the set of natural numbers less than 5.

22. Set D is the set of natural numbers between 27 and 51, inclusive.

In Exercises 23–26, express each set with a written description.

23. $A = \{x \mid x \text{ is a capital letter of the English alphabet from E through M inclusive}\}$

24. $B = \{\text{penny, nickel, dime, quarter, half-dollar}\}$

25. $C = \{x, y, z\}$

26. $D = \{x \mid 3 \le x < 9\}$

In Exercises 27–36, let

$$U = \{1, 2, 3, 4, \ldots, 10\}$$
$$A = \{1, 3, 5, 7\}$$
$$B = \{5, 7, 9, 10\}$$
$$C = \{1, 7, 10\}$$

Determine the following.

27. $A \cap B$

28. $A \cup B'$

29. $A' \cap B$

30. $(A \cup B)' \cup C$

31. $A - B$

32. $A - C'$

33. $A \times C$

34. $B \times A$

35. The number of subsets of set B

36. The number of proper subsets of set A

37. For the following sets, construct a Venn diagram and place the elements in the proper region.

$U = \{\text{lion, tiger, leopard, cheetah, puma, lynx, panther, jaguar}\}$

$A = \{\text{tiger, puma, lynx}\}$

$B = \{\text{lion, tiger, jaguar, panther}\}$

$C = \{\text{tiger, lynx, cheetah, panther}\}$

In Exercises 38–43, use Fig. 2.30 to determine the sets.

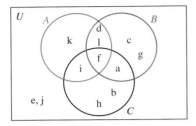

Figure 2.30

38. $A \cup B$

39. $A \cap B'$

40. $A \cup B \cup C$

41. $A \cap B \cap C$

42. $(A \cup B) \cap C$

43. $(A \cap B) \cup C$

Construct a Venn diagram to determine whether the following statements are true for all sets A, B, and C.

44. $(A' \cup B')' = A \cap B$

45. $(A \cup B') \cup (A \cup C') = A \cup (B \cap C)'$

In Exercises 46–51, use the following table, which shows the amount of sugar, in grams (g) and caffeine, in milligrams (mg), in an 8-oz serving of selected beverages. Let the beverages listed represent the universal set.

Beverage	Sugar (grams, g)	Caffeine (milligrams, mg)
Mountain Dew	31	37
Coca-Cola	27	23
Pepsi	27	25
Sprite	25	0
Brewed Coffee	0	85
Brewed tea	0	40
Orange juice	24	0
Grape juice	40	0
Gatorade	14	0
Water	0	0

Source: International Food Information Council

Let A be the set of beverages that contain at least 20 g of sugar.
Let B be the set of beverages that contain at least 20 mg of caffeine.
Indicate in Fig 2.31 in which region, I–IV, each of the following beverages belongs.

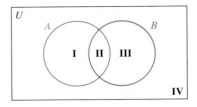

Figure 2.31

46. Pepsi

47. Brewed coffee

48. Orange juice

49. Water

50. Gatorade

51. Mountain Dew

2.5

52. *Pizza Survey* A pizza chain was willing to pay $1 to each person interviewed about his or her likes and dislikes of types of pizza crust. Of the people interviewed, 200 liked thin crust, 270 liked thick crust, 70 liked both, and 50 did not like pizza at all. What was the total cost of the survey?

53. *Cookie Preferences* The Cookie Shoppe conducted a survey to determine its customers' preferences.

    200 people liked chocolate chip cookies.
    190 people liked peanut butter cookies.
    210 people liked sugar cookies.
    100 people liked chocolate chip cookies and peanut butter cookies.
    150 people liked peanut butter cookies and sugar cookies.
    110 people liked chocolate chip cookies and sugar cookies.
    70 people liked all three.
    5 people did not like any of these cookies.

Draw a Venn diagram and then determine how many people

a) completed the survey.

b) liked only peanut butter cookies.

c) liked peanut butter cookies and chocolate chip cookies, but not sugar cookies.

d) liked peanut butter cookies or sugar cookies, but not chocolate chip cookies.

54. TV Choices *TV Guide* surveyed 510 subscribers asking which of the following three crime investigation shows they watched on a regular basis: *CSI:Crime Scene Investigation, CSI:Miami,* and *CSI:NY.* The results of the 510 questionnaires that were returned showed that

    175 watched *CSI:NY.*
    227 watched *CSI:Miami.*
    285 watched *CSI:Crime Scene Investigation.*
    100 watched *CSI:NY* and *CSI:Miami*
    96 watched *CSI:NY* and *CSI:Crime Scene Investigation.*
    87 watched *CSI:Miami* and *CSI:Crime Scene Investigation.*
    59 watched all three shows.

Construct a Venn diagram and determine how many people

a) watched only *CSI:NY.*

b) watched exactly one of these shows.

c) watched *CSI:Miami* and *CSI:Crime Scene Investigation,* but not *CSI:NY.*

d) watched *CSI:NY* or *CSI:Crime Scene Investigation,* but not *CSI:Miami.*

e) watched exactly two of these shows.

▲ Actors from *CSI:NY*

2.6

In Exercises 55 and 56, show that the sets are infinite by placing each set in a one-to-one correspondence with a proper subset of itself.

55. $\{2, 4, 6, 8, 10, \dots\}$ **56.** $\{3, 5, 7, 9, 11, \dots\}$

In Exercises 57 and 58, show that each set has cardinal number $\aleph_0$ by setting up a one-to-one correspondence between the set of counting numbers and the given set.

57. $\{5, 8, 11, 14, 17, \dots\}$ **58.** $\{4, 9, 14, 19, 24, \dots\}$

CHAPTER ❷ TEST

In Exercises 1–9, state whether each is true or false. If the statement is false, explain why.

1. $\{1, y, \triangle, \$\}$ is equivalent to $\{p, \#, 5, \square\}$.

2. $\{3, 5, 9, h\} = \{9, 5, 3, j\}$

3. $\{\text{star, moon, sun}\} \subset \{\text{star, moon, sun, planet}\}$

4. $\{7\} \subseteq \{x \mid x \in N \text{ and } x < 7\}$

5. $\{\ \} \not\subseteq \{0\}$

6. $\{p, q, r, s\}$ has 15 subsets.

7. If $A \cap B = \{\ \}$, then A and B are disjoint sets.

8. For any set A, $A \cup A' = \{\ \}$.

9. For any set A, $A \cap U = A$.

In Exercises 10 and 11, use set
$$A = \{x \mid x \in N \text{ and } x < 9\}$$

10. Write set A in roster form.

11. Write a description of set A.

In Exercises 12–17, use the following information.
$$U = \{3, 5, 7, 9, 11, 13, 15\}$$
$$A = \{3, 5, 7, 9\}$$
$$B = \{7, 9, 11, 13\}$$
$$C = \{3, 11, 15\}$$

Determine the following.

12. $A \cap B$ **13.** $A \cup C'$

14. $A \cap (B \cap C)'$ **15.** $n(A \cap B')$

16. $A - B$

17. $A \times C$

18. Using the sets provided for Exercises 12–17, draw a Venn diagram illustrating the relationship among the sets.

19. Use a Venn diagram to determine whether

$$A \cap (B \cup C') = (A \cap B) \cup (A \cap C')$$

for all sets A, B, and C. Show your work.

20. *Snacks at a Circus* Of the 155 people who purchased snacks at a circus,

    76 purchased cotton candy.
    90 purchased peanuts.
   107 purchased popcorn.
    52 purchased cotton candy and peanuts.
    54 purchased cotton candy and popcorn.
    57 purchased peanuts and popcorn.
    35 purchased all three snacks.

Construct a Venn diagram and then determine how many people purchased

a) exactly one of these snacks.

b) none of these snacks.

c) at least two of these snacks.

d) cotton candy and peanuts, but not popcorn.

e) cotton candy or peanuts, but not popcorn.

f) only popcorn.

21. Show that the following set is infinite by setting up a one-to-one correspondence between the set and a proper subset of itself.

$$\{7, 8, 9, 10, \dots \}$$

22. Show that the following set has cardinal number $\aleph_0$ by setting up a one-to-one correspondence between the set of counting numbers and the set.

$$\{1, 3, 5, 7, \dots \}$$

G R O U P   P R O J E C T S

SELECTING A FAMILY PET

1. The Wilcox family is considering buying a dog. They have established several criteria for the family dog: It must be one of the breeds listed in the table, must not shed, must be less than 16 in. tall, and must be good with children.

  a) Using the information in the table,* construct a Venn diagram in which the universal set is the dogs listed. Indicate the set of dogs to be placed in each region of the Venn diagram.

  b) From the Venn diagram constructed in part (a), determine which dogs will meet the criteria set by the Wilcox family. Explain.

Breed	Sheds	Less than 16 in.	Good with children
Airedale	no	no	no
Basset hound	yes	yes	yes
Beagle	yes	yes	yes
Border terrier	no	yes	yes
Cairn terrier	no	yes	no
Cocker spaniel	yes	yes	yes
Collie	yes	no	yes
Dachshund	yes	yes	no
Poodle, miniature	no	yes	no
Schnauzer, miniature	no	yes	no
Scottish terrier	no	yes	no
Wirehaired fox terrier	no	yes	no

*The information is a collection of the opinions of an animal psychologist, Dr. Daniel Tortora, and a group of veterinarians.

CLASSIFICATION OF THE DOMESTIC CAT

2. Read the Did You Know? feature on page 57. Do research and indicate the name of the following groupings to which the domestic cat belongs.

   a) Kingdom

   b) Phylum

   c) Class

   d) Order

   e) Family

   f) Genus

   g) Species

WHO LIVES WHERE

3. On Diplomat Row, an area of Washington, D.C., there are five houses. Each owner is a different nationality, each has a different pet, each has a different favorite food, each has a different favorite drink, and each house is painted a different color.

   The green house is directly to the right of the ivory house.

   The Senegalese has the red house.

The dog belongs to the Spaniard.

The Afghanistani drinks tea.

The person who eats cheese lives next door to the fox.

The Japanese eats fish.

Milk is drunk in the middle house.

Apples are eaten in the house next to the horse.

Ale is drunk in the green house.

The Norwegian lives in the first house.

The peach eater drinks whiskey.

Apples are eaten in the yellow house.

The banana eater owns a snail.

The Norwegian lives next door to the blue house.

For each house find

   a) the color.

   b) the nationality of the occupant.

   c) the owner's favorite food.

   d) the owner's favorite drink.

   e) the owner's pet.

   f) Finally, the crucial question is: Does the zebra's owner drink vodka or ale?

CHAPTER 3

Logic

▲ Logic is used to communicate effectively and make convincing arguments.

WHAT YOU WILL LEARN

- Statements, quantifiers, and compound statements
- Statements involving the words *not, and, or, if . . . then . . .,* and *if and only if*
- Truth tables for negations, conjunctions, disjunctions, conditional statements, and biconditional statements
- Self-contradictions, tautologies, and implications
- Equivalent statements, De Morgan's laws, and variations of conditional statements
- Symbolic arguments and standard forms of arguments
- Euler diagrams and syllogistic arguments
- Using logic to analyze switching circuits

WHY IT IS IMPORTANT

The study of logic enables us to communicate effectively, make more convincing arguments, and develop patterns of reasoning for decision making. The study of logic also prepares an individual to better understand the thought processes involved in learning other areas of mathematics and other subjects.

3.1 STATEMENTS AND LOGICAL CONNECTIVES

▲ "When it rains it pours." Logic symbols can be used to help us analyze statements made by advertisers.

Almost everyday we see or hear advertisements that attempt to influence our buying habits. Advertisements often rely on spoken or written statements that are used to favorably portray the advertised product and form a convincing argument that will persuade us to purchase the product. Some familiar advertising statements are: *Don't leave home without it; It takes a licking and keeps on ticking; Sometimes you feel like a nut, sometimes you don't;* and *When it rains it pours.* In this section, we will learn how to represent statements using logic symbols that may help us better understand the nature of the statement. We will use these symbols throughout the chapter to analyze more complicated statements. Such statements appear in everyday life in, for example, legal documents, product instructions, and game rules in addition to advertising.

History

The ancient Greeks were the first people to systematically analyze the way humans think and arrive at conclusions. Aristotle (384–322 B.C.) organized the study of logic for the first time in a work called *Organon*. As a result of his work, Aristotle is called the father of logic. The logic from this period, called *Aristotelian logic*, has been taught and studied for more than 2000 years.

Since Aristotle's time, the study of logic has been continued by other great philosophers and mathematicians. Gottfried Wilhelm Leibniz (1646–1716) had a deep conviction that all mathematical and scientific concepts could be derived from logic. As a result, he became the first serious student of *symbolic logic*. One difference between symbolic logic and Aristotelian logic is that in symbolic logic, as its name implies, symbols (usually letters) represent written statements. A self-educated English mathematician, George Boole (1815–1864), is considered to be the founder of symbolic logic because of his impressive work in this area. Among Boole's publications are *The Mathematical Analysis of Logic* (1847) and *An Investigation of the Law of Thought* (1854). Mathematician Charles Dodgson, better known as Lewis Carroll, incorporated many interesting ideas from logic into his books *Alice's Adventures in Wonderland* and *Through the Looking Glass* and his other children's stories.

Logic has been studied through the ages to exercise the mind's ability to reason. Understanding logic will enable you to think clearly, communicate effectively, make more convincing arguments, and develop patterns of reasoning that will help you in making decisions. It will also help you to detect the fallacies in the reasoning or arguments of others such as advertisers and politicians. Studying logic has other practical applications, such as helping you to understand wills, contracts, and other legal documents.

The study of logic is also good preparation for other areas of mathematics. If you preview Chapter 12, on probability, you will see formulas for the probability of A or B and the probability of A and B, symbolized as $P(A$ or $B)$ and $P(A$ and $B)$, respectively. Special meanings of common words such as *or* and *and* apply to all areas of mathematics. The meaning of these and other special words is discussed in this chapter.

Logic and the English Language

In reading, writing, and speaking, we use many words such as *and, or,* and *if . . . then . . .* to connect thoughts. In logic we call these words *connectives*. How are these words interpreted in daily communication? A judge announces to a convicted offender, "I hereby sentence you to five months of community service *and* a fine of $100." In this case, we normally interpret the word *and* to indicate that *both* events will take place. That is, the person must perform community service and must also pay a fine.

Now suppose a judge states, "I sentence you to six months in prison *or* 10 months of community service." In this case, we interpret the connective *or* as meaning the convicted person must either spend the time in jail or perform community service, but not both. The word *or* in this case is the *exclusive or*. When the exclusive *or* is used, one or the other of the events can take place, but *not both*.

In a restaurant, a waiter asks, "May I interest you in a cup of soup or a sandwich?" This question offers three possibilities: You may order soup, you may order a sandwich, or you may order both soup and a sandwich. The *or* in this case is the *inclusive or*. When the inclusive *or* is used, one or the other, *or both* events can take place. *In this chapter, when we use the word* or *in a logic statement, it will mean the* inclusive or *unless stated otherwise.*

If–then statements are often used to relate two ideas, as in the bank policy statement "If the average daily balance is greater than $500, then there will be no service charge." If–then statements are also used to emphasize a point or add humor, as in the statement "If the Cubs win, then I will be a monkey's uncle."

Now let's look at logic from a mathematical point of view.

Statements and Logical Connectives

A sentence that can be judged either true or false is called a *statement*. Labeling a statement true or false is called *assigning a truth value* to the statement. Here are some examples of statements.

1. The Brooklyn Bridge goes over San Francisco Bay.
2. Disney World is in Idaho.
3. The Mississippi River is the longest river in the United States.

In each case, we can say that the sentence is either true or false. Statement 1 is false because the Brooklyn Bridge does not go over San Francisco Bay. Statement 2 is false because Disney World is in Florida. By looking at a map or reading an almanac, we can determine that the Mississippi River is the longest river in the United States; therefore, statement 3 is true.

The three sentences discussed above are examples of *simple statements* because they convey one idea. Sentences combining two or more ideas that can be assigned a truth value are called *compound statements*. Compound statements are discussed shortly.

▲ The Brooklyn Bridge in New York City

Quantifiers

Sometimes it is necessary to change a statement to its opposite meaning. To do so, we use the *negation* of a statement. For example, the negation of the statement "Emily is at home" is "Emily is not at home." The negation of a true statement is always a false

statement, and the negation of a false statement is always a true statement. We must use special caution when negating statements containing the words *all, none* (or *no*), and *some*. These words are referred to as *quantifiers*.

Consider the statement "All lakes contain fresh water." We know this statement is false because the Great Salt Lake in Utah contains salt water. Its negation must therefore be true. We may be tempted to write its negation as "No lake contains fresh water," but this statement is also false because Lake Superior contains fresh water. Therefore, "No lakes contain fresh water" is not the negation of "All lakes contain fresh water." The correct negation of "All lakes contain fresh water" is "Not all lakes contain fresh water" or "At least one lake does not contain fresh water" or "Some lakes do not contain fresh water." These statements all imply that at least one lake does not contain fresh water, which is a true statement.

Now consider the statement "No birds can swim." This statement is false because at least one bird, the penguin, can swim. Therefore, the negation of this statement must be true. We may be tempted to write the negation as "All birds can swim," but because this statement is also false it cannot be the negation. The correct negation of the statement is "Some birds can swim" or "At least one bird can swim," each of which is a true statement.

Now let's consider statements involving the quantifier *some*, as in "Some students have a driver's license." This statement is true, meaning that at least one student has a driver's license. The negation of this statement must therefore be false. The negation is "No student has a driver's license," which is a false statement.

Consider the statement "Some students do not ride motorcycles." This statement is true because it means "At least one student does not ride a motorcycle." The negation of this statement must therefore be false. The negation is "All students ride motorcycles," which is a false statement.

The negation of quantified statements is summarized as follows:

Form of statement	Form of negation
All are.	Some are not.
None are.	Some are.
Some are.	None are.
Some are not.	All are.

The following diagram might help you to remember the statements and their negations:

The quantifiers diagonally opposite each other are the negations of each other.

EXAMPLE ❶ *Write Negations*

Write the negation of each statement.
a) Some snakes are poisonous.
b) All swimming pools are rectangular.

SOLUTION

a) Since *some* means "at least one," the statement "Some snakes are poisonous" is the same as "At least one snake is poisonous." Because it is a true statement, its negation must be false. The negation is "No snakes are poisonous," which is a false statement.

b) The statement "All swimming pools are rectangular" is a false statement since some pools are circular, some are oval, and some have other shapes. Its negation must therefore be true. The negation may be written as "Some swimming pools are not rectangular" or "Not all swimming pools are rectangular" or "At least one swimming pool is not rectangular." Each of these statements is true. ●

Compound Statements

Statements consisting of two or more simple statements are called **compound statements**. The connectives often used to join two simple statements are

and,   or,   if, … then … ,   if and only if

In addition, we consider a simple statement that has been negated to be a compound statement. The word *not* is generally used to negate a statement.

To reduce the amount of writing in logic, it is common to represent each simple statement with a lowercase letter. For example, suppose we are discussing the simple statement "Leland is a farmer." Instead of writing "Leland is a farmer" over and over again, we can let p represent the statement "Leland is a farmer." Thereafter we can simply refer to the statement with the letter p. It is customary to use the letters p, q, r, and s to represent simple statements, but other letters may be used instead. Let's now look at the connectives used to make compound statements.

Not Statements

The negation is symbolized by $\sim$ and read "not." For example, the negation of the statement "Steve is a college student" is "Steve is not a college student." If p represents the simple statement "Steve is a college student," then $\sim p$ represents the compound statement "Steve is not a college student." For any statement p, $\sim(\sim p) = p$. For example, the negation of the statement "Steve is not a college student" is "Steve is a college student."

Consider the statement "Inga is not at home." This statement contains the word *not*, which indicates that it is a negation. To write this statement symbolically, we let p represent "Inga *is* at home." Then $\sim p$ would be "Inga is not at home." *We will use this convention of letting letters such as p, q, or r represent statements that are not negated. We will represent negated statements with the negation symbol, $\sim$.*

And Statements

The *conjunction* is symbolized by $\wedge$ and read "and." The $\wedge$ looks like an A (for And) with the bar missing. Let p and q represent the simple statements.

p: You will perform 5 months of community service.
q: You will pay a $100 fine.

Then the following is the conjunction written in symbolic form.

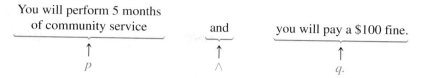

The conjunction is generally expressed as *and*. Other words sometimes used to express a conjunction are *but, however,* and *nevertheless.*

EXAMPLE ② *Write a Conjunction*

Write the following conjunction in symbolic form.

Green Day is not on tour, but Green Day is recording a new CD.

SOLUTION Let *t* and *r* represent the simple statements.

t: Green Day is on tour.
r: Green Day is recording a new CD.

In symbolic form, the compound statement is $\sim t \wedge r$.   ●

In Example 2, the compound statement is "Green Day is not on tour, but Green Day is recording a new CD." This statement could also be represented as "Green Day is not on tour, but *they* are recording a new CD." In this problem, it should be clear the word *they* means *Green Day*. Therefore, the statement, "Green Day is not on tour, but they are recording a new CD" would also be symbolized as $\sim t \wedge r$.

Or Statements

The *disjunction* is symbolized by $\vee$ and read "or." The *or* we use in this book (except where indicated in the exercise sets) is the *inclusive or* described on page 102.

EXAMPLE ③ *Write a Disjunction*

Let

p: Maria will go to the circus.
q: Maria will go to the zoo.

Write the following statements in symbolic form.
a) Maria will go to the circus or Maria will go to the zoo.
b) Maria will go to the zoo or Maria will not go to the circus.
c) Maria will not go to the circus or Maria will not go to the zoo.

SOLUTION
a) $p \vee q$ b) $q \vee \sim p$ c) $\sim p \vee \sim q$ ●

◄ Billie Joe Armstrong of Green Day

Because *or* represents the *inclusive or*, the statement "Maria will go to the circus or Maria will go to the zoo" in Example 3(a) may mean that Maria will go to the circus, or that Maria will go to the zoo, or that Maria will go to both the circus *and* the zoo. The statement in Example 3(a) could also be written as "Maria will go to the circus or the zoo."

When a compound statement contains more than one connective, a comma can be used to indicate which simple statements are to be grouped together. When we write the compound statement symbolically, *the simple statements on the same side of the comma are to be grouped together within parentheses.*

For example, "Pink is a singer (p) or Geena Davis is an actress (g), and Dallas is in Texas (d)" is written $(p \lor g) \land d$. Note that the p and g are both on the same side of the comma in the written statement. They are therefore grouped together within parentheses. The statement "Pink is a singer, or Geena Davis is an actress and Dallas is in Texas" is written $p \lor (g \land d)$. In this case, g and d are on the same side of the comma and are therefore grouped together within parentheses.

EXAMPLE ❹   *Understand How Commas Are Used to Group Statements*

Let

> p: Dinner includes soup.
> q: Dinner includes salad.
> r: Dinner includes the vegetable of the day.

Write the following statements in symbolic form.

a) Dinner includes soup, and salad or the vegetable of the day.

b) Dinner includes soup and salad, or the vegetable of the day.

SOLUTION

a) The comma tells us to group the statement "Dinner includes salad" with the statement "Dinner includes the vegetable of the day." Note that both statements are on the same side of the comma. The statement in symbolic form is $p \land (q \lor r)$.

   In mathematics, we always evaluate the information within the parentheses first. Since the conjunction, $\land$, is outside the parentheses and is evaluated *last*, this statement is considered a *conjunction*.

b) The comma tells us to group the statement "Dinner includes soup" with the statement "Dinner includes salad." Note that both statements are on the same side of the comma. The statement in symbolic form is $(p \land q) \lor r$. Since the disjunction, $\lor$, is outside the parentheses and is evaluated *last*, this statement is considered a *disjunction*. ●

The information provided in Example 4 is summarized below.

Statement	Symbolic representation	Type of statement
Dinner includes soup, and salad or the vegetable of the day.	$p \land (q \lor r)$	conjunction
Dinner includes soup and salad, or the vegetable of the day.	$(p \land q) \lor r$	disjunction

A negation symbol has the effect of negating only the statement that directly fol-lows it. To negate a compound statement, we must use parentheses. When a negation symbol is placed in front of a statement in parentheses, it negates the entire statement in parentheses. The negation symbol in this case is read, "It is not true that . . . " or "It is false that . . . "

┌─ **EXAMPLE ❺** *Change Symbolic Statements to Words*
Let

$$p: \quad \text{Jozsef is making breakfast.}$$
$$q: \quad \text{Arum is setting the table.}$$

Write the following symbolic statements in words.

a) $p \wedge \sim q$ b) $\sim p \vee \sim q$ c) $\sim(p \wedge q)$

SOLUTION

a) Jozsef is making breakfast and Arum is not setting the table.
b) Jozsef is not making breakfast or Arum is not setting the table.
c) It is false that Jozsef is making breakfast and Arum is setting the table.   ●

Recall that the word *but* may also be used in a conjunction. Therefore, Example 5(a) could also be written "Jozsef is making breakfast, *but* Arum is not setting the table."

Part (b) of Example 5 is a disjunction, since it can be written $(\sim p) \vee (\sim q)$. Part (c), which is $\sim(p \wedge q)$, is a negation since the negation symbol negates the entire statement within parentheses. The similarity of these two statements is discussed in Section 3.4.

Occasionally, we come across a *neither–nor* statement, such as "John is neither handsome nor rich." This statement means that John is not handsome *and* John is not rich. If p represents "John is handsome" and q represents "John is rich," this statement is symbolized by $\sim p \wedge \sim q$.

If–Then Statements

The *conditional* is symbolized by $\rightarrow$ and is read "if–then." The statement $p \rightarrow q$ is read "If p, then q."* The conditional statement consists of two parts: the part that precedes the arrow is the *antecedent,* and the part that follows the arrow is the *consequent.*† In the conditional statement $p \rightarrow q$, the p is the antecedent and the q is the consequent.

In the conditional statement $\sim(p \vee q) \rightarrow (p \wedge q)$, the antecedent is $\sim(p \vee q)$ and the consequent is $(p \wedge q)$. An example of a conditional statement is "If you drink your milk, then you will grow up to be healthy." A conditional symbol may be placed between any two statements even if the statements are not related.

---

*Some books indicate that $p \rightarrow q$ may also be read "p implies q." Many higher-level mathematics books, however, indicate that $p \rightarrow q$ may be read "p implies q" only under certain conditions. Implications are discussed in Section 3.3.

†Some books refer to the antecedent as the hypothesis or premise and the consequent as the conclusion.

Sometimes the word *then* in a conditional statement is not explicitly stated. For example, the statement "If you get an A, I will buy you a car" is a conditional statement because it actually means "If you get an A, then I will buy you a car."

▲ *Zoe* by Beth Anderson

EXAMPLE ❻ *Write Conditional Statements*

Let

> p: The portrait is a pastel.
>
> q: The portrait is by Beth Anderson.

Write the following statements symbolically.
a) If the portrait is a pastel, then the portrait is by Beth Anderson.
b) If the portrait is by Beth Anderson, then the portrait is not a pastel.
c) It is false that if the portrait is by Beth Anderson then the portrait is a pastel.

SOLUTION
a) $p \rightarrow q$ b) $q \rightarrow \sim p$ c) $\sim(q \rightarrow p)$ ●

EXAMPLE ❼ *Use Commas When Writing a Symbolic Statement in Words*

Let

> p: Jorge is enrolled in calculus.
>
> q: Jorge's major is criminal justice.
>
> r: Jorge's major is engineering.

Write the following symbolic statements in words and indicate whether the statement is a negation, conjunction, disjunction, or conditional.
a) $(q \rightarrow \sim p) \vee r$ b) $q \rightarrow (\sim p \vee r)$

SOLUTION The parentheses indicate where to place the commas in the sentences.
a) "If Jorge's major is criminal justice then Jorge is not enrolled in calculus, or Jorge's major is engineering." This statement is a disjunction because $\vee$ is outside the parentheses.
b) "If Jorge's major is criminal justice, then Jorge is not enrolled in calculus or Jorge's major is engineering." This statement is a conditional because $\rightarrow$ is outside the parentheses.   ●

If and Only if Statements

The *biconditional* is symbolized by $\leftrightarrow$ and is read "if and only if." The phrase *if and only if* is sometimes abbreviated as "iff." The statement $p \leftrightarrow q$ is read "p if and only if q."

▲ Martin St. Louis

EXAMPLE 8 *Write Statements Using the Biconditional*

Let

p: The Tampa Bay Lightning win the Stanley Cup.

q: Martin St. Louis is the MVP.

Write the following symbolic statements in words.

a) $p \leftrightarrow \sim q$ b) $\sim(q \leftrightarrow \sim p)$

SOLUTION

a) The Tampa Bay Lightning win the Stanley Cup if and only if Martin St. Louis is not the MVP.

b) It is false that Martin St. Louis is the MVP if and only if the Tampa Bay Lightning do not win the Stanley Cup.   ●

You will learn later that $p \leftrightarrow q$ means the same as $(p \rightarrow q) \wedge (q \rightarrow p)$. Therefore, the statement "I will go to college if and only if I can pay the tuition" has the same logical meaning as "If I go to college then I can pay the tuition, and if I can pay the tuition then I will go to college."

A summary of the connectives discussed in this section is given in Table 3.1.

Table 3.1 Logical Connectives

Formal Name	Symbol	Read	Symbolic Form
Negation	$\sim$	"Not"	$\sim p$
Conjunction	$\wedge$	"And"	$p \wedge q$
Disjunction	$\vee$	"Or"	$p \vee q$
Conditional	$\rightarrow$	"If-then"	$p \rightarrow q$
Biconditional	$\leftrightarrow$	"If and only if"	$p \leftrightarrow q$

SECTION 3.1   EXERCISES

CONCEPT/WRITING EXERCISES

1. a) What is a statement?

    b) What is a simple statement?

    c) What is a compound statement?

2. Fill in the blanks to make the following statements true.

    a) The negation of a true statement is always a _____ statement.

    b) The negation of a _____ statement is always a true statement.

3. Give three words that can be used as a quantifier in a statement.

4. Represent the statement, "The telephone does not have caller ID" symbolically. Explain your answer.

5. Write the general form of the negation for statements of the form

   a) none are.

   b) some are not.

   c) all are.

   d) some are.

6. Draw the symbol used to represent the

   a) conditional.

   b) disjunction.

   c) conjunction.

   d) negation.

   e) biconditional.

7. a) When the *exclusive or* is used as a connective between two events, can both events take place? Explain.

   b) When the *inclusive or* is used as a connective between two events, can both events take place? Explain.

   c) Which *or*, the *inclusive or* or the *exclusive or*, is used in this chapter?

8. Explain how a comma is used to indicate the grouping of simple statements.

PRACTICE THE SKILLS/PROBLEM SOLVING

In Exercises 9–22, indicate whether the statement is a simple statement or a compound statement. If it is a compound statement, indicate whether it is a negation, conjunction, disjunction, conditional, or biconditional by using both the word and its appropriate symbol (for example, "a negation," ~).

9. Jana Bryant is teaching statistics or she is teaching calculus.

10. If you burn the chicken wings, then you can feed them to the dog.

11. Time will go backwards if and only if you travel faster than the speed of light.

12. Louis Armstrong did not play the drums.

▲ Louis Armstrong, see Exercise 12

13. Bobby Glewen joined the Army and he got married.

14. The book was neither a novel nor an autobiography.

15. The hurricane did $400,000 worth of damage to DeSoto County.

16. Inhibor Melendez will be admitted to law school if and only if he earns his bachelor's degree.

17. It is false that Jeffery Hilt is a high school teacher and a grade school teacher.

18. If Cathy Smith walks 4 miles today, then she will be sore tomorrow.

19. Mary Jo Woo ran 4 miles today and she lifted weights for 30 minutes.

20. Nancy Wallin went to the game, but she did not eat a hot dog.

21. It is false that if John Wubben fixes your car then you will need to pay him in cash.

22. If Buddy and Evelyn Cordova are residents of Budville, then they must vote for mayor on Tuesday.

In Exercises 23–34, write the negation of the statement.

23. All butterflies are insects.

24. All houses are wired using parallel circuits.

25. No aldermen are running for mayor.

26. Some diet sodas contain saccharin.

27. Some turtles do not have claws.

28. No teachers made the roster.

29. No bicycles have three wheels.

30. All horses have manes.

31. Some pine trees do not produce pinecones.

32. No one likes asparagus.

33. Some pedestrians are in the crosswalk.

34. Some dogs with long hair do not get cold.

In Exercises 35–40, write the statement in symbolic form.
Let

p: The tent is pitched.
q: The bonfire is burning.

35. The tent is not pitched.

36. The tent is pitched and the bonfire is burning.

37. The bonfire is not burning or the tent is not pitched.

38. The bonfire is not burning if and only if the tent is not pitched.

39. If the tent is not pitched, then the bonfire is not burning.

40. The bonfire is not burning, however the tent is pitched.

In Exercises 41–46, write the statement in symbolic form.
Let

p: The chili is spicy.
q: The sour cream is cold.

41. The chili is not spicy, but the sour cream is cold.

42. Neither is the chili spicy nor is the sour cream cold.

43. The sour cream is not cold if and only if the chili is spicy.

44. If the chili is spicy, then the sour cream is not cold.

45. It is false that the chili is spicy or the sour cream is cold.

46. It is false that if the sour cream is not cold then the chili is spicy.

In Exercises 47–56, write the compound statement in words.
Let

p: Ken Jennings won 74 games of *Jeopardy!*
q: Ken Jennings won more than $3 million.

▲ Alex Trebek and Ken Jennings

47. ~q

48. ~p

49. p ∧ q

50. q ∨ p

51. ~p → q

52. ~p ↔ ~q

53. ~p ∨ ~q

54. ~(q ∨ p)

55. ~(p ∧ q)

56. ~p ∧ ~q

In Exercises 57–66, write the statements in symbolic form.
Let

p: The temperature is 90°.
q: The air conditioner is working.
r: The apartment is hot.

57. The temperature is 90° and the air conditioner is not working, and the apartment is hot.

58. The temperature is not 90° and the air conditioner is working, but the apartment is hot.

59. The temperature is 90° and the air conditioner is working, or the apartment is hot.

60. If the apartment is hot and the air conditioner is working, then the temperature is 90°.

61. If the temperature is 90°, then the air conditioner is working or the apartment is not hot.

62. The temperature is not 90° if and only if the air conditioner is not working, or the apartment is not hot.

63. The apartment is hot if and only if the air conditioner is working, and the temperature is 90°.

64. It is false that if the apartment is hot then the air conditioner is not working.

65. If the air conditioner is working, then the temperature is 90° if and only if the apartment is hot.

66. The apartment is hot or the air conditioner is not working, if and only if the temperature is 90°.

In Exercises 67–76, write each symbolic statement in words. Let

p: The water is 70°.

q: The sun is shining.

r: We go swimming.

67. $(p \lor q) \land \sim r$

68. $(p \land q) \lor r$

69. $\sim p \land (q \lor r)$

70. $(q \rightarrow p) \lor r$

71. $\sim r \rightarrow (q \land p)$

72. $(q \land r) \rightarrow p$

73. $(q \rightarrow r) \land p$

74. $\sim p \rightarrow (q \lor r)$

75. $(q \leftrightarrow p) \land r$

76. $q \rightarrow (p \leftrightarrow r)$

Dinner Menu In Exercises 77–80, use the following information to arrive at your answers. Many restaurant dinner menus include statements such as the following. All dinners are served with a choice of: Soup or Salad, and Potatoes or Pasta, and Carrots or Peas. Which of the following selections are permissible? If a selection is not permissible, explain why. See the discussion of the exclusive or on page 102.

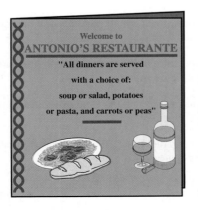

Welcome to
ANTONIO'S RESTAURANTE

"All dinners are served

with a choice of:

soup or salad, potatoes

or pasta, and carrots or peas"

77. Soup, salad, and peas

78. Salad, pasta, and carrots

79. Soup, potatoes, pasta, and peas

80. Soup, pasta, and potatoes

In Exercises 81–89, (a) select letters to represent the simple statements and write each statement symbolically by using parentheses and (b) indicate whether the statement is a negation, conjunction, disjunction, conditional, or biconditional.

81. I bought the watch in Tijuana and I did not pay $100.

82. If the conference is in Las Vegas, then we can see Wayne Newton or we can play poker.

83. It is false that if your speed is below the speed limit then you will not get pulled over.

84. If dinner is ready then we can eat, or we cannot go to the restaurant.

85. If the food has fiber or the food has vitamins, then you will be healthy.

86. If Corliss is teaching then Faye is in the math lab, if and only if it is not a weekend.

87. You may take this course, if and only if you did not fail the previous course or you passed the placement test.

88. If the car has gas and the battery is charged, then the car will start.

89. The classroom is empty if and only if it is the weekend, or it is 7 A.M.

CHALLENGE PROBLEMS/GROUP ACTIVITIES

90. **An Ancient Question** If Zeus could do anything, could he build a wall that he could not jump over? Explain your answer.

91. **a)** Make up three simple statements and label them p, q, and r. Then write compound statements to represent $(p \lor q) \land r$ and $p \lor (q \land r)$.

   b) Do you think that the statements for $(p \lor q) \land r$ and $p \lor (q \land r)$ mean the same thing? Explain.

RECREATIONAL MATHEMATICS

92. *Sudoku* Sudoku is a logic-based puzzle that originated in Japan. The goal is to enter numerical digits in each of the empty squares so that every digit from 1 to 9 appears exactly one time in each of the rows, in each of the columns, and in each of the nine 3 by 3 boxes. Completing the puzzle requires patience and logical ability. For more information, see www.websudoku.com. Complete the following Sudoku puzzle.

	1		4	8		5	6	
5					9	8		
	3				1	4		7
8	2			9		1		
6			1		4			9
		3		6			4	5
9		1	5				2	
		7	2					4
	5	2		7	8		3	

INTERNET/RESEARCH ACTIVITIES

93. *Legal Documents* Obtain a legal document such as a will or rental agreement and copy one page of the document. Circle every connective used. Then list the number of times each connective appeared. Be sure to include conditional statements from which the word *then* was omitted from the sentence. Give the page and your listing to your instructor.

94. Write a report on the life and accomplishments of George Boole, who was an important contributor to the development of logic. In your report, indicate how his work eventually led to the development of the computer. References include encyclopedias, history of mathematics books, and the Internet.

3.2 TRUTH TABLES FOR NEGATION, CONJUNCTION, AND DISJUNCTION

▲ Under what conditions is the statement *Idaho grows the most potatoes or Iowa grows the most corn* true?

Consider the following statement: Idaho grows the most potatoes or Iowa grows the most corn. Under what conditions can the statement be considered true? Under what conditions can the statement be considered false? In this section, we will introduce a tool used to help us analyze such statements.

A *truth table* is a device used to determine when a compound statement is true or false. Five basic truth tables are used in constructing other truth tables. Three are discussed in this section (Tables 3.2, 3.4, and 3.7), and two are discussed in the next section. Section 3.5 uses truth tables in determining whether a logical argument is valid or invalid.

Negation

The first truth table is for *negation*. If p is a true statement, then the negation of p, "not p," is a false statement. If p is a false statement, then "not p" is a true statement. For

Table 3.2 Negation

	p	~*p*
Case 1	T	F
Case 2	F	T

Table 3.3

	p	*q*
Case 1	T	T
Case 2	T	F
Case 3	F	T
Case 4	F	F

Table 3.4 Conjunction

	p	*q*	*p* ∧ *q*
Case 1	T	T	T
Case 2	T	F	F
Case 3	F	T	F
Case 4	F	F	F

example, if the statement "The shirt is blue" is true, then the statement "The shirt is not blue" is false. These relationships are summarized in Table 3.2. For a simple statement, there are exactly two true–false cases, as shown.

If a compound statement consists of two simple statements *p* and *q*, there are four possible cases, as illustrated in Table 3.3. Consider the statement "The test is today and the test covers Chapter 5." The simple statement "The test is today" has two possible truth values, true or false. The simple statement "The test covers Chapter 5" also has two truth values, true or false. Thus, for these two simple statements there are four distinct possible true–false arrangements. Whenever we construct a truth table for a compound statement that consists of two simple statements, we begin by listing the four true–false cases shown in Table 3.3.

Conjunction

To illustrate the conjunction, consider the following situation. You have recently purchased a new house. To decorate it, you ordered a new carpet and new furniture from the same store. You explain to the salesperson that the carpet must be delivered before the furniture. He promises that the carpet will be delivered on Thursday and that the furniture will be delivered on Friday.

To help determine whether the salesperson kept his promise, we assign letters to each simple statement. Let *p* be "The carpet will be delivered on Thursday" and *q* be "The furniture will be delivered on Friday." The salesperson's statement written in symbolic form is *p* ∧ *q*. There are four possible true–false situations to be considered (Table 3.4).

CASE 1: *p* is true and *q* is true. The carpet is delivered on Thursday and the furniture is delivered on Friday. The salesperson has kept his promise and the compound statement is true. Thus, we put a T in the *p* ∧ *q* column.

CASE 2: *p* is true and *q* is false. The carpet is delivered on Thursday but the furniture is not delivered on Friday. Since the furniture was not delivered as promised, the compound statement is false. Thus, we put an F in the *p* ∧ *q* column.

CASE 3: *p* is false and *q* is true. The carpet is not delivered on Thursday but the furniture is delivered on Friday. Since the carpet was not delivered on Thursday as promised, the compound statement is false. Thus, we put an F in the *p* ∧ *q* column.

CASE 4: *p* is false and *q* is false. The carpet is not delivered on Thursday and the furniture is not delivered on Friday. Since the carpet and furniture were not delivered as promised, the compound statement is false. Thus, we put an F in the *p* ∧ *q* column.

Examining the four cases, we see that in only one case did the salesperson keep his promise: in case 1. Therefore, case 1 (T, T) is true. In cases 2, 3, and 4, the salesperson did not keep his promise and the compound statement is false. The results are summarized in Table 3.4, the truth table for the conjunction.

The **conjunction** *p* ∧ *q* is true only when both *p* and *q* are true.

EXAMPLE 1 *Construct a Truth Table*

Construct a truth table for $p \wedge \sim q$.

SOLUTION Because there are two statements, p and q, construct a truth table with four cases; see Table 3.5(a). Then write the truth values under the p in the compound statement and label this column 1, as in Table 3.5(b). Copy these truth values directly from the p column on the left. Write the corresponding truth values under the q in the compound statement and call this column 2, as in Table 3.5(c). Copy the truth values for column 2 directly from the q column on the left. Now find the truth values of $\sim q$ by negating the truth values in column 2 and call this column 3,

Table 3.5

(a)

	p	q	$p \wedge \sim q$
Case 1	T	T	
Case 2	T	F	
Case 3	F	T	
Case 4	F	F	

(b)

p	q	$p \wedge \sim q$
T	T	T
T	F	T
F	T	F
F	F	F
		1

(c)

p	q	p	$\wedge$	$\sim$	q
T	T	T			T
T	F	T			F
F	T	F			T
F	F	F			F
		1			2

(d)

p	q	p	$\wedge$	$\sim$	q
T	T	T		F	T
T	F	T		T	F
F	T	F		F	T
F	F	F		T	F
		1		3	2

(e)

p	q	p	$\wedge$	$\sim$	q
T	T	T	F	F	T
T	F	T	T	T	F
F	T	F	F	F	T
F	F	F	F	T	F
		1	4	3	2

as in Table 3.5(d). Use the conjunction table, Table 3.4, and the entries in the columns labeled 1 and 3 to complete the column labeled 4, as in Table 3.5(e). The results in column 4 are obtained as follows:

Row 1: $T \wedge F$ is F.   Row 2: $T \wedge T$ is T.
Row 3: $F \wedge F$ is F.   Row 4: $F \wedge T$ is F.

The answer is always the last column completed. The columns labeled 1, 2, and 3 are only aids in arriving at the answer labeled column 4. ●

The statement $p \wedge \sim q$ in Example 1 actually means $p \wedge (\sim q)$. In the future, instead of listing a column for q and a separate column for its negation, we will make one column for $\sim q$, which will have the opposite values of those in the q column on the left. Similarly, when we evaluate $\sim p$, we will use the opposite values of those in the p column on the left. This procedure is illustrated in Example 2.

In Example 1, we spoke about *cases* and also *columns*. Consider Table 3.5(e). This table has four cases indicated by the four different rows of the two left-hand (unnumbered) columns. The four *cases* are TT, TF, FT, and FF. In every truth table with two letters, we list the four cases (the first two columns) first. Then we complete the remaining columns in the truth table. In Table 3.5(e), after completing the two left-hand columns, we complete the remaining columns in the order indicated by the numbers below the columns. We will continue to place numbers below the columns to show the order in which the columns are completed.

In discussion of the truth table in Example 2, and all following truth tables, if we say column 1, it means the column labeled 1. Column 2 will mean the column labeled 2, and so on.

> **TIMELY TIP** When constructing truth tables it is very important to keep your entries in neat columns and rows. If you are using lined paper, put only one row of the table on each line. If you are not using lined paper, using a straightedge may help you correctly enter the information into the truth table's rows and columns.

EXAMPLE ❷ *Construct and Interpret a Truth Table*

a) Construct a truth table for the following statement: Jose is not an artist and Jose is not a musician.

b) Under which conditions will the compound statement be true?

c) Suppose "Jose is an artist" is a false statement and "Jose is a musician" is a true statement. Is the compound statement given in part (a) true or false?

> **SOLUTION**

a) First write the simple statements in symbolic form by using simple nonnegated statements.

Let

$$p: \quad \text{Jose is an artist.}$$
$$q: \quad \text{Jose is a musician.}$$

Table 3.6

p	q	$\sim p$	$\wedge$	$\sim q$
T	T	F	F	F
T	F	F	F	T
F	T	T	Ⓕ	F
F	F	T	Ⓣ	T
		1	3	2

Therefore, the compound statement may be written $\sim p \wedge \sim q$. Now construct a truth table with four cases, as shown in Table 3.6.

Fill in the column labeled 1 by negating the truth values under p on the far left. Fill in the column labeled 2 by negating the values under q in the second column from the left. Fill in the column labeled 3 by using the columns labeled 1 and 2 and the definition of conjunction.

In the first row, to determine the entry for column 3, we use false for $\sim p$ and false for $\sim q$. Since false $\wedge$ false is false (see case 4 of Table 3.4), we place an F in column 3, row 1. In the second row, we use false for $\sim p$ and true for $\sim q$. Since false $\wedge$ true is false (see case 3 of Table 3.4), we place an F in column 3, row 2. In the third row, we use true for $\sim p$ and false for $\sim q$. Since true $\wedge$ false is false (see case 2 of Table 3.4), we place an F in column 3, row 3. In the fourth row, we use true for $\sim p$ and true for $\sim q$. Since true $\wedge$ true is true (see case 1 of Table 3.4), we place a T in column 3, row 4.

b) The compound statement in part (a) will be true only in case 4 (circled in blue) when both simple statements, p and q, are false, that is, when Jose is not an artist and Jose is not a musician.

c) We are told that p, "Jose is an artist," is a false statement and that q, "Jose is a musician," is a true statement. From the truth table (Table 3.6), we can determine that when p is false and q is true, the compound statement, case 3, (circled in red) is false.

Disjunction

Consider the job description in the margin that describes several job requirements. Who qualifies for the job? To help analyze the statement, translate it into symbolic form. Let p be "A requirement for the job is a two-year college degree in civil technology" and q be "A requirement for the job is five years of related experience." The statement in symbolic form is $p \vee q$. For the two simple statements, there are four distinct cases (see Table 3.7).

CASE 1: p is true and q is true. A candidate has a two-year college degree in civil technology and five years of related experience. The candidate has both requirements and qualifies for the job. Consider qualifying for the job as a true statement and not qualifying as a false statement. Since the candidate qualifies for the job, we put a T in the $p \vee q$ column.

CASE 2: p is true and q is false. A candidate has a two-year college degree in civil technology but does not have five years of related experience. The candidate still qualifies for the job with the two-year college degree. Thus, we put a T in the $p \vee q$ column.

CASE 3: p is false and q is true. The candidate does not have a two-year college degree in civil technology but does have five years of related experience. The candidate qualifies for the job with the five years of related experience. Thus, we put a T in the $p \vee q$ column.

CASE 4: p is false and q is false. The candidate does not have a two-year college degree in civil technology and does not have five years of related experience. The candidate does not meet either of the two requirements and therefore does not qualify for the job. Thus, we put an F in the $p \vee q$ column.

In examining the four cases, we see that there is only one case in which the candidate does not qualify for the job: case 4. As this example indicates, an *or* statement will be true in every case, except when both simple statements are false. The results are summarized in Table 3.7, the truth table for the disjunction.

Civil Technician

Municipal program for redevelopment seeks on-site technician. **The applicant must have a two-year college degree in civil technology or five years of related experience**. Interested candidates please call 555-1234.

Table 3.7 Disjunction

p	q	$p \vee q$
T	T	T
T	F	T
F	T	T
F	F	F

The **disjunction**, $p \vee q$, is true when either p is true, q is true, or both p and q are true.

The disjunction $p \vee q$ is false only when p and q are both false.

EXAMPLE ❸ *Truth Table with a Negation*

Construct a truth table for $\sim(\sim q \wedge p)$.

SOLUTION First construct the standard truth table listing the four cases. Then work within parentheses. The order to be followed is indicated by the numbers below the columns (see Table 3.8). Under $\sim q$, column 1, write the negation of the q column. Then, in column 2, copy the values from the p column. Next, complete the *and* column, column 3, using columns 1 and 2 and the truth table for the conjunction. The *and* column is true only when both statements are true, as in case 2. Finally, negate the values in the *and* column, column 3, and place these negated values in column 4. By examining the truth table you can see that the compound statement $\sim(\sim q \wedge p)$ is false only in case 2, that is, when p is true and q is false. ●

Table 3.8

p	q	$\sim$	$(\sim q$	$\wedge$	$p)$
T	T	T	F	F	T
T	F	F	T	T	T
F	T	T	F	F	F
F	F	T	T	F	F
		4	1	3	2

A GENERAL PROCEDURE FOR CONSTRUCTING TRUTH TABLES

1. Study the compound statement and determine whether it is a negation, conjunction, disjunction, conditional, or biconditional statement, as was done in Section 3.1. The answer to the truth table will appear under $\sim$ if the statement is a negation, under $\wedge$ if the statement is a conjunction, under $\vee$ if the statement is a disjunction, under $\rightarrow$ if the statement is a conditional, and under $\leftrightarrow$ if the statement is a biconditional.

2. Complete the columns under the simple statements, p, q, r, and their negations, $\sim p$, $\sim q$, $\sim r$, within parentheses, if present. If there are nested parentheses (one pair of parentheses within another pair), work with the innermost pair first.

3. Complete the column under the connective within the parentheses, if present. You will use the truth values of the connective in determining the final answer in step 5.

4. Complete the column under any remaining statements and their negations.

5. Complete the column under any remaining connectives. Recall that the answer will appear under the column determined in step 1. If the statement is a conjunction, disjunction, conditional, or biconditional, you will obtain the truth values for the connective by using the last column completed on the left side and on the right side of the connective. If the statement is a negation, you will obtain the truth values by negating the truth values of the last column completed within the grouping symbols on the right side of the negation. Be sure to circle or highlight your answer column or number the columns in the order they were completed.

EXAMPLE ❹ *Use the General Procedure to Construct a Truth Table*

Construct a truth table for the statement $(\sim p \vee q) \wedge \sim p$.

SOLUTION We will follow the general procedure outlined in the box. This statement is a conjunction, so the answer will be under the conjunction symbol. Complete columns under $\sim p$ and q within the parentheses and call these columns 1 and 2, respectively (see Table 3.9). Complete the column under the disjunction, $\vee$, using the truth values in columns 1 and 2, and call this column 3. Next complete the column under $\sim p$, and call this column 4. The answer, column 5, is determined from the definition of the conjunction and the truth values in column 3, the last column completed on the left side of the conjunction, and column 4. ●

Table 3.9

p	q	$(\sim p$	$\vee$	$q)$	$\wedge$	$\sim p$
T	T	F	T	T	F	F
T	F	F	F	F	F	F
F	T	T	T	T	T	T
F	F	T	T	F	T	T
		1	3	2	5	4

Table 3.10

	p	q	r
Case 1	T	T	T
Case 2	T	T	F
Case 3	T	F	T
Case 4	T	F	F
Case 5	F	T	T
Case 6	F	T	F
Case 7	F	F	T
Case 8	F	F	F

So far, all the truth tables we have constructed have contained at most two simple statements. Now we will explain how to construct a truth table that consists of three simple statements, such as $(p \wedge q) \wedge r$. When a compound statement consists of three simple statements, there are eight different true–false possibilities, as illustrated in Table 3.10. To begin such a truth table, write four Ts and four Fs in the column under p. Under the second statement, q, pairs of Ts alternate with pairs of Fs. Under the third statement, r, T alternates with F. This technique is not the only way of listing the cases, but it ensures that each case is unique and that no cases are omitted.

EXAMPLE ❺ *Construct a Truth Table with Eight Cases*

a) Construct a truth table for the statement "Santana is home and he is not at his desk, or he is sleeping."

b) Suppose that "Santana is home" is a false statement, that "Santana is at his desk" is a true statement, and that "Santana is sleeping" is a true statement. Is the compound statement in part (a) true or false?

SOLUTION

a) First we will translate the statement into symbolic form.
Let

p: Santana is home.
q: Santana is at his desk.
r: Santana is sleeping.

In symbolic form, the statement is $(p \wedge \sim q) \vee r$.

Since the statement is composed of three simple statements, there are eight cases. Begin by listing the eight cases in the three left-hand columns; see Table 3.11. By examining the statement, you can see that it is a disjunction. Therefore, the answer will be in the $\vee$ column. Fill out the truth table by working in parentheses first. Place values under p, column 1, and $\sim q$, column 2. Then find the conjunctions of columns 1 and 2 to obtain column 3. Place the values of r in column 4. To obtain the answer, column 5, use columns 3 and 4 and the information for the disjunction contained in Table 3.7 on page 117.

Table 3.11

p	q	r	(p	∧	~q)	∨	r
T	T	T	T	F	F	T	T
T	T	F	T	F	F	F	F
T	F	T	T	T	T	T	T
T	F	F	T	T	T	T	F
F	T	T	F	F	F	(T)	T
F	T	F	F	F	F	F	F
F	F	T	F	F	T	T	T
F	F	F	F	F	T	F	F
			1	3	2	5	4

b) We are given the following:

p: Santana is home—false.

q: Santana is at his desk—true.

r: Santana is sleeping—true.

We need to find the truth value of the following case: false, true, true. In case 5 of the truth table, p, q, and r are F, T, and T, respectively. Therefore, under these conditions, the original compound statement is true (as circled in the table).   ●

We have learned that a truth table with one simple statement has two cases, a truth table with two simple statements has four cases, and a truth table with three simple statements has eight cases. In general, *the number of distinct cases in a truth table with n distinct simple statements is 2^n.* The compound statement $(p \vee q) \vee (r \wedge \sim s)$ has four simple statements, p, q, r, s. Thus, a truth table for this compound statement would have 2^4, or 16, distinct cases.

When we construct a truth table, we determine the truth values of a compound statement for every possible case. If we want to find the truth value of the compound statement for any specific case when we know the truth values of the simple statements, we do not have to develop the entire table. For example, to determine the truth value for the statement

$$2 + 3 = 5 \quad \text{and} \quad 1 + 1 = 3$$

we let p be $2 + 3 = 5$ and q be $1 + 1 = 3$. Now we can write the compound statement as $p \wedge q$. We know that p is a true statement and q is a false statement. Thus, we can substitute T for p and F for q and evaluate the statement:

$$p \wedge q$$
$$T \wedge F$$
$$F$$

Therefore, the compound statement $2 + 3 = 5$ and $1 + 1 = 3$ is a false statement.

┌EXAMPLE ❻ *Determine the Truth Value of a Compound Statement*

Determine the truth value for each simple statement. Then, using these truth values, determine the truth value of the compound statement.

a) 15 is less than or equal to 9.

b) George Washington was the first U.S. president or Abraham Lincoln was the second U.S. president, but there has not been a U.S. president born in Antarctica.

SOLUTION

a) Let

p: 15 is less than 9.

q: 15 is equal to 9.

The statement "15 is less than or equal to 9" means that 15 is less than 9 or 15 is equal to 9. The compound statement can be expressed as $p \vee q$. We know that both p and q are false statements since 15 is greater than 9, so we substitute F for p and F for q and evaluate the statement:

$$p \vee q$$
$$F \vee F$$
$$F$$

Therefore, the compound statement "15 is less than or equal to 9" is a false statement.

b) Let

p: George Washington was the first U.S. president.

q: Abraham Lincoln was the second U.S. president.

r: There has been a U.S. president who was born in Antarctica .

The compound statement can be written in symbolic form as $(p \vee q) \wedge \sim r$. Recall that *but* is used to express a conjunction. We know that p is a true statement and that q is a false statement. We also know that r is a false statement since all U.S. presidents must be born in the United States. Thus, since r is a false statement, the negation, $\sim r$, is a true statement. So we will substitute T for p, F for q, and T for $\sim r$ and then evaluate the statement:

$$(p \vee q) \wedge \sim r$$
$$(T \vee F) \wedge T$$
$$T \wedge T$$
$$T$$

Therefore, the original compound statement is a true statement.   ●

EXAMPLE ❼ *Pet Ownership in the United States*

The number of pets owned in the United States in 2005 is shown in Fig. 3.1. Use this graph to determine the truth value of the following statement: There are more dogs owned than cats and there are fewer reptiles owned than birds, or the most numerous pets owned are not fish.

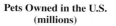

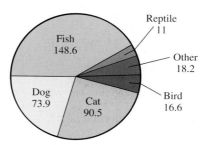

Source: American Pet Products Manufacturing Association

Figure 3.1

SOLUTION Let

> p: There are more dogs owned than cats.
>
> q: There are fewer reptiles owned than birds.
>
> r: The most numerous pets owned are fish.

The given compound statement can be written in symbolic form as $(p \wedge q) \vee \sim r$. From Fig. 3.1, we see that statement p is false: there are actually more cats owned than dogs. We also see that statement q is true: there are fewer reptiles owned than birds. We also see that statement r is true: the most numerous pets owned are fish. Since r is true, its negation, $\sim r$, is false. Therefore, we substitute F for p, T for q, and F for $\sim r$, which gives

$$(p \wedge q) \vee \sim r$$
$$(F \wedge T) \vee F$$
$$F \vee F$$
$$F$$

Thus, the original compound statement is a false statement.   ●

SECTION 3.2   EXERCISES

CONCEPT/WRITING EXERCISES

1. a) How many distinct cases must be listed in a truth table that contains two simple statements?

    b) List all the cases.

2. a) How many distinct cases must be listed in a truth table that contains three simple statements?

    b) List all the cases.

3. a) Construct the truth table for the conjunction $p \wedge q$.

    b) Under what circumstances is the conjunction true?

    c) Construct the truth table for the disjunction $p \vee q$.

    d) Under what circumstances is the disjunction false?

4. Suppose a compound statement contains five simple statements. How many distinct cases would the truth table for this compound statement have?

PRACTICE THE SKILLS/PROBLEM SOLVING

In Exercises 5–20, construct a truth table for the statement.

5. $p \wedge \sim p$

6. $p \vee \sim p$

7. $q \vee \sim p$

8. $p \wedge \sim q$

9. $\sim p \vee \sim q$

10. $\sim(p \vee \sim q)$

11. $\sim(p \wedge \sim q)$

12. $\sim(\sim p \wedge \sim q)$

13. $\sim q \vee (p \wedge r)$

14. $(p \vee \sim q) \wedge r$

15. $r \vee (p \wedge \sim q)$

16. $(r \wedge q) \wedge \sim p$

17. $(r \vee \sim p) \wedge \sim q$

18. $\sim p \wedge (q \vee r)$

19. $(\sim q \wedge r) \vee p$

20. $\sim r \vee (\sim p \wedge q)$

In Exercises 21–30, write the statement in symbolic form and construct a truth table.

21. The cookies are warm and the milk is cold.

22. The zoo is open, but it is not a nice day.

23. I have a new cell phone, but I do not have a new battery.

24. It is false that Wanda Garner is the president or that Judy Ackerman is the treasurer.

25. It is false that Jasper Adams is a tutor and Mark Russo is a secretary.

26. Mike made pizza and Dennis made a chef salad, but Gil burned the lemon squares.

27. The copier is out of toner, or the lens is dirty or the corona wires are broken.

28. I am hungry, and I want to eat a healthy lunch and I want to eat in a hurry.

29. The Congress must act on the bill, and the president must sign the bill or not sign the bill.

30. Gordon Langeneger likes the Mac Pro and he likes the MacBook Pro, but he does not like the Pentium IV.

In Exercises 31–42, determine the truth value of the statement if

a) p is true, q is false, and r is true.

b) p is false, q is true, and r is true.

31. $(\sim p \wedge r) \wedge q$ **32.** $\sim p \vee (q \wedge r)$

33. $(\sim p \vee \sim q) \vee \sim r$ **34.** $(\sim q \wedge \sim p) \vee \sim r$

35. $(p \vee \sim q) \wedge \sim (p \wedge \sim r)$ **36.** $(p \wedge \sim q) \vee r$

37. $(\sim r \wedge p) \vee q$ **38.** $\sim q \vee (r \wedge p)$

39. $(\sim q \vee \sim p) \wedge r$ **40.** $(\sim r \vee \sim p) \vee \sim q$

41. $(\sim p \vee \sim q) \vee (\sim r \vee q)$ **42.** $(\sim r \wedge \sim q) \wedge (\sim r \vee \sim p)$

In Exercises 43–50, determine the truth value for each simple statement. Then use these truth values to determine the truth value of the compound statement. (You may have to use a reference source such as the Internet or an encyclopedia.)

43. $18 \div 3 = 9$ or $56 \div 8 = 7$

44. $17 \geq 17$ and $-3 > -2$

45. Virginia borders the Atlantic Ocean or California borders the Indian Ocean.

46. Hawaii is the 50th state or Alaska lies on the equator, and Birmingham is the capital of Missouri.

47. Steven Spielberg is a movie director and Tom Hanks is an actor, but John Madden is not a sports announcer.

▲ John Madden and Melissa Stark

48. Quebec is in Texas or Toronto is in California, and Cedar Rapids is in Iowa.

49. Iraq is in Africa or Iran is in South America, and Syria is in the Middle East.

50. Holstein is a breed of cattle and collie is a breed of dogs, or beagle is not a breed of cats.

Carbon Dioxide Emissions In Exercises 51–54, use the table to determine the truth value of each simple statement. Then determine the truth value of the compound statement.

Countries with the Highest Carbon Dioxide (CO_2) Emissions in 2004

Country	CO_2 Emissions (in megatons)	Per Capita CO_2 Emissions (in tons)
United States	5652	19.66
China	3271	2.55
Russia	1503	10.43
Japan	1207	9.47
India	1016	0.97

Source: International Energy Agency

51. The United States had the lowest per capita CO_2 emissions and China had the highest per capita CO_2 emissions.

52. The United States had more CO_2 emissions than China and Russia had combined or the United States had more CO_2 emissions than Russia, Japan, and India had combined.

53. India had lower per capita CO_2 emissions than Japan had or China had lower per capita CO_2 emissions than India had.

54. Russia had lower per capita CO_2 emissions than the United States had, but Russia had higher per capita CO_2 emissions than Japan had.

Sleep Time In Exercises 55–58, use the graph, which shows the number of hours Americans sleep, to determine the truth value of each simple statement. Then determine the truth value of the compound statement.

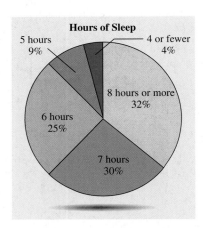

Hours of Sleep

5 hours 9%
4 or fewer 4%
8 hours or more 32%
6 hours 25%
7 hours 30%

55. It is false that 30% of Americans get 6 hours of sleep each night and 9% get 5 hours of sleep each night.

56. Twenty-five percent of Americans get 6 hours of sleep each night, and 30% get 7 hours of sleep each night or 9% do not get 5 hours of sleep each night.

57. Thirteen percent of Americans get 5 or fewer hours of sleep each night or 32% get 6 or more hours of sleep each night, and 30% get 8 or more hours of sleep each night.

58. Over one-half of all Americans get 7 or fewer hours of sleep each night, and over one-quarter get 6 or fewer hours of sleep each night.

In Exercises 59–62, let

       p: Tanisha owns a convertible.

       q: Joan owns a Volvo.

Translate each statement into symbols. Then construct a truth table for each and indicate under what conditions the compound statement is true.

59. Tanisha owns a convertible and Joan does not own a Volvo.

60. Tanisha does not own a convertible, but Joan owns a Volvo.

61. Tanisha owns a convertible or Joan does not own a Volvo.

62. Tanisha does not own a convertible or Joan does not own a Volvo.

In Exercises 63–66, let

       p: The house is owned by an engineer.

       q: The heat is solar generated.

       r: The car is run by electric power.

Translate each statement into symbols. Then construct a truth table for each and indicate under what conditions the compound statement is true.

63. The car is run by electric power or the heat is solar generated, but the house is owned by an engineer.

64. The house is owned by an engineer and the heat is solar generated, or the car is run by electric power.

65. The heat is solar generated, or the house is owned by an engineer and the car is not run by electric power.

66. The house is not owned by an engineer, and the car is not run by electric power and the heat is solar generated.

Obtaining a Loan In Exercises 67 and 68, read the requirements and each applicant's qualifications for obtaining a loan.

a) Identify which of the applicants would qualify for the loan.

b) For the applicants who do not qualify for the loan, explain why.

67. To qualify for a loan of $40,000, an applicant must have a gross income of $28,000 if single, $46,000 combined income if married, and assets of at least $6,000.

   Mrs. Rusinek, married with three children, earns $42,000. Mr. Rusinek does not have an income. The Rusineks have assets of $42,000.

   Mr. Duncan is not married, works in sales, and earns $31,000. He has assets of $9000.

   Mrs. Tuttle and her husband have total assets of $43,000. One earns $35,000, and the other earns $23,500.

68. To qualify for a loan of $45,000, an applicant must have a gross income of $30,000 if single, $50,000 combined income if married, and assets of at least $10,000.

   Mr. Argento, married with two children, earns $37,000. Mrs. Argento earns $15,000 at a part-time job. The Argentos have assets of $25,000.

   Ms. McVey, single, has assets of $19,000. She works in a store and earns $25,000.

   Mr. Siewert earns $24,000 and Ms. Fox, his wife, earns $28,000. Their assets total $8000.

69. *Airline Special Fares* An airline advertisement states, "To get the special fare you must purchase your tickets between January 1 and February 15 and fly round trip between March 1 and April 1. You must depart on a Monday, Tuesday, or Wednesday, and return on a Tuesday, Wednesday, or Thursday, and stay over at least one Saturday."

a) Determine which of the following individuals will qualify for the special fare.

b) If the person does not qualify for the special fare, explain why.

   Wing Park plans to purchase his ticket on January 15, depart on Monday, March 3, and return on Tuesday, March 18.

   Gina Vela plans to purchase her ticket on February 1, depart on Wednesday, March 12, and return on Thursday, April 3.

   Kara Shavo plans to purchase her ticket on February 14, depart on Tuesday, March 4, and return on Monday, March 19.

   Christos Supernaw plans to purchase his ticket on January 4, depart on Monday, March 10, and return on Thursday, March 13.

   Alex Chang plans to purchase his ticket on January 1, depart on Monday, March 3, and return on Monday, March 10.

▲ See Exercise 69

PROBLEM SOLVING/GROUP ACTIVITIES

In Exercises 70 and 71, construct a truth table for the symbolic statement.

70. $\sim[(\sim(p \vee q)) \vee (q \wedge r)]$

71. $[(q \wedge \sim r) \wedge (\sim p \vee \sim q)] \vee (p \vee \sim r)$

72. On page 120, we indicated that a compound statement consisting of n simple statements had 2^n distinct true–false cases.

a) How many distinct true–false cases does a truth table containing simple statements p, q, r, and s have?

b) List all possible true–false cases for a truth table containing the simple statements p, q, r, and s.

c) Use the list in part (b) to construct a truth table for $(q \wedge p) \vee (\sim r \wedge s)$.

d) Construct a truth table for $(\sim r \wedge \sim s) \wedge (\sim p \vee q)$.

73. Must $(p \wedge \sim q) \vee r$ and $(q \wedge \sim r) \vee p$ have the same number of trues in their answer columns? Explain.

INTERNET/RESEARCH ACTIVITIES

74. Do research and write a report on each of the following.

a) The relationship between *negation* in logic and *complement* in set theory.

b) The relationship between *conjunction* in logic and *intersection* in set theory.

c) The relationship between *disjunction* in logic and *union* in set theory.

3.3   TRUTH TABLES FOR THE CONDITIONAL AND BICONDITIONAL

▲ Under what conditions is the statement *If you get an A, then I will buy you a car* true?

Suppose I said to you, "If you get an A, then I will buy you a car." As we discussed in Section 3.1, this statement is called a *conditional* statement. In this section, we will discuss under what conditions a conditional statement is true and under what conditions a conditional statement is false.

Conditional

In Section 3.1, we mentioned that the statement preceding the conditional symbol is called the *antecedent* and that the statement following the conditional symbol is called the *consequent*. For example, consider $(p \lor q) \rightarrow [\sim(q \land r)]$. In this statement, $(p \lor q)$ is the antecedent and $[\sim(q \land r)]$ is the consequent.

To develop a truth table for the conditional statement, consider the statement "If you get an A, then I will buy you a car." Assume this statement is true except when I have actually broken my promise to you.

Let

p: You get an A.

q: I buy you a car.

Translated into symbolic form, the statement becomes $p \rightarrow q$. Let's examine the four cases shown in Table 3.12.

CASE 1: (T, T) You get an A, and I buy a car for you. I have met my commitment, and the statement is true.

CASE 2: (T, F) You get an A, and I do not buy a car for you. I have broken my promise, and the statement is false.

What happens if you don't get an A? If you don't get an A, I no longer have a commitment to you, and therefore I cannot break my promise.

CASE 3: (F, T) You do not get an A, and I buy you a car. I have not broken my promise, and therefore the statement is true.

CASE 4: (F, F) You do not get an A, and I don't buy you a car. I have not broken my promise, and therefore the statement is true.

The conditional statement is false when the antecedent is true and the consequent is false. In every other case the conditional statement is true.

Table 3.12 Conditional

p	q	$p \rightarrow q$
T	T	T
T	F	F
F	T	T
F	F	T

> The **conditional statement** $p \rightarrow q$ is true in every case except when p is a true statement and q is a false statement.

EXAMPLE ❶   *A Truth Table with a Conditional*

Construct a truth table for the statement $\sim p \rightarrow \sim q$.

Table 3.13

p	q	~p	→	~q
T	T	F	T	F
T	F	F	T	T
F	T	T	F	F
F	F	T	T	T
		1	3	2

Table 3.14

p	q	r	p	→	(~q	∧	r)
T	T	T	T	F	F	F	T
T	T	F	T	F	F	F	F
T	F	T	T	T	T	T	T
T	F	F	T	F	T	F	F
F	T	T	F	T	F	F	T
F	T	F	F	T	F	F	F
F	F	T	F	T	T	T	T
F	F	F	F	T	T	F	F
			4	5	1	3	2

SOLUTION Because this statement is a conditional, the answer will lie under the → . Fill out the truth table by placing the appropriate truth values under ~p, column 1, and under ~q, column 2 (see Table 3.13). Then, using the information given in the truth table for the conditional and the truth values in columns 1 and 2, determine the solution, column 3. In row 1, the antecedent, ~p, is false and the consequent, ~q, is also false. Row 1 is F → F, which according to row 4 of Table 3.12, is T. Likewise, row 2 of Table 3.13 is F → T, which is T. Row 3 is T → F, which is F. Row 4 is T → T, which is T. ●

EXAMPLE ② *A Conditional Truth Table with Three Simple Statements*

Construct a truth table for the statement $p \rightarrow (\sim q \wedge r)$.

SOLUTION Because this statement is a conditional, the answer will lie under the → . Work within the parentheses first. Place the truth values under ~q, column 1, and r, column 2 (Table 3.14). Then take the conjunction of columns 1 and 2 to obtain column 3. Next, place the truth values under p in column 4. To determine the answer, column 5, use columns 3 and 4 and the information of the conditional statement given in Table 3.12. Column 4 represents the truth values of the antecedent, and column 3 represents the truth values of the consequent. Remember that the conditional is false only when the antecedent is true and the consequent is false, as in cases (rows) 1, 2, and 4 of column 5. ●

EXAMPLE ③ *Examining an Advertisement*

An advertisement for Perky Morning coffee makes the following claim: "If you drink Perky Morning coffee, then you will not be sluggish and you will have a great day." Translate the statement into symbolic form and construct a truth table.

SOLUTION Let

>   *p*: You drink Perky Morning coffee.
>   *q*: You will be sluggish.
>   *r*: You will have a great day.

In symbolic form, the claim is

$$p \rightarrow (\sim q \wedge r)$$

This symbolic statement is identical to the statement in Table 3.14, and the truth tables are the same. Column 3 represents the truth values of $(\sim q \wedge r)$, which corresponds to the statement "You will not be sluggish and you will have a great day." Note that column 3 is true in cases (rows) 3 and 7. In case 3, since p is true, you drank Perky Morning coffee. In case 7, however, since p is false, you did not drink Perky Morning coffee. From this information we can conclude that it is possible for you to not be sluggish and for you to have a great day without drinking Perky Morning coffee. ●

A truth table alone cannot tell us whether a statement is true or false. It can, however, be used to examine the various possibilities.

Biconditional

The *biconditional statement*, $p \leftrightarrow q$, means that $p \rightarrow q$ and $q \rightarrow p$, or, symbolically, $(p \rightarrow q) \wedge (q \rightarrow p)$. To determine the truth table for $p \leftrightarrow q$, we will construct the truth table for $(p \rightarrow q) \wedge (q \rightarrow p)$ (Table 3.15). Table 3.16 shows the truth values for the biconditional statement.

Table 3.15

p	q	$(p$	$\rightarrow$	$q)$	$\wedge$	$(q$	$\rightarrow$	$p)$
T	T	T	T	T	T	T	T	T
T	F	T	F	F	F	F	T	T
F	T	F	T	T	F	T	F	F
F	F	F	T	F	T	F	T	F
		1	3	2	7	4	6	5

Table 3.16 Biconditional

p	q	$p \leftrightarrow q$
T	T	T
T	F	F
F	T	F
F	F	T

From Table 3.16 we see that the biconditional statement is true when the antecedent and the consequent have the same truth value and false when the antecedent and consequent have different truth values.

> The **biconditional statement**, $p \leftrightarrow q$, is true only when p and q have the same truth value, that is, when both are true or both are false.

EXAMPLE ❹ *A Truth Table Using a Biconditional*

Construct a truth table for the statement $p \leftrightarrow (q \rightarrow \sim r)$.

SOLUTION Since there are three letters, there must be eight cases. The parentheses indicate that the answer must be under the biconditional (Table 3.17). Use columns 3 and 4 to obtain the answer in column 5. When columns 3 and 4 have the same truth values, place a T in column 5. When columns 3 and 4 have different truth values, place an F in column 5.

Table 3.17

p	q	r	p	$\leftrightarrow$	$(q$	$\rightarrow$	$\sim r)$
T	T	T	T	F	T	F	F
T	T	F	T	T	T	T	T
T	F	T	T	T	F	T	F
T	F	F	T	T	F	T	T
F	T	T	F	T	T	F	F
F	T	F	F	F	T	T	T
F	F	T	F	F	F	T	F
F	F	F	F	F	F	T	T
			4	5	1	3	2

In Section 3.2, we showed that finding the truth value of a compound statement for a specific case does not require constructing an entire truth table. Examples 5 and 6 illustrate this technique for the conditional and the biconditional.

EXAMPLE 5 Determine the Truth Value of a Compound Statement

Determine the truth value of the statement $(\sim p \leftrightarrow q) \rightarrow (\sim q \leftrightarrow r)$ when p is false, q is true, and r is false.

SOLUTION   Substitute the truth value for each simple statement:

$$(\sim p \leftrightarrow q) \rightarrow (\sim q \leftrightarrow r)$$
$$(T \leftrightarrow T) \;\rightarrow\; (F \leftrightarrow F)$$
$$T \quad\rightarrow\quad T$$
$$T$$

For this specific case, the statement is true.   ●

EXAMPLE 6 Determine the Truth Value of a Compound Statement

Determine the truth value for each simple statement. Then use the truth values to determine the truth value of the compound statement.

a) If 15 is an even number, then 29 is an even number.

b) Northwestern University is in Illinois and Marquette University is in Alaska, if and only if Purdue University is in Alabama.

SOLUTION

a) Let

$$p:\quad \text{15 is an even number.}$$
$$q:\quad \text{29 is an even number.}$$

Then the statement "If 15 is an even number, then 29 is an even number" can be written $p \rightarrow q$. Since 15 is not an even number, p is a false statement. Also, since 29 is not an even number, q is a false statement. We substitute F for p and F for q and evaluate the statement:

$$p \rightarrow q$$
$$F \rightarrow F$$
$$T$$

Therefore, "If 15 is an even number, then 29 is an even number" is a true statement.

b) Let

$$p:\quad \text{Northwestern University is in Illinois.}$$
$$q:\quad \text{Marquette University is in Alaska.}$$
$$r:\quad \text{Purdue University is in Alabama.}$$

The original compound statement can be written $(p \wedge q) \leftrightarrow r$. By checking the Internet or other references we can find that Northwestern University is in Illinois, Marquette University is in Wisconsin, and Purdue University is in Indiana. Therefore, p is a true statement, but q and r are false statements. We will substitute T for p, F for q, and F for r and evaluate the compound statement:

$$(p \ \wedge \ q) \leftrightarrow r$$
$$(\text{T} \ \wedge \ \text{F}) \leftrightarrow \text{F}$$
$$\text{F} \quad \leftrightarrow \text{F}$$
$$\text{T}$$

Therefore, the original compound statement is true.   ●

EXAMPLE ❼ *Using Real Data in Compound Statements*

The graph in Fig. 3.2 represents the student population by age group in 2005 for Everett Community College (EvCC). Use this graph to determine the truth value of the following compound statements.

a) If 18- to 21-year-old students account for 25% of the EvCC student population, then 22- to 25-year-old students account for 12% of the EvCC student population and 31- to 35-year-old students account for 16% of the EvCC student population.

b) Students under age 18 years old account for 10% of the EvCC student population, if and only if 26- to 30-year-old students account for 25% of the EvCC student population or 36- to 40-year-old students account for 9% of the EvCC student population.

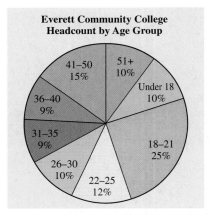

Everett Community College Headcount by Age Group

Source: Everett Community College Web Site

Figure 3.2

SOLUTION

a) Let

p: 18- to 21-year-old students account for 25% of the EvCC student population.

q: 22- to 25-year-old students account for 12% of the EvCC student population.

r: 31- to 35-year-old students account for 16% of the EvCC student population.

Then the original statement can be written $p \rightarrow (q \wedge r)$. We can see from Fig. 3.2 that both p and q are true statements and that r is a false statement. Substitute T for p, T for q, and F for r and evaluate the statement:

$$p \rightarrow (q \wedge r)$$
$$T \rightarrow (T \wedge F)$$
$$T \rightarrow \quad F$$
$$F$$

Therefore, "If 18- to 21-year-old students account for 25% of the EvCC student population, then 22- to 25-year-old students account for 12% of the EvCC student population and 31- to 35-year-old students account for 16% of the EvCC student population" is a false statement.

b) Let

p: Students under age 18 years old account for 10% of the EvCC student population.

q: 26- to 30-year-old students account for 25% of the EvCC student population.

r: 36- to 40-year-old students account for 9% of the EvCC student population.

Then the original statement can be written $p \leftrightarrow (q \vee r)$. We can see from Fig. 3.2 that p is true, q is false, and r is true. Substitute T for p, F for q, and T for r and evaluate the statement:

$$p \leftrightarrow (q \vee r)$$
$$T \leftrightarrow (F \vee T)$$
$$T \leftrightarrow \quad T$$
$$T$$

Therefore, the original statement, "Students under age 18 years old account for 10% of the EvCC student population, if and only if 26- to 30-year-old students account for 25% of the EvCC student population or 36- to 40-year-old students account for 9% of the EvCC student population" is a true statement. ●

Self-Contradictions, Tautologies, and Implications

Two special situations can occur in the truth table of a compound statement: The statement may always be false, or the statement may always be true. We give such statements special names.

A **self-contradiction** is a compound statement that is always false.

When every truth value in the answer column of the truth table is false, then the statement is a self-contradiction.

Table 3.18

p	q	$(p \leftrightarrow q)$	$\wedge$	$(p$	$\leftrightarrow$	$\sim q)$
T	T	T	F	T	F	F
T	F	F	F	T	T	T
F	T	F	F	F	T	F
F	F	T	F	F	F	T
		1	5	2	4	3

┌EXAMPLE ⑧ *All Falses, a Self-Contradiction*

Construct a truth table for the statement $(p \leftrightarrow q) \wedge (p \leftrightarrow \sim q)$.

SOLUTION See Table 3.18. In this example, the truth values are false in each case of column 5. This statement is an example of a self-contradiction or a *logically false statement.* ●

A **tautology** is a compound statement that is always true.

When every truth value in the answer column of the truth table is true, the statement is a tautology.

EXAMPLE ❾ *All Trues, a Tautology*

Construct a truth table for the statement $(p \land q) \to (p \lor r)$.

SOLUTION The answer is given in column 3 of Table 3.19. The truth values are true in every case. Thus, the statement is an example of a tautology or a *logically true statement*.

▲ "Heads I win, tails you lose." Do you think that this statement is a tautology, self-contradiction, or neither? See Problem-Solving Exercise 81.

Table 3.19

p	q	r	$(p \land q)$	$\to$	$(p \lor r)$
T	T	T	T	T	T
T	T	F	T	T	T
T	F	T	F	T	T
T	F	F	F	T	T
F	T	T	F	T	T
F	T	F	F	T	F
F	F	T	F	T	T
F	F	F	F	T	F
			1	3	2

The conditional statement $(p \land q) \to (p \lor r)$ is a tautology. Conditional statements that are tautologies are called *implications*. In Example 9, we can say that $p \land q$ implies $p \lor r$.

An **implication** is a conditional statement that is a tautology.

In any implication the antecedent of the conditional statement implies the consequent. In other words, if the antecedent is true, then the consequent must also be true. That is, the consequent will be true whenever the antecedent is true.

EXAMPLE ❿ *An Implication?*

Determine whether the conditional statement $[(p \land q) \land p] \to q$ is an implication.

SOLUTION If the conditional statement is a tautology, the conditional statement is an implication. Because the conditional statement is a tautology (see Table 3.20), the conditional statement is an implication. The antecedent $[(p \land q) \land p]$ implies the consequent q. Note that the antecedent is true only in case 1 and that the consequent is also true in case 1.

Table 3.20

p	q	$[(p \land q)$	$\land$	$p]$	$\to$	q
T	T	T	T	T	T	T
T	F	F	F	T	T	F
F	T	F	F	F	T	T
F	F	F	F	F	T	F
		1	3	2	5	4

SECTION 3.3 EXERCISES

CONCEPT/WRITING EXERCISES

1. a) Construct the truth table for the conditional statement $p \to q$.

   b) Explain when the conditional statement is true and when it is false.

   c) Construct the truth table for the biconditional statement $p \leftrightarrow q$.

   d) Explain when the biconditional statement is true and when it is false.

2. a) What is the statement preceding the conditional symbol called?

   b) What is the statement following the conditional symbol called?

3. a) Explain the procedure to determine the truth value of a compound statement when specific truth values are provided for the simple statements.

   b) Follow the procedure in part (a) and determine the truth value of the symbolic statement

   $$[(p \leftrightarrow q) \lor (\sim r \to q)] \to \sim r$$

   when p is true, q is true, and r is false.

4. What is a tautology?

5. What is a self-contradiction?

6. What is an implication?

PRACTICE THE SKILLS

In Exercises 7–16, construct a truth table for the statement.

7. $\sim p \to q$

8. $\sim p \to \sim q$

9. $\sim(p \to \sim q)$

10. $\sim(\sim p \leftrightarrow q)$

11. $\sim q \leftrightarrow p$

12. $(p \leftrightarrow q) \to p$

13. $p \leftrightarrow (q \lor p)$

14. $(\sim q \land p) \to \sim q$

15. $q \to (p \to \sim q)$

16. $(p \lor q) \leftrightarrow (p \land q)$

In Exercises 17–26, construct a truth table for the statement.

17. $\sim p \to (q \land r)$

18. $q \lor (p \to \sim r)$

19. $p \leftrightarrow (\sim q \to r)$

20. $(\sim p \to \sim r) \to q$

21. $(q \lor \sim r) \leftrightarrow \sim p$

22. $(p \land r) \to (q \lor r)$

23. $(\sim r \lor \sim q) \to p$

24. $[r \land (q \lor \sim p)] \leftrightarrow \sim p$

25. $(p \to q) \leftrightarrow (\sim q \to \sim r)$

26. $(\sim p \leftrightarrow \sim q) \to (\sim q \leftrightarrow r)$

In Exercises 27–32, write the statement in symbolic form. Then construct a truth table for the symbolic statement.

27. If I take niacin, then I will stay healthy and I will have lower cholesterol.

28. The goalie will make the save if and only if the stopper is in position, or the forward cannot handle the ball.

29. The election was fair if and only if the polling station stayed open until 8 P.M., or we will request a recount.

30. If the dam holds then we can go fishing, if and only if the pole is not broken.

31. If Mary Andrews does not send me an e-mail then we can call her, or we can write to Mom.

32. It is false that if Eileen Jones went to lunch, then she cannot take a message and we will have to go home.

In Exercises 33–38, determine whether the statement is a tautology, self-contradiction, or neither.

33. $p \to \sim p$

34. $(p \land \sim q) \leftrightarrow \sim p$

35. $p \land (q \land \sim p)$

36. $(p \wedge {\sim}q) \rightarrow q$

37. $({\sim}q \rightarrow p) \vee {\sim}q$

38. $[(p \rightarrow q) \vee r] \leftrightarrow [(p \wedge q) \rightarrow r]$

In Exercises 39–44, determine whether the statement is an implication.

39. ${\sim}p \rightarrow (p \vee q)$

40. $(p \wedge q) \rightarrow ({\sim}p \vee q)$

41. $(q \wedge p) \rightarrow (p \wedge q)$

42. $(p \vee q) \rightarrow (p \vee {\sim}r)$

43. $[(p \rightarrow q) \wedge (q \rightarrow p)] \rightarrow (p \leftrightarrow q)$

44. $[(p \vee q) \wedge r] \rightarrow (p \vee q)$

In Exercises 45–56, if p is true, q is false, and r is true, find the truth value of the statement.

45. ${\sim}p \rightarrow (q \rightarrow r)$

46. $(p \vee q) \rightarrow {\sim}r$

47. $q \leftrightarrow ({\sim}p \vee r)$

48. $r \rightarrow ({\sim}p \leftrightarrow {\sim}q)$

49. $({\sim}p \wedge {\sim}q) \vee {\sim}r$

50. ${\sim}[p \rightarrow (q \wedge r)]$

51. $(p \wedge r) \leftrightarrow (p \vee {\sim}q)$

52. $({\sim}p \vee q) \rightarrow {\sim}r$

53. $({\sim}p \leftrightarrow r) \vee ({\sim}q \leftrightarrow r)$

54. $(r \rightarrow {\sim}p) \wedge (q \rightarrow {\sim}r)$

55. ${\sim}[(p \vee q) \leftrightarrow (p \rightarrow {\sim}r)]$

56. $[({\sim}r \rightarrow {\sim}q) \vee (p \wedge {\sim}r)] \rightarrow q$

PROBLEM SOLVING

In Exercises 57–64, determine the truth value for each simple statement. Then, using the truth values, determine the truth value of the compound statement.

57. If $2 + 7 = 9$, then $15 - 3 = 12$.

58. If $\frac{3}{4} < 1$ and $\frac{7}{8} > 1$, then $\frac{15}{16} < 1$.

59. A cat has whiskers or a fish can swim, and a chicken lays eggs.

60. Tallahassee is in Florida and Atlanta is in Georgia, or Chicago is in Mississippi.

61. Apple makes computers, if and only if Nike makes sports shoes or Rolex makes watches.

62. Spike Lee is a movie director, or if Halle Berry is a schoolteacher then George Clooney is a circus clown.

63. Valentine's Day is in February or President's Day is in March, and Thanksgiving is in November.

64. Honda makes automobiles or Honda makes motorcycles, if and only if Toyota makes cereal.

In Exercises 65–68, use the information provided about the moons for the planets Jupiter and Saturn to determine the truth values of the simple statements. Then determine the truth value of the compound statement.

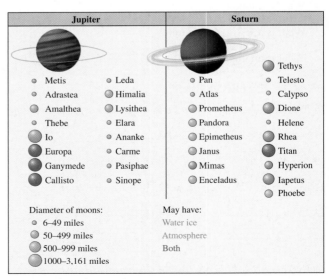

Source: Data from *Time* Magazine

65. *Jupiter's Moons* Io has a diameter of 1000–3161 miles or Thebe may have water, and Io may have atmosphere.

66. *Moons of Saturn* Titan may have water and Titan may have atmosphere, if and only if Janus may have water.

67. *Moon Comparisons* Phoebe has a larger diameter than Rhea if and only if Callisto may have water ice, and Calypso has a diameter of 6–49 miles.

68. *Moon Comparisons* If Jupiter has 16 moons or Saturn does not have 18 moons, then Saturn has 7 moons that may have water ice.

In Exercises 69 and 70, use the graphs to determine the truth values of each simple statement. Then determine the truth value of the compound statement.

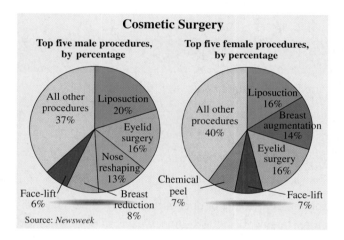

Cosmetic Surgery

Top five male procedures, by percentage

Top five female procedures, by percentage

Source: *Newsweek*

69. *Most Common Cosmetic Surgery* The most common cosmetic surgery procedure for females is liposuction or the most common procedure for males is eyelid surgery, and 20% of male cosmetic surgery is for nose reshaping.

70. *Face-lifts and Eyelid Surgeries* 7% of female cosmetic surgeries are for face-lifts and 10% of male cosmetic surgeries are for face-lifts, if and only if males have a higher percent of eyelid surgeries than females.

In Exercises 71–76, suppose both of the following statements are true.

p: Muhundan spoke at the teachers' conference.
q: Muhundan received the outstanding teacher award.

Find the truth values of each compound statement.

71. If Muhundan received the outstanding teacher award, then Muhundan spoke at the teachers' conference.

72. If Muhundan spoke at the teachers' conference, then Muhundan did not receive the outstanding teacher award.

73. If Muhundan did not receive the outstanding teacher award, then Muhundan spoke at the teachers' conference.

74. Muhundan did not receive the outstanding teacher award if and only if Muhundan spoke at the teachers' conference.

75. Muhundan received the outstanding teacher award if and only if Muhundan spoke at the teachers' conference.

76. If Muhundan did not receive the outstanding teacher award, then Muhundan did not speak at the teachers' conference.

77. *A New Computer* Your parents make the following statement to your sister, "If you get straight A's this semester, then we will buy you a new computer." At the end of the semester your parents buy your sister a new computer. Can you conclude that your sister got straight A's? Explain.

78. *Job Interview* Consider the statement "If your interview goes well, then you will be offered the job." If you are interviewed and then offered the job, can you conclude that your interview went well? Explain.

CHALLENGE PROBLEMS/GROUP ACTIVITIES

In Exercises 79 and 80, construct truth tables for the symbolic statement.

79. $[p \vee (q \to \sim r)] \leftrightarrow (p \wedge \sim q)$

80. $[(r \to \sim q) \to \sim p] \vee (q \leftrightarrow \sim r)$

81. Is the statement "Heads I win, tails you lose" a tautology, a self-contradiction, or neither? Explain your answer.

82. Construct a truth table for

 a) $(p \vee q) \to (r \wedge s)$.

 b) $(q \to \sim p) \vee (r \leftrightarrow s)$.

RECREATIONAL MATHEMATICS

83. *Cat Puzzle* Solve the following puzzle. The Joneses have four cats. The parents are Tiger and Boots, and the kittens are Sam and Sue. Each cat insists on eating out of its own bowl. To complicate matters, each cat will eat only its own brand of cat food. The colors of the bowls are red, yellow, green, and blue. The different types of cat food are Whiskas, Friskies, Nine Lives, and Meow Mix. Tiger will eat Meow Mix if and only if it is in a yellow bowl. If Boots is to eat her food, then it must be in a yellow bowl. Mrs. Jones knows that the label on the can containing Sam's food is the same color as his bowl. Boots eats Whiskas. Meow Mix and Nine Lives are packaged in a brown paper bag. The color of Sue's bowl is green if and only if she eats Meow Mix. The label on the Friskies can is red. Match each cat with its food and the bowl of the correct color.

84. ***The Youngest Triplet*** The Barr triplets have an annoying habit: Whenever a question is asked of the three of them, two tell the truth and the third lies. When I asked them which of them was born last, they replied as follows.

Mary: Katie was born last.
Katie: I am the youngest.
Annie: Mary is the youngest.

Which of the Barr triplets was born last?

INTERNET/RESEARCH ACTIVITY

85. Select an advertisement from the Internet, a newspaper, or a magazine that makes or implies a conditional statement. Analyze the advertisement to determine whether the consequent necessarily follows from the antecedent. Explain your answer. (See Example 3.)

3.4   EQUIVALENT STATEMENTS

▲ Which statement is equivalent to *If it is sunny, then we go to the beach*?

Suppose your friend makes the following statements:

If it is sunny, then we go to the beach.

If we go to the beach, then it is sunny.

If it is not sunny, then we do not go to the beach.

If we do not go to the beach, then it is not sunny.

Are these statements all saying the same thing, or does each one say something completely different from each other statement? In this section, we will study how we can answer this question by using logic symbols and truth tables. We also will learn to identify variations of conditional statements.

Equivalent statements are an important concept in the study of logic.

> Two statements are **equivalent,** symbolized ⇔ ,* if both statements have exactly the same truth values in the answer columns of the truth tables.

Sometimes the words *logically equivalent* are used in place of the word *equivalent.*
    To determine whether two statements are equivalent, construct a truth table for each statement and compare the answer columns of the truth tables. If the answer columns are identical, the statements are equivalent. If the answer columns are not identical, the statements are not equivalent.

---

*The symbol ≡ is also used to indicate equivalent statements.

PROFILE IN MATHEMATICS

Charles Dodgson

One of the more interesting and well-known students of logic was Charles Dodgson (1832–1898), better known to us as Lewis Carroll, the author of *Alice's Adventures in Wonderland* and *Through the Looking-Glass*. Although the books have a child's point of view, many argue that the audience best equipped to enjoy them is an adult one. Dodgson, a mathematician, logician, and photographer (among other things), uses the naïveté of a 7-year-old girl to show what can happen when the rules of logic are taken to absurd extremes.

"You should say what you mean," the March Hare went on.

"I do," Alice hastily replied; "at least—at least I mean what I say—that's the same thing, you know."

"Not the same thing a bit!" said the Hatter. "You might as well say that 'I see what I eat' is the same thing as 'I eat what I see'!"

EXAMPLE 1 *Equivalent Statements*

Determine whether the following two statements are equivalent.

$$p \wedge (q \vee r)$$
$$(p \wedge q) \vee (p \wedge r)$$

SOLUTION Construct a truth table for each statement (see Table 3.21).

Table 3.21

p	q	r	p	$\wedge$	$(q \vee r)$	$(p \wedge q)$	$\vee$	$(p \wedge r)$
T	T	T	T	T	T	T	T	T
T	T	F	T	T	T	T	T	F
T	F	T	T	T	T	F	T	T
T	F	F	T	F	F	F	F	F
F	T	T	F	F	T	F	F	F
F	T	F	F	F	T	F	F	F
F	F	T	F	F	T	F	F	F
F	F	F	F	F	F	F	F	F
			1	3	2	1	3	2

Because the truth tables have the same answer (column 3 for both tables), the statements are equivalent. Therefore, we can write

$$p \wedge (q \vee r) \Leftrightarrow (p \wedge q) \vee (p \wedge r)$$

EXAMPLE 2 *Are the Following Equivalent Statements?*

Determine whether the following statements are equivalent.
a) If you work hard and obey all of the rules, then you will succeed in life.
b) If you do not work hard or do not obey all of the rules, then you will not succeed in life.

SOLUTION First write each statement in symbolic form, then construct a truth table for each statement. If the answer columns of both truth tables are identical, then the statements are equivalent. If the answer columns are not identical, then the statements are not equivalent.

Let

p: You work hard.
q: You obey all of the rules.
r: You will succeed in life.

In symbolic form, the statements are
a) $(p \wedge q) \to r$.   b) $(\sim p \vee \sim q) \to \sim r$.

The truth tables for these statements are given in Tables 3.22 and 3.23, respectively. The answers in the columns labeled 5 are not identical, so the statements are not equivalent.

Table 3.22

p	q	r	(p	$\wedge$	q)	$\rightarrow$	r
T	T	T	T	T	T	T	T
T	T	F	T	T	T	F	F
T	F	T	T	F	F	T	T
T	F	F	T	F	F	T	F
F	T	T	F	F	T	T	T
F	T	F	F	F	T	T	F
F	F	T	F	F	F	T	T
F	F	F	F	F	F	T	F
			1	3	2	5	4

Table 3.23

p	q	r	($\sim p$	$\vee$	$\sim q$)	$\rightarrow$	$\sim r$
T	T	T	F	F	F	T	F
T	T	F	F	F	F	T	T
T	F	T	F	T	T	F	F
T	F	F	F	T	T	T	T
F	T	T	T	T	F	F	F
F	T	F	T	T	F	T	T
F	F	T	T	T	T	F	F
F	F	F	T	T	T	T	T
			1	3	2	5	4

•

EXAMPLE ❸ *Which Statements Are Logically Equivalent?*

Determine which statement is logically equivalent to "It is not true that the tire is both out of balance and flat."

a) If the tire is not flat, then the tire is not out of balance.
b) The tire is not out of balance or the tire is not flat.
c) The tire is not flat and the tire is not out of balance.
d) If the tire is not out of balance, then the tire is not flat.

SOLUTION To determine whether any of the choices are equivalent to the given statement, first write the given statements and the choices in symbolic form. Then construct truth tables and compare the answer columns of the truth tables.

Let

p: The tire is out of balance.
q: The tire is flat.

The given statement may be written "It is not true that the tire is out of balance and the tire is flat." The statement is expressed in symbolic form as $\sim(p \wedge q)$. Using p and q as indicated, choices (a) through (d) may be expressed symbolically as

a) $\sim q \rightarrow \sim p$.   b) $\sim p \vee \sim q$.   c) $\sim q \wedge \sim p$.   d) $\sim p \rightarrow \sim q$.

Now construct a truth table for the given statement (Table 3.24) and for each statement (a) through (d), given in Table 3.25(a) through (d). By examining the truth tables, we see that the given statement, $\sim(p \wedge q)$, is logically equivalent to choice (b), $\sim p \vee \sim q$. Therefore, the correct answer is "The tire is not out of balance or the tire is not flat." This statement is logically equivalent to the statement "It is not true that the tire is both out of balance and flat."

Table 3.24

p	q	~	(p	∧	q)
T	T	F	T	T	T
T	F	T	T	F	F
F	T	T	F	F	T
F	F	T	F	F	F
		4	1	3	2

Table 3.25

		(a)			(b)			(c)			(d)		
p	q	~q	→	~p	~p	∨	~q	~q	∧	~p	~p	→	~q
T	T	F	T	F	F	F	F	F	F	F	F	T	F
T	F	T	F	F	F	T	T	T	F	F	F	T	T
F	T	F	T	T	T	T	F	F	F	T	T	F	F
F	F	T	T	T	T	T	T	T	T	T	T	T	T

De Morgan's Laws

Example 3 showed that a statement of the form $\sim(p \wedge q)$ is equivalent to a statement of the form $\sim p \vee \sim q$. Thus, we may write $\sim(p \wedge q) \Leftrightarrow \sim p \vee \sim q$. This equivalent statement is one of two special laws called De Morgan's laws. The laws, named after Augustus De Morgan, an English mathematician, were first introduced in Section 2.4, where they applied to sets.

DE MORGAN'S LAWS

1. $\sim(p \wedge q) \Leftrightarrow \sim p \vee \sim q$
2. $\sim(p \vee q) \Leftrightarrow \sim p \wedge \sim q$

You can demonstrate that De Morgan's second law is true by constructing and comparing truth tables for $\sim(p \vee q)$ and $\sim p \wedge \sim q$. Do so now.

When using De Morgan's laws, if it becomes necessary to negate an already negated statement, use the fact that $\sim(\sim p)$ is equivalent to p. For example, the negation of the statement "Today is not Monday" is "Today is Monday."

EXAMPLE 4 Use De Morgan's Laws

Select the statement that is logically equivalent to "I do not have investments, but I do not have debts."

a) I do not have investments or I do not have debts.
b) It is false that I have investments and I have debts.
c) It is false that I have investments or I have debts.
d) I have investments or I have debts.

SOLUTION To determine which statement is equivalent, write each statement in symbolic form.

Let

p: I have investments.
q: I have debts.

The statement, "I do not have investments, but I do not have debts" written symbolically is $\sim p \wedge \sim q$. Recall that the word *but* means the same thing as *and*. Now, write parts (a) through (d) symbolically.

a) $\sim p \vee \sim q$ b) $\sim (p \wedge q)$ c) $\sim (p \vee q)$ d) $p \vee q$

De Morgan's law shows that $\sim p \wedge \sim q$ is equivalent to $\sim (p \vee q)$. Therefore, the answer is (c): "It is false that I have investments or I have debts."   ●

EXAMPLE ❺   *Using De Morgan's Laws to Write an Equivalent Statement*

Write a statement that is logically equivalent to "It is not true that tomatoes are poisonous or eating peppers cures the common cold."

SOLUTION Let

p: Tomatoes are poisonous.

q: Eating peppers cures the common cold.

The given statement is of the form $\sim (p \vee q)$. Using the second of De Morgan's laws, we see that an equivalent statement in symbols is $\sim p \wedge \sim q$. Therefore, an equivalent statement in words is "Tomatoes are not poisonous and eating peppers does not cure the common cold."   ●

Consider $\sim (p \wedge q) \Leftrightarrow \sim p \vee \sim q$, one of De Morgan's laws. To go from $\sim (p \wedge q)$ to $\sim p \vee \sim q$, we negate both the p and the q within parentheses; change the conjunction, $\wedge$, to a disjunction, $\vee$; and remove the negation symbol preceding the left parentheses and the parentheses themselves. We can use a similar procedure to obtain equivalent statements. For example,

$$\sim (\sim p \wedge q) \Leftrightarrow p \vee \sim q$$
$$\sim (p \wedge \sim q) \Leftrightarrow \sim p \vee q$$

We can use a similar procedure to obtain equivalent statements when a disjunction is within parentheses. Note that

$$\sim (\sim p \vee q) \Leftrightarrow p \wedge \sim q$$
$$\sim (p \vee \sim q) \Leftrightarrow \sim p \wedge q$$

EXAMPLE ❻   *Using De Morgan's Laws to Write an Equivalent Statement*

Use De Morgan's laws to write a statement logically equivalent to "Benjamin Franklin was not a U.S. president, but he signed the Declaration of Independence."

SOLUTION Let

p: Benjamin Franklin was a U.S. president.

q: Benjamin Franklin signed the Declaration of Independence.

The statement written symbolically is $\sim p \wedge q$. Earlier we showed that

$$\sim p \wedge q \Leftrightarrow \sim(p \vee \sim q)$$

Therefore, the statement "It is false that Benjamin Franklin was a U.S. president or Benjamin Franklin did not sign the Declaration of Independence" is logically equivalent to the given statement.

There are strong similarities between the topics of sets and logic. We can see them by examining De Morgan's laws for sets and logic.

De Morgan's laws: set theory	De Morgan's laws: logic
$(A \cap B)' = A' \cup B'$	$\sim(p \wedge q) \Leftrightarrow \sim p \vee \sim q$
$(A \cup B)' = A' \cap B'$	$\sim(p \vee q) \Leftrightarrow \sim p \wedge \sim q$

The complement in set theory, $'$, is similar to the negation, $\sim$, in logic. The intersection, $\cap$, is similar to the conjunction, $\wedge$; and the union, $\cup$, is similar to the disjunction, $\vee$. If we were to interchange the set symbols with the logic symbols, De Morgan's laws would remain, but in a different form.

Both $'$ and $\sim$ can be interpreted as *not*.

Both $\cap$ and $\wedge$ can be interpreted as *and*.

Both $\cup$ and $\vee$ can be interpreted as *or*.

For example, the set statement $A' \cup B$ can be written as a statement in logic as $\sim a \vee b$.

Statements containing connectives other than *and* and *or* may have equivalent statements. To illustrate this point, construct truth tables for $p \rightarrow q$ and for $\sim p \vee q$. The truth tables will have the same answer columns and therefore the statements are equivalent. That is,

$$p \rightarrow q \Leftrightarrow \sim p \vee q$$

With these equivalent statements, we can write a conditional statement as a disjunction or a disjunction as a conditional statement. For example, the statement "If the game is polo, then you ride a horse" can be equivalently stated as "The game is not polo or you ride a horse."

To change a conditional statement to a disjunction, negate the antecedent, change the conditional symbol to a disjunction symbol, and keep the consequent the same. To change a disjunction statement to a conditional statement, negate the first statement, change the disjunction symbol to a conditional symbol, and keep the second statement the same.

EXAMPLE 7 *Rewriting a Disjunction as a Conditional Statement*

Write a conditional statement that is logically equivalent to "The Oregon Ducks will win or the Oregon State Beavers will lose." Assume that the negation of winning is losing.

SOLUTION Let

p: The Oregon Ducks will win.

q: The Oregon State Beavers will win.

The original statement may be written symbolically as $p \vee \sim q$. To write an equivalent conditional statement, negate the first statement, p, change the disjunction symbol to a conditional symbol, and keep the second statement the same. Symbolically, the equivalent statement is $\sim p \rightarrow \sim q$. The equivalent statement in words is "If the Oregon Ducks lose, then the Oregon State Beavers will lose." ●

Negation of the Conditional Statement

Now we will discuss how to negate a conditional statement. To negate a statement we use the fact that $p \rightarrow q \Leftrightarrow \sim p \vee q$ and De Morgan's laws. Examples 8 and 9 show the process.

EXAMPLE 8 *The Negation of a Conditional Statement*

Determine a statement equivalent to $\sim(p \rightarrow q)$.

SOLUTION Begin with $p \rightarrow q \Leftrightarrow \sim p \vee q$, negate both statements, and use De Morgan's laws.

$$p \rightarrow q \Leftrightarrow \sim p \vee q$$
$$\sim(p \rightarrow q) \Leftrightarrow \sim(\sim p \vee q) \quad \text{Negate both statements}$$
$$\Leftrightarrow p \wedge \sim q \quad \text{De Morgan's laws}$$

Therefore, $\sim(p \rightarrow q)$ is equivalent to $p \wedge \sim q$. ●

EXAMPLE 9 *Write an Equivalent Statement*

Write a statement that is equivalent to "It is false that if it is snowing then we cannot go to the basketball game."

SOLUTION Let

p: It is snowing.

q: We can go to the basketball game.

The given statement can then be represented symbolically as $\sim(p \rightarrow \sim q)$. Using the procedure illustrated in Example 8 we can determine that $\sim(p \rightarrow \sim q)$ is equivalent to $p \wedge q$. You should verify that the two statements are equivalent now. Therefore, an equivalent statement is "It is snowing and we can go to the basketball game." ●

Variations of the Conditional Statement

We know that $p \rightarrow q$ is equivalent to $\sim p \lor q$. Are any other statements equivalent to $p \rightarrow q$? Yes, there are many. Now let's look at the variations of the conditional statement to determine whether any are equivalent to the conditional statement. *The variations of the conditional statement are made by switching and/or negating the antecedent and the consequent of a conditional statement.* The variations of the conditional statement are the *converse* of the conditional, the *inverse* of the conditional, and the *contrapositive* of the conditional.

Listed here are the variations of the conditional with their symbolic form and the words we say to read each one.

VARIATIONS OF THE CONDITIONAL STATEMENT

Name	Symbolic form	Read
Conditional	$p \rightarrow q$	"If p, then q"
Converse of the conditional	$q \rightarrow p$	"If q, then p"
Inverse of the conditional	$\sim p \rightarrow \sim q$	"If not p, then not q"
Contrapositive of the conditional	$\sim q \rightarrow \sim p$	"If not q, then not p"

To write the converse of the conditional statement, switch the order of the antecedent and the consequent. To write the inverse, negate both the antecedent and the consequent. To write the contrapositive, switch the order of the antecedent and the consequent and then negate both of them.

Are any of the variations of the conditional statement equivalent? To determine the answer, we can construct a truth table for each variation, as shown in Table 3.26. It reveals that the conditional statement is equivalent to the contrapositive statement and that the converse statement is equivalent to the inverse statement.

Table 3.26

p	q	Conditional $p \rightarrow q$	Contrapositive $\sim q \rightarrow \sim p$	Converse $q \rightarrow p$	Inverse $\sim p \rightarrow \sim q$
T	T	T	T	T	T
T	F	F	F	T	T
F	T	T	T	F	F
F	F	T	T	T	T

EXAMPLE ⑩ *The Converse, Inverse and Contrapositive*

For the conditional statement "If the song contains sitar music, then the song was written by George Harrison," write the

a) converse.   b) inverse.   c) contrapositive.

▲ A sitar

SOLUTION

a) Let

> p: The song contains sitar music.
> q: The song was written by George Harrison.

The conditional statement is of the form $p \rightarrow q$, so the converse must be of the form $q \rightarrow p$. Therefore, the converse is "If the song was written by George Harrison, then the song contains sitar music."

b) The inverse is of the form $\sim p \rightarrow \sim q$. Therefore, the inverse is "If the song does not contain sitar music, then the song was not written by George Harrison."

c) The contrapositive is of the form $\sim q \rightarrow \sim p$. Therefore, the contrapositive is "If the song was not written by George Harrison, then the song does not contain sitar music." •

EXAMPLE ⑪ *Determine the Truth Values*

Let

> p: The number is divisible by 9.
> q: The number is divisible by 3.

Write the following statements and determine which are true.

a) The conditional statement, $p \rightarrow q$

b) The converse of $p \rightarrow q$

c) The inverse of $p \rightarrow q$

d) The contrapositive of $p \rightarrow q$

SOLUTION

a) *Conditional statement:* $(p \rightarrow q)$
   If the number is divisible by 9, then the number is divisible by 3. This statement is true. A number divisible by 9 must also be divisible by 3, since 3 is a divisor of 9.

b) *Converse of the conditional:* $(q \rightarrow p)$
   If the number is divisible by 3, then the number is divisible by 9. This statement is false. For instance, 6 is divisible by 3, but 6 is not divisible by 9.

c) *Inverse of the conditional:* $(\sim p \rightarrow \sim q)$
   If the number is not divisible by 9, then the number is not divisible by 3. This statement is false. For instance, 6 is not divisible by 9, but 6 is divisible by 3.

d) *Contrapositive of the conditional:* $(\sim q \rightarrow \sim p)$
   If the number is not divisible by 3, then the number is not divisible by 9. The statement is true, since any number that is divisible by 9 must be divisible by 3. •

EXAMPLE ⑫ *Use the Contrapositive*

Use the contrapositive to write a statement logically equivalent to "If you don't eat your meat, then you can't have pudding."

SOLUTION Let

$$p: \quad \text{You do eat your meat.}$$
$$q: \quad \text{You can have pudding.}$$

The given statement written symbolically is

$$\sim p \rightarrow \sim q$$

The contrapositive of the statement is

$$q \rightarrow p$$

Therefore, an equivalent statement is "If you can have pudding, then you do eat your meat." ●

The contrapositive of the conditional is very important in mathematics. Consider the statement "If a^2 is not a whole number, then a is not a whole number." Is this statement true? You may find this question difficult to answer. Writing the statement's contrapositive may enable you to answer the question. The contrapositive is "If a is a whole number, then a^2 is a whole number." Since the contrapositive is a true statement, the original statement must also be true.

EXAMPLE ⑬ *Which Are Equivalent?*

Determine which, if any, of the following statements are equivalent. You may use De Morgan's laws, the fact that $p \rightarrow q \Leftrightarrow \sim p \vee q$, information from the variations of the conditional, or truth tables.

a) If you leave by 9 A.M., then you will get to your destination on time.
b) You do not leave by 9 A.M. or you will get to your destination on time.
c) It is false that you will get to your destination on time or you did not leave by 9 A.M.
d) If you do not get to your destination on time, then you did not leave by 9 A.M.

SOLUTION Let

$$p: \quad \text{You leave by 9 A.M.}$$
$$q: \quad \text{You will get to your destination on time.}$$

In symbolic form, the four statements are

a) $p \rightarrow q$.   b) $\sim p \vee q$.   c) $\sim(q \vee \sim p)$.   d) $\sim q \rightarrow \sim p$.

Which of these statements are equivalent? Earlier in this section, you learned that $p \rightarrow q$ is equivalent to $\sim p \vee q$. Therefore, statements (a) and (b) are equivalent. Statement (d) is the contrapositive of statement (a). Therefore, statement (d) is also equivalent to statement (a) and statement (b). All these statements have the same truth table (Table 3.27 on page 146).

Table 3.27

p	q	(a) $p \rightarrow q$	(b) $\sim p \vee q$	(d) $\sim q \rightarrow \sim p$
T	T	T	T	T
T	F	F	F	F
F	T	T	T	T
F	F	T	T	T

Now let's look at statement (c). To determine whether $\sim(q \vee \sim p)$ is equivalent to the other statements, we will construct its truth table (Table 3.28) and compare the answer column with the answer columns in Table 3.27.

Table 3.28

p	q	(c) $\sim$	$(q$	$\vee$	$\sim p)$
T	T	F	T	T	F
T	F	T	F	F	F
F	T	F	T	T	T
F	F	F	F	T	T
		4	1	3	2

None of the three answer columns of the truth table in Table 3.27 is the same as the answer column of the truth table in Table 3.28. Therefore $\sim(q \vee \sim p)$ is not equivalent to any of the other statements. Therefore, statements (a), (b), and (d) are equivalent to each other. ●

SECTION 3.4   EXERCISES

CONCEPT/WRITING EXERCISES

1. **a)** What are equivalent statements?

   b) Explain how you can determine whether two statements are equivalent.

2. Suppose two statements are connected with the biconditional and the truth table is constructed. If the answer column of the truth table has all trues, what must be true about these two statements? Explain.

3. Write De Morgan's laws for logic.

4. For a statement of the form $p \rightarrow q$, symbolically indicate the form of the

   a) converse.

   b) inverse.

   c) contrapositive.

5. Which of the following are equivalent statements?

   a) The converse

   b) The contrapositive

   c) The inverse

   d) The conditional

6. Write a disjunction that is logically equivalent to $p \to q$.

7. If $p \to q$ is equivalent to $\sim p \vee q$, write a conjunction that is equivalent to $\sim(p \to q)$.

8. Write a conjunction involving two conditional statements that is logically equivalent to $p \leftrightarrow q$. See page 128.

PRACTICE THE SKILLS

In Exercises 9–18, use De Morgan's laws to determine whether the two statements are equivalent.

9. $\sim(p \wedge q),\ \sim p \wedge q$

10. $\sim(p \vee \sim q),\ \sim p \wedge q$

11. $\sim(p \wedge q),\ \sim(q \vee \sim p)$

12. $\sim p \vee \sim q,\ \sim(p \wedge q)$

13. $\sim(p \vee q),\ \sim p \wedge \sim q$

14. $\sim(p \wedge q),\ \sim p \wedge \sim q$

15. $(\sim p \vee \sim q) \to r,\ \sim(p \wedge q) \to r$

16. $q \to \sim(p \wedge \sim r),\ q \to \sim p \vee r$

17. $\sim(p \to \sim q),\ p \wedge q$

18. $\sim(\sim p \to q),\ \sim p \wedge \sim q$

In Exercises 19–30, use a truth table to determine whether the two statements are equivalent.

19. $p \to q,\ \sim p \vee q$

20. $\sim(p \to q),\ p \wedge \sim q$

21. $\sim q \to \sim p,\ p \to q$

22. $q \to p,\ \sim p \to \sim q$

23. $(p \vee q) \vee r,\ p \vee (q \vee r)$

24. $p \vee (q \wedge r),\ \sim p \to (q \wedge r)$

25. $p \wedge (q \vee r),\ (p \wedge q) \vee r$

26. $\sim(q \to p) \vee r,\ (p \vee q) \wedge \sim r$

27. $(p \to q) \wedge (q \to r),\ (p \to q) \to r$

28. $\sim q \to (p \wedge r),\ \sim(p \vee r) \to q$

29. $(p \to q) \wedge (q \to p),\ (p \leftrightarrow q)$

30. $[\sim(p \to q)] \wedge [\sim(q \to p)],\ \sim(p \leftrightarrow q)$

PROBLEM SOLVING

In Exercises 31–38, use De Morgan's laws to write an equivalent statement for the sentence.

31. It is false that the Rocky Mountains are in the East and the Appalachian Mountains are in the West.

32. It is false that Johanna Chan is the secretary or Davidson Pierre is the treasurer.

33. The watch was neither a Swatch watch nor was the watch a Swiss Army watch.

34. The pot roast is hot, but it is not well done.

35. The hotel does not have a weight room or the conference center does not have an auditorium.

36. Robert Farinelli is an authorized WedgCor dealer or he is not going to work for Prism Construction Company.

37. If Ashley Tabai takes the new job, then she will not move or she will buy a new house in town.

38. If Phil Murphy buys us dinner, then we will not go to the top of the CN Tower but we will be able to walk to the Red Bistro Restaurant.

In Exercises 39–46, use the fact that $p \to q$ is equivalent to $\sim p \vee q$ to write an equivalent form of the given statement.

39. If Ena Salter selects a new textbook, then she will have to write a new syllabus.

40. Maxwell's favorite TV show is *Jimmy Neutron* or his favorite TV show is *Danny Phantom*.

▲ Jimmy Neutron

41. Bob the Tomato visited the nursing home or he did not visit the Cub Scout meeting.

42. If Joanne Ernst goes to the Lightning game, then she will not go to the Devil Rays game.

43. If the plumbers meet in Kansas City then the Rainmakers will provide the entertainment.

44. Mary Beth Headlee organized the conference or John Waters does not work at Sinclair Community College.

45. Chase is not hiding or the pitcher is broken.

46. If Weezer is not on the radio, then Tim Ollendick is working.

In Exercises 47–54, use the fact that $\sim(p \rightarrow q)$ is equivalent to $p \wedge \sim q$ to write the statement in an equivalent form.

47. It is false that if we go to Cincinnati, then we will go to the zoo.

48. It is false that if General Electric makes the telephone, then the telephone is made in the United States.

49. I am cold and the heater is not working.

50. The Badgers beat the Nittany Lions and the Bucks beat the 76ers.

51. It is not true that if Borders has a sale then we will buy $100 worth of books.

52. Thompson is sick today but Allen didn't go to school.

53. John Deere will hire new workers and the city of Dubuque will retrain the workers.

54. My cell phone is not made by Motorola and my carrier is Alltel.

In Exercises 55–60, write the converse, inverse, and contrapositive of the statement. (For Exercise 60, use De Morgan's laws.)

55. If we work every night, then we can finish the quilt in 1 week.

56. If your cell phone is beeping, then you need to charge the battery.

57. If I go to Mexico, then I buy silver jewelry.

58. If Bob Dylan records a new CD, then he will go on tour.

59. If that annoying paper clip shows up on my computer screen, then I will scream.

60. If the sun is shining, then we will go down to the marina and we will take out the sailboat.

In Exercises 61–66, write the contrapositive of the statement. Use the contrapositive to determine whether the conditional statement is true or false.

61. If a natural number is not divisible by 5, then the natural number is not divisible by 10.

62. If the opposite sides of the quadrilateral are not parallel, then the quadrilateral is not a parallelogram.

63. If a natural number is divisible by 3, then the natural number is divisible by 6.

64. If $1/n$ is not a natural number, then n is not a natural number.

65. If two lines do not intersect in at least one point, then the two lines are parallel.

66. If $\dfrac{m \cdot a}{m \cdot b} \neq \dfrac{a}{b}$, then m is not a counting number.

In Exercises 67–82, determine which, if any, of the three statements are equivalent (see Example 13).

67. a) Bill Rush is not the editor or Bill Rush is the vice president.

   b) If Bill Rush is the vice president, then Bill Rush is not the editor.

   c) If Bill Rush is the editor, then Bill Rush is not the vice president.

68. a) If Fido is our dog's name, then Rex is not our dog's name.

   b) It is false that Fido is our dog's name and Rex is not our dog's name.

   c) Fido is not our dog's name or Rex is our dog's name.

69. a) The office is not cool and the copier is jammed.

   b) If the office is not cool, then the copier is not jammed.

   c) It is false that the office is cool or the copier is not jammed.

70. a) The test is not written or the review sheet is not ready.

   b) If the test is written, then the review sheet is ready.

   c) It is false that the review sheet is ready and the test is not written.

71. a) Today is not Sunday or the library is open.

   b) If today is Sunday, then the library is not open.

   c) If the library is open, then today is not Sunday.

72. a) If you are fishing at 1 P.M., then you are driving a car at 1 P.M.

   b) You are not fishing at 1 P.M. or you are driving a car at 1 P.M.

   c) It is false that you are fishing at 1 P.M. and you are not driving a car at 1 P.M.

▲ See Exercise 72

73. a) The grass grows and the trees are blooming.

   b) If the trees are blooming, then the grass does not grow.

   c) The trees are not blooming or the grass does not grow.

74. a) Johnny Patrick is chosen as department chair if and only if he is the only candidate.

   b) If Johnny Patrick is chosen as department chair then he is the only candidate, and if Johnny Patrick is the only candidate then he is chosen as department chair.

   c) Johnny Patrick is not chosen as department chair and he is not the only candidate.

75. a) It is false that if you do not drink milk then your cholesterol count will be lower.

   b) Your cholesterol count will be lower if and only if you drink milk.

   c) It is false that if you drink milk then your cholesterol count will not be lower.

76. a) Bruce Springsteen will not go on tour if and only if Clarence Clemmons does not play the saxophone in his band.

   b) It is false that Bruce Springsteen will go on tour if and only if Clarence Clemmons does not play the saxophone in his band.

   c) If Bruce Springsteen goes on tour, then Clarence Clemmons plays saxophone in his band.

77. a) If the pay is good and today is Monday, then I will take the job.

   b) If I do not take the job, then it is false that the pay is good or today is Monday.

   c) The pay is good and today is Monday, or I will take the job.

78. a) If you are 18 years old and a citizen of the United States, then you can vote in the presidential election.

b) You can vote in the presidential election, if and only if you are a citizen of the United States and you are 18 years old.

c) You cannot vote in the presidential election, or you are 18 years old and you are not a citizen of the United States.

79. a) The package was sent by Federal Express, or the package was not sent by United Parcel Service but the package arrived on time.

b) The package arrived on time, if and only if it was sent by Federal Express or it was not sent by United Parcel Service.

c) If the package was not sent by Federal Express, then the package was not sent by United Parcel Service but the package arrived on time.

80. a) If we put the dog outside or we feed the dog, then the dog will not bark.

b) If the dog barks, then we did not put the dog outside and we did not feed the dog.

c) If the dog barks, then it is false that we put the dog outside or we feed the dog.

81. a) The car needs oil, and the car needs gas or the car is new.

b) The car needs oil, and it is false that the car does not need gas and the car is not new.

c) If the car needs oil, then the car needs gas or the car is not new.

82. a) The mortgage rate went down, if and only if Tim purchased the house and the down payment was 10%.

b) The down payment was 10%, and if Tim purchased the house then the mortgage rate went down.

c) If Tim purchased the house, then the mortgage rate went down and the down payment was not 10%.

83. If p and q represent two simple statements, and if $p \to q$ is a false statement, what must be the truth value of the converse, $q \to p$? Explain.

84. If p and q represent two simple statements, and if $p \to q$ is a false statement, what must be the truth value of the inverse, $\sim p \to \sim q$? Explain.

85. If p and q represent two simple statements, and if $p \to q$ is a false statement, what must be the truth value of the contrapositive, $\sim q \to \sim p$? Explain.

86. If p and q represent two simple statements, and if $p \to q$ is a true statement, what must be the truth value of the contrapositive, $\sim q \to \sim p$? Explain.

CHALLENGE PROBLEMS/GROUP ACTIVITIES

87. We learned that $p \to q \Leftrightarrow \sim p \vee q$. Determine a conjunction that is equivalent to $p \to q$. (*Hint:* There are many answers.)

88. Determine whether $\sim[\sim(p \vee \sim q)] \Leftrightarrow p \vee \sim q$. Explain the method(s) you used to determine your answer.

89. In an appliance or device that uses fuzzy logic, a change in one condition causes a change in a second condition. For example, in a camera, if the brightness increases, the lens aperture automatically decreases to get the proper exposure on the film. Name at least 10 appliances or devices that make use of fuzzy logic and explain how fuzzy logic is used in each appliance or device. See the Did You Know? on page 146.

90. In symbolic logic, a statement is either true or false (consider true to have a value of 1 and false a value of 0). In fuzzy logic, nothing is true or false, but everything is a matter of degree. For example, consider the statement "The sun is shining." In fuzzy logic, this statement may have a value between 0 and 1 and may be constantly changing. For example, if the sun is partially blocked by clouds, the value of this statement may be 0.25. In fuzzy logic, the values of connective statements are found as follows for statements p and q.

Not p has a truth value of $1 - p$.

$p \wedge q$ has a truth value equal to the lesser of p and q.

$p \vee q$ has a truth value equal to the greater of p and q.

$p \rightarrow q$ has a truth value equal to the lesser of 1 and $1 - p + q$.

$p \leftrightarrow q$ has a truth value equal to $1 - |p - q|$, that is, 1 minus the absolute value* of p minus q.

Suppose the statement "p: The sun is shining" has a truth value of 0.25 and the statement "q: Mary is getting a tan" has a truth value of 0.20. Find the truth value of

a) $\sim p$.   **b)** $\sim q$.

c) $p \wedge q$.   **d)** $p \vee q$.

e) $p \rightarrow q$.   **f)** $p \leftrightarrow q$.

INTERNET/RESEARCH ACTIVITIES

91. Do research and write a report on fuzzy logic.

92. Read one of Lewis Carroll's books and write a report on how he used logic in the book. Give at least five specific examples.

93. Do research and write a report on the life and achievements of Augustus De Morgan. Indicate in your report his contributions to sets and logic.

3.5   SYMBOLIC ARGUMENTS

▲ John Mellencamp and his band sing the national anthem.

Consider the following statements.

> If John Mellencamp sings the national anthem, then U2 will play at halftime.
>
> John Mellencamp sings the national anthem.

If you accept these two statements as true, then what logical conclusion could you draw? Do you agree that you can logically conclude that U2 will play at halftime? In this section, we will use our knowledge of logic to study the structure of such statements to draw logical conclusions.

Previously in this chapter, we used symbolic logic to determine the truth value of a compound statement. We now extend those basic ideas to determine whether we can draw logical conclusions from a set of given statements. Consider once again the two statements.

> If John Mellencamp sings the national anthem, then U2 will play at halftime.
>
> John Mellencamp sings the national anthem.

*Absolute values are discussed in Section 13.8.

These statements in the following form constitute what we will call a *symbolic argument*.

Premise 1:   If John Mellencamp sings the national anthem, then U2 will play at halftime.

Premise 2:   John Mellencamp sings the national anthem.

Conclusion: U2 will play at halftime.

A *symbolic argument* consists of a set of *premises* and a *conclusion*. It is called a symbolic argument because we generally write it in symbolic form to determine its validity.

> An **argument is valid** when its conclusion necessarily follows from a given set of premises.
>   An **argument is invalid** or a **fallacy** when the conclusion does not necessarily follow from the given set of premises.

An argument that is not valid is invalid. The argument just presented is an example of a valid argument, as the conclusion necessarily follows from the premises. Now we will discuss a procedure to determine whether an argument is valid or invalid. We begin by writing the argument in symbolic form. To write the argument in symbolic form, we let p and q be

p: John Mellencamp sings the national anthem.

q: U2 will play at halftime.

Symbolically, the argument is written

Premise 1: $p \rightarrow q$

Premise 2: p

Conclusion: $\therefore q$ (The three-dot triangle is read "therefore.")

Write the argument in the following form.

If   [*premise 1* **and** *premise 2*] **then** *conclusion*

$[(p \rightarrow q) \quad \wedge \quad p] \quad \rightarrow \quad q$

Then construct a truth table for the statement $[(p \rightarrow q) \wedge p] \rightarrow q$ (Table 3.29). *If the truth table answer column is true in every case, then the statement is a tautology, and the argument is valid. If the truth table is not a tautology, then the argument is invalid.* Since the statement is a tautology (see column 5), the conclusion necessarily follows from the premises and the argument is valid.

Table 3.29

p	q	$[(p \rightarrow q)$	$\wedge$	$p]$	$\rightarrow$	q
T	T	T	T	T	T	T
T	F	F	F	T	T	F
F	T	T	F	F	T	T
F	F	T	F	F	T	F
		1	3	2	5	4

Once we have demonstrated that an argument in a particular form is valid, all arguments with exactly the same form will also be valid. In fact, many of these forms have been assigned names. The argument form just discussed,

$$p \rightarrow q$$
$$\underline{p}$$
$$\therefore q$$

is called the *law of detachment*, or *modus ponens*.

EXAMPLE ❶ *Determining Validity without a Truth Table*

Determine whether the following argument is valid or invalid.

If Canada is north of the United States, then Alaska is in Mexico.
Canada is north of the United States.
∴ Alaska is in Mexico.

SOLUTION Translate the argument into symbolic form.

Let

c: Canada is north of the United States.
a: Alaska is in Mexico.

In symbolic form, the argument is

$$c \rightarrow a$$
$$\underline{c}$$
$$\therefore a$$

This argument is also the law of detachment. Therefore, it is a valid argument.   ●

▲ Alaska

Note that the argument in Example 1 is valid even though the conclusion, "Alaska is in Mexico," is a false statement. It is also possible to have an invalid argument in which the conclusion is a true statement. When an argument is valid, the conclusion necessarily follows from the premises. It is not necessary for the premises or the conclusion to be true statements in an argument.

PROCEDURE TO DETERMINE WHETHER AN ARGUMENT IS VALID

1. Write the argument in symbolic form.
2. Compare the form of the argument with forms that are known to be valid or invalid. If there are no known forms to compare it with, or you do not remember the forms, go to step 3.
3. If the argument contains two premises, write a conditional statement of the form

   [(premise 1) ∧ (premise 2)] → conclusion

4. Construct a truth table for the statement in step 3.
5. If the answer column of the truth table has all trues, the statement is a tautology, and the argument is valid. If the answer column does not have all trues, the argument is invalid.

Examples 1 through 4 contain two premises. When an argument contains more than two premises, step 3 of the procedure will change slightly, as will be explained shortly.

EXAMPLE ❷ *Determining Validity with a Truth Table*

Determine whether the following argument is valid or invalid.

> If you score 90% on the final exam, then you will get an A in the course.
> You will not get an A in the course.
> ∴ You do not score 90% on the final exam.

SOLUTION We first write the argument in symbolic form.

Let

p: You score 90% on the final exam.
q: You will get an A in the course.

In symbolic form, the argument is

$$p \to q$$
$$\frac{\sim q}{\therefore \sim p}$$

As we have not tested an argument in this form, we will construct a truth table to determine whether the argument is valid or invalid. We write the argument in the form $[(p \to q) \wedge \sim q] \to \sim p$, and construct a truth table (Table 3.30). Since the answer, column 5, has all T's, the argument is valid.

Table 3.30

p	q	$[(p \to q)$	$\wedge$	$\sim q]$	$\to$	$\sim p$
T	T	T	F	F	T	F
T	F	F	F	T	T	F
F	T	T	F	F	T	T
F	F	T	T	T	T	T
		1	3	2	5	4

The argument form in Example 2 is an example of the *law of contraposition*, or *modus tollens*.

EXAMPLE ❸ *Another Symbolic Argument*

Determine whether the following argument is valid or invalid.

> The grass is green or the grass is full of weeds.
> The grass is not green.
> ∴ The grass is full of weeds.

SOLUTION Let

p: The grass is green.

q: The grass is full of weeds.

In symbolic form, the argument is

$$p \lor q$$
$$\underline{\sim p}$$
$$\therefore q$$

As this form is not one of those we are familiar with, we will construct a truth table. We write the argument in the form $[(p \lor q) \land \sim p] \to q$. Next we construct a truth table, as shown in Table 3.31. The answer to the truth table, column 5, is true in *every case*. Therefore, the statement is a tautology, and the argument is valid.

Table 3.31

p	q	$[(p \lor q)$	$\land$	$\sim p]$	$\to$	q
T	T	T	F	F	T	T
T	F	T	F	F	T	F
F	T	T	T	T	T	T
F	F	F	F	T	T	F
		1	3	2	5	4

The argument form in Example 3 is an example of *disjunctive syllogism*. Other standard forms of arguments are given in the following chart.

STANDARD FORMS OF ARGUMENTS				
Valid Arguments	*Law of Detachment* $p \to q$ $\underline{p}$ $\therefore q$	*Law of Contraposition* $p \to q$ $\underline{\sim q}$ $\therefore \sim p$	*Law of Syllogism* $p \to q$ $\underline{q \to r}$ $\therefore p \to r$	*Disjunctive Syllogism* $p \lor q$ $\underline{\sim p}$ $\therefore q$
Invalid Arguments	*Fallacy of the Converse* $p \to q$ $\underline{q}$ $\therefore p$	*Fallacy of the Inverse* $p \to q$ $\underline{\sim p}$ $\therefore \sim q$		

As we saw in Example 1, it is not always necessary to construct a truth table to determine whether or not an argument is valid. The next two examples will show how we can identify an argument as one of the standard arguments given in the chart above.

EXAMPLE ❹ Identifying the Law of Syllogism in an Argument

Determine whether the following argument is valid or invalid.

> If my laptop battery is dead, then I use my home computer.
> If I use my home computer, then my kids will play outside.
> ∴ If my laptop battery is dead, then my kids will play outside.

SOLUTION Let

p:	My laptop battery is dead.
q:	I use my home computer.
r:	My kids will play outside.

In symbolic form, the argument is

$$
\begin{array}{l}
p \rightarrow q \\
\underline{q \rightarrow r} \\
\therefore\, p \rightarrow r
\end{array}
$$

The argument is in the form of the law of syllogism. Therefore, the argument is valid, and there is no need to construct a truth table. ●

EXAMPLE ❺ Identifying Common Fallacies in Arguments

Determine whether the following arguments are valid or invalid.

a)

> If it is snowing, then we put salt on the driveway.
> We put salt on the driveway.
> ∴ It is snowing.

b)

> If it is snowing, then we put salt on the driveway.
> It is not snowing.
> ∴ We do not put salt on the driveway.

SOLUTION

a) Let

p:	It is snowing.
q:	We put salt on the driveway.

In symbolic form, the argument is

$$
\begin{array}{l}
p \rightarrow q \\
\underline{q} \\
\therefore\, p
\end{array}
$$

This argument is in the form of the fallacy of the converse. Therefore, the argument is a fallacy, or invalid.

b) Using the same symbols defined in the solution to part (a), in symbolic form, the argument is

$$p \rightarrow q$$
$$\underline{\sim p}$$
$$\therefore \sim q$$

This argument is in the form of the fallacy of the inverse. Therefore, the argument is a fallacy, or invalid.

●

TIMELY TIP If you are not sure whether an argument with two premises is one of the standard forms or if you do not remember the standard forms, you can always determine whether a given argument is valid or invalid by using a truth table. To do so, follow the boxed procedure on page 153.

In Example 5(b), if you did not recognize that this argument was of the same form as the fallacy of the inverse you could construct the truth table for the conditional statement

$$[(p \rightarrow q) \wedge \sim p] \rightarrow \sim q$$

The true–false values under the conditional column, $\rightarrow$, would be T, T, F, T. Since the statement is not a tautology, the argument is invalid.

Now we consider an argument that has more than two premises. When an argument contains more than two premises, the statement we test, using a truth table, is formed by taking the conjunction of all the premises as the antecedent of a conditional statement and the conclusion as the consequent of the conditional statement. One example is an argument of the form

$$p_1$$
$$p_2$$
$$\underline{p_3}$$
$$\therefore c$$

We evaluate the truth table for $[p_1 \wedge p_2 \wedge p_3] \rightarrow c$. When we evaluate $[p_1 \wedge p_2 \wedge p_3]$, it makes no difference whether we evaluate $[(p_1 \wedge p_2) \wedge p_3]$ or $[p_1 \wedge (p_2 \wedge p_3)]$ because both give the same answer. In Example 6, we evaluate $[p_1 \wedge p_2 \wedge p_3]$ from left to right; that is, $[(p_1 \wedge p_2) \wedge p_3]$.

EXAMPLE ❻ An Argument with Three Premises

Use a truth table to determine whether the following argument is valid or invalid.

If my cell phone company is Verizon, then I can call you free of charge.
I can call you free of charge or I can send you an e-mail.
I can send you an e-mail or my cell phone company is Verizon.
∴ My cell phone company is Verizon.

SOLUTION This argument contains three simple statements.

Let

p: My cell phone company is Verizon.

q: I can call you free of charge.

r: I can send you an e-mail.

In symbolic form, the argument is

$$p \rightarrow q$$
$$q \vee r$$
$$\underline{r \vee p}$$
$$\therefore p$$

Write the argument in the form

$$[(p \rightarrow q) \wedge (q \vee r) \wedge (r \vee p)] \rightarrow p.$$

Now construct the truth table (Table 3.32). The answer, column 7, is not true in every case. Thus, the argument is a fallacy, or invalid.

Table 3.32

p	q	r	$[(p \rightarrow q)$	$\wedge$	$(q \vee r)$	$\wedge$	$(r \vee p)]$	$\rightarrow$	p
T	T	T	T	T	T	T	T	T	T
T	T	F	T	T	T	T	T	T	T
T	F	T	F	F	T	F	T	T	T
T	F	F	F	F	F	F	T	T	T
F	T	T	T	T	T	T	T	F	F
F	T	F	T	T	T	F	F	T	F
F	F	T	T	T	T	T	T	F	F
F	F	F	T	F	F	F	F	T	F
			1	3	2	5	4	7	6

Let's now investigate how we can arrive at a valid conclusion from a given set of premises.

EXAMPLE ❼ Determine a Logical Conclusion

Determine a logical conclusion that follows from the given statements. "If the price of gas is below $3.00 per gallon, then we will drive to the Offspring concert. We will not drive to the Offspring concert. Therefore . . ."

SOLUTION If you recognize a specific form of an argument, you can use your knowledge of that form to draw a logical conclusion.

Let

p: The price of gas is below \$3.00 per gallon.

q: We will drive to the Offspring concert.

The argument is of the following form.

$$p \rightarrow q$$
$$\underline{\sim q}$$
$$\therefore ?$$

If the question mark is replaced with a $\sim p$, this argument is of the form of the law of contraposition. Thus, a logical conclusion is "Therefore, the price of gas is not below \$3.00 per gallon."

SECTION 3.5 EXERCISES

CONCEPT/WRITING EXERCISES

1. a) What does it mean when an argument is a valid argument?

   b) What does it mean when an argument is a fallacy?

2. Explain how to determine whether an argument with premises p_1 and p_2 and conclusion c is a valid argument or an invalid argument.

3. Is it possible for an argument to be invalid if its conclusion is true? Explain your answer.

4. Is it possible for an argument to be valid if its conclusion is false? Explain your answer.

5. Is it possible for an argument to be invalid if the premises are all true? Explain your answer.

6. Is it possible for an argument to be valid if the premises are all false? Explain your answer.

In Exercises 7–10, (a) indicate the form of the valid argument and (b) write an original argument in words for each form.

7. Law of detachment   8. Law of syllogism

9. Law of contraposition   10. Disjunctive syllogism

In Exercises 11 and 12, (a) indicate the form of the fallacy, and (b) write an original argument in words for each form.

11. Fallacy of the converse   12. Fallacy of the inverse

PRACTICE THE SKILLS

In Exercises 13–32, determine whether the argument is valid or invalid. You may compare the argument to a standard form, given on page 155, or use a truth table.

13. $a \rightarrow b$
$\underline{\sim a}$
$\therefore \sim b$

14. $c \vee d$
$\underline{\sim c}$
$\therefore d$

15. $e \rightarrow f$
$\underline{e}$
$\therefore f$

16. $g \rightarrow h$
$\underline{h \rightarrow i}$
$\therefore g \rightarrow i$

17. $j \vee k$
$\underline{\sim k}$
$\therefore j$

18. $l \rightarrow m$
$\underline{\sim m}$
$\therefore \sim l$

19. $n \rightarrow o$
$\underline{o}$
$\therefore n$

20. $r \rightarrow s$
$\underline{r}$
$\therefore s$

21. $t \rightarrow u$
$\underline{\sim u}$
$\therefore \sim t$

22. $v \rightarrow w$
$\underline{w}$
$\therefore v$

23. $x \rightarrow y$
$\underline{y \rightarrow z}$
$\therefore x \rightarrow z$

24. $x \rightarrow y$
$\underline{\sim x}$
$\therefore \sim y$

25. $p \leftrightarrow q$
$\underline{q \wedge r}$
$\therefore p \vee r$

26. $p \leftrightarrow q$
$\underline{q \rightarrow r}$
$\therefore \sim r \rightarrow \sim p$

27. $r \leftrightarrow p$
$\underline{\sim p \wedge q}$
$\therefore p \wedge r$

28. $p \vee q$
$\underline{r \wedge p}$
$\therefore q$

29. $p \rightarrow q$
$q \vee r$
$\underline{r \vee p}$
$\therefore p$

30. $p \rightarrow q$
$q \rightarrow r$
$\underline{r \rightarrow p}$
$\therefore q \rightarrow p$

31. $p \rightarrow q$
$r \rightarrow \sim p$
$\underline{p \lor r}$
$\therefore q \lor \sim p$

32. $p \leftrightarrow q$
$p \lor r$
$\underline{q \rightarrow r}$
$\therefore q \lor r$

PROBLEM SOLVING

In Exercises 33–50, (a) translate the argument into symbolic form and (b) determine if the argument is valid or invalid. You may compare the argument to a standard form or use a truth table.

33. If Will Smith wins an Academy Award, then he will retire from acting.
Will Smith did not win an Academy Award.

∴ Will Smith will not retire from acting.

34. If the car is a Road Runner, then the car is fast.
The car is fast.

∴ The car is a Road Runner.

35. If the baby is a boy, then we will name him Alexander Martin.
The baby is a boy.

∴ We will name him Alexander Martin.

36. If I can get my child to preschool by 8:45 A.M., then I can take the 9:00 A.M. class.
If I can take the 9:00 A.M. class, then I can be done by 2:00 P.M.

∴ If I can get my child to preschool by 8:45 A.M., then I can be done by 2:00 P.M.

37. If the guitar is a Les Paul model, then the guitar is made by Gibson.
The guitar is not made by Gibson.

∴ The guitar is not a Les Paul model.

▲ Les Paul

38. We will go for a bike ride or we will go shopping.
We will not go shopping.

∴ We will go for a bike ride.

39. If we planted the garden by the first Friday in April, then we will have potatoes by the Fourth of July.
We will have potatoes by the Fourth of July.

∴ We planted the garden by the first Friday in April.

40. If you pass general chemistry, then you can take organic chemistry.
You pass general chemistry.

∴ You can take organic chemistry.

41. Sarah Hughes will win an Olympic gold medal in figure skating or Joey Cheek will win an Olympic gold medal in speed skating.
Sarah Hughes will not win an Olympic gold medal in figure skating.

∴ Joey Cheek will win an Olympic gold medal in speed skating.

42. If Nicholas Thompson teaches this course, then I will get a passing grade.
I did not get a passing grade.

∴ Nicholas Thompson did not teach the course.

43. If it is cold, then graduation will be held indoors.
If graduation is held indoors, then the fireworks will be postponed.

∴ If it is cold, then the fireworks will be postponed.

44. If the canteen is full, then we can go for a walk.
We can go for a walk and we will not get thirsty.

∴ If we go for a walk, then the canteen is not full.

45. Marie works at the post office and Jim works for Target.
If Jim works for Target, then Tommy gets an internship.

∴ If Tommy gets an internship, then Marie works at the post office.

46. Vitamin C helps your immune system or niacin helps reduce cholesterol.

If niacin helps reduce cholesterol, then vitamin E enhances your skin.

∴ Vitamin C helps your immune system and vitamin E enhances your skin.

47. It is snowing and I am going skiing.

If I am going skiing, then I will wear a coat.

∴ If it is snowing, then I will wear a coat.

48. The garden has vegetables or the garden has flowers.

If the garden does not have flowers, then the garden has vegetables.

∴ The garden has flowers or the garden has vegetables.

49. If the house has electric heat, then the Flynns will buy the house.

If the price is not less than $100,000, then the Flynns will not buy the house.

∴ If the house has electric heat, then the price is less than $100,000.

50. If there is an atmosphere, then there is gravity.

If an object has weight, then there is gravity.

∴ If there is an atmosphere, then an object has weight.

In Exercises 51–60, translate the argument into symbolic form. Then determine whether the argument is valid or invalid.

51. If the prescription was called in to Walgreen's, then you can pick it up by 4:00 P.M. You cannot pick it up by 4:00 P.M. Therefore, the prescription was not called in to Walgreen's.

52. The printer has a clogged nozzle or the printer does not have toner. The printer has toner. Therefore, the printer has a clogged nozzle.

53. Max is playing Game Boy with the sound off or Max is wearing headphones. Max is not playing Game Boy with the sound off. Therefore, Max is wearing headphones.

54. If the cat is in the room, then the mice are hiding. The mice are not hiding. Therefore, the cat is not in the room.

55. The test was easy and I received a good grade. The test was not easy or I did not receive a good grade. Therefore, the test was not easy.

56. If Bonnie passes the bar exam, then she will practice law. Bonnie will not practice law. Therefore, Bonnie did not pass the bar exam.

57. The baby is crying but the baby is not hungry. If the baby is hungry then the baby is crying. Therefore, the baby is hungry.

58. If the car is new, then the car has air conditioning. The car is not new and the car has air conditioning. Therefore, the car is not new.

59. If the football team wins the game, then Dave played quarterback. If Dave played quarterback, then the team is not in second place. Therefore, if the football team wins the game, then the team is in second place.

60. The engineering courses are difficult and the chemistry labs are long. If the chemistry labs are long, then the art tests are easy. Therefore, the engineering courses are difficult and the art tests are not easy.

In Exercises 61–67, using the standard forms of arguments and other information you have learned, supply what you believe is a logical conclusion to the argument. Verify that the argument is valid for the conclusion you supplied.

61. If you eat an entire bag of M & M's, then your face will break out.

You eat an entire bag of M & M's.

Therefore, . . .

62. If the temperature hits 100°, then we will go swimming.

We did not go swimming.

Therefore, . . .

63. I am stressed out or I have the flu.

I do not have the flu.

Therefore, . . .

64. If I can get Nick to his piano lesson by 3:30 P.M., then I can do my shopping.

If I can do my shopping, then we do not need to order pizza again.

Therefore, . . .

65. If you close the deal, then you will get a commission.

You did not get a commission.

Therefore, . . .

66. If Katherine is at her ballet lesson, then Allyson will take a nap.
Katherine is at her ballet lesson.
Therefore, . . .

67. If you do not pay off your credit card bill, then you will have to pay interest.
If you have to pay interest, then the bank makes money.
Therefore, . . .

CHALLENGE PROBLEMS/GROUP ACTIVITIES

68. Determine whether the argument is valid or invalid.

If Lynn wins the contest or strikes oil, then she will be rich.
If Lynn is rich, then she will stop working.
∴. If Lynn does not stop working, she did not win the contest.

69. Is it possible for an argument to be invalid if the conjunction of the premises is false in every case of the truth table? Explain your answer.

RECREATIONAL MATHEMATICS

70. René Descartes was a seventeenth-century French mathematician and philosopher. One of his most memorable statements is, "I think, therefore, I am." This statement is the basis for the following joke.

Descartes walks into an inn. The innkeeper asks Descartes if he would like something to drink. Descartes replies, "I think not," and promptly vanishes into thin air!

This joke can be summarized in the following argument: If I think, then I am. I think not. Therefore, I am not.

a) Represent this argument symbolically.

b) Is it a valid argument?

c) Explain your answer using either a standard form of argument or using a truth table.

INTERNET/RESEARCH ACTIVITIES

71. Show how logic is used in advertising. Discuss several advertisements and show how logic is used to persuade the reader.

72. Find examples of valid (or invalid) arguments in printed matter such as newspaper or magazine articles. Explain why the arguments are valid (or invalid).

3.6 EULER DIAGRAMS AND SYLLOGISTIC ARGUMENTS

▲ Adam Brody and Meg Ryan in the movie *In the Land of Women.*

While trying to choose a movie to watch on Valentine's Day, your spouse says to you, "All Meg Ryan movies are romantic comedies. Meg Ryan is in the movie *In the Land of Women*. Therefore, *In the Land of Women* is a romantic comedy." This argument uses a type of argument that we will discuss and analyze in this section.

In Section 3.5, we showed how to determine the validity of *symbolic arguments* using truth tables and comparing the arguments to standard forms. This section presents another form of argument called a *syllogistic argument*, better known by the shorter name *syllogism*. The validity of a syllogistic argument is determined by using Euler (pronounced "oiler") diagrams, as is explained shortly.

Syllogistic logic, a deductive process of arriving at a conclusion, was developed by Aristotle in about 350 B.C. Aristotle considered the relationships among the four types of statements that follow.

All _____ are _____.
No _____ are _____.
Some _____ are _____.
Some _____ are not _____.

Examples of these statements are: *All doctors are tall. No doctors are tall. Some doctors are tall. Some doctors are not tall.* Since Aristotle's time, other types of statements have been added to the study of syllogistic logic, two of which are

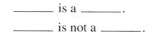

_____ is a _____.

_____ is not a _____.

Examples of these statements are: *Maria is a doctor. Maria is not a doctor.*

The difference between a symbolic argument and a syllogistic argument can be seen in the following chart. Symbolic arguments use the connectives *and, or, not, if–then,* and *if and only if*. Syllogistic arguments use the quantifiers *all, some,* and *none,* which were discussed in Section 3.1.

SYMBOLIC ARGUMENTS VERSUS SYLLOGISTIC ARGUMENTS		
	Words or phrases used	*Method of determining validity*
Symbolic argument	and, or, not, if–then, if and only if	Truth tables or by comparison with standard forms of arguments
Syllogistic argument	all are, some are, none are, some are not	Euler diagrams

As with symbolic logic, the premises and the conclusion together form an argument. An example of a syllogistic argument is

All German shepherds are dogs.

All dogs bark.

∴ All German shepherds bark.

This is an example of a valid argument. Recall from Section 3.5 that an argument is *valid* when its conclusion necessarily follows from a given set of premises. Recall that an argument in which the conclusion does not necessarily follow from the given premises is said to be an *invalid argument* or a *fallacy*.

Before we give another example of a syllogism, let's review the Venn diagrams discussed in Section 2.3 in relationship with Aristotle's four statements.

All *A*s are *B*s	No *A*s are *B*s	Some *A*s are *B*s	Some *A*s are not *B*s
If an element is in set *A*, then it is in set *B*.	If an element is in set *A*, then it is not in set *B*.	There is at least one element that is in both set *A* and set *B*.	There is at least one element that is in set *A* that is not in set *B*.

One method used to determine whether an argument is valid or is a fallacy is by means of an *Euler diagram*, named after Leonhard Euler, who used circles to represent sets in syllogistic arguments. The technique of using Euler diagrams is illustrated in Example 1.

EXAMPLE ❶ *Using an Euler Diagram*

Determine whether the following syllogism is valid or invalid.

All keys are made of brass.

All things made of brass are valuable.

∴ All keys are valuable.

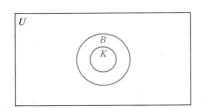

Figure 3.3

SOLUTION To determine whether this syllogism is valid or not valid, we will construct an Euler diagram. We begin with the first premise, "All keys are made of brass." As shown in Fig. 3.3, the inner blue circle labeled *K* represents the set of all keys and the outer red circle labeled *B* represents the set of all brass objects. The first premise requires that the inner blue circle must be entirely contained within the outer red circle. Next, we will represent the second premise, "All things made of brass are valuable." As shown in Fig. 3.4, the outermost black circle labeled *V* represents the set of all valuable objects. The second premise dictates that the red circle, representing the set of brass objects, must be entirely contained within the black circle, representing the set of valuable objects. Now, examine the completed Euler diagram in Fig. 3.4. Note that the premises force the set of keys to be within the set of valuable objects. Therefore, the argument is valid since the conclusion, "All keys are valuable," necessarily follows from the set of premises.   ●

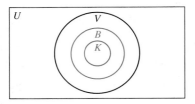

Figure 3.4

The syllogism in Example 1 is valid even though the conclusion, "All keys are valuable," is not a true statement. Similarly, a syllogism can be invalid, or a fallacy, even if the conclusion is a true statement.

When we determine the validity of an argument, we are determining whether the conclusion necessarily follows from the premises. When we say that an argument is valid, we are saying that if all the premises are true statements, then the conclusion must also be a true statement.

The form of the argument determines its validity, not the particular statements. For example, consider the syllogism

All Earth people have two heads.

All people with two heads can fly.

∴ All Earth people can fly.

The form of this argument is the same as that of the previous valid argument in Example 1. Therefore, this argument is also valid.

EXAMPLE ❷ *Analyzing a Syllogism*

Determine whether the following syllogism is valid or invalid.

All judges are lawyers.

William is a judge.

∴ William is a lawyer.

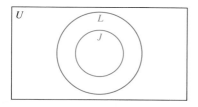

Figure 3.5

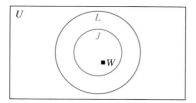

Figure 3.6

SOLUTION The statement "All judges are lawyers" is illustrated in Fig. 3.5. Note that the *J* circle must be completely inside the *L* circle. The second premise, "William is a judge," tells us that William must be placed in the inner circle labeled *J* (Fig. 3.6). The Euler diagram illustrates that by placing William inside the *J* circle William must also be inside the *L* circle. Therefore, the conclusion "William is a lawyer" necessarily follows from the premises and the argument is valid. ●

In both Example 1 and Example 2, we had no choice as to where the second premise was to be placed in the Euler diagram. In Example 1, the set of brass objects had to be placed inside the set of valuable objects. In Example 2, William had to be placed inside the set of judges. Often when determining the truth value of a syllogism, a premise can be placed in more than one area in the diagram. *We always try to draw the Euler diagram so that the conclusion does not necessarily follow from the premises. If that can be done, then the conclusion does not necessarily follow from the premises and the argument is invalid.* If we cannot show that the argument is invalid, only then do we accept the argument as valid. We illustrate this process in Example 3.

EXAMPLE ❸ *Ballerinas and Athletes*

Determine whether the following syllogism is valid or is invalid.

> All ballerinas are athletic.
> Keyshawn is athletic.
> ∴ Keyshawn is a ballerina.

SOLUTION The premise "All ballerinas are athletic" is illustrated in Fig. 3.7(a). The next premise, "Keyshawn is athletic," tells us that Keyshawn must be placed in the set of athletic people. Two diagrams in which both premises are satisfied are shown in Fig. 3.7(b) and (c). By examining Fig. 3.7(b), however, we see that Keyshawn is not a ballerina. Therefore, the conclusion "Keyshawn is a ballerina" does not necessarily follow from the set of premises. Thus, the argument is invalid, or a fallacy.

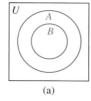

(a)   (b)   (c)

Figure 3.7 ●

EXAMPLE ❹ *Parrots and Chickens*

Determine whether the following syllogism is valid or invalid.

> No parrots eat chicken.
> Fletch does not eat chicken.
> ∴ Fletch is a parrot.

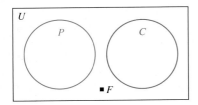

Figure 3.8

Figure 3.9

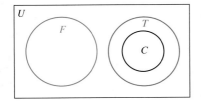

Figure 3.11

SOLUTION The first premise tells us that parrots and things that eat chicken are disjoint sets—that is, sets that do not intersect. The diagram in Fig. 3.8 satisfies the two given premises and also shows that Fletch is not a parrot. Therefore, the argument is invalid, or is a fallacy. ●

TIMELY TIP Note that in Example 4 if we placed Fletch in circle *P*, the argument would appear to be valid. Remember that *whenever testing the validity of an argument, always try to show that the argument is invalid.* If there is any way of showing that the conclusion does not necessarily follow from the premises, then the argument is invalid.

EXAMPLE ⑤ *A Syllogism Involving the Word Some*

Determine whether the following syllogism is valid or invalid.

All *A*s are *B*s.

Some *B*s are *C*s.

∴ Some *A*s are *C*s.

SOLUTION The premise "All *A*s are *B*s" is illustrated in Fig. 3.9. The premise "Some *B*s are *C*s" means that there is at least one *B* that is a *C*. We can illustrate this set of premises in four ways, as illustrated in Fig. 3.10.

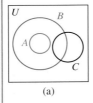

(a)   (b)   (c)   (d)

Figure 3.10

In all four illustrations, we see that (1) all *A*s are *B*s and (2) some *B*s are *C*s. The conclusion is "Some *A*s are *C*s." Since at least one of the illustrations, Fig. 3.10(a), shows that the conclusion does not necessarily follow from the given premises, the argument is invalid. ●

EXAMPLE ⑥ *Frogs and Cats*

Determine whether the following syllogism is valid or invalid.

No frogs eat tuna.

All cats eat tuna.

∴ No frogs are cats.

SOLUTION The first premise tells us that frogs and the things that eat tuna are disjoint sets as shown in Fig. 3.11. The second premise tells us that the set of cats is a subset of the things that eat tuna. Therefore, the circle representing the set of cats must go within the circle representing the set of the things that eat tuna.

Note that the set of frogs and the set of cats cannot be made to intersect without violating a premise. Thus, the conclusion "No frogs are cats" necessarily follows from the premises and the argument is valid. Note that we did not say that this conclusion is true, only that the argument is valid.

SECTION 3.6 EXERCISES

CONCEPT/WRITING EXERCISES

1. **a)** If an Euler diagram can only be drawn in a way in which the conclusion necessarily follows from the premises, what can be said about the syllogistic argument under consideration?

   b) If an Euler diagram can be drawn in a way in which the conclusion does not necessarily follow from the premises, what can be said about the syllogistic argument under consideration?

2. Explain the difference between a symbolic argument and a syllogistic argument.

3. Represent the given statement with two circles as you would when constructing an Euler diagram.

   a) All *A*s are *B*s.

   b) Some *C*s are *D*s.

   c) No *E*s are *F*s.

4. **a)** What does it mean when we determine that an argument is a valid argument?

   b) What does it mean when we determine that an argument is invalid?

5. Can an argument be valid if the conclusion is a false statement? Explain your answer.

6. Can an argument be invalid if the conclusion is a true statement? Explain.

PRACTICE THE SKILLS/PROBLEM SOLVING

In Exercises 7–30, use an Euler diagram to determine whether the syllogism is valid or invalid.

7. All gingerbread men can sing.
   Gingy is a gingerbread man.
   ∴ Gingy can sing.

▲ See Exercise 7

8. All cats have whiskers.
   All things with whiskers are dogs.
   ∴ All cats are dogs.

9. No candy bars are health foods.
   All Snickers are candy bars.
   ∴ No Snickers are health foods.

10. All dolphins are mammals.
    All mammals are vertebrates.
    ∴ All dolphins are vertebrates.

11. All theme parks have walkways.
    Metropolitan Community College has walkways.
    ∴ Metropolitan Community College is a theme park.

12. All golfers have rain gear.
    John Pearse has rain gear.
    ∴ John Pearse is a golfer.

13. No horses buck.
    Palominos are horses.
    ∴ Palominos do not buck.

14. No jockeys weigh more than 200 pounds.
    Deb Otto is not a jockey.
    ∴ Deb Otto weighs more than 200 pounds.

15. Some mushrooms are poisonous.
A morel is a mushroom.

∴ A morel is poisonous.

16. Some policemen are polite.
Jarod Harshbarger is a policeman.

∴ Jarod Harshbarger is not polite.

17. Some farmers are politicians.
Some politicians are senators.

∴ Some farmers are senators.

18. Some professional golfers give golf lessons.
All people who belong to the PGA are professional
golfers.

∴ All people who belong to the PGA give golf lessons.

19. No lawn weeds are flowers.
Sedge is not a flower.

∴ Sedge is a lawn weed.

20. Some caterpillars are furry.
All furry things are mammals.

∴ Some caterpillars are mammals.

21. Some flowers love sunlight.
All things that love sunlight love water.

∴ Some flowers love water.

22. Some CD players are MP3 players.
All iPods are MP3 players.

∴ Some CD players are iPods.

23. No scarecrows are tin men.
No tin men are lions.

∴ No scarecrows are lions.

24. All pilots can fly.
All astronauts can fly.

∴ Some pilots are astronauts.

25. Some dogs wear glasses.
Fido wears glasses.

∴ Fido is a dog.

26. All rainy days are cloudy.
Today it is cloudy.

∴ Today is a rainy day.

27. All sweet things taste good.
All things that taste good are fattening.
All things that are fattening put on pounds.

∴ All sweet things put on pounds.

28. All books have red covers.
All books that have red covers contain 200 pages.
Some books that contain 200 pages are novels.

∴ All books that contain 200 pages are novels.

29. All country singers play the guitar.
All country singers play the drums.
Some people who play the guitar are rock singers.

∴ Some country singers are rock singers.

30. Some hot dogs are made of turkey.
All things made of turkey are edible.
Some things that are made of beef are edible.

∴ Some hot dogs are made of beef.

CHALLENGE PROBLEM/GROUP ACTIVITY

31. *Sets and Logic* Statements in logic can be translated into set
statements: for example, $p \wedge q$ is similar to $P \cap Q$; $p \vee q$
is similar to $P \cup Q$; and $p \rightarrow q$ is equivalent to $\sim p \vee q$,
which is similar to $P' \cup Q$. Euler diagrams can also be
used to show that arguments similar to those discussed in
Section 3.5 are valid or invalid. Use Euler diagrams to
show that the following symbolic argument is invalid.

$$p \rightarrow q$$
$$\underline{p \vee q}$$
$$\therefore \sim p$$

32. Leonhard Euler is considered one of the greatest mathematicians of all time. Do research and write a report on Euler's life. Include information on his contributions to sets and to logic. Also indicate other areas of mathematics in which he made important contributions. References include encyclopedias, history of mathematics books, and the Internet.

3.7 SWITCHING CIRCUITS

▲ What must be true for a lamp to produce light?

Suppose you are sitting at your desk and want to turn on a lamp so you can read a book. If a wall switch controls the power to the outlet that the lamp is plugged into, and the lamp has an on/off switch, what conditions must be true for the lamp's bulb to light? The wiring in our homes can be explained and described using logic. In this section, we will learn how to analyze electrical circuits using logic.

Using Symbolic Statements to Represent Circuits

A common application of logic is switching circuits. To understand the basic concepts of switching circuits, let us examine a few simple circuits that are common in most homes. The typical lamp has a cord, which is plugged into a wall outlet. Somewhere between the bulb in the lamp and the outlet is a switch to turn the lamp on and off. A switch is often referred to as being on or off. When the switch is in the *on* position, the current flows through the switch and the bulb lights up. When the switch is in the *on* position, we can say that the switch is *closed* and that current will flow through the switch. When the switch is in the *off* position, the current does not flow through the switch and the bulb does not light. When the switch is in the *off* position, we can say that the switch is *open*, and the current does not flow through the switch. The basic configuration of a switch is shown in Fig. 3.12.

Electric circuits can be expressed as logical statements. We represent switches as letters, using T to represent a closed switch (or current flow) and F to represent an open switch (or no current flow). This relationship is indicated in Table 3.33.

Occasionally, we have a wall switch connected to a wall outlet and a lamp plugged into the wall outlet (Fig. 3.13). We then say that the wall switch and the switch on the lamp are in *series*, meaning that for the bulb in the lamp to light, both switches must be on at the same time (Fig. 3.14 on page 170). On the other hand, the bulb will not light if either switch is off or if both switches are off. In either of these conditions, the electricity will not flow through the circuit. In a *series circuit*, the current can take only one path. If any switch in the path is open, the current cannot flow.

To illustrate this situation symbolically, let p represent the wall switch and q the lamp switch. The letter T will be used to represent both a closed switch and the bulb lighting. The letter F will represent an open switch and the bulb not lighting. Thus, we have four possible cases.

Figure 3.12

Table 3.33

Switch	Lightbulb
T	on (switch closed)
F	off (switch open)

Figure 3.13

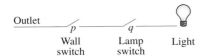

Figure 3.14

Table 3.34

p	q	Light	p ∧ q
T	T	on (T)	T
T	F	off (F)	F
F	T	off (F)	F
F	F	off (F)	F

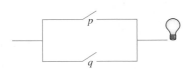

Figure 3.15

Table 3.35

p	q	Light	p ∨ q
T	T	on (T)	T
T	F	on (T)	T
F	T	on (T)	T
F	F	off (F)	F

Figure 3.16

CASE 1: Both switches are closed; that is, p is T and q is T. The light is on, T.

CASE 2: Switch p is closed and switch q is open; that is, p is T and q is F. The light is off, F.

CASE 3: Switch p is open and switch q is closed; that is, p is F and q is T. The light is off, F.

CASE 4: Both switches are open; that is, p is F and q is F. The light is off, F.

Table 3.34 summarizes the results.

The on–off results are the same as the truth table for the conjunction $p \wedge q$ if we think of "on" as true and "off" as false.

> Switches in series will always be represented with a conjunction, ∧.

Another type of electric circuit used in the home is the *parallel circuit*, in which there are two or more paths that the current can take. If the current can pass through either path or both (see Fig. 3.15), the light will go on. The letter T will be used to represent both a closed switch and the bulb lighting. The letter F will represent an open switch and the bulb not lighting. Thus, we have four possible cases.

CASE 1: Both switches are closed; that is, p is T and q is T. The light is on, T.

CASE 2: Switch p is closed and switch q is open; that is, p is T and q is F. The light is on, T.

CASE 3: Switch p is open and switch q is closed; that is, p is F and q is T. The light is on, T.

CASE 4: Both switches are open; that is, p is F and q is F. The light is off, F.

Table 3.35 summarizes the results. The on–off results are the same as the $p \vee q$ truth table if we think of "on" as true and "off" as false.

> Switches in parallel will always be represented with a disjunction, ∨.

Sometimes it is necessary to have two or more switches in the same circuit that will both be open at the same time and both be closed at the same time. In such circuits, we will use the same letter to represent both switches. For example, in the circuit shown in Fig. 3.16, there are two switches labeled p. Therefore, both of these switches must be open at the same time and both must be closed at the same time. One of the p switches cannot be open at the same time the other p switch is closed.

We can now combine some of these basic concepts to analyze more circuits.

┌─ **EXAMPLE ❶** *Representing a Switching Circuit with Symbolic Statements*

a) Write a symbolic statement that represents the circuit shown in Fig. 3.16.

b) Construct a truth table to determine when the light will be on.

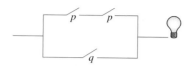

Figure 3.17

Table 3.36

p	*q*	*p*	∧	(*p* ∨ *q*)
T	T	T	T	T
T	F	T	T	T
F	T	F	F	T
F	F	F	F	F
		1	3	2

SOLUTION

a) In Fig. 3.16, there is a blue switch *p* on the left, and to the right there is a branch containing a red switch *p* and a switch *q*. The current must flow through the blue switch *p* into the branch on its right. Therefore, the blue switch *p* is in series with the branch containing the red switch *p* and switch *q*. After the current flows through the blue switch *p* it reaches the branch on its right. At this point, the current has the option of flowing into the red switch *p*, switch *q*, or both of these switches. Therefore, the branch containing the red switch *p* and switch *q* is a parallel branch. We say these two switches are in parallel. The entire circuit in symbolic form is $p \land (p \lor q)$. Note that the parentheses are very important. Without parentheses, the symbolic statement could be interpreted as $(p \land p) \lor q$. The diagram for $(p \land p) \lor q$ is illustrated in Fig. 3.17. We shall see later in this section that the circuits in Fig. 3.16 and Fig. 3.17 are not the same.

b) The truth table for the statement (Table 3.36) indicates that the light will be on only in the cases in which *p* is true or when switch *p* is closed. ●

EXAMPLE ② *Representing a Switching Circuit with Symbolic Statements*

a) Write a symbolic statement that represents the circuit in Fig. 3.18.

b) Construct a truth table to determine when the light will be on.

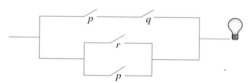

Figure 3.18

SOLUTION

a) The upper branch of the circuit contains two switches, *p* and *q*, in series. We can represent that branch with the statement $p \land q$. The lower branch of the circuit has two switches, *r* and *p*, in parallel. We can represent that branch with the statement $r \lor p$. The upper branch is in parallel with the lower branch. Putting the two branches together, we get the statement $(p \land q) \lor (r \lor p)$.

b) The truth table for the statement (Table 3.37) shows that cases 6 and 8 are false. Thus, the light will be off in these cases and on in all the other cases. In examining the truth values, we see that the statement is false only in the cases in which both *p* and *r* are false or when both switches are open. By examining the diagram or truth table, we can see that the current will flow if switch *p* is closed or switch *r* is closed. ●

Table 3.37

p	*q*	*r*	(*p* ∧ *q*)	∨	(*r* ∨ *p*)
T	T	T	T	T	T
T	T	F	T	T	T
T	F	T	F	T	T
T	F	F	F	T	T
F	T	T	F	T	T
F	T	F	F	F	F
F	F	T	F	T	T
F	F	F	F	F	F
			1	3	2

Drawing Switching Circuits That Represent Symbolic Statements

We will next study how to draw a switching circuit that represents a given symbolic statement. Suppose we are given the statement $(p \land q) \lor r$ and are asked to construct a circuit corresponding to it. Remember that ∧ indicates a series branch

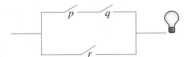

Figure 3.19

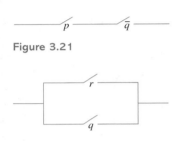

Figure 3.20

Figure 3.21

Figure 3.22

and $\vee$ indicates a parallel branch. Working first within parentheses, we see that switches p and q are in series. This series branch is in parallel with switch r, as indicated in Fig. 3.19.

Occasionally, it is necessary to have two switches in the same circuit such that when one switch is open, the other switch is closed; and when one switch is closed, the other switch is open. Therefore, the two switches will never both be open together and never be closed together. This situation can be represented by using p for one of the switches and $\overline{p}$ for the other switch. The switch labeled $\overline{p}$ corresponds to $\sim p$ in a logic statement. For example, in a series circuit, $p \wedge \sim p$ would be represented by Fig. 3.20. In this case, the light would never go on; the switches would counteract each other. When switch p is closed, switch $\overline{p}$ is open; and when p is open, $\overline{p}$ is closed.

EXAMPLE ❸ *Representing a Symbolic Statement as a Switching Circuit*

Draw a switching circuit that represents $[(p \wedge \sim q) \vee (r \vee q)] \wedge s$.

SOLUTION In the statement, p and $\sim q$ have $\wedge$ between them, so switches p and $\overline{q}$ are in series, as represented in Fig. 3.21. Also in the statement, r and q have $\vee$ between them, so switches r and q are in parallel, as represented in Fig. 3.22.

Because $(p \wedge \sim q)$ and $(r \vee q)$ are connected with $\vee$, the two branches are in parallel with each other. The parallel branches are represented in Fig. 3.23. Finally, s in the statement is connected to the rest of the statement with $\wedge$. Therefore, switch s is in series with the entire rest of the circuit, as illustrated in Fig. 3.24.

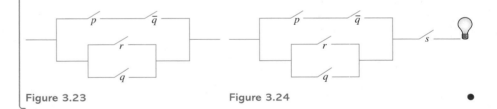

Figure 3.23   Figure 3.24

Equivalent Circuits

Sometimes two circuits that look very different will actually have the exact same conditions under which the light will be on. If we were to analyze the truth tables for the corresponding symbolic statements for such circuits, we would find that they have identical answer columns. In other words, the corresponding symbolic statements are equivalent.

Equivalent circuits are two circuits that have equivalent corresponding symbolic statements.

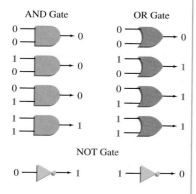
To determine whether two circuits are equivalent, we will analyze the answer columns of the truth tables of their corresponding symbolic statements. If the answer columns from their corresponding symbolic statements are identical, then the circuits are equivalent.

EXAMPLE ④ Are the Circuits Equivalent?

Determine whether the two circuits are equivalent.

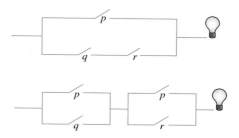

SOLUTION The symbolic statement that represents the first circuit is $p \vee (q \wedge r)$. The symbolic statement that represents the second circuit is $(p \vee q) \wedge (p \vee r)$. The truth tables for these statements are shown in Table 3.38.

Table 3.38

p	q	r	p	$\vee$	$(q \wedge r)$	$(p \vee q)$	$\wedge$	$(p \vee r)$
T	T	T	T	T	T	T	T	T
T	T	F	T	T	F	T	T	T
T	F	T	T	T	F	T	T	T
T	F	F	T	T	F	T	T	T
F	T	T	F	T	T	T	T	T
F	T	F	F	F	F	T	F	F
F	F	T	F	F	F	F	F	T
F	F	F	F	F	F	F	F	F

Note that the answer columns for the two statements are identical. Therefore, $p \vee (q \wedge r)$ is equivalent to $(p \vee q) \wedge (p \vee r)$ and the two circuits are equivalent.

SECTION 3.7   EXERCISES

CONCEPT/WRITING EXERCISES

1. **a)** In your own words, describe a series circuit.

   b) Which type of logical connective can be used to represent a series circuit?

2. **a)** In your own words, describe a parallel circuit.

   b) Which type of logical connective can be used to represent a parallel circuit?

3. Explain why the lightbulb will never go on in the following circuit.

4. Explain why the lightbulb will always be on in the following circuit.

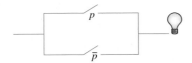

PRACTICE THE SKILLS/PROBLEM SOLVING

In Exercises 5–12, (a) write a symbolic statement that represents the circuit and (b) construct a truth table to determine when the lightbulb will be on. That is, determine which switches must be open and which switches must be closed for the lightbulb to be on.

5.

6.

7.

8.

9.

10.
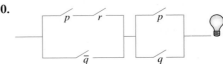

11.
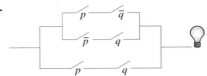

12.
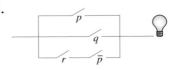

In Exercises 13–20, draw a switching circuit that represents the symbolic statement.

13. $p \vee q$

14. $p \vee (q \wedge r)$

15. $(p \vee q) \wedge r$

16. $\sim p \wedge (q \vee r)$

17. $(p \vee q) \wedge (r \vee s)$

18. $(p \wedge q) \vee (r \wedge s)$

19. $[(p \vee q) \vee (r \wedge q)] \wedge (\sim p)$

20. $[(p \vee q) \wedge r] \vee (\sim p \wedge q)$

In Exercises 21–26, represent each circuit with a symbolic statement. Then use a truth table to determine if the circuits are equivalent.

21.
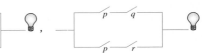

22.

23.

24.

25.

26.

CHALLENGE PROBLEMS/GROUP ACTIVITIES

27. Design a circuit that can be represented by

  a) $p \rightarrow q$

  b) $\sim(p \rightarrow q)$

  (*Hint:* See Section 3.4.)

28. Design two circuits that each involve switches labeled p, q, r, and s that appear to be different but are actually equivalent circuits.

INTERNET/RESEARCH ACTIVITIES

29. Digital computers use gates that work like switches to perform calculations. (See Did You Know? on page 173.) Information is fed into the gates and information leaves the gates, according to the type of gate. The three basic gates used in computers are the NOT gate, the AND gate, and the OR gate. Do research on the three types of gates.

  a) Explain how each gate works.

  b) Explain the relationship between each gate and the corresponding logic connectives *not, and,* and *or*.

  c) Illustrate how two or more gates can be combined to form a more complex gate.

CHAPTER ❸ SUMMARY

Important Facts

Quantifiers

Form of Statement	Form of Negation
All are.	Some are not.
None are.	Some are.
Some are.	None are.
Some are not.	All are.

Summary of connectives

Formal Name	Symbol	Read	Symbolic Form
Negation	$\sim$	not	$\sim p$
Conjunction	$\wedge$	and	$p \wedge q$
Disjunction	$\vee$	or	$p \vee q$
Conditional	$\rightarrow$	if–then	$p \rightarrow q$
Biconditional	$\leftrightarrow$	if and only if	$p \leftrightarrow q$

Basic truth tables

				Conjunction	Disjunction	Conditional	Biconditional
Negation							
p	$\sim p$	p	q	$p \wedge q$	$p \vee q$	$p \rightarrow q$	$p \leftrightarrow q$
T	F	T	T	T	T	T	T
F	T	T	F	F	T	F	F
		F	T	F	T	T	F
		F	F	F	F	T	T

De Morgan's laws

$$\sim(p \wedge q) \Leftrightarrow \sim p \vee \sim q$$
$$\sim(p \vee q) \Leftrightarrow \sim p \wedge \sim q$$

Other equivalent forms

$$p \rightarrow q \Leftrightarrow \sim p \vee q$$
$$\sim (p \rightarrow q) \Leftrightarrow p \wedge \sim q$$
$$p \leftrightarrow q \Leftrightarrow [(p \rightarrow q) \wedge (q \rightarrow p)]$$

Variations of the conditional statement

Name	Symbolic Form	Read
Conditional	$p \rightarrow q$	If p, then q.
Converse of the conditional	$q \rightarrow p$	If q, then p.
Inverse of the conditional	$\sim p \rightarrow \sim q$	If not p, then not q.
Contrapositive of the conditional	$\sim q \rightarrow \sim p$	If not q, then not p.

Standard forms of arguments
Valid arguments

Law of Detachment	Law of Contra-position	Law of Syllogism	Disjunctive Syllogism
$p \rightarrow q$	$p \rightarrow q$	$p \rightarrow q$	$p \vee q$
p	$\sim q$	$q \rightarrow r$	$\sim p$
$\therefore q$	$\therefore \sim p$	$\therefore p \rightarrow r$	$\therefore q$

Invalid arguments

Fallacy of the Converse	Fallacy of the Inverse
$p \rightarrow q$	$p \rightarrow q$
q	$\sim p$
$\therefore p$	$\therefore \sim q$

Symbolic argument vs. syllogistic argument

	Words or Phrases Used	Method of Determining Validity
Symbolic argument	and, or, not, if–then, if and only if	Truth tables or by comparison with standard forms of arguments
Syllogistic argument	all are, some are, none are, some are not	Euler diagrams

Switching Circuits as Symbolic Statements

Switches in series will always be represented with a conjunction, $\wedge$.

Switches in parallel will always be represented with a disjunction, $\vee$.

CHAPTER ③ REVIEW EXERCISES

3.1

In Exercises 1–4, write the negation of the statement.

1. No gift cards are exchangeable.

2. All bears are mammals.

3. Some women are presidents.

▲ Ellen Johnson-Sirleaf, President of Liberia

4. Some pine trees are not green.

In Exercises 5–10, write each compound statement in words.

p: The coffee is Maxwell House.
q: The coffee is hot.
r: The coffee is strong.

5. $p \vee q$

6. $\sim q \wedge r$

7. $q \rightarrow (r \wedge \sim p)$

8. $p \leftrightarrow \sim r$

9. $\sim p \leftrightarrow (r \wedge \sim q)$

10. $(p \vee \sim q) \wedge \sim r$

3.2

In Exercises 11–16, use the statements for p, q, and r as in Exercises 5–10 to write the statement in symbolic form.

11. The coffee is strong and the coffee is hot.

12. If the coffee is Maxwell House, then the coffee is strong.

13. If the coffee is strong then the coffee is hot, or the coffee is not Maxwell House.

14. The coffee is hot if and only if the coffee is Maxwell House, and the coffee is not strong.

15. The coffee is strong and the coffee is hot, or the coffee is not Maxwell House.

16. It is false that the coffee is strong and the coffee is hot.

In Exercises 17–22, construct a truth table for the statement.

17. $(p \lor q) \land \sim p$

18. $q \leftrightarrow (p \lor \sim q)$

19. $(p \lor q) \leftrightarrow (p \lor r)$

20. $p \land (\sim q \lor r)$

21. $p \rightarrow (q \land \sim r)$

22. $(p \land q) \rightarrow \sim r$

3.2, 3.3

In Exercises 23–26, determine the truth value of the statement.

23. If the IRS collects taxes or the Postal Service delivers mail, then the FBI investigates crop damage.

24. $17 + 4 = 21$, and $\frac{15}{5} = -7$ or $3 - 9 = -6$.

25. If Oregon borders the Pacific Ocean or California borders the Atlantic Ocean, then Minnesota is south of Texas.

26. $15 - 7 = 22$ or $4 + 9 = 13$, and $9 - 8 = 1$.

3.3

In Exercises 27–30, determine the truth value of the statement when p is T, q is F, and r is F.

27. $(p \rightarrow \sim r) \lor (p \land q)$

28. $(p \lor q) \leftrightarrow (\sim r \land p)$

29. $\sim r \leftrightarrow [(p \lor q) \leftrightarrow \sim p]$

30. $\sim[(q \land r) \rightarrow (\sim p \lor r)]$

3.4

In Exercises 31–34, determine whether the pairs of statements are equivalent. You may use De Morgan's laws, the fact that $(p \rightarrow q) \Leftrightarrow (\sim p \lor q)$, the fact that $\sim(p \rightarrow q) \Leftrightarrow (p \land \sim q)$, truth tables, or equivalent forms of the conditional statement.

31. $\sim p \lor \sim q, \qquad \sim p \leftrightarrow q$

32. $\sim p \rightarrow \sim q, \qquad p \lor \sim q$

33. $\sim p \lor (q \land r), \quad (\sim p \lor q) \land (\sim p \lor r)$

34. $(\sim q \rightarrow p) \land p, \quad \sim(\sim p \leftrightarrow q) \lor p$

In Exercises 35–39, use De Morgan's laws, the fact that $(p \rightarrow q) \Leftrightarrow (\sim p \lor q)$, or the fact that $\sim(p \rightarrow q) \Leftrightarrow (p \land \sim q)$, to write an equivalent statement for the given statement.

35. Bobby Darin sang *Mack the Knife* and Elvis did not write *Memphis*.

▲ Bobby Darin and Sandra Dee

36. Lynn Swann played for the Steelers or Jack Tatum played for the Raiders.

37. It is not true that Altec Lansing only produces speakers or Harman Kardon only produces stereo receivers.

38. Travis Tritt did not win an Academy Award and Randy Jackson does not do commercials for Milk Bone Dog Biscuits.

39. If the temperature is not above 32°, then we will go ice fishing at O'Leary's Lake.

In Exercises 40–44, write the (a) converse, (b) inverse, and (c) contrapositive for the given statement.

40. If you hear a new voice today, then you soften your opinion.

41. If we take the table to *Antiques Roadshow*, then we will learn the table's value.

42. If Maureen Gerald is not in attendance, then she is helping at the school.

43. If the desk is made by Winner's Only and the desk is in the Rose catalog, then we will not buy a desk at Miller's Furniture.

44. If you get straight A's on your report card, then I will let you attend the prom.

In Exercises 45–48, determine which, if any, of the three statements are equivalent.

45. a) If you read 10 books in the summer, then you reach your goal.

  b) You do not read 10 books in the summer or you reach your goal.

  c) It is false that you read 10 books in the summer and you do not reach your goal.

46. a) The screwdriver is on the workbench if and only if the screwdriver is not on the counter.

  b) If the screwdriver is not on the counter, then the screwdriver is not on the workbench.

  c) It is false that the screwdriver is on the counter and the screwdriver is not on the workbench.

47. a) If $2 + 3 = 6$, then $3 + 1 = 5$.

  b) $2 + 3 = 6$ if and only if $3 + 1 \neq 5$.

  c) If $3 + 1 \neq 5$, then $2 + 3 \neq 6$.

48. a) If the sale is on Tuesday and I have money, then I will go to the sale.

  b) If I go to the sale, then the sale is on Tuesday and I have money.

  c) I go to the sale, or the sale is on Tuesday and I have money.

3.5

In Exercises 49–52, determine whether the argument is valid or invalid. You may compare the argument to a standard form or use a truth table.

49. $p \rightarrow q$
$\underline{\sim p}$
$\therefore q$

50. $p \land q$
$\underline{q \rightarrow r}$
$\therefore p \rightarrow r$

51. If Jose Macias is the manager, then Kevin Geis is the coach.
If Kevin Geis is the coach, then Tim Weisman is the umpire.
$\therefore$ If Jose Macias is the manager, then Tim Weisman is the umpire.

52. If we eat at Joe's, then we will get heartburn. We get heartburn or we take Tums. Therefore, we do not get heartburn.

3.6

In Exercises 53–56, use an Euler diagram to determine whether the argument is valid or invalid.

53. All plumbers wear overalls.
Some electricians wear overalls.
$\therefore$ Some electricians are plumbers.

54. Some submarines are yellow.
All dandelions are yellow.
$\therefore$ Some dandelions are submarines.

55. No Beatles are Rolling Stones.
Some Rolling Stones are Small Faces.
$\therefore$ No Beatles are Small Faces.

56. All bears are furry.
Teddy is furry.
$\therefore$ Teddy is a bear.

3.7

57. a) Write the corresponding symbolic statement of the circuit shown.

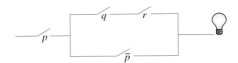

  b) Construct a truth table to determine when the lightbulb will be on.

58. Construct a diagram of a circuit that corresponds to the symbolic statement $(p \lor q) \lor (p \land q)$.

59. Determine whether the circuits shown are equivalent.

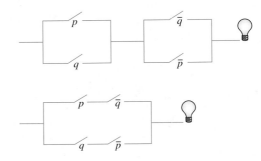

CHAPTER ❸ TEST

In Exercises 1–3, write the statement in symbolic form.

> *p*:   Ann is the secretary.
>
> *q*:   Dick is the vice president.
>
> *r*:   Elaine is the president.

1. Ann is the secretary but Elaine is the president, or Dick is not the vice president.

2. If Elaine is the president then Dick is the vice president, or Ann is not the secretary.

3. It is false that Elaine is the president if and only if Dick is not the vice president.

In Exercises 4 and 5, use p, q, and r as above to write each symbolic statement in words.

4. $(\sim p \wedge r) \leftrightarrow \sim q$ **5.** $(p \vee \sim q) \rightarrow r$

In Exercises 6 and 7, construct a truth table for the given statement.

6. $[\sim(p \rightarrow r)] \wedge q$ **7.** $(q \leftrightarrow \sim r) \vee p$

In Exercises 8 and 9, find the truth value of the statement.

8. $2 + 6 = 8$ or $7 - 12 = 5$.

9. Harrison Ford is an actor or Gerald Ford was a president, if and only if the Mississippi is a river.

In Exercises 10 and 11, given that p is true, q is false, and r is true, determine the truth value of the statement.

10. $(r \vee q) \leftrightarrow (p \wedge \sim q)$

11. $[\sim(r \rightarrow \sim p)] \wedge (q \rightarrow p)$

12. Determine whether the pair of statements are equivalent.

$$\sim p \vee q, \qquad \sim(p \wedge \sim q)$$

In Exercises 13 and 14, determine which, if any, of the three statements are equivalent.

13. a) If the bird is red, then it is a cardinal.

b) The bird is not red or it is a cardinal.

c) If the bird is not red, then it is not a cardinal.

14. a) It is not true that the test is today or the concert is tonight.

b) The test is not today and the concert is not tonight.

c) If the test is not today, then the concert is not tonight.

15. *Translate the following argument into symbolic form. Determine whether the argument is valid or invalid by comparing the argument to a recognized form or by using a truth table.*

> If the soccer team wins the game, then Sue played fullback. If Sue played fullback, then the team is in second place. Therefore, if the soccer team wins the game, then the team is in second place.

16. *Use an Euler diagram to determine whether the syllogism is valid or is a fallacy.*

> All living things contain carbon.
> Roger contains carbon.
> ─────────────────────────
>
> ∴ Therefore, Roger is a living thing.

In Exercises 17 and 18, write the negation of the statement.

17. All highways are roads.

18. Nick played football and Max played baseball.

19. Write the converse, inverse, and contrapositive of the conditional statement, "If the garbage truck comes, then today is Saturday."

20. Construct a diagram of a circuit that corresponds to $(p \wedge q) \vee (\sim p \vee \sim q)$

G R O U P   P R O J E C T S

1. Gates in computers work on the same principles as switching circuits. The three basic types of gate are the NOT gate, the AND gate, and the OR gate. Each is illustrated along with a table that indicates current flow entering and exiting the gate. If current flows into a NOT gate, then no current exits, and vice versa. Current exits an AND gate only when both inputs have a current flow. Current exits an OR gate if current flows through either, or both, inputs. In the table, a 1 represents a current flow and a 0 indicates no current flow. For example, in the AND gate, if there is a current flow in input A (I_a has a value of 1) and no current flow in input B (I_b has a value of 0), there is no current flow in the output (O has a value of 0); see row 2 of the AND Gate table.

NOT gate

Input ─▷○─ Output

NOT gate

I	O
1	0
0	1

AND gate

Input A ─┐
         ├D─ Output
Input B ─┘

AND gate

I_a	I_b	O
1	1	1
1	0	0
0	1	0
0	0	0

OR gate

Input A ─┐
         ├D─ Output
Input B ─┘

OR gate

I_a	I_b	O
1	1	1
1	0	1
0	1	1
0	0	0

a) If 1 is considered true and 0 is considered false, explain how these tables are similar to the *not, and,* and *or* truth tables.

   For the inputs indicated in the following figures determine whether the output is 1 or 0.

b)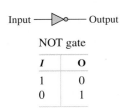
   I_a 1
   I_b 0 ──── Output

c) I_a 1
   I_b 0 ──── Output

d) I_a 1
   I_b 1 ──── Output

e) What values for I_a and I_b will give an output of 1 in the figure in part (d)? Explain how you determined your answer.

f) Construct a truth table using 1's and 0's for the following gate. Your truth table should have columns I_a, I_b, and O and should indicate the four possible cases for the inputs and each corresponding output.

   I_a ─▷○─┐
            ├D─ Output
   I_b ────┘

2. a) Shown is a photograph of a logic game at the Ontario Science Centre. There are 12 balls on top of the game board, numbered from left to right, with ball 1 on the extreme left and ball 12 on the extreme right. On the platform in front of the players are 12 buttons. Button 1 corresponds to ball 1, button 2 corresponds to ball 2, and so on. When 6 buttons are pushed, the 6 respective balls are released. When 1 or 2 balls reach an *and* gate or an *or* gate, a single ball may or may not pass through the gate. The object of the game is to select a proper combination of 6 buttons that will allow 1 ball to reach the bottom. Using your knowledge of *and* and *or*, select a combination of 6 buttons that will result in a win. (There is more than one answer.) Explain how you determined your answer.

   b) Construct a game similar to this one where 15 balls are at the top and 8 balls must be selected to allow 1 ball to reach the bottom.

   c) Indicate all solutions to the game you constructed in part (c).

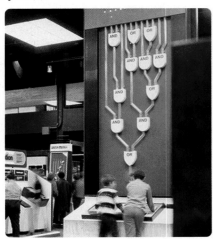

CHAPTER 7

Systems of Linear Equations and Inequalities

▲ Business owners may solve systems of equations to determine under what conditions their business will be profitable.

WHAT YOU WILL LEARN

- Solving systems of linear equations by graphing, by using the substitution method, by using the addition method, and by using matrices
- Solving systems of linear inequalities
- Adding, subtracting, and multiplying matrices
- Solving application problems using linear programming

WHY IT IS IMPORTANT

Imagine that you and a friend enter the T-shirt business. To make a profit in your business, you need to keep track of the cost of your materials, your overhead, the quantity of T-shirts sold, the price at which you sell the T-shirts, and many other items. To do so, you may need to develop and solve systems of equations.

7.1   SYSTEMS OF LINEAR EQUATIONS

Suppose you needed to have some landscaping work done at your home. In your local newspaper, two different landscaping services each have advertised specials. One company charges a lower consultation fee than the other company but charges a higher hourly rate for labor. How do you determine the number of hours of service needed for both services to have the same cost? How do you decide which company is less expensive for the services you need? In this section, we will introduce one way to use algebra to answer these questions.

▲ Solving a system of equations can help determine which of two landscaping companies offers the least expensive service.

In algebra, it is often necessary to find the common solution to two or more equations. We refer to the equations in this type of problem as a *system of linear equations* or as *simultaneous linear equations*. The solution to a system of linear equations may be found by a number of techniques. In this section, we illustrate how to solve a system of linear equations by graphing.

Solutions to Systems of Linear Equations

A *solution to a system of equations* is the ordered pair or ordered pairs that satisfy *all* equations in the system. A system of linear equations may have exactly one solution, no solution, or infinitely many solutions.

┌─ **EXAMPLE ❶** *Is the Ordered Pair a Solution?*

Determine which of the ordered pairs is a solution to the following system of linear equations.

$$x + 2y = 8$$
$$2x - 3y = 2$$

a) $(6, 1)$ b) $(4, 2)$ c) $(1, 0)$

SOLUTION For the ordered pair to be a solution to the system, it must satisfy each equation in the system. Substitute the values of x and y into each equation.

a) $x + 2y = 8$ $2x - 3y = 2$
      $6 + 2(1) = 8$ $2(6) - 3(1) = 2$
          $8 = 8$ True $9 = 2$ False

Since $(6, 1)$ does not satisfy *both* equations, it is not a solution to the system.

b) $x + 2y = 8$ $2x - 3y = 2$
      $4 + 2(2) = 8$ $2(4) - 3(2) = 2$
          $8 = 8$ True $2 = 2$ True

Since $(4, 2)$ satisfies *both* equations, it is a solution to the system.

c) $x + 2y = 8$ $2x - 3y = 2$
      $1 + 2(0) = 8$ $2(1) - 3(0) = 2$
          $1 = 8$ False $2 = 2$ True

Since $(1, 0)$ does not satisfy *both* equations, it is not a solution to the system.   ●

Solving a System of Linear Equations by Graphing

To find the solution to a system of linear equations graphically, we graph both of the equations on the same axes. The coordinates of the point or points of intersection of the graphs are the solution or solutions to the system of equations.

$x + y = 4$		$2x - y = -1$	
x	y	x	y
0	4	0	1
1	3	1	3
4	0	−2	−3

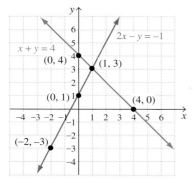

Figure 7.1

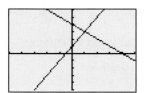

Figure 7.2

PROCEDURE FOR SOLVING A SYSTEM OF EQUATIONS BY GRAPHING

1. Determine three ordered pairs that satisfy each equation.
2. Plot the points that correspond to the ordered pairs and sketch the graphs of *both* equations on the same axes.
3. The coordinates of the point or points of intersection of the graphs are the solution or solutions to the system of equations.

When two linear equations are graphed, three situations are possible. The two lines may intersect at one point, as in Example 2; or the two lines may be parallel and not intersect, as in Example 3; or the two equations may represent the same line, as in Example 4.

Since the solution to a system of equations may not be integer values, you may not be able to obtain the exact solution by graphing.

EXAMPLE ❷ A System with One Solution

Determine the solution to the following system of equations graphically.

$$x + y = 4$$
$$2x - y = -1$$

SOLUTION To determine the solution, graph both $x + y = 4$ and $2x - y = -1$ on the same axes (Fig. 7.1). Three points that satisfy each equation are shown in the tables above Fig. 7.1. Figure 7.2 shows the system $x + y = 4$ and $2x - y = -1$ graphed on a Texas Instrument TI-84 Plus graphing calculator.

The graphs intersect at (1, 3), which is the solution to the system of equations. This point is the only point that satisfies *both* equations.

CHECK:

$x + y = 4$	$2x - y = -1$
$1 + 3 = 4$	$2(1) - 3 = -1$
$4 = 4$ True	$2 - 3 = -1$
	$-1 = -1$ True

TIMELY TIP When checking the solution to a system of equations, it is important to check the solution in both equations. The ordered pair solution must satisfy *both* equations of the system.

The system of equations in Example 2 is an example of a *consistent system of equations*. A consistent system of equations is one that has a solution.

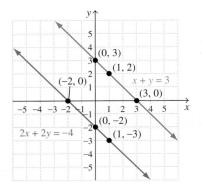

Figure 7.3

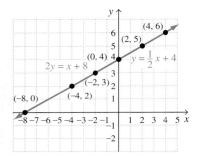

Figure 7.4

EXAMPLE ❸ *A System with No Solution*

Determine the solution to the following system of equations graphically.

$$x + y = 3$$
$$2x + 2y = -4$$

SOLUTION Three ordered pairs that satisfy the equation $x + y = 3$ are $(0, 3)$, $(3, 0)$, and $(1, 2)$. Three ordered pairs that satisfy the equation $2x + 2y = -4$ are $(-2, 0)$, $(0, -2)$, and $(1, -3)$. The graphs of both equations are given in Fig. 7.3. Since the two lines are parallel, they do not intersect; therefore, the system has *no solution.* •

The system of equations in Example 3 has no solution. A system of equations that has no solution is called an *inconsistent system.*

EXAMPLE ❹ *A System with an Infinite Number of Solutions*

Determine the solution to the following system of equations graphically.

$$y = \frac{1}{2}x + 4$$
$$2y = x + 8$$

SOLUTION Three ordered pairs that satisfy the equation $y = \frac{1}{2}x + 4$ are $(0, 4)$, $(2, 5)$, and $(-2, 3)$. Three ordered pairs that satisfy the equation $2y = x + 8$ are $(-8, 0)$, $(4, 6)$, and $(-4, 2)$. Graph the equations on the same axes (Fig. 7.4). Because all six points are on the same line, the two equations represent the same line. Therefore, every ordered pair that is a solution to one equation is also a solution to the other equation. Every point on the line satisfies both equations; thus, this system has an *infinite number of solutions*. Solving the second equation for y reveals that the equations are equivalent. •

When a system of equations has an infinite number of solutions, as in Example 4, it is called a *dependent system*. Note that because it has a solution, a dependent system is also a consistent system.

Figure 7.5 summarizes the three possibilities for a system of linear equations.

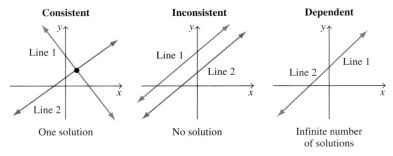

Figure 7.5

In Chapter 6, we introduced *modeling*. Recall that a *mathematical model* is an equation or system of equations that represents a real-life situation. In Examples 5 and 6, we develop equations that model a real-life situation.

EXAMPLE ⑤ MODELING - *A Landscape Service Application*

Tom's Tree and Landscape Service charges a consultation fee of $200 plus $50 per hour for labor for landscaping. Lawn Perfect Landscape Service charges a consultation fee of $300 plus $25 per hour for labor for landscaping.

a) Write a system of equations to represent the cost, C, of the two landscaping services, each with h hours of labor.

b) Graph both equations on the same axes and determine the number of hours needed for both services to have the same cost.

c) If the Johnsons need 7 hours of landscaping service done at their home, which service is less expensive?

SOLUTION Let $h =$ the number of hours of labor. The total cost of each service is the consultation fee plus the cost of the labor.

a) Tom's Tree and Landscape Service: $C = 200 + 50h$
   Lawn Perfect Landscape Service: $C = 300 + 25h$

b) We graphed the cost, C, versus the number of hours of labor, h, for 0 to 10 hours (Fig. 7.6). On the graph, the lines intersect at the point (4, 400). Thus, for 4 hours of service, both services would have the same cost, $400.

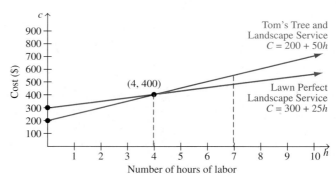

Figure 7.6

c) The graph shows that for more than 4 hours, Lawn Perfect is the least expensive service. Thus, for 7 hours, Lawn Perfect is less expensive than Tom's Tree and Landscape Service. ●

Break-Even Analysis

Manufacturers use a technique called *break-even analysis* to determine how many units of an item must be sold for the business to "break even," that is, for its total revenue to equal its total cost. Suppose we let the horizontal axis represent the number of units manufactured and sold and the vertical axis represent dollars. Then linear equations for cost, C, and revenue, R, can both be sketched on the same axes (Fig. 7.7). Both C and R are expressed in dollars, and both are a function of the number of units. Profit, P, is the difference between revenue, R, and cost, C. Thus, $P = R - C$. If revenue is greater than cost, the company makes a profit. If cost is greater than revenue, the company has a loss.

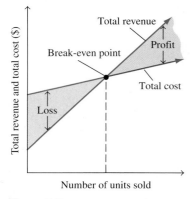

Figure 7.7

Initially, the cost graph is higher than the revenue graph because of fixed (over-head) costs such as rent and utilities. During low levels of sales, the manufacturer suffers a loss (the cost graph is greater). During higher levels of sales, the manufacturer realizes a profit (the revenue graph is greater). The point at which the two graphs intersect is called the *break-even point*. At that number of units sold, revenue equals cost and the manufacturer breaks even.

─ EXAMPLE ➏ MODELING - *Profit and Loss in Business*

At a collectibles show, Richard Lane can sell model cars for $25. The costs for making the cars are a fixed cost of $150 and a production cost of $10 apiece.

a) Write an equation that represents Richard's revenue. Write an equation that represents Richard's cost.

b) How many model cars must Richard sell to break even?

c) Write an equation for the profit formula. Use the formula to determine Richard's profit if he sells 14 model cars.

d) How many model cars must Richard sell to make a profit of $450?

SOLUTION

a) Let x denote the number of model cars made and sold. The revenue is given by the equation

$$R = 25x \quad \text{($25 times the number of units)}$$

and the cost is given by the equation

$$C = 150 + 10x \quad \text{($150 plus $10 times the number of units)}$$

b) The break-even point is the point at which the revenue and cost graphs intersect. In Fig. 7.8, the graphs intersect at the point (10, 250), which is the break-even point. Thus, for Richard to break even, he must sell 10 model cars. When 10 model cars are made and sold, the cost and revenue are both $250.

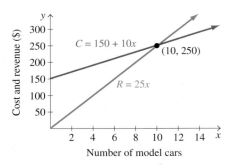

Figure 7.8

c) Profit is equal to the revenue minus the cost. Therefore, the profit formula is

$$
\begin{aligned}
P &= R - C \\
&= 25x - (150 + 10x) \\
&= 25x - 150 - 10x \\
&= 15x - 150
\end{aligned}
$$

For 14 cars, the profit is found as follows.

$$P = 15x - 150$$
$$= 15(14) - 150 = 60$$

Richard has a profit of $60 if he sells 14 model cars. By observing the graph, we can see that if Richard sells 14 model cars, he will have a profit since at 14 cars the revenue line is greater than the cost line.

d) We can determine the number of model cars that Richard must sell to have a profit of $450 by using the profit formula. Substituting 450 for P we have

$$P = 15x - 150$$
$$450 = 15x - 150$$
$$600 = 15x$$
$$40 = x$$

Thus, Richard must sell 40 model cars to make a profit of $450.

TIMELY TIP Following is a summary of the different types of systems of linear equations.

- A *consistent system of equations* is one that has a solution.
- An *inconsistent system of equations* is one that has no solution.
- A *dependent system of equations* is one that has an infinite number of solutions.

SECTION 7.1 EXERCISES

CONCEPT/WRITING EXERCISES

1. What is a system of linear equations?

2. What is the solution to a system of linear equations?

3. Define an *inconsistent system of equations*.

4. Define a *consistent system of equations*.

5. Define a *dependent system of equations*.

6. **a)** Outline the procedure for solving a system of linear equations by graphing.

   b) What is a disadvantage of solving a system of linear equations by graphing?

7. If a system of linear equations has no solution, what does that mean about the graphs of the equations in the system?

8. If a system of linear equations has one solution, what does that mean about the graphs of the equations in the system?

9. If a system of linear equations has an infinite number of solutions, what does that mean about the graphs of the equations in the system?

10. Can a system of linear equations have exactly two solutions? Explain.

PRACTICE THE SKILLS

In Exercises 11 and 12, determine which ordered pairs are solutions to the given system.

11. $y = 3x - 4$ $(3, 5)$ $(2, 2)$ $(1, 7)$
    $y = -x + 8$

12. $x + 2y = 6$ $(-2, 4)$ $(2, 2)$ $(3, -9)$
    $x - y = -6$

In Exercises 13–16, solve the system of equations graphically.

13. $x = 2$
$y = 4$

14. $x = -1$
$y = 3$

15. $x = 4$
$y = -3$

16. $x = -5$
$y = -3$

In Exercises 17–32, solve the system of equations graphically. If the system does not have a single ordered pair as a solution, state whether the system is inconsistent or dependent.

17. $x = 3$
$y = -x - 2$

18. $y = 2$
$y = x - 1$

19. $y = 4x - 8$
$y = -x + 7$

20. $x + y = 6$
$-x + y = 4$

21. $x + 2y = 0$
$2x - 3y = -14$

22. $3x - y = 1$
$4x - 3y = 3$

23. $2x + y = 3$
$2y = 6 - 4x$

24. $y = 2x - 4$
$2x + y = 0$

25. $y = x + 3$
$y = -1$

26. $x = 1$
$x + y + 3 = 0$

27. $2x - y = -3$
$2x + y = -9$

28. $3x + 2y = 6$
$6x + 4y = 12$

29. $2x - 3y = 12$
$3y - 2x = 9$

30. $y = \frac{1}{3}x - 4$
$3y - x = 4$

31. $y = \frac{4}{3}x - 2$
$2x + 2y = 10$

32. $2(x - 1) + 2y = 0$
$3x + 2(y + 2) = 0$

33. a) If the two lines in a system of equations have different slopes, how many solutions will the system have? Explain your answer.

    b) If the two lines in a system of equations have the same slope but different y-intercepts, how many solutions will the system have? Explain.

    c) If the two lines in a system of equations have the same slope and the same y-intercept, how many solutions will the system have? Explain.

34. Indicate whether the graph shown represents a consistent, inconsistent, or dependent system. Explain your answer.

a)

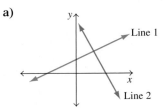

b)

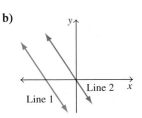

c)

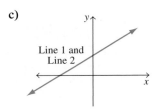

In Exercises 35–46, determine without graphing whether the system of equations has exactly one solution, no solution, or an infinite number of solutions. (Consider your answers to Exercise 33.)

35. $3x + y = 9$
$y = -3x + 9$

36. $4x + 3y = 8$
$6y = -8x + 4$

37. $3x + y = -6$
$4x - 2y = -8$

38. $x - 3y = 8$
$3x - y = 6$

39. $3x + y = 7$
$y = -3x + 9$

40. $x + 4y = 12$
$x = 4y + 3$

41. $2x - 3y = 6$
$x - \frac{3}{2}y = 3$

42. $x - 2y = 6$
$x + 2y = 4$

43. $3x = 6y + 5$
$y = \frac{1}{2}x - 3$

44. $3y = 6x + 4$
$-2x + y = \frac{4}{3}$

45. $4x + 7y = 2$
$4x = 6 + 7y$

46. $12x - 5y = 4$
$3x + 4y = 6$

PROBLEM SOLVING

Two lines are perpendicular *to each other when they meet at a right angle (a 90° angle). Two lines are perpendicular when their slopes are* negative reciprocals. *The negative reciprocal of 2 is* $-\frac{1}{2}$, *the negative reciprocal of* $\frac{3}{5}$ *is* $-1/(\frac{3}{5})$ *or* $-\frac{5}{3}$, *and so on. If a represents any real number, except 0, its negative reciprocal is* $-1/a$. *Note that the product of a number and its negative reciprocal is* -1. *In Exercises 47–50, determine, by finding the slope of each line, whether the lines will be perpendicular to each other when graphed.*

47. $4y - 2x = 15$
   $3y - 5x = 9$

48. $4y - x = 6$
   $y = x + 8$

49. $2x + y = 3$
   $2y - x = 5$

50. $6x + 5y = 3$
   $-10x = 2 + 12y$

In Exercises 51–55, part of the question involves determining a system of equations that models the situation.

51. MODELING - *Hot-Water Heater Repair* Phillip Hoffman's plumber says it will cost Phillip $250 to repair his water heater. Phillip can purchase a new, more efficient heater for $700. His current heater costs $375 per year for energy costs, and the new heater would cost $225 per year.

   a) Write a system of equations with one equation representing the total cost of repairing the heater plus annual energy costs and the other equation representing the total cost of replacing the heater plus annual energy costs.

   b) Graph both equations (for up to and including 6 years) on the same axes.

   c) Determine the number of years it would take for the total cost of repair to equal the total cost of replacement.

52. MODELING - *Landscaping Revisited* In Example 5, assume that Tom's Tree and Landscape Service charges $200 for a consultation fee plus $60 per hour for labor and that Lawn Perfect Landscape Service charges $305 for a consultation fee plus $25 per hour for labor.

   a) Write the system of equations to represent the cost of the two landscaping services.

   b) Graph both equations for 0 to 10 hours on the same axes.

   c) Determine the number of hours of landscaping that must be used for both services to have the same cost.

53. MODELING - *Selling Backpacks* Benjamin's Backpacks can sell backpacks for $25 per backpack. The costs for making the backpacks are a fixed cost of $400 and a production cost of $15 per backpack (see Example 6 for an example of cost and revenue equations).

   a) Write the cost and revenue equations.

   b) Graph both equations, for 0 to 50 backpacks, on the same axes.

   c) Use the graph to determine the number of backpacks Benjamin's Backpacks must sell to break even.

   d) Write the profit formula.

   e) Use the profit formula to determine whether Benjamin's Backpacks makes a profit or loss if it sells 30 backpacks. What is the profit or loss?

   f) How many backpacks must Benjamin's Backpacks sell to realize a profit of $1000?

54. MODELING - *Purchasing Stocks* When buying or selling stock for a customer, the Mark Demo Agency charges $40 plus 8 cents per share of stock purchased or sold. Andy Harris and Associates charges $15 plus 18 cents per share of stock purchased or sold.

a) Write a system of equations to represent the cost of purchasing or selling stock with each company.

b) Graph both equations (for up to and including 350 shares of stock) on the same axes.

c) Determine the number of shares of stock that must be purchased or sold for the total cost to be the same.

d) If 300 shares of stock are to be purchased, which firm would be less expensive?

55. MODELING - *Manufacturing PDAs* A manufacturer sells a certain personal digital assistant, or PDA, for $300 per unit. Manufacturing costs consist of a fixed cost of $8400 and a production cost of $230 per unit.

a) Write the cost and revenue equations.

b) Graph both equations (for up to and including 150 units) on the same axes.

c) Use the graph to determine the number of units the manufacturer must sell to break even.

d) Write the profit formula.

e) Use the profit formula to determine the manufacturer's profit or loss if 100 units are sold.

f) How many units must the manufacturer sell to make a profit of $1260?

56. Explain how you can determine whether a system of two linear equations will be consistent, dependent, or inconsistent without graphing the equations.

CHALLENGE PROBLEMS/GROUP ACTIVITIES

57. MODELING - *Job Offers* Hubert Hotchkiss had two job offers for sales positions. One pays a salary of $500 per week plus a 15% commission on his dollar sales volume. The second position pays a salary of $650 per week with no commission.

a) For each offer, write an equation that expresses the weekly pay.

b) Graph the system of equations and determine the solution.

c) For what dollar sales volume will the two offers result in the same pay?

58. MODELING - *Long-Distance Calling*

a) In September 2006, an AT&T One Rate Plan charged 7 cents per minute for long-distance calls with a monthly fee of $3.95. The Sprint Nickel Anytime Plan charged 5 cents per minute for long-distance calls with a monthly fee of $8.95. Write an equation to determine the monthly cost for long-distance service with the AT&T One Rate Plan and write an equation to determine the monthly cost for long-distance service with the Sprint Nickel Anytime Plan.

b) Graph the system of equations and determine the solution.

c) After how many minutes will the cost for the two long-distance service plans be the same?

59. *Points of Intersection* a) If two lines have different slopes, what is the maximum possible number of points of intersection?

b) If three lines all have different slopes, what is the maximum possible number of points of intersection of any two lines?

c) If four lines all have different slopes, what is the maximum possible number of points of intersection of any two lines?

d) If five lines all have different slopes, what is the maximum possible number of points of intersection of any two lines?

e) Is there a pattern in the number of points of intersection? If so, explain the pattern. Use the pattern to determine the maximum possible number of points of intersection for six lines.

RECREATIONAL MATHEMATICS

60. Connect all the following points using exactly four straight-line segments. Do not lift your pencil off the paper.

· · ·

· · ·

· · ·

INTERNET/RESEARCH ACTIVITY

61. *The Rhind Papyrus* The Rhind Papyrus indicates that the early Egyptians used linear equations. Do research and write a paper on the symbols used in linear equations and the use of the linear equations by the early Egyptians. (References include history of mathematics books, encyclopedias, and the Internet.)

7.2 SOLVING SYSTEMS OF LINEAR EQUATIONS BY THE SUBSTITUTION AND ADDITION METHODS

▲ Solving a system of equations may help determine which of two cell phone plans offers the least expensive service.

Bill Ramierez is considering two cell phone plans. Both plans offer 300 free minutes each month. One plan charges $30 per month plus 45 cents for each additional minute after 300 minutes. The other plan charges $35 per month plus 20 cents for each additional minute after 300 minutes. How would Bill determine how long he would have to talk on the phone, in 1 month, for the two plans to have the same cost? In this section, we will illustrate two different algebraic methods, the substitution method and the addition method, for answering this question.

We first discuss the substitution method.

Substitution Method

PROCEDURE FOR SOLVING A SYSTEM OF EQUATIONS USING THE SUBSTITUTION METHOD

1. Solve one of the equations for one of the variables. If possible, solve for a variable with a numerical coefficient of 1. By doing so, you may avoid working with fractions.
2. Substitute the expression found in step 1 into the other equation. This step yields an equation in terms of a single variable.
3. Solve the equation found in step 2 for the variable.
4. Substitute the value found in step 3 into the equation you rewrote in step 1 and solve for the remaining variable.

Examples 1, 2, and 3 illustrate the *substitution method*. These systems of equations are the same as in Examples 2, 3, and 4 in Section 7.1.

EXAMPLE ❶ *A Single Solution, by the Substitution Method*

Solve the following system of equations by substitution.

$$x + y = 4$$
$$2x - y = -1$$

SOLUTION The numerical coefficients of the x and y terms in the equation $x + y = 4$ are both 1. Thus, we can solve this equation for either x or y. Let's solve for x in the first equation.

STEP 1.

$$x + y = 4$$
$$x + y - y = 4 - y \qquad \text{Subtract } y \text{ from both sides of the equation.}$$
$$x = 4 - y$$

STEP 2. Substitute $4 - y$ for x in the second equation.

$$2x - y = -1$$
$$2(4 - y) - y = -1$$

STEP 3. Now solve the equation for y.

$$8 - 2y - y = -1 \qquad \text{Distributive property}$$
$$8 - 3y = -1$$
$$8 - 8 - 3y = -1 - 8 \qquad \text{Subtract 8 from both sides of the equation.}$$
$$-3y = -9$$
$$\frac{-3y}{-3} = \frac{-9}{-3} \qquad \text{Divide both sides of the equation by } -3.$$
$$y = 3$$

STEP 4. Substitute $y = 3$ in the equation solved for x and determine the value of x.

$$x = 4 - y$$
$$x = 4 - 3$$
$$x = 1$$

Thus, the solution is the ordered pair (1, 3). This answer checks with the solution obtained graphically in Section 7.1, Example 2. ●

TIMELY TIP   When solving a system of equations, once you successfully solve for one of the variables, make sure you solve for the other variable. Remember that a solution to a system of equations must contain a numerical value for each variable in the system.

EXAMPLE ❷ *No Solution, by the Substitution Method*

Solve the following system of equations by substitution.

$$x + y = 3$$
$$2x + 2y = -4$$

SOLUTION The numerical coefficients of the x and y terms in the equation $x + y = 3$ are both 1. Thus, we can solve this equation for either x or y. Let us solve for y in the first equation.

$$x + y = 3$$
$$x - x + y = 3 - x \qquad \text{Subtract } x \text{ from both sides of the equation.}$$
$$y = 3 - x$$

Now substitute $3 - x$ for y in the second equation.

$$2x + 2y = -4$$
$$2x + 2(3 - x) = -4$$
$$2x + 6 - 2x = -4 \qquad \text{Distributive property}$$
$$6 = -4 \qquad \text{False}$$

Since 6 cannot be equal to -4, there is no solution to the system of equations. Thus, the system of equations is inconsistent. This answer checks with the solution obtained graphically in Section 7.1, Example 3. ●

When solving the system in Example 2, we obtained $6 = -4$ and indicated that the system was inconsistent and that there was no solution. When solving a system of equations, if you obtain a false statement, such as $4 = 0$ or $-2 = 0$, the system is *inconsistent* and has *no solution*.

EXAMPLE ❸ *An Infinite Number of Solutions, by the Substitution Method*

Solve the following system of equations by substitution.

$$y = \frac{1}{2}x + 4$$
$$2y = x + 8$$

SOLUTION The first equation $y = \frac{1}{2}x + 4$ is already solved for y, so we will substitute $\frac{1}{2}x + 4$ for y in the second equation.

$$2y = x + 8$$
$$2\left(\frac{1}{2}x + 4\right) = x + 8$$
$$x + 8 = x + 8 \qquad \text{Distributive property}$$
$$x - x + 8 = x - x + 8 \qquad \text{Subtract } x \text{ from both sides of the equation.}$$
$$8 = 8 \qquad \text{True}$$

Since 8 equals 8, the system has an infinite number of solutions. Thus, the system of equations is dependent. This answer checks with the solution obtained in Section 7.1, Example 4. ●

When solving Example 3, we obtained $8 = 8$ and indicated that the system was dependent and had an infinite number of solutions. When solving a system of equations, if you obtain a true statement, such as $0 = 0$ or $8 = 8$, the system is *dependent* and has an *infinite number of solutions*.

Addition Method

If neither of the equations in a system of linear equations has a variable with a coefficient of 1, it is generally easier to solve the system by using the *addition* (or *elimination*) *method*.

To solve a system of linear equations by the addition method, it is necessary to obtain two equations whose sum will be a single equation containing only one variable. To achieve this goal, we rewrite the system of equations as two equations where the coefficients of one of the variables are opposites (or additive inverses) of each other. For example, if one equation has a term of $2x$, we might rewrite the other equation so that its x term will be $-2x$. To obtain the desired equations, it might be necessary to multiply one or both equations in the original system by a number. When an equation is to be multiplied by a number, we will place brackets around the equation and place the number that is to multiply the equation before the brackets. For example, $4[2x + 3y = 6]$ means that each term on both sides of the equal sign in the equation $2x + 3y = 6$ is to be multiplied by 4:

$$4[2x + 3y = 6] \qquad \text{gives} \qquad 8x + 12y = 24$$

This notation will make our explanations much more efficient and easier for you to follow.

PROCEDURE FOR SOLVING A SYSTEM OF EQUATIONS BY THE ADDITION METHOD

1. If necessary, rewrite the equations so that the terms containing the variables appear on one side of the equal sign and the constants appear on the other side of the equal sign.
2. If necessary, multiply one or both equations by a constant(s) so that when you add the equations, the sum will be an equation containing only one variable.
3. Add the equations to obtain a single equation in one variable.
4. Solve for the variable in the equation obtained in step 3.
5. Substitute the value found in step 4 into either of the original equations and solve for the other variable.

EXAMPLE ④ *Eliminating a Variable by the Addition Method*

Solve the following system of equations by the addition method.

$$x + y = 5$$
$$2x - y = 7$$

SOLUTION Since the coefficients of the y terms, 1 and -1, are additive inverses, the sum of the y terms will be zero when the equations are added. Thus, the sum of the two equations will contain only one variable, x. Add the two equations to obtain one equation in one variable. Then solve for the remaining variable.

$$
\begin{aligned}
x + y &= 5 \\
\underline{2x - y} &= \underline{7} \\
3x &= 12 \\
x &= 4
\end{aligned}
$$

Now substitute 4 for x in either of the original equations to find the value of y.

$$x + y = 5$$
$$4 + y = 5$$
$$y = 1$$

The solution to the system is (4, 1).

EXAMPLE ❺ *Multiplying by −1 in the Addition Method*

Solve the following system of equations by the addition method.

$$x + 4y = 10$$
$$x + 2y = 6$$

SOLUTION We want the sum of the two equations to have only one variable. We can eliminate the variable x by multiplying either equation by −1 and then adding the two equations. We will multiply the first equation by −1.

$$-1[x + 4y = 10] \quad \text{gives} \quad -x - 4y = -10$$
$$x + 2y = 6 \qquad\qquad\qquad x + 2y = 6$$

We now have a system of equations equivalent to the original system.
   Now add the two equations.

$$-x - 4y = -10$$
$$\underline{x + 2y = 6}$$
$$-2y = -4$$
$$y = 2$$

Now we solve for x by substituting 2 for y in either of the original equations.

$$x + 4y = 10$$
$$x + 4(2) = 10$$
$$x + 8 = 10$$
$$x = 2$$

The solution is (2, 2).

EXAMPLE ❻ *Multiplying One Equation in the Addition Method*

Solve the following system of equations by the addition method.

$$4x + y = 6$$
$$3x + 2y = 7$$

SOLUTION We can multiply the top equation by -2 and then add the two equations to eliminate the variable y.

$$-2[4x + y = 6] \qquad \text{gives} \qquad -8x - 2y = -12$$
$$3x + 2y = 7 \qquad\qquad\qquad\qquad 3x + 2y = \quad 7$$

$$-8x - 2y = -12$$
$$\underline{3x + 2y = \quad 7}$$
$$-5x \qquad\quad = -5$$
$$x = 1$$

Now we find y by substituting 1 for x in either of the original equations.

$$4x + y = 6$$
$$4(1) + y = 6$$
$$4 + y = 6$$
$$y = 2$$

The solution is $(1, 2)$. ●

Note that in Example 6 we could have eliminated the variable x by multiplying the top equation by 3 and the bottom equation by -4, then adding the two equations. Try this method now.

EXAMPLE ❼ *Multiplying Both Equations*

Solve the following system of equations by the addition method.

$$3x - 4y = 8$$
$$2x + 3y = 9$$

SOLUTION In this system, we cannot eliminate a variable by multiplying only one equation by an integer value and then adding. To eliminate a variable, we can multiply each equation by a different number. To eliminate the variable x, we can multiply the top equation by 2 and the bottom by -3 (or the top by -2 and the bottom by 3) and then add the two equations. If we want, we can instead eliminate the variable y by multiplying the top equation by 3 and the bottom by 4 and then adding the two equations. Let's eliminate the variable x.

$$2[3x - 4y = 8] \qquad \text{gives} \qquad 6x - 8y = 16$$
$$-3[2x + 3y = 9] \qquad \text{gives} \qquad -6x - 9y = -27$$

$$6x - 8y = \quad 16$$
$$\underline{-6x - 9y = -27}$$
$$-17y = -11$$
$$y = \frac{11}{17}$$

We could now find x by substituting $\frac{11}{17}$ for y in either of the original equations. Although it can be done, it gets messy. Instead, let's solve for x by eliminating the variable y from the two original equations. To do so, we multiply the first equation by 3 and the second equation by 4.

$$3[3x - 4y = 8] \quad \text{gives} \quad 9x - 12y = 24$$
$$4[2x + 3y = 9] \quad \text{gives} \quad 8x + 12y = 36$$

$$
\begin{array}{r}
9x - 12y = 24 \\
8x + 12y = 36 \\
\hline
17x \quad\quad\; = 60
\end{array}
$$

$$x = \frac{60}{17}$$

The solution to the system is $\left(\frac{60}{17}, \frac{11}{17}\right)$.   ●

TIMELY TIP If you obtain an equation such as $0 = 6$, or any other equation that is false when solving a system of linear equations, the system is *inconsistent* (the two equations represent parallel lines; see Fig. 7.3 on page 416) and there is no solution.

If you obtain the equation $0 = 0$ when solving a system of linear equations by either the substitution or the addition method, the system is *dependent* (both equations represent the same line; see Fig. 7.4 on page 416) and there are an infinite number of solutions.

EXAMPLE ❽ MODELING - *When Are Repair Costs the Same?*

Melinda Melendez needs to purchase a new radiator for her car and have it installed by a mechanic. She is considering two garages: Steve's Repair and Greg's Garage. At Steve's Repair, the parts cost $200 and the labor cost is $50 per hour. At Greg's Garage, the parts cost $375 and the labor cost is $25 per hour. How many hours would the repair need to take for the total cost at each garage to be the same?

SOLUTION We are asked to find the number of hours the repair would need to take for each garage to have the same total cost, C. First write a system of equations to represent the total cost for each of the garages. The total cost consists of the cost of the parts and the labor cost. The labor cost depends on the number of hours of labor.

Let x = the number of hours of labor.

$$\text{Total cost} = \text{cost of parts} + \text{labor cost}$$
$$\text{Steve's Repair: } C = 200 + 50x$$
$$\text{Greg's Garage: } C = 375 + 25x$$

We want to determine when the cost will be the same, so we set the two costs equal to each other (substitution method) and solve the resulting equation.

$$200 + 50x = 375 + 25x$$
$$200 - 200 + 50x = 375 - 200 + 25x \qquad \text{Subtract 200 from both sides of the equation.}$$
$$50x = 175 + 25x$$
$$50x - 25x = 175 + 25x - 25x \qquad \text{Subtract 25x from both sides of the equation.}$$
$$25x = 175$$
$$\frac{25x}{25} = \frac{175}{25} \qquad \text{Divide both sides of the equation by 25.}$$
$$x = 7$$

Thus, for 7 hours of labor, the cost at both garages would be the same. If we construct a graph (Fig. 7.9) of the two cost equations, the point of intersection is (7, 550). If the repair were to require 7 hours of labor, the total cost at either garage would be $550.

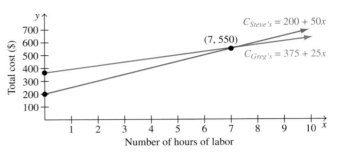

Figure 7.9

EXAMPLE 9 MODELING - *A Mixture Problem*

Pat Kuby, a pharmacist, needs 500 milliliters (mℓ) of a 10% phenobarbital solution. She has only a 5% phenobarbital solution and a 25% phenobarbital solution available. How many milliliters of each solution should she mix to obtain the desired solution?

SOLUTION First we set up a system of equations. The unknown quantities are the amount of 5% solution and the amount of the 25% solution that must be used. Let

$$x = \text{number of m}\ell \text{ of 5\% solution}$$
$$y = \text{number of m}\ell \text{ of 25\% solution}$$

We know that 500 mℓ of solution are needed. Thus,

$$x + y = 500$$

The total amount of phenobarbital in a solution is determined by multiplying the percent of phenobarbital by the number of milliliters of solution. The second equation comes from the fact that

$$\begin{pmatrix} \text{Total amount of} \\ \text{phenobarbital in} \\ \text{5\% solution} \end{pmatrix} + \begin{pmatrix} \text{total amount of} \\ \text{phenobarbital in} \\ \text{25\% solution} \end{pmatrix} = \begin{pmatrix} \text{total amount of} \\ \text{phenobarbital} \\ \text{in 10\% mixture} \end{pmatrix}$$
$$0.05x \quad + \quad 0.25y \quad = \quad 0.10(500)$$
$$\text{or} \quad 0.05x + 0.25y = 50$$

The system of equations is

$$x + y = 500$$
$$0.05x + 0.25y = 50$$

Let's solve this system of equations by using the addition method. There are various ways of eliminating one variable. To obtain integer values in the second equation, we can multiply both sides of the equation by 100. The result will be an x term of $5x$. If we multiply both sides of the first equation by -5, that will result in an x term of $-5x$. By following this process, we can eliminate the x terms from the system.

$$-5[x + y = 500] \quad \text{gives} \quad -5x - 5y = -2500$$
$$100[0.05x + 0.25y = 50] \quad \text{gives} \quad 5x + 25y = 5000$$

$$
\begin{array}{r}
-5x - 5y = -2500 \\
\underline{5x + 25y = 5000} \\
20y = 2500
\end{array}
$$

$$\frac{20y}{20} = \frac{2500}{20}$$

$$y = 125$$

Now we determine x.

$$x + y = 500$$
$$x + 125 = 500$$
$$x = 375$$

Therefore, 375 mℓ of a 5% phenobarbital solution must be mixed with 125 mℓ of a 25% phenobarbital solution to obtain 500 mℓ of a 10% phenobarbital solution. ●

Example 9 can also be solved by using substitution. Try to do so now.

SECTION 7.2 EXERCISES

CONCEPT/WRITING EXERCISES

1. In your own words, explain how to solve a system of linear equations by using the substitution method.

2. In your own words, explain how to solve a system of linear equations by using the addition method.

3. How will you know, when solving a system of linear equations by either the substitution or the addition method, whether the system is dependent?

4. How will you know, when solving a system of linear equations by either the substitution or the addition method, whether the system is inconsistent?

5. When solving the following system of equations by the substitution method, which variable, in which equation, would you choose to solve for in order to make the solution easier to obtain? Explain your answer. Do not solve the system.

$$x + 3y = 3$$
$$3x + 4y = -1$$

6. When solving the following system of equations by the addition method, what will your first step be in solving the system? Explain your answer. Do not solve the system.

$$2x + y = 6$$
$$3x + 3y = 9$$

PRACTICE THE SKILLS

In Exercises 7–24, solve the system of equations by the substitution method. If the system does not have a single ordered pair as a solution, state whether the system is inconsistent or dependent.

7. $y = x + 8$
   $y = -x + 4$

8. $y = 4x - 3$
   $y = 3x - 1$

9. $6x + 5y = 1$
   $x - 3y = 4$

10. $4x - y = 3$
    $3x - y = 1$

11. $y - x = 4$
    $x - y = 3$

12. $x + y = 3$
    $y + x = 5$

13. $3y + 2x = 4$
$3y = 6 - x$

14. $x = 5y - 12$
$x - y = 0$

15. $y - 2x = 3$
$2y = 4x + 6$

16. $y = 2$
$y + x + 3 = 0$

17. $x = y + 3$
$x = -3$

18. $x + 2y = 6$
$y = 2x + 3$

19. $y + 3x - 4 = 0$
$2x - y = 7$

20. $x + 4y = 7$
$2x + 3y = 5$

21. $x = 2y + 3$
$y = 3x - 1$

22. $x + 4y = 9$
$2x - y - 6 = 0$

23. $y = -2x + 3$
$4x + 2y = 12$

24. $2x + y = 12$
$x = -\frac{1}{2}y + 6$

In Exercises 25–40, solve the system of equations by the addition method. If the system does not have a single ordered pair as a solution, state whether the system is inconsistent or dependent.

25. $3x + y = 9$
$2x - y = 6$

26. $x + 3y = 9$
$x - 3y = -3$

27. $x + y = 12$
$x - 2y = -3$

28. $2x + y = 10$
$-2x + 2y = -16$

29. $2x - y = -4$
$-3x - y = 6$

30. $x + y = 6$
$-2x + y = -3$

31. $4x + 3y = -1$
$2x - y = -13$

32. $2x + y = 6$
$3x + y = 5$

33. $2x + y = 11$
$x + 3y = 18$

34. $5x - 2y = 11$
$-3x + 2y = 1$

35. $3x - 4y = 11$
$3x + 5y = -7$

36. $4x - 2y = 6$
$4y = 8x - 12$

37. $4x + y = 6$
$-8x - 2y = 13$

38. $2x + 3y = 6$
$5x - 4y = -8$

39. $3x - 4y = 2$
$4x + 3y = 11$

40. $6x + 6y = 1$
$4x + 9y = 4$

PROBLEM SOLVING

In Exercises 41–52, write a system of equations that can be used to solve the problem. Then solve the system and determine the answer.

41. MODELING - *Owning a Business* Sosena Milion can join a small business as a full partner and receive a salary of $12,000 per year plus 15% of the year's profit, or she can join as a sales manager with a salary of $27,000 per year plus 5% of the year's profit. What must the year's profit be for her total earnings to be the same whether she joins as a full partner or as a sales manager?

42. MODELING - *Investments* David Stewart invested $25,000 in two different corporate bonds for 1 year. One bond pays a 4.5% simple interest rate, and the other pays a 6% simple interest rate. The total annual interest David received from both bonds was $1380. Find the amount he invested in each bond. For 1 year, the simple interest on a specific corporate bond is found by multiplying the amount invested by the simple interest rate.

43. MODELING - *Pizza Orders* Pizza Corner sells medium and large specialty pizzas. A medium Meat Lovers pizza costs $10.95, and a large Meat Lovers pizza costs $14.95. One Saturday a total of 50 Meat Lovers pizzas were sold, and the receipts from the Meat Lovers pizzas were $663.50. How many medium and how many large Meat Lovers pizzas were sold?

44. MODELING - *Basketball Game* The University of Maryland women's basketball team made 45 field goals in a recent game; some were 2-pointers and some were 3-pointers. How many 2-point baskets were made and how many 3-point baskets were made if Maryland scored 101 points?

45. MODELING - *Chemical Mixture* Antonio Gonzalez is a chemist and needs 10 liters (ℓ) of a 40% hydrochloric acid solution. He discovers he is out of the 40% hydrochloric acid solution and does not have sufficient time to reorder. He checks his supply shelf and finds he has a large supply of both 25% and 50% hydrochloric acid solutions. He decides to use the 25% and 50% solutions to make 10 ℓ of a 40% solution. How many liters of the 25% solution and of the 50% solution should he mix?

46. MODELING - *Sets of Dishes* A restaurant manager purchased 100 sets of dishes. One design cost $30 per set, and another design cost $40 per set. If the manager spent $3200 on the dishes, how many sets of each design did she purchase?

47. MODELING - *Choosing a Copy Service* Lori Lanier recently purchased a high-speed copier for her home office and wants to purchase a service contract on the copier. She is considering two sources for the contract. The Economy Sales and Service Company charges $18 a month plus 2 cents per copy. Office Superstore charges $24 a month but only 1.5 cents per copy. How many copies would Lori need to make for the monthly costs of both plans to be the same?

48. MODELING - *Hardwood Floor Installation* The cost to purchase a particular type of hardwood flooring at Home Depot is $2.65 per square foot. In addition, the installation cost is $468.75. The cost to purchase the same flooring at Hardwood Guys is $3.10 per square foot. In addition, the installation cost is $412.50.

a) Determine the number of square feet of this flooring that Roberto Cruz must purchase for the total cost of the flooring and installation to be the same from both stores.

b) If Roberto needs to purchase and have installed 196 square feet of this flooring, which store would be less expensive?

49. MODELING - *Nut and Pretzel Mix* Dave Chwalik wants to purchase 20 pounds of party mix for a total of $30. To obtain the mixture, he will mix nuts that cost $3 per pound with pretzels that cost $1 per pound. How many pounds of each type of mix should he use?

50. MODELING - *Laboratory Research* Animals in an experiment are to be kept on a strict diet. Each animal is to receive, among other things, 20 g of protein and 6 g of carbohydrates. The scientist has only two food mixes of the following compositions available.

	Protein (%)	Carbohydrates (%)
Mix A	10	6
Mix B	20	2

How many grams of each mix should she use to obtain the right diet for a single animal?

51. MODELING - *Concert Ticket Prices* Finger Lakes Performing Arts Center sold 4600 tickets for a summer jazz concert. Covered amphitheatre tickets cost $27 and lawn seats cost $14. If $104,700 in ticket sales was collected for the concert, how many tickets of each type were sold?

52. MODELING - *Golf Club Membership* Membership in Oakwood Country Club costs $3000 per year and entitles a member to play a round of golf for a greens fee of $18. At Pinecrest Country Club, membership costs $2500 per year and the greens fee is $20.

a) How many rounds must a golfer play in a year for the costs at the two clubs to be the same?

b) If Tamika Johnson planned to play 30 rounds of golf in a year, which club would be the least expensive?

53. MODELING - *Car Sales* The following graph shows that General Motors' (GM's) share of the U.S. car and truck market has declined from 2001 through 2005 and is expected to continue to decline through 2010. The graph also shows that Toyota cars and trucks sales are increasing and are expected to continue to increase through 2010. GM's percentage of the U.S. market share can be modeled by the equation $y = -0.83x + 28.33$, and Toyota's market share can be modeled by the equation $y = 0.89x + 9.11$, where x represents the number of years since 2000 and $x \geq 1$. Assuming this trend continues, use the substitution method to approximate when GM's percentage of market share will equal Toyota's.

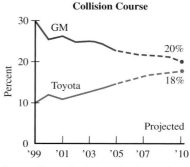

Source: Center for Automotive Research

54. MODELING - *Printing Photos* The graph on the top of page 434 shows that the number of traditional photos printed at retail photography labs has declined from 2000 through 2005. The graph also shows that the number of digital photos printed at retail photography labs has increased over this time period. The number of traditional photos printed at labs can be modeled by the equation $y = -2.3x + 29.9$, and the number of digital photos printed at labs can be modeled by the equation $y = 1.5x + 0.4$, where x represents the number of years since 2000. Assuming this trend continues, use the substitution method to approximate when the number of traditional photos printed will equal the number of digital photos printed at retail photography labs.

Prints Made at Labs

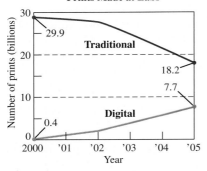

Source: Data from Photo Marketing Association International

CHALLENGE PROBLEMS/GROUP ACTIVITIES

55. Solve the following system of equations for u and v by first substituting x for $\frac{1}{u}$ and y for $\frac{1}{v}$.

$$\frac{1}{u} + \frac{2}{v} = 8$$

$$\frac{3}{u} - \frac{1}{v} = 3$$

56. Develop a system of equations that has (6, 5) as its solution. Explain how you developed your system of equations.

57. The substitution or addition methods can also be used to solve a system of three equations in three variables. Consider the following system.

$$x + y + z = 7$$
$$x - y + 2z = 9$$
$$-x + 2y + z = 4$$

The *ordered triple* (x, y, z) is the solution to the system if it satisfies all three equations.

a) Show that the ordered triple (2, 1, 4) is a solution to the system.

b) Use the substitution or addition method to determine the solution to the system. (*Hint:* Eliminate one variable by using two equations. Then eliminate the same variable by using two different equations.)

58. Construct a system of two equations that has no solution. Explain how you know the system has no solution.

59. Construct a system of two equations that has an infinite number of solutions. Explain how you know the system has an infinite number of solutions.

60. When solving a system of equations by the substitution method, a student obtained the equation $0 = 0$ and gave the solution as (0, 0). What is the student's error?

61. In parts (a)–(d), make up a system of linear equations whose solution will be the ordered pair given. *Hint:* It may be helpful to visualize possible graphs that have the given solution. There are many possible answers for each part.

a) (0, 0) b) (1, 0) c) (0, 1) d) (1, 1)

7.3 MATRICES

▲ In this section, we introduce a method to display information from a survey such as opinions of college students.

Five hundred students at the University of Delaware were asked if they were in favor of or opposed to an increase in their student fees to pay for building a new meeting room for student clubs. Each student was also asked to indicate whether he or she was a freshman, sophomore, junior, or senior. How can the responses from the survey be displayed? In this section, we will introduce a method used to display information such as responses from a survey.

A *matrix* is a rectangular array of elements. An array is a systematic arrangement of numbers or symbols in rows and columns. Matrices (the plural of matrix) may be used

DID YOU KNOW?

Matrices Are Everywhere

You are already familiar with matrices, although you may not be aware of it. The matrix is a good way to display numerical data, as illustrated on this trail sign in Yosemite National Park.

to display information and to solve systems of linear equations. The following matrix displays the responses from the survey of 500 students at the University of Delaware regarding an increase in their student fees.

Rows \ Columns	Freshmen	Sophomores	Juniors	Seniors
In favor	102	93	22	35
Opposed	82	94	23	49

The numbers in the rows and columns of a matrix are called the *elements* of the matrix. The matrix given above contains eight elements. The *dimensions* of a matrix may be indicated with the notation $r \times s$, where r is the number of rows and s is the number of columns in the matrix. Because the matrix given above has 2 rows and 4 columns, it is a 2 by 4, written 2×4, matrix. In this text, from this point onward, we use brackets, [ ], to indicate a matrix. Consider the two matrices below. A matrix that contains the same number of rows and columns is called a *square matrix*. Following is an example of a 2×2 square matrix and a 3×3 square matrix.

$$\begin{bmatrix} 2 & 3 \\ 5 & 2 \end{bmatrix} \qquad \begin{bmatrix} 4 & 6 & -1 \\ 2 & 3 & 0 \\ 5 & 2 & 1 \end{bmatrix}$$

Two matrices are equal if and only if they have the same elements in the same relative positions.

EXAMPLE 1 ***Equal Matrices***

Given $A = B$, determine x and y.

$$A = \begin{bmatrix} 3 & 7 \\ 4 & 9 \end{bmatrix}, \qquad B = \begin{bmatrix} x & 7 \\ 4 & y \end{bmatrix}$$

SOLUTION Since the matrices are equal, the corresponding elements must be the same, so $x = 3$ and $y = 9$.

Addition of Matrices

Two matrices can be added only if they have the same dimensions (same number of rows and same number of columns). To obtain the sum of two matrices with the same dimensions, add the corresponding elements of the two matrices.

EXAMPLE 2 ***Adding Matrices***

Determine $A + B$ if

$$A = \begin{bmatrix} 3 & 4 \\ -1 & 7 \end{bmatrix} \quad \text{and} \quad B = \begin{bmatrix} 2 & 8 \\ 4 & 0 \end{bmatrix}$$

SOLUTION

$$A + B = \begin{bmatrix} 3 & 4 \\ -1 & 7 \end{bmatrix} + \begin{bmatrix} 2 & 8 \\ 4 & 0 \end{bmatrix}$$

$$= \begin{bmatrix} 3 + 2 & 4 + 8 \\ -1 + 4 & 7 + 0 \end{bmatrix} = \begin{bmatrix} 5 & 12 \\ 3 & 7 \end{bmatrix}$$

EXAMPLE ③ MODELING - *Sales of Bicycles*

Peddler's Bicycle Corporation owns and operates two stores, one in Pennsylvania and one in New Jersey. The number of mountain bicycles (MB) and racing bicycles (RB) sold in each store during January through June and during July through December are indicated in the matrices that follow. We will call the matrices *A* and *B*.

$$
\begin{array}{cc}
& \textit{Pennsylvania} \\
& \begin{array}{cc} MB & RB \end{array} \\
\begin{array}{c} \text{Jan.--June} \\ \text{July--Dec.} \end{array} & \begin{bmatrix} 515 & 425 \\ 290 & 250 \end{bmatrix} = A
\end{array}
\qquad
\begin{array}{cc}
& \textit{New Jersey} \\
& \begin{array}{cc} MB & RB \end{array} \\
& \begin{bmatrix} 520 & 350 \\ 180 & 271 \end{bmatrix} = B
\end{array}
$$

Determine the total number of each type of bicycle sold by the corporation during each time period.

SOLUTION To solve the problem, we add matrices *A* and *B*.

$$
\begin{array}{c}
\begin{array}{cc} MB & RB \end{array} \\
\begin{array}{c} \text{Jan.--June} \\ \text{July--Dec.} \end{array}
\begin{bmatrix} 515 + 520 & 425 + 350 \\ 290 + 180 & 250 + 271 \end{bmatrix}
=
\begin{array}{c}
\begin{array}{cc} MB & RB \end{array} \\
\begin{bmatrix} 1035 & 775 \\ 470 & 521 \end{bmatrix}
\end{array}
\end{array}
$$

We can see from the sum matrix that during the period from January through June, a total of 1035 mountain bicycles and 775 racing bicycles were sold. During the period from July through December, a total of 470 mountain bicycles and 521 racing bicycles were sold. ●

Subtraction of Matrices

Only matrices with the same dimension may be subtracted. To do so, we subtract each entry in one matrix from the corresponding entry in the other matrix.

EXAMPLE ④ *Subtracting Matrices*

Determine $A - B$ if

$$
A = \begin{bmatrix} 3 & 6 \\ 5 & -1 \end{bmatrix} \quad \text{and} \quad B = \begin{bmatrix} 2 & -4 \\ 8 & -3 \end{bmatrix}
$$

SOLUTION

$$
\begin{aligned}
A - B &= \begin{bmatrix} 3 & 6 \\ 5 & -1 \end{bmatrix} - \begin{bmatrix} 2 & -4 \\ 8 & -3 \end{bmatrix} \\
&= \begin{bmatrix} 3 - 2 & 6 - (-4) \\ 5 - 8 & -1 - (-3) \end{bmatrix} = \begin{bmatrix} 1 & 10 \\ -3 & 2 \end{bmatrix}
\end{aligned}
$$

●

Multiplying a Matrix by a Real Number

A matrix may be multiplied by a real number by multiplying each entry in the matrix by the real number. Sometimes when we multiply a matrix by a real number, we call that real number a *scalar*.

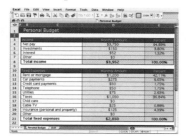
EXAMPLE ❺ *Multiplying a Matrix by a Scalar*

For matrices A and B, determine (a) $3A$ and (b) $3A - 2B$.

$$A = \begin{bmatrix} 1 & 4 \\ -3 & 5 \end{bmatrix}, \qquad B = \begin{bmatrix} -1 & 3 \\ 5 & 6 \end{bmatrix}$$

SOLUTION

a) $3A = 3\begin{bmatrix} 1 & 4 \\ -3 & 5 \end{bmatrix} = \begin{bmatrix} 3(1) & 3(4) \\ 3(-3) & 3(5) \end{bmatrix} = \begin{bmatrix} 3 & 12 \\ -9 & 15 \end{bmatrix}$

b) We determined $3A$ in part (a). Now we find $2B$.

$$2B = 2\begin{bmatrix} -1 & 3 \\ 5 & 6 \end{bmatrix} = \begin{bmatrix} 2(-1) & 2(3) \\ 2(5) & 2(6) \end{bmatrix} = \begin{bmatrix} -2 & 6 \\ 10 & 12 \end{bmatrix}$$

$$3A - 2B = \begin{bmatrix} 3 & 12 \\ -9 & 15 \end{bmatrix} - \begin{bmatrix} -2 & 6 \\ 10 & 12 \end{bmatrix}$$

$$= \begin{bmatrix} 3 - (-2) & 12 - 6 \\ -9 - 10 & 15 - 12 \end{bmatrix} = \begin{bmatrix} 5 & 6 \\ -19 & 3 \end{bmatrix}$$ •

Multiplication of Matrices

Multiplication of matrices is slightly more difficult than addition of matrices. Multiplication of matrices is possible only when the number of *columns* of the first matrix, A, is the same as the number of *rows* of the second matrix, B. We use the notation

$$A$$
$$3 \times 4$$

to indicate that matrix A has three rows and four columns. Suppose matrix A is a 3×4 matrix and matrix B is a 4×5 matrix. Then

$$\begin{array}{cc} A & B \\ 3 \times 4 & 4 \times 5 \end{array}$$

$$\boxed{\text{Same}}$$

Product matrix 3×5

This notation indicates that matrix A has four columns and matrix B has four rows. Therefore, we can multiply these two matrices. The product matrix will have the same number of rows as matrix A and the same number of columns as matrix B. Thus, the dimensions of the product matrix are 3×5.

EXAMPLE ❻ *Can These Matrices Be Multiplied?*

Determine which of the following pairs of matrices can be multiplied.

a) $A = \begin{bmatrix} 3 & 2 \\ 5 & 7 \end{bmatrix}, \qquad B = \begin{bmatrix} 0 & 6 \\ 4 & 1 \end{bmatrix}$

b) $A = \begin{bmatrix} 2 & 3 \\ 5 & 6 \end{bmatrix}, \qquad B = \begin{bmatrix} 2 & 4 & -1 \\ 6 & 8 & 0 \end{bmatrix}$

c) $A = \begin{bmatrix} 2 & 1 & 4 \\ 3 & 2 & 8 \end{bmatrix}, \qquad B = \begin{bmatrix} 2 & 1 & 3 \\ 1 & 0 & -2 \end{bmatrix}$

SOLUTION
a)

$$
\begin{array}{cc}
A & B \\
2 \times 2 & 2 \times 2
\end{array}
$$

Same

Because matrix A has two columns and matrix B has two rows, the two matrices can be multiplied. The product is a 2×2 matrix.

b)

$$
\begin{array}{cc}
A & B \\
2 \times 2 & 2 \times 3
\end{array}
$$

Same

Because matrix A has two columns and matrix B has two rows, the two matrices can be multiplied. The product is a 2×3 matrix.

c)

$$
\begin{array}{cc}
A & B \\
2 \times 3 & 2 \times 3
\end{array}
$$

Not Same

Because matrix A has three columns and matrix B has two rows, the two matrices cannot be multiplied.   ●

To explain matrix multiplication, let's use matrices A and B that follow.

$$
A = \begin{bmatrix} 3 & 2 \\ 5 & 7 \end{bmatrix} \quad \text{and} \quad B = \begin{bmatrix} 0 & 6 \\ 4 & 1 \end{bmatrix}
$$

Since A contains two rows and B contains two columns, the product matrix will contain two rows and two columns. To multiply two matrices, we use a row–column scheme of multiplying. The numbers in the *first row* of matrix A are multiplied by the numbers in the *first column* of matrix B. These products are then added to determine the entry in the product matrix.

$$
A \times B = \begin{bmatrix} 3 & 2 \\ 5 & 7 \end{bmatrix}\begin{bmatrix} 0 & 6 \\ 4 & 1 \end{bmatrix}
$$

First row   First column

$$
\begin{bmatrix} 3 & 2 \\ 5 & 7 \end{bmatrix} \qquad \begin{bmatrix} 0 & 6 \\ 4 & 1 \end{bmatrix}
$$

$$
(3 \times 0) + (2 \times 4) = 0 + 8
$$
$$
= 8
$$

The 8 is placed in the first-row, first-column position of the product matrix. The other numbers in the product matrix are obtained similarly, as illustrated in the matrix that follows.

First row   First column

$$\begin{bmatrix} 3 & 2 \\ 5 & 7 \end{bmatrix} \quad \begin{bmatrix} 0 & 6 \\ 4 & 1 \end{bmatrix}$$

$(3 \times 0) + (2 \times 4) = 8$

First row   Second column

$$\begin{bmatrix} 3 & 2 \\ 5 & 7 \end{bmatrix} \quad \begin{bmatrix} 0 & 6 \\ 4 & 1 \end{bmatrix}$$

$(3 \times 6) + (2 \times 1) = 20$

$$A \times B = \begin{bmatrix} 8 & 20 \\ 28 & 37 \end{bmatrix}$$

Second row   First column

$$\begin{bmatrix} 3 & 2 \\ 5 & 7 \end{bmatrix} \quad \begin{bmatrix} 0 & 6 \\ 4 & 1 \end{bmatrix}$$

$(5 \times 0) + (7 \times 4) = 28$

Second row   Second column

$$\begin{bmatrix} 3 & 2 \\ 5 & 7 \end{bmatrix} \quad \begin{bmatrix} 0 & 6 \\ 4 & 1 \end{bmatrix}$$

$(5 \times 6) + (7 \times 1) = 37$

We can shorten the procedure as follows.

$$\begin{aligned}
A \times B &= \begin{bmatrix} 3 & 2 \\ 5 & 7 \end{bmatrix}\begin{bmatrix} 0 & 6 \\ 4 & 1 \end{bmatrix} \\
&= \begin{bmatrix} 3(0) + 2(4) & 3(6) + 2(1) \\ 5(0) + 7(4) & 5(6) + 7(1) \end{bmatrix} \\
&= \begin{bmatrix} 8 & 20 \\ 28 & 37 \end{bmatrix}
\end{aligned}$$

In general, if

$$A = \begin{bmatrix} a & b \\ c & d \end{bmatrix} \quad \text{and} \quad B = \begin{bmatrix} e & f \\ g & h \end{bmatrix}$$

then

$$A \times B = \begin{bmatrix} a & b \\ c & d \end{bmatrix}\begin{bmatrix} e & f \\ g & h \end{bmatrix} = \begin{bmatrix} ae + bg & af + bh \\ ce + dg & cf + dh \end{bmatrix}$$

Let's do one more multiplication of matrices.

EXAMPLE 7 *Multiplying Matrices*

Determine $A \times B$ if

$$A = \begin{bmatrix} 1 & 5 \\ 4 & 7 \end{bmatrix} \quad \text{and} \quad B = \begin{bmatrix} 5 & -1 & 3 \\ 2 & 8 & 0 \end{bmatrix}$$

SOLUTION Matrix A contains two columns, and matrix B contains two rows. Thus, the matrices can be multiplied. Since matrix A contains two rows and matrix B contains three columns, the product matrix will contain two rows and three columns.

$$\begin{aligned}
A \times B &= \begin{bmatrix} 1 & 5 \\ 4 & 7 \end{bmatrix}\begin{bmatrix} 5 & -1 & 3 \\ 2 & 8 & 0 \end{bmatrix} \\
&= \begin{bmatrix} 1(5) + 5(2) & 1(-1) + 5(8) & 1(3) + 5(0) \\ 4(5) + 7(2) & 4(-1) + 7(8) & 4(3) + 7(0) \end{bmatrix} \\
&= \begin{bmatrix} 15 & 39 & 3 \\ 34 & 52 & 12 \end{bmatrix}
\end{aligned}$$

It should be noted that multiplication of matrices *is not* commutative; that is, $A \times B \neq B \times A$, except in special instances.

Square matrices have a *multiplicative identity matrix*. The multiplicative identity matrices for a 2×2 and a 3×3 matrix, denoted I, follow. Note that in any multiplicative identity matrix, 1's go diagonally from top left to bottom right and all other elements in the matrix are 0's.

$$I = \begin{bmatrix} 1 & 0 \\ 0 & 1 \end{bmatrix} \qquad I = \begin{bmatrix} 1 & 0 & 0 \\ 0 & 1 & 0 \\ 0 & 0 & 1 \end{bmatrix}$$

For any square matrix, A, $A \times I = I \times A = A$.

EXAMPLE 8 *Using the Identity Matrix in Multiplication*

Use the multiplicative identity matrix for a 2×2 matrix and matrix A to show that $A \times I = A$.

$$A = \begin{bmatrix} 4 & 3 \\ 2 & 1 \end{bmatrix}$$

SOLUTION The identity matrix is $I = \begin{bmatrix} 1 & 0 \\ 0 & 1 \end{bmatrix}$.

$$A \times I = \begin{bmatrix} 4 & 3 \\ 2 & 1 \end{bmatrix} \begin{bmatrix} 1 & 0 \\ 0 & 1 \end{bmatrix}$$

$$= \begin{bmatrix} 4(1) + 3(0) & 4(0) + 3(1) \\ 2(1) + 1(0) & 2(0) + 1(1) \end{bmatrix}$$

$$= \begin{bmatrix} 4 & 3 \\ 2 & 1 \end{bmatrix} = A$$

Verify for yourself that $I \times A = A$ as well. ●

Example 9 illustrates an application of multiplication of matrices.

EXAMPLE 9 *A Manufacturing Application*

The Fancy Frock Company manufactures three types of women's outfits: a dress, a two-piece suit (skirt and jacket), and a three-piece suit (skirt, jacket, and a vest). On a particular day, the firm produces 20 dresses, 30 two-piece suits, and 50 three-piece suits. Each dress requires 4 units of material and 1 hour of work to produce, each two-piece suit requires 5 units of material and 2 hours of work to produce, and each three-piece suit requires 6 units of material and 3 hours to produce. Use matrix multiplication to determine the total number of units of material and the total number of hours needed for that day's production.

SOLUTION Let matrix A represent the number of each type of women's outfits produced.

$$A = \begin{matrix} & \text{Dress} & \begin{matrix}\text{Two} \\ \text{piece}\end{matrix} & \begin{matrix}\text{Three} \\ \text{piece}\end{matrix} \\ & [\ 20 & 30 & 50\ ] \end{matrix}$$

The units of material and time requirements for each type are indicated in matrix B.

$$B = \begin{bmatrix} 4 & 1 \\ 5 & 2 \\ 6 & 3 \end{bmatrix} \begin{matrix} \text{Dress} \\ \text{Two piece} \\ \text{Three piece} \end{matrix}$$

with column headers: Material   Hours

The product of A and B, or $A \times B$, will give the total number of units of material and the total number of hours of work needed for that day's production.

$$A \times B = \begin{bmatrix} 20 & 30 & 50 \end{bmatrix} \begin{bmatrix} 4 & 1 \\ 5 & 2 \\ 6 & 3 \end{bmatrix}$$

$$= \begin{bmatrix} 20(4) + 30(5) + 50(6) & 20(1) + 30(2) + 50(3) \end{bmatrix}$$

$$= \begin{bmatrix} 530 & 230 \end{bmatrix}$$

Thus, a total of 530 units of material and a total of 230 hours of work are needed that day.

TIMELY TIP Matrices can only be added or subtracted if they have the same dimensions.
Matrices can only be multiplied if the number of *columns* in the first matrix is the same as the number of *rows* in the second matrix.

SECTION 7.3 EXERCISES

CONCEPT/WRITING EXERCISES

1. What is a matrix?

2. Explain how to determine the dimensions of a matrix.

3. What is a square matrix?

4. How many columns does a 3×2 matrix have?

5. How many rows does a 4×3 matrix have?

6. To add or subtract two matrices, what must be true about the dimensions of those matrices?

7. a) In your own words, explain the procedure used to add matrices.

   b) Use the procedure given in part (a) to add

   $$\begin{bmatrix} 5 & 4 & -1 \\ 3 & 9 & 5 \end{bmatrix} \text{ and } \begin{bmatrix} 2 & 5 & -6 \\ -1 & 7 & 4 \end{bmatrix}$$

8. a) In your own words, explain the procedure used to subtract matrices.

   b) Use the procedure given in part (a) to subtract

   $$\begin{bmatrix} 8 & 4 & 2 \\ 0 & -2 & 4 \end{bmatrix} \text{ from } \begin{bmatrix} 3 & -5 & 6 \\ -2 & 3 & 4 \end{bmatrix}$$

9. a) To multiply two matrices, what must be true about the dimensions of those matrices?

   b) What will be the dimensions of the product matrix when multiplying a 2×2 matrix with a 2×3 matrix?

10. a) In your own words, explain the procedure used to multiply matrices.

    b) Use the procedure given in part (a) to multiply

    $$\begin{bmatrix} 8 & -1 \\ 6 & 0 \end{bmatrix} \text{ by } \begin{bmatrix} 2 & -3 \\ 5 & -4 \end{bmatrix}$$

11. a) What is the multiplicative identity matrix for a 2×2 matrix?

b) What is the multiplicative identity matrix for a 3×3 matrix?

12. A company has three offices: East, West, and Central. Each office has five divisions. The number of employees in each division of the three offices is as follows:

East: 110, 232, 103, 190, 212
West: 107, 250, 135, 203, 189
Central: 115, 218, 122, 192, 210

Express this information in the form of a 3×5 matrix.

PRACTICE THE SKILLS

In Exercises 13–16, determine $A + B$.

13. $A = \begin{bmatrix} 1 & 8 \\ 2 & 7 \end{bmatrix}$, $B = \begin{bmatrix} -4 & 1 \\ 7 & 2 \end{bmatrix}$

14. $A = \begin{bmatrix} 5 & 6 & -7 \\ 0 & 1 & -1 \end{bmatrix}$, $B = \begin{bmatrix} -4 & 2 & -8 \\ 7 & -3 & 0 \end{bmatrix}$

15. $A = \begin{bmatrix} 2 & 1 \\ -1 & 4 \\ 6 & 0 \end{bmatrix}$, $B = \begin{bmatrix} -3 & 3 \\ -4 & 0 \\ 1 & 6 \end{bmatrix}$

16. $A = \begin{bmatrix} 2 & 6 & 3 \\ -1 & -6 & 4 \\ 3 & 0 & 5 \end{bmatrix}$, $B = \begin{bmatrix} -1 & 3 & 1 \\ 7 & -2 & 1 \\ 2 & 3 & 8 \end{bmatrix}$

In Exercises 17–20, determine $A - B$.

17. $A = \begin{bmatrix} 4 & -2 \\ -3 & 5 \end{bmatrix}$, $B = \begin{bmatrix} -2 & 5 \\ 9 & 1 \end{bmatrix}$

18. $A = \begin{bmatrix} 10 & 1 \\ 12 & 2 \\ -3 & -9 \end{bmatrix}$, $B = \begin{bmatrix} -3 & 3 \\ 4 & 7 \\ -2 & 6 \end{bmatrix}$

19. $A = \begin{bmatrix} -5 & 1 \\ 8 & 6 \\ 1 & -5 \end{bmatrix}$, $B = \begin{bmatrix} -6 & -8 \\ -10 & -11 \\ 3 & -7 \end{bmatrix}$

20. $A = \begin{bmatrix} 5 & 3 & -1 \\ 7 & 4 & 2 \\ 6 & -1 & -5 \end{bmatrix}$, $B = \begin{bmatrix} 4 & 3 & 6 \\ -2 & -4 & 9 \\ 0 & -2 & 4 \end{bmatrix}$

In Exercises 21–26,

$A = \begin{bmatrix} 1 & 2 \\ 0 & 5 \end{bmatrix}$, $B = \begin{bmatrix} 3 & 2 \\ 5 & 0 \end{bmatrix}$, and $C = \begin{bmatrix} -2 & 3 \\ 4 & 0 \end{bmatrix}$.

Determine the following.

21. $2B$

22. $-3B$

23. $2B + 4C$

24. $2B + 3A$

25. $4B - 2C$

26. $3C - 2A$

In Exercises 27–32, determine $A \times B$.

27. $A = \begin{bmatrix} 1 & 3 \\ 0 & 6 \end{bmatrix}$, $B = \begin{bmatrix} 2 & 6 \\ 8 & 4 \end{bmatrix}$

28. $A = \begin{bmatrix} 1 & -1 \\ 2 & 6 \end{bmatrix}$, $B = \begin{bmatrix} 4 & -2 \\ -3 & -2 \end{bmatrix}$

29. $A = \begin{bmatrix} 2 & 3 & -1 \\ 0 & 4 & 6 \end{bmatrix}$, $B = \begin{bmatrix} 2 \\ 4 \\ 1 \end{bmatrix}$

30. $A = \begin{bmatrix} 1 & 1 \\ 1 & 1 \end{bmatrix}$, $B = \begin{bmatrix} 1 & -1 \\ -1 & 2 \end{bmatrix}$

31. $A = \begin{bmatrix} 4 & 7 & 6 \\ -2 & 3 & 1 \\ 5 & 1 & 2 \end{bmatrix}$, $B = \begin{bmatrix} 1 & 0 & 0 \\ 0 & 1 & 0 \\ 0 & 0 & 1 \end{bmatrix}$

32. $A = \begin{bmatrix} 1 & -3 \\ 7 & 2 \end{bmatrix}$, $B = \begin{bmatrix} 0 & 4 \\ 6 & 1 \end{bmatrix}$

In Exercises 33–38, determine $A + B$ and $A \times B$. If an operation cannot be performed, explain why.

33. $A = \begin{bmatrix} 2 & 3 & 5 \\ 4 & 0 & 3 \end{bmatrix}$, $B = \begin{bmatrix} 7 & -2 & 3 \\ 2 & -1 & 1 \end{bmatrix}$

34. $A = \begin{bmatrix} 6 & 4 & -1 \\ 2 & 3 & 4 \end{bmatrix}$, $B = \begin{bmatrix} 1 & 0 \\ 4 & -1 \end{bmatrix}$

35. $A = \begin{bmatrix} 4 & 5 & 3 \\ 6 & 2 & 1 \end{bmatrix}$, $B = \begin{bmatrix} 3 & 2 \\ 4 & 6 \\ -2 & 0 \end{bmatrix}$

36. $A = \begin{bmatrix} 6 & 5 \\ 4 & 3 \\ 2 & 1 \end{bmatrix}$, $B = \begin{bmatrix} 6 & 5 \\ 4 & 3 \\ 2 & 1 \end{bmatrix}$

37. $A = \begin{bmatrix} 1 & 2 \\ 3 & 4 \end{bmatrix}$, $B = \begin{bmatrix} -3 \\ 2 \end{bmatrix}$

38. $A = \begin{bmatrix} 5 & -1 \\ 6 & -2 \end{bmatrix}$, $B = \begin{bmatrix} 1 & 2 \\ 3 & 4 \end{bmatrix}$

In Exercises 39–41, show the commutative property of addition, $A + B = B + A$, holds for matrices A and B.

39. $A = \begin{bmatrix} 3 & 5 \\ -2 & -3 \end{bmatrix}, \quad B = \begin{bmatrix} 4 & 5 \\ 6 & 7 \end{bmatrix}$

40. $A = \begin{bmatrix} 9 & 4 \\ 1 & 7 \end{bmatrix}, \quad B = \begin{bmatrix} 2 & 0 \\ -1 & 6 \end{bmatrix}$

41. $A = \begin{bmatrix} 0 & -1 \\ 3 & -4 \end{bmatrix}, \quad B = \begin{bmatrix} 8 & 1 \\ 3 & -4 \end{bmatrix}$

42. Create two matrices with the same dimensions, A and B, and show that $A + B = B + A$.

In Exercises 43–45, show that the associative property of addition, $(A + B) + C = A + (B + C)$, holds for the matrices given.

43. $A = \begin{bmatrix} 5 & 2 \\ 3 & 6 \end{bmatrix}, \quad B = \begin{bmatrix} 3 & 4 \\ -2 & 7 \end{bmatrix}, \quad C = \begin{bmatrix} -1 & 4 \\ 5 & 0 \end{bmatrix}$

44. $A = \begin{bmatrix} 4 & 1 \\ 6 & 7 \end{bmatrix}, \quad B = \begin{bmatrix} -9 & 1 \\ -7 & 2 \end{bmatrix}, \quad C = \begin{bmatrix} -6 & -3 \\ 3 & 6 \end{bmatrix}$

45. $A = \begin{bmatrix} 7 & 4 \\ 9 & -36 \end{bmatrix}, \quad B = \begin{bmatrix} 5 & 6 \\ -1 & -4 \end{bmatrix}, \quad C = \begin{bmatrix} -7 & -5 \\ -1 & 3 \end{bmatrix}$

46. Create three matrices with the same dimensions, A, B, and C, and show that $(A + B) + C = A + (B + C)$.

In Exercises 47–51, determine whether the commutative property of multiplication, $A \times B = B \times A$, holds for the matrices given.

47. $A = \begin{bmatrix} 1 & -2 \\ 4 & -3 \end{bmatrix}, \quad B = \begin{bmatrix} -1 & -3 \\ 2 & 4 \end{bmatrix}$

48. $A = \begin{bmatrix} 3 & 1 \\ 6 & 6 \end{bmatrix}, \quad B = \begin{bmatrix} 1 & 0 \\ 0 & 1 \end{bmatrix}$

49. $A = \begin{bmatrix} 4 & 2 \\ 1 & -3 \end{bmatrix}, \quad B = \begin{bmatrix} 2 & 4 \\ -3 & 1 \end{bmatrix}$

50. $A = \begin{bmatrix} -3 & 2 \\ 6 & -5 \end{bmatrix}, \quad B = \begin{bmatrix} -\frac{5}{3} & -\frac{2}{3} \\ -2 & -1 \end{bmatrix}$

51. $A = \begin{bmatrix} 3 & 2 & 1 \\ 4 & 2 & 0 \\ 0 & -2 & 5 \end{bmatrix}, \quad B = \begin{bmatrix} 1 & 0 & 0 \\ 0 & 1 & 0 \\ 0 & 0 & 1 \end{bmatrix}$

52. Create two square matrices A and B with the same dimensions, and determine whether $A \times B = B \times A$.

In Exercises 53–57, show that the associative property of multiplication, $(A \times B) \times C = A \times (B \times C)$, holds for the matrices given.

53. $A = \begin{bmatrix} 1 & 3 \\ 4 & 0 \end{bmatrix}, \quad B = \begin{bmatrix} 4 & 2 \\ 3 & 1 \end{bmatrix}, \quad C = \begin{bmatrix} 2 & 1 \\ 3 & 0 \end{bmatrix}$

54. $A = \begin{bmatrix} -2 & 3 \\ 0 & 4 \end{bmatrix}, \quad B = \begin{bmatrix} 4 & 0 \\ 3 & 5 \end{bmatrix}, \quad C = \begin{bmatrix} 3 & 4 \\ -2 & 5 \end{bmatrix}$

55. $A = \begin{bmatrix} 4 & 3 \\ -6 & 2 \end{bmatrix}, \quad B = \begin{bmatrix} 1 & 2 \\ 0 & 1 \end{bmatrix}, \quad C = \begin{bmatrix} 4 & 3 \\ 0 & -2 \end{bmatrix}$

56. $A = \begin{bmatrix} -1 & -2 \\ -3 & -4 \end{bmatrix}, \quad B = \begin{bmatrix} 1 & 0 \\ 0 & 1 \end{bmatrix}, \quad C = \begin{bmatrix} 0 & 0 \\ 0 & 0 \end{bmatrix}$

57. $A = \begin{bmatrix} 3 & 4 \\ -1 & -2 \end{bmatrix}, \quad B = \begin{bmatrix} 0 & 1 \\ 1 & 0 \end{bmatrix}, \quad C = \begin{bmatrix} 2 & 0 \\ 3 & 0 \end{bmatrix}$

58. Create three matrices, A, B, and C, and show that $(A \times B) \times C = A \times (B \times C)$.

PROBLEM SOLVING

59. **MODELING - *Purchasing Produce*** Matrix A represents the weight, in pounds, of tomatoes, onions, and carrots that Wegmans Food Markets purchased from two different local farmers in 1 week. Matrix B represents the weight, in pounds, of tomatoes, onions, and carrots that Wegmans Food Markets purchased from the same farmers the following week.

$A =$

	Tomatoes	Onions	Carrots
Chase's Farm	40	22	31
Gro-More Farms	38	25	34

$B =$

	Tomatoes	Onions	Carrots
Chase's Farm	48	36	39
Gro-More Farms	40	29	37

Use matrix addition to determine the total weight, in pounds, Wegmans purchased over the 2-week period for each item from each farm.

60. MODELING - *Sweatshirt Inventory* Dick's Sporting Goods sells sweatshirts for adults and youth. Each type of sweatshirt comes in four sizes: small, medium, large, and extra large. Matrix *A* represents the stock on hand at the beginning of a given week for each type of sweatshirt. Matrix *B* represents the stock on hand at the end of the same week for the same three types of sweatshirts.

$$A = \begin{matrix} & \text{Adult} & \text{Youth} & \\ & \begin{bmatrix} 31 & 18 \\ 39 & 16 \\ 41 & 22 \\ 34 & 21 \end{bmatrix} & \begin{matrix} \text{Small} \\ \text{Medium} \\ \text{Large} \\ \text{Extra large} \end{matrix} \end{matrix} \quad B = \begin{matrix} & \text{Adult} & \text{Youth} & \\ & \begin{bmatrix} 14 & 9 \\ 18 & 9 \\ 19 & 15 \\ 15 & 9 \end{bmatrix} & \begin{matrix} \text{Small} \\ \text{Medium} \\ \text{Large} \\ \text{Extra large} \end{matrix} \end{matrix}$$

Use matrix subtraction to determine the number of sweatshirts sold in the given week for each size of each type.

61. MODELING - *Supplying Muffins* A bakery supplies chocolate chip, blueberry, and coffee cake muffins to Java's Coffee Shop and to Spot Coffee Shop. Matrix *A* shows the number of each type of muffin, in dozens, supplied to each coffee shop in 1 week. The bakery's cost for ingredients, per dozen, for chocolate chip, blueberry, and coffee cake muffins is $3, $2, and $1.5, respectively. Matrix *B* represents the bakery's cost for ingredients, per dozen, for each type of muffin.

$$A = \begin{matrix} \text{Chocolate} & \text{Blue-} & \text{Coffee} \\ \text{chip} & \text{berry} & \text{cake} \\ \begin{bmatrix} 7 & 8.5 & 10 \\ 7.5 & 8 & 11 \end{bmatrix} & & \begin{matrix} \text{Java's Coffee Shop} \\ \text{Spot Coffee Shop} \end{matrix} \end{matrix}$$

$$B = \begin{bmatrix} 3 \\ 2 \\ 1.5 \end{bmatrix} \begin{matrix} \text{Chocolate chip} \\ \text{Blueberry} \\ \text{Coffee cake} \end{matrix}$$

Use matrix multiplication to determine the total weekly cost of ingredients for each shop.

62. MODELING - *Menu Choices* The cafeteria manager at the University of Virginia recently added three new meals that each consist of a meat, a vegetable, a salad, and a dessert to the lunch menu. The first day these new meals were offered, 35 students purchased meal 1, 28 students purchased meal 2, and 23 students purchased meal 3. Matrix *A* represents the number of students who purchased each type of meal. Matrix *B* represents the cost per serving, in cents, for each item from the three meals.

$$A = \begin{matrix} \text{Meal} & \text{Meal} & \text{Meal} \\ 1 & 2 & 3 \\ [35 & 28 & 23] \end{matrix}$$

$$B = \begin{matrix} \text{Meat} & \text{Vegetable} & \text{Salad} & \text{Dessert} \\ \begin{bmatrix} 45 & 12 & 8 & 10 \\ 52 & 8 & 6 & 15 \\ 49 & 7 & 9 & 11 \end{bmatrix} & & & \begin{matrix} \text{Meal 1} \\ \text{Meal 2} \\ \text{Meal 3} \end{matrix} \end{matrix}$$

Use matrix multiplication to determine the total cost for each item.

63. MODELING - *Cookie Company Costs* The Original Cookie Factory bakes and sells four types of cookies: chocolate chip, sugar, molasses, and peanut butter. Matrix *A* shows the number of units of various ingredients used in baking a dozen of each type of cookie.

$$A = \begin{matrix} \text{Sugar} & \text{Flour} & \text{Milk} & \text{Eggs} \\ \begin{bmatrix} 2 & 2 & \frac{1}{2} & 1 \\ 3 & 2 & 1 & 2 \\ 0 & 1 & 0 & 3 \\ \frac{1}{2} & 1 & 0 & 0 \end{bmatrix} & & & \begin{matrix} \text{Chocolate chip} \\ \text{Sugar} \\ \text{Molasses} \\ \text{Peanut butter} \end{matrix} \end{matrix}$$

The cost, in cents per cup or per egg, for each ingredient when purchased in small quantities and in large quantities is given in matrix *B*.

$$B = \begin{matrix} \text{Large} & \text{Small} \\ \text{quantities} & \text{quantities} \\ \begin{bmatrix} 10 & 12 \\ 5 & 8 \\ 8 & 8 \\ 4 & 6 \end{bmatrix} & \begin{matrix} \text{Sugar} \\ \text{Flour} \\ \text{Milk} \\ \text{Eggs} \end{matrix} \end{matrix}$$

Use matrix multiplication to find a matrix representing the comparative cost per item for small and large quantities purchased.

In Exercises 64 and 65, use the information given in Exercise 63. Suppose a typical day's order consists of 40 dozen chocolate chip cookies, 30 dozen sugar cookies, 12 dozen molasses cookies, and 20 dozen peanut butter cookies.

64. a) Express these orders as a 1×4 matrix.

b) Use matrix multiplication to determine the amount of each ingredient needed to fill the day's order.

65. Use matrix multiplication to determine the cost under the two purchase options (small and large quantities) to fill the day's order.

66. MODELING - *Food Prices* To raise money for a local charity, the Spanish Club at Montclair High School sold hot dogs, soft drinks, and candy bars for 3 days in the student lounge. The sales for the 3 days are summarized in matrix A.

$$A = \begin{bmatrix} 52 & 50 & 75 \\ 48 & 43 & 60 \\ 62 & 57 & 81 \end{bmatrix} \begin{matrix} \text{Day 1} \\ \text{Day 2} \\ \text{Day 3} \end{matrix}$$

Hot dogs, Soft drinks, Candy bars

The cost and revenue (in dollars) for hot dogs, soft drinks, and candy are summarized in matrix B.

$$B = \begin{bmatrix} 0.30 & 0.75 \\ 0.25 & 0.50 \\ 0.15 & 0.45 \end{bmatrix} \begin{matrix} \text{Hot dogs} \\ \text{Soft drinks} \\ \text{Candy bars} \end{matrix}$$

Cost, Revenue

Multiply the two matrices to form a 3×2 matrix that shows the total cost and revenue for each item.

In Exercises 67 and 68, there are many acceptable answers.

67. a) Construct two matrices A and B whose product is a 3×1 matrix. Explain how you determined your answer.

b) For your matrices, determine $A \times B$.

68. a) Construct two matrices A and B whose product is a 4×1 matrix. Explain how you determined your answer.

b) For your matrices, determine $A \times B$.

*Two matrices whose product is the multiplicative identity matrix are said to be **multiplicative inverses**. That is, if $A \times B = B \times A = I$, where I is the multiplicative identity matrix, then A and B are multiplicative inverses.*

In Exercises 69 and 70, determine whether A and B are multiplicative inverses.

69. $A = \begin{bmatrix} 5 & -2 \\ -2 & 1 \end{bmatrix}, \qquad B = \begin{bmatrix} 1 & 2 \\ 2 & 5 \end{bmatrix}$

70. $A = \begin{bmatrix} 7 & 3 \\ 2 & 1 \end{bmatrix}, \qquad B = \begin{bmatrix} 1 & -3 \\ -2 & 7 \end{bmatrix}$

CHALLENGE PROBLEMS/GROUP ACTIVITIES

In Exercises 71 and 72, determine whether the statement is true or false. Give an example to support your answer.

71. $A - B = B - A$, where A and B are any matrices.

72. For scalar a and matrices B and C, $a(B + C) = aB + aC$.

73. MODELING - *Sofa Manufacturing Costs* The number of hours of labor required to manufacture one sofa of various sizes is summarized in matrix L.

$$L = \begin{bmatrix} 1.4\text{ hr} & 0.7\text{ hr} & 0.3\text{ hr} \\ 1.8\text{ hr} & 1.4\text{ hr} & 0.3\text{ hr} \\ 2.7\text{ hr} & 2.8\text{ hr} & 0.5\text{ hr} \end{bmatrix} \begin{matrix} \text{Small} \\ \text{Medium} \\ \text{Large} \end{matrix}$$

Department: Cutting, Assembly, Packing; Sofa size

The hourly labor rates for cutting, assembly, and packing at the Ames City Plant and at the Bay City Plant are given in matrix C.

$$C = \begin{bmatrix} \$14 & \$12 \\ \$10 & \$9 \\ \$7 & \$5 \end{bmatrix} \begin{matrix} \text{Cutting} \\ \text{Assembly} \\ \text{Packaging} \end{matrix}$$

Plant: Ames City, Bay City; Department

a) What is the total labor cost for manufacturing a small-sized sofa at the Ames City plant?

b) What is the total cost for manufacturing a large-sized sofa at the Bay City plant?

c) Determine the product $L \times C$ and explain the meaning of the results.

74. Is it possible that two matrices could be added but not multiplied? If so, give an example.

75. Is it possible that two matrices could be multiplied but not added? If so, give an example.

RECREATIONAL MATHEMATICS

76. Make up two matrices A and B such that

$$A + B = \begin{bmatrix} 1 & 0 \\ 0 & 1 \end{bmatrix} \text{ and } A \times B = \begin{bmatrix} 0 & 0 \\ 0 & 0 \end{bmatrix}.$$

INTERNET/RESEARCH ACTIVITIES

77. Find an article that shows information illustrated in matrix form. Write a short paper explaining how to interpret the information provided by the matrix. Include the article with your report.

78. *Messages* The study of encoding and decoding messages is called *cryptography*. Do research on current real-life uses of cryptography and write a paper on how matrix multiplication is used to encode and decode messages. In your paper, include current real-life uses of cryptography.

7.4 SOLVING SYSTEMS OF LINEAR EQUATIONS BY USING MATRICES

▲ If you know the total cost of two different types of candy in a box and the weight of each type of candy, you can use a system of equations to determine the cost of 1 pound of each item.

Consider the following situation. One package of chocolate-covered mints and chocolate-covered cherries sells for $23. A different package of chocolate-covered mints and chocolate-covered cherries sells for $14. If you know the weight of the chocolate-covered mints and the weight of the chocolate-covered cherries in each package, would you be able to determine the cost of 1 pound of the chocolate-covered mints and the cost of 1 pound of the chocolate-covered cherries? There are several ways to determine these costs. In this section, we will illustrate a method for answering this question by using matrices.

In Section 7.3, we introduced matrices. Now we will discuss the procedure to solve a system of linear equations using matrices. We will illustrate how to solve a system of two equations and two unknowns. Systems of equations containing three equations and three unknowns (called third-order systems) and higher-order systems can also be solved by using matrices, but we will not discuss third or higher order systems in this book.

The first step in solving a system of equations using matrices is to represent the system of equations with an *augmented matrix*. An augmented matrix consists of two smaller matrices, one for the coefficients of the variables in the equations and one for the constants in the equations. To determine the augmented matrix, first write each equation in standard form, $ax + by = c$. For the system of equations below, its augmented matrix is shown to its right.

System of equations	Augmented matrix
$a_1 x + b_1 y = c_1$ $a_2 x + b_2 y = c_2$	$\begin{bmatrix} a_1 & b_1 & c_1 \\ a_2 & b_2 & c_2 \end{bmatrix}$

Following is another example.

System of equations	Augmented matrix
$x + 2y = 8$	$\begin{bmatrix} 1 & 2 & \vert & 8 \\ 3 & -1 & \vert & 7 \end{bmatrix}$
$3x - y = 7$	

Note that the vertical bar in the augmented matrix separates the numerical coefficients from the constants. The matrix is just a shortened way of writing the system of equations. Thus, we can solve a system of equations by using matrices in a manner very similar to solving a system of equations with the addition method.

To solve a system of equations by using matrices, we use *row transformations* to obtain new matrices that have the same solution as the original system. We will discuss three row transformation procedures.

PROCEDURES FOR ROW TRANSFORMATIONS

1. Any two rows of a matrix may be interchanged (which is the same as interchanging any two equations in the system of equations).

2. All the numbers in any row may be multiplied by any nonzero real number (which is the same as multiplying both sides of an equation by any nonzero real number).

3. All the numbers in any row may be multiplied by any nonzero real number, and these products may be added to the corresponding numbers in any other row of numbers.

We use row transformations to obtain an augmented matrix whose numbers to the left of the vertical bar are the same as in the *multiplicative identity matrix*. From this type of augmented matrix, we can determine the solution to the system of equations. For example, if we get

$$\begin{bmatrix} 1 & 0 & \vert & 3 \\ 0 & 1 & \vert & -2 \end{bmatrix}$$

it tells us that $1x + 0y = 3$ or $x = 3$, and $0x + 1y = -2$ or $y = -2$. Thus, the solution to the system of equations that yielded this augmented matrix is $(3, -2)$. Now let's work an example.

EXAMPLE ❶ *Using Row Transformations*

Solve the following system of equations by using matrices.

$$x + 2y = 5$$
$$3x - y = 8$$

SOLUTION First we write the augmented matrix.

$$\begin{bmatrix} 1 & 2 & \vert & 5 \\ 3 & -1 & \vert & 8 \end{bmatrix}$$

Our goal is to obtain a matrix of the form

$$\begin{bmatrix} 1 & 0 & | & c_1 \\ 0 & 1 & | & c_2 \end{bmatrix}$$

where c_1 and c_2 may represent any real numbers. It is generally easier to work by columns. Therefore, we will try to get the first column of the augmented matrix to be $\begin{smallmatrix}1\\0\end{smallmatrix}$ and the second column to be $\begin{smallmatrix}0\\1\end{smallmatrix}$. Since the element in the top left position is already a 1, we must work to change the 3 in the first column, second row, into a 0. We use row transformation procedure 3 to change the 3 into a 0. If we multiply the top row of numbers by -3 and add these products to the second row of numbers, the element in the first column, second row will become a 0:

$$\begin{bmatrix} 1 & 2 & | & 5 \\ 3 & -1 & | & 8 \end{bmatrix} \quad \text{Original augmented matrix}$$

The top row of numbers multiplied by -3 gives

$$1(-3), \qquad 2(-3), \qquad \text{and} \qquad 5(-3)$$

Now add these products to their respective numbers in row 2.

$$\begin{bmatrix} 1 & 2 & | & 5 \\ 3 + 1(-3) & -1 + 2(-3) & | & 8 + 5(-3) \end{bmatrix} = \begin{bmatrix} 1 & 2 & | & 5 \\ 0 & -7 & | & -7 \end{bmatrix}$$

The next step is to obtain a 1 in the second column, second row. At present, -7 is in that position. To change the -7 to a 1, we use row transformation procedure 2. If we multiply -7 by $-\frac{1}{7}$, the product will be 1. Therefore, we multiply all the numbers in the second row by $-\frac{1}{7}$ to get

$$\begin{bmatrix} 1 & 2 & | & 5 \\ 0(-\frac{1}{7}) & -7(-\frac{1}{7}) & | & -7(-\frac{1}{7}) \end{bmatrix} = \begin{bmatrix} 1 & 2 & | & 5 \\ 0 & 1 & | & 1 \end{bmatrix}$$

The next step is to obtain a 0 in the second column, first row. At present, a 2 is in that position. Multiplying the numbers in the second row by -2 and adding the products to the corresponding numbers in the first row gives a 0 in the desired position.

$$\begin{bmatrix} 1 + 0(-2) & 2 + 1(-2) & | & 5 + 1(-2) \\ 0 & 1 & | & 1 \end{bmatrix} = \begin{bmatrix} 1 & 0 & | & 3 \\ 0 & 1 & | & 1 \end{bmatrix}$$

We now have the desired augmented matrix:

$$\begin{bmatrix} 1 & 0 & | & 3 \\ 0 & 1 & | & 1 \end{bmatrix}$$

With this matrix, we see that $1x + 0y = 3$, or $x = 3$, and $0x + 1y = 1$, or $y = 1$. The solution to the system is $(3, 1)$.

CHECK: $x + 2y = 5$ $3x - y = 8$
              $3 + 2(1) = 5$ $3(3) - 1 = 8$
              $5 = 5$ True $8 = 8$ True   ●

Now we give a general procedure to change an augmented matrix to the desired form.

TO CHANGE AN AUGMENTED MATRIX TO THE FORM
$$\begin{bmatrix} 1 & 0 & c_1 \\ 0 & 1 & c_2 \end{bmatrix}$$

Use row transformations to:
1. Change the element in the first column, first row, to a 1.
2. Change the element in the first column, second row, to a 0.
3. Change the element in the second column, second row, to a 1.
4. Change the element in the second column, first row, to a 0.

Generally, when changing an element in the augmented matrix to a 1, we use step 2 in the row transformation box on page 447. When changing an element to a 0, we use step 3 in the row transformation box.

EXAMPLE 2 *Using Matrices to Solve a System of Equations*

Solve the following system of equations using matrices.

$$2x + 4y = 6$$
$$4x - 2y = -8$$

SOLUTION First write the augmented matrix.

$$\begin{bmatrix} 2 & 4 & 6 \\ 4 & -2 & -8 \end{bmatrix}$$

To obtain a 1 in the first column, first row, multiply the numbers in the first row by $\frac{1}{2}$.

$$\begin{bmatrix} 1 & 2 & 3 \\ 4 & -2 & -8 \end{bmatrix}$$

To obtain a 0 in the first column, second row, multiply the numbers in the first row by -4 and add the products to the corresponding numbers in the second row.

$$\begin{bmatrix} 1 & 2 & 3 \\ 4 + 1(-4) & -2 + 2(-4) & -8 + 3(-4) \end{bmatrix} = \begin{bmatrix} 1 & 2 & 3 \\ 0 & -10 & -20 \end{bmatrix}$$

To obtain a 1 in the second column, second row, multiply the numbers in the second row by $-\frac{1}{10}$.

$$\begin{bmatrix} 1 & 2 & \bigm| & 3 \\ 0(-\frac{1}{10}) & -10(-\frac{1}{10}) & \bigm| & -20(-\frac{1}{10}) \end{bmatrix} = \begin{bmatrix} 1 & 2 & \bigm| & 3 \\ 0 & 1 & \bigm| & 2 \end{bmatrix}$$

To obtain a 0 in the second column, first row, multiply the numbers in the second row by -2 and add the products to the corresponding numbers in the first row.

$$\begin{bmatrix} 1 + 0(-2) & 2 + 1(-2) & \bigm| & 3 + 2(-2) \\ 0 & 1 & \bigm| & 2 \end{bmatrix} = \begin{bmatrix} 1 & 0 & \bigm| & -1 \\ 0 & 1 & \bigm| & 2 \end{bmatrix}$$

The solution to the system of equations is $(-1, 2)$.   ●

Inconsistent and Dependent Systems

Assume that you solve a system of two equations and obtain an augmented matrix in which one row of numbers on the left side of the vertical line are all zeroes but a zero does not appear in the same row on the right side of the vertical line. This situation indicates that the system is inconsistent and has no solution. For example, a system of equations that yields the following augmented matrix is an inconsistent system.

$$\begin{bmatrix} 1 & 2 & \bigm| & 5 \\ 0 & 0 & \bigm| & 4 \end{bmatrix} \quad \text{Inconsistent system}$$

The second row of the matrix represents the equation

$$0x + 0y = 4 \quad \text{or} \quad 0 = 4$$

which is never true. This matrix represents a system of equations that has no solution.

If you obtain a matrix in which a 0 appears across an entire row, the system of equations is dependent. For example, a system of equations that yields the following matrix is a dependent system.

$$\begin{bmatrix} 1 & 5 & \bigm| & -6 \\ 0 & 0 & \bigm| & 0 \end{bmatrix} \quad \text{Dependent system}$$

The second row of the matrix represents the equation

$$0x + 0y = 0 \quad \text{or} \quad 0 = 0$$

which is always true. This matrix represents a system of equations that has an infinite number of solutions.

Triangularization Method

Another procedure to solve a system of two equations is to use row transformation procedures to obtain an augmented matrix of the form

$$\begin{bmatrix} 1 & a & \bigm| & b \\ 0 & 1 & \bigm| & c \end{bmatrix}$$

where a, b, and c represent real numbers. This procedure is called the *triangularization method* because the ones and zeroes form a triangle.

When the matrix is in this form, we can write the following system of equations.

$$\begin{array}{cc} 1x + ay = b & x + ay = b \\ 0x + 1y = c & y = c \end{array}$$

or

Using substitution, we can solve the system.

─EXAMPLE ❸ *Solving a System of Equations Using the Triangularization Method*

Solve the following system of equations using the triangularization method.

$$2x + 4y = 6$$
$$4x - 2y = -8$$

SOLUTION In Example 2, in the process of solving the system we obtained the augmented matrix

$$\left[\begin{array}{cc|c} 1 & 2 & 3 \\ 0 & 1 & 2 \end{array}\right]$$

This matrix represents the following system of equations.

$$x + 2y = 3$$
$$y = 2$$

To solve for x, we substitute 2 for y in the equation

$$x + 2y = 3$$
$$x + 2(2) = 3$$
$$x + 4 = 3$$
$$x = -1$$

Thus, the solution to the system is $(-1, 2)$, as was obtained in Example 2. You may use either method when solving a system of equations with matrices unless your instructor specifies otherwise.

●

SECTION 7.4   EXERCISES

CONCEPT/WRITING EXERCISES

1. **a)** What is an augmented matrix?

   b) Determine the augmented matrix for the following system.
$$x + 3y = 7$$
$$2x - y = 4$$

2. In your own words, write the three row transformation procedures.

3. How will you know, when solving a system of equations by using matrices, whether the system is dependent?

4. How will you know, when solving a system of equations by using matrices, whether the system is inconsistent?

5. If you obtained the following augmented matrix when solving a system of equations, what would be your next step in completing the process? Explain your answer.
$$\begin{bmatrix} 1 & 3 & | & 5 \\ 0 & -2 & | & 1 \end{bmatrix}$$

6. If you obtained the following augmented matrix when solving a system of equations, what would be your next step in completing the process? Explain your answer.
$$\begin{bmatrix} 1 & -2 & | & 1 \\ 0 & 1 & | & 3 \end{bmatrix}$$

PRACTICE THE SKILLS

In Exercises 7–20, use matrices to solve the system of equations.

7. $x + 3y = 7$
   $-x + y = 1$

8. $x - y = 2$
   $2x - y = 4$

9. $x - 2y = -1$
   $2x + y = 8$

10. $x + y = -1$
    $2x + 3y = -5$

11. $2x - 5y = -6$
    $-4x + 10y = 12$

12. $x + y = 5$
    $3x - y = 3$

13. $2x - 3y = 10$
    $2x + 2y = 5$

14. $x + 3y = 1$
    $-2x + y = 5$

15. $4x + 2y = 6$
    $5x + 4y = 9$

16. $4x + 2y = -10$
    $-2x + y = -7$

17. $-3x + 6y = 5$
    $2x - 4y = 8$

18. $2x - 5y = 10$
    $3x + y = 15$

19. $3x + y = 13$
    $x + 3y = 15$

20. $4x - 3y = 7$
    $-2x + 5y = 14$

PROBLEM SOLVING

In Exercises 21–24, use matrices to solve the problem.

21. **MODELING -** *Selling Baseball Caps* Lids sells fitted baseball caps for $35 and stretch-fit baseball caps for $25. Recently, the company sold a total of 32 baseball caps in a single day. If the baseball cap receipts for the day totaled $980, how many of each type of baseball cap were sold?

22. **MODELING -** *TV Dimensions* Vita Gunta just purchased a new high-definition television. She noticed that the perimeter of the screen is 124 in. The width of the screen is 8 in. greater than its height. Find the dimensions of the screen.

23. **MODELING -** *On the Job* Peoplepower, Inc., a daily employment agency, charges $10 per hour for a truck driver and $8 per hour for a laborer. On a certain job, the laborer worked two more hours than the truck driver, and together they cost $144. How many hours did each work?

24. **MODELING -** *Snack Mix* If Andy DaLora buys 2 lb of caramel corn and 3 lb of mixed nuts, his total cost would be $27. If he buys 1 lb of caramel corn and 2 lb of mixed nuts, his total cost would be $17. Find the cost of 1 lb of caramel corn and 1 lb of mixed nuts.

25. MODELING - *Fill in the Missing Information* Hammer-Mill sells two types of laser printer paper to office supply stores. The premium laser paper sells for $6 a ream, and the paper for color laser printers sells for $7.50 a ream. HammerMill received an order for 200 reams of paper and a check for $1275. When placing the order, the office supply store clerk failed to specify the number of reams of each type of paper being ordered. Can HammerMill fill the order with the information given? If so, determine the number of reams of premium laser paper and the number of reams of paper for the color laser printer the clerk ordered.

INTERNET/RESEARCH ACTIVITY

26. Do research and write a paper on the development of matrices. In your paper, cover the contributions of James Joseph Sylvester, Arthur Cayley, and William Rowan Hamilton. References include history of mathematics books, encyclopedias, and the Internet.

7.5 SYSTEMS OF LINEAR INEQUALITIES

▲ A system of inequalities may be used to determine how many camcorders should be stocked to satisfy store requirements.

Assume that Circuit City sells only two different camcorders, one made by Panasonic and one made by Sony. Based on demand, the store must stock at least twice as many Panasonic units as Sony units. The costs to the store for the two camcorders are $300 and $600, respectively. The management wants at least 10 Panasonic camcorders and 5 Sony camcorders in inventory at all times and does not want more than $18,000 in camcorder inventory at any one time. To determine how many camcorders of each type should be stocked to satisfy the store's requirements, we could set up and solve a system of linear inequalities. In this section, we will explore the techniques of finding the solution set to a system of linear inequalities.

The solution set of a system of linear inequalities is the set of points that satisfy all inequalities in the system. The solution set of a system of linear inequalities may consist of infinitely many ordered pairs. To determine the solution set to a system of linear inequalities, graph each inequality on the same axes. The ordered pairs common to all the inequalities are the solution set to the system.

PROCEDURE FOR SOLVING A SYSTEM OF LINEAR INEQUALITIES

1. Select one of the inequalities. Replace the inequality symbol with an equal sign and draw the graph of the equation. Draw the graph with a dashed line if the inequality is $<$ or $>$ and with a solid line if the inequality is $\leq$ or $\geq$.

2. Select a test point on one side of the line and determine whether the point is a solution to the inequality. If so, shade the area on the side of the line containing the point. If the point is not a solution, shade the area on the other side of the line.

3. Repeat steps 1 and 2 for the other inequality.

4. The intersection of the two shaded areas and any solid line common to both inequalities form the solution set to the system of inequalities.

┌─ **EXAMPLE ❶** *Solving a System of Inequalities*

Graph the following system of inequalities and indicate the solution set.

$$x + y < 5$$
$$x - y < 3$$

SOLUTION Graph both inequalities on the same axes. First draw the graph of $x + y < 5$. When drawing the graph, remember to use a dashed line, since the inequality is "less than" (see Fig. 7.10a). If you have forgotten how to graph inequalities, review Section 6.8. Shade the half plane that satisfies the inequality $x + y < 5$.

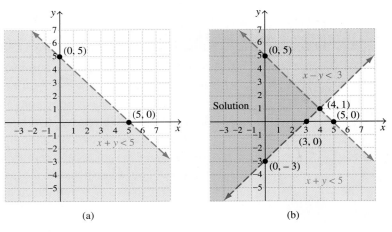

(a)   (b)

Figure 7.10

Now, on the same axes, shade the half plane that satisfies the inequality $x - y < 3$ (see Fig. 7.10b). The solution set consists of all the points common to the two shaded half planes. These are the points in the region on the graph containing both color shadings. In Figure 7.10(b), we have indicated this region in green. Figure 7.10(b) shows that the two lines intersect at $(4, 1)$. This ordered pair can also be found by any of the algebraic methods discussed in Sections 7.2 and 7.3.   ●

┌─ **EXAMPLE ❷** *Solving a System of Linear Inequalities*

Graph the following system of inequalities and indicate the solution set.

$$4x - 2y \geq 8$$
$$2x + 3y < 6$$

SOLUTION Graph the inequality $4x - 2y \geq 8$. Remember to use a solid line because the inequality is "greater than or equal to"; see Fig. 7.11(a).

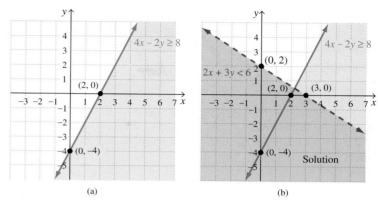

Figure 7.11

On the same set of axes, draw the graph of $2x + 3y < 6$. Use a dashed line since the inequality is "less than"; see Fig. 7.11(b). The solution is the region of the graph that contains both color shadings and the part of the solid line that satisfies the inequality $2x + 3y < 6$. Note that the point of intersection of the two lines is not a part of the solution set. •

EXAMPLE ❸ *Another System of Inequalities*

Graph the following system of inequalities and indicate the solution set.

$$x \geq -2$$
$$y < 3$$

SOLUTION Graph the inequality $x \geq -2$; see Fig. 7.12(a). On the same axes, graph the inequality $y < 3$; see Fig. 7.12(b). The solution set is that region of the graph that is shaded in both colors and the part of the solid line that satisfies the inequality $y < 3$. The point of intersection of the two lines, $(-2, 3)$, is not part of the solution because it does not satisfy the inequality $y < 3$.

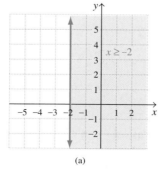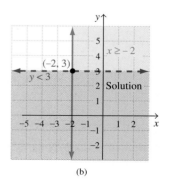

Figure 7.12

SECTION 7.5   EXERCISES

CONCEPT/WRITING EXERCISES

1. What is the solution set of a system of linear inequalities?

2. If in a system of inequalities one inequality contains $\leq$ and the other inequality contains $>$, is the point of intersection of the two boundary lines of the inequalities in the solution set? Explain.

3. If in a system of inequalities one inequality contains $\leq$ and the other inequality contains $\geq$, is the point of intersection of the two boundary lines of the inequalities in the solution set? Explain.

4. If in a system of inequalities one inequality contains $<$ and the other inequality contains $>$, is the point of intersection of the two boundary lines of the inequalities in the solution set? Explain.

PRACTICE THE SKILLS

In Exercises 5–20, graph the system of linear inequalities and indicate the solution set.

5. $y > x + 4$
   $y > 3x$

6. $y > -3x$
   $y \leq -2x + 1$

7. $x + y \geq 1$
   $x - y > 3$

8. $x + y < 4$
   $3x + 2y \geq 6$

9. $x - y < 4$
   $x + y < 5$

10. $3x - y \leq 6$
    $x - y > 4$

11. $x + 2y \geq 4$
    $3x - y \geq -6$

12. $x - 3y \leq 3$
    $x + 2y \geq 4$

13. $y \leq 3x$
    $x \geq 3y$

14. $y \leq 4$
    $x - y < 1$

15. $x \leq 0$
    $y \leq 0$

16. $x \geq 1$
    $y \leq 1$

17. $4x + 2y > 8$
    $x \geq y - 1$

18. $5y > 3x + 10$
    $3y < -2x - 3$

19. $3x + 2y > 8$
    $x < 5y - 5$

20. $3x \geq 2y + 10$
    $x \leq y + 8$

CHALLENGE PROBLEMS/GROUP ACTIVITIES

21. **MODELING - *Craft Sales*** Julie Gratien makes small and large decorated bowls. It takes Julie 20 minutes to decorate a small bowl and 30 minutes to decorate a large bowl. She

can spend no more than a total of 600 minutes decorating the bowls. The number of small bowls made needs to be at least twice the number of large bowls made. Julie must also make at least 10 small bowls and 5 large bowls.

a) Using x to represent the number of small bowls made and y to represent the number of large bowls made, translate the problem into a system of linear inequalities.

b) Solve the system graphically. Graph sales for small bowls on the horizontal axis and sales for large bowls on the vertical axis.

c) Select a point in the solution set. Determine the sales for the two types of bowls that corresponds to the point selected.

22. **MODELING - *Special Diet*** Ruben Gonzalez is on a special diet. He must consume fewer than 500 calories at a meal that consists of one serving of chicken and one serving of rice. The meal must contain at least 150 calories from each source.

a) Using x to represent the number of calories from chicken and y to represent the number of calories from rice, translate the problem into a system of linear inequalities.

b) Solve the system graphically. Graph calories from chicken on the horizontal axis and calories from rice on the vertical axis.

c) There are about 180 calories in 3 oz of chicken and about 200 calories in 8 oz of rice. Select a point in the solution set. For the point selected, determine the number of ounces of chicken and the number of ounces of rice to be served.

23. Write a system of linear inequalities whose solution is the second quadrant, including the axes.

24. a) Do all systems of linear inequalities have solutions? Explain.

b) Write a system of inequalities that has no solution.

25. Can a system of linear inequalities have a solution set consisting of a single point? Explain.

26. Can a system of linear inequalities have as its solution set all the points on the coordinate plane? Explain your answer, giving an example to support it.

27. Write a system of linear inequalities that has the ordered pair (0, 0) as its only solution. There are many possible answers.

28. Write a system of linear inequalities that has the following ordered pairs as some of its solutions. There are many possible answers.

$$\dots(-3, -3), (-2, -2), (-1, -1), (0, 0), (1, 1), (2, 2), (3, 3),\dots$$

7.6   LINEAR PROGRAMMING

▲ Linear programming can be used to determine how many skateboards and in-line skates a company should make in order to maximize profit.

Consider a small company that manufactures skateboards and in-line skates. The maximum number of skateboards and pairs of in-line skates that can be produced per day is 20. To meet demand, the company must make at least 2 pairs of in-line skates per day. The company wants to make at least 3 skateboards but no more than 6 skateboards per day. The company makes a profit of $25 on a skateboard and a profit of $20 on a pair of in-line skates. How many skateboards and pairs of in-line skates should be made to maximize profit while satisfying all requirements? In this section, we will discuss how to solve questions such as this one by using a method called linear programming.

Government, business, and industry often require decision makers to find cost-effective solutions to a variety of problems. Linear programming provides businesses and governments with a mathematical form of decision making that makes the most efficient use of time and resources. Linear programming often serves as a method of expressing the relationships in many of these problems and uses systems of linear inequalities.

The typical linear programming problem has many variables and is generally so lengthy that it is solved on a computer by a technique called the *simplex method*. The simplex method was developed in the 1940s by George B. Dantzig (see the Profile in Mathematics on page 459). Linear programming is used to solve problems in the social sciences, health care, land development, nutrition, military, and many other fields.

We will not discuss the simplex method in this textbook. We will merely give a brief introduction to how linear programming works. You can find a detailed explanation in books on finite mathematics.

In a linear programming problem, there are restrictions called *constraints*. Each constraint is represented as a linear inequality. The list of constraints forms a system of linear inequalities. When the system of inequalities is graphed, we often obtain a region bounded on all sides by line segments (Fig. 7.13). This region is called the *feasible region*. The points where two or more boundaries intersect are called the *vertices* of the feasible region. The points on the boundary of the region and the points inside the feasible region are the solution set for the system of inequalities.

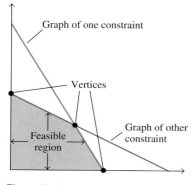

Figure 7.13

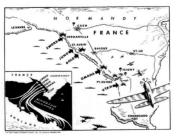
For each linear programming problem, we will obtain a formula of the form $K = Ax + By$, called the *objective function*. The objective function is the formula for the quantity K (or some other variable) that we want to maximize or minimize. The values we substitute for x and y determine the value of K. From the information given in the problem, we determine the real number constants A and B. In a particular linear programming problem, a typical equation that might be used to find the maximum profit, P, is $P = 3x + 7y$. We would find the maximum profit by substituting the ordered pairs (x, y) of the vertices of the feasible region into the formula $P = 3x + 7y$ to see which ordered pair yields the greatest value of P and therefore the maximum profit. The ordered pair that yields the smallest value of P determines the minimum profit.

Linear programming is used to determine which ordered pair will yield the maximum (or minimum) value of the variable that is being maximized (or minimized). The fundamental principle of linear programming provides a rule for finding those maximum and minimum values.

> ### FUNDAMENTAL PRINCIPLE OF LINEAR PROGRAMMING
> If the objective function, $K = Ax + By$, is evaluated at each point in a feasible region, the maximum and minimum values of the equation occur at vertices of the region.

Linear programming is a powerful tool for finding the maximum and minimum values of an objective function. Using the fundamental principle of linear programming, we are quickly able to determine the maximum and minimum values of an objective function by using just a few of the infinitely many points in the feasible region.

Example 1 illustrates how the fundamental principle is used to solve a linear programming problem.

EXAMPLE ❶ MODELING - *Using the Fundamental Principle of Linear Programming*

The Ric Shaw Chair company makes two types of rocking chairs, a plain chair and a fancy chair. Each rocking chair must be assembled and then finished. The plain chair takes 4 hours to assemble and 4 hours to finish. The fancy chair takes 8 hours to assemble and 12 hours to finish. The company can provide at most 160 worker-hours of assembling and 180 worker-hours of finishing a day. If the profit on a plain chair is $40 and the profit on a fancy chair is $65, how many rocking chairs of each type should the company make per day to maximize profits? What is the maximum profit?

SOLUTION From the information given, we know the following facts.

	Assembly Time (hr)	Finishing Time (hr)	Profit ($)
Plain chair	4	4	40.00
Fancy chair	8	12	65.00

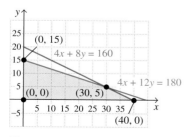

Figure 7.14

Let

$$x = \text{the number of plain chairs made per day}$$
$$y = \text{the number of fancy chairs made per day}$$
$$40x = \text{profit on the plain chairs}$$
$$65y = \text{profit on the fancy chairs}$$
$$P = \text{the total profit}$$

The total profit is the sum of the profit on the plain chairs and the profit on the fancy chairs. Since $40x$ is the profit on the plain chairs and $65y$ is the profit on the fancy chairs, the profit formula is $P = 40x + 65y$.

The maximum profit, P, is dependent on several conditions, called *constraints*. The number of chairs manufactured each day cannot be a negative amount. This condition gives us the constraints $x \geq 0$ and $y \geq 0$. Another constraint is determined by the total number of hours allocated for assembling. Four hours are needed to assemble the plain chair, so the total number of hours per day to assemble x plain chairs is $4x$. Eight hours are required to assemble a fancy chair, so the total number of hours needed to assemble y fancy chairs is $8y$. The maximum number of hours allocated for assembling is 160 per day. Thus, the third constraint is $4x + 8y \leq 160$. The final constraint is determined by the number of hours allotted for finishing. Finishing a plain chair takes 4 hours, or $4x$ hours to finish x plain chairs. Finishing a fancy chair takes 12 hours, or $12y$ hours to finish y fancy chairs. The total number of hours allotted for finishing is 180 per day. Therefore, the fourth constraint is $4x + 12y \leq 180$. Thus, the four constraints are

$$x \geq 0$$
$$y \geq 0$$
$$4x + 8y \leq 160$$
$$4x + 12y \leq 180$$

The list of constraints is a system of linear inequalities in two variables. The solution to the system of inequalities is the set of ordered pairs that satisfy all the constraints. These points are plotted in Fig. 7.14. Note that the solution to the system consists of the colored region and the solid boundaries. The points (0, 0), (0, 15), (30, 5), and (40, 0) are the points at which the boundaries intersect. These points can also be found by the addition or substitution method described in Section 7.2.

The goal in this example is to maximize the profit. The objective function is given by the profit formula $P = 40x + 65y$. According to the fundamental principle, the maximum profit will be found at one of the vertices of the feasible region.

Calculate P for each one of the vertices.

$$P = 40x + 65y$$

At (0, 0), $P = 40(0) + 65(0) = 0$

At (0, 15), $P = 40(0) + 65(15) = 975$

At (30, 5), $P = 40(30) + 65(5) = 1525$

At (40, 0), $P = 40(40) + 65(0) = 1600$

The maximum profit is at (40, 0), which means that the company should manufacture 40 plain rocking chairs and no fancy rocking chairs. The maximum profit would be $1600. The minimum profit would be at (0, 0), when no rocking chairs of either style were manufactured. ●

A variation of the problem in Example 1 could be that the company knows that it cannot make more than 15 plain rocking chairs per day. With this additional constraint, we now have the following set of constraints.

$$x \geq 0$$
$$x \leq 15$$
$$y \geq 0$$
$$4x + 8y \leq 160$$
$$4x + 12y \leq 180$$

The graph of the feasible region of these constraints is shown in Fig. 7.15.

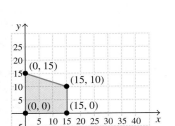

Figure 7.15

The vertices of the feasible region are (0, 0), (0, 15), (15, 10), and (15, 0). To determine the maximum profit, we calculate P for each of these vertices:

$$P = 40x + 65y$$

At (0, 0),	$P = 40(0) + 65(0) = 0$
At (0, 15),	$P = 40(0) + 65(15) = 975$
At (15, 10),	$P = 40(15) + 65(10) = 1250$
At (15, 0),	$P = 40(15) + 65(0) = 600$

This set of constraints gives the maximum profit of $1250 when the company manufactures 15 plain rocking chairs and 10 fancy rocking chairs.

EXAMPLE ② MODELING - *Washers and Dryers, Maximizing Profit*

The Admiral Appliance Company makes washers and dryers. The company must manufacture at least one washer per day to ship to one of its customers. No more than 6 washers can be manufactured due to production restrictions. The number of dryers manufactured cannot exceed 7 per day. Also, the number of washers manufactured cannot exceed the number of dryers manufactured per day. If the profit on each washer is $20 and the profit on each dryer is $30, how many of each appliance should the company make per day to maximize profits? What is the maximum profit?

SOLUTION Let

$$x = \text{the number of washers manufactured per day}$$
$$y = \text{the number of dryers manufactured per day}$$
$$20x = \text{the profit on washers}$$
$$30y = \text{the profit on dryers}$$
$$P = \text{the total profit}$$

The maximum profit is dependent on several constraints. The number of appliances manufactured each day cannot be a negative amount. This condition gives us the constraints $x \geq 0$ and $y \geq 0$. The company must manufacture at least one washer

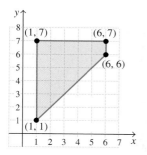

Figure 7.16

per day; therefore, $x \geq 1$. No more than 6 washers can be manufactured per day; therefore, $x \leq 6$. No more than 7 dryers can be manufactured per day; therefore, $y \leq 7$. The number of washers cannot exceed the number of dryers manufactured per day; therefore, $x \leq y$. Thus, the six constraints are

$$x \geq 0, y \geq 0, x \geq 1, x \leq 6, y \leq 7, x \leq y$$

In this example, the objective function is the profit formula. Since $20x$ is the profit on x washers and $30y$ is the profit on y dryers, the profit formula is $P = 20x + 30y$. Figure 7.16 shows the feasible region. The feasible region consists of the shaded region and the boundaries. The vertices of the feasible region are at $(1, 1)$, $(1, 7)$, $(6, 7)$, and $(6, 6)$.

Next we calculate the value of the objective function, P, at each one of the vertices.

$$P = 20x + 30y$$

At $(1, 1)$, $P = 20(1) + 30(1) = 50$

At $(1, 7)$, $P = 20(1) + 30(7) = 230$

At $(6, 7)$, $P = 20(6) + 30(7) = 330$

At $(6, 6)$, $P = 20(6) + 30(6) = 300$

The maximum profit is at $(6, 7)$. Therefore, the company should manufacture 6 washers and 7 dryers to maximize its profit. The maximum profit is $330. •

Use the following steps to solve a linear programming problem.

SOLVING A LINEAR PROGRAMMING PROBLEM

1. Determine all necessary constraints.

2. Determine the objective function.

3. Graph the constraints and determine the feasible region.

4. Determine the vertices of the feasible region.

5. Determine the value of the objective function at each vertex.

The solution is determined by the values in the ordered pair of the vertex that yields the maximum or minimum value of the objective function.

SECTION 7.6 EXERCISES

CONCEPT/WRITING EXERCISES

1. What are constraints in a linear programming problem? How are they represented?

2. In a linear programming problem, how is a feasible region formed?

3. What are the points of intersection of the boundaries of the feasible region called?

4. a) What is the general form of the objective function?

   b) What is the purpose of the objective function in a linear programming problem?

5. In your own words, state the fundamental principle of linear programming.

6. A profit function is $P = 4x + 6y$ and the vertices of the feasible region are $(1, 1)$, $(1, 4)$, $(5, 1)$, and $(7, 1)$. Determine the maximum profit. Explain how you determined your answer.

PRACTICE THE SKILLS

Exercises 7–10 show a feasible region and its vertices. Find the maximum and minimum values of the given objective function.

7. $K = 6x + 4y$

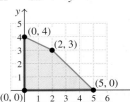

8. $K = 10x + 8y$

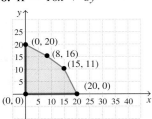

9. $K = 2x + 3y$

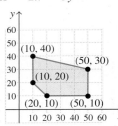

10. $K = 40x + 50y$

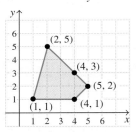

In Exercises 11–16, a set of constraints and a profit formula are given.

a) *Draw the graph of the constraints and find the vertices of the feasible region.*

b) *Use the vertices as obtained in part (a) to determine the maximum and minimum profit.*

11. $x + y \leq 6$
$2x + y \leq 8$
$x \geq 0$
$y \geq 0$
$P = 4x + 5y$

12. $2x + 3y \leq 8$
$4x + 2y \leq 8$
$x \geq 0$
$y \geq 0$
$P = 2x + 6y$

13. $x + y \leq 4$
$x + 3y \leq 6$
$x \geq 0$
$y \geq 0$
$P = 7x + 6y$

14. $x + y \leq 50$
$x + 3y \leq 90$
$x \geq 0$
$y \geq 0$
$P = 20x + 40y$

15. $2x + 3y \geq 18$
$4x + 2y \leq 20$
$x \geq 1$
$y \geq 4$
$P = 2.20x + 1.65y$

16. $x + 2y \leq 14$
$7x + 4y \geq 28$
$x \geq 2$
$x \leq 10$
$y \geq 1$
$P = 15.13x + 9.35y$

PROBLEM SOLVING

17. MODELING - *Stocking Cameras* A small electronics store stocks two brands of digital cameras, Kodak and Canon. The manager does not want to keep more than 24 cameras on hand. The number of Kodak cameras stocked needs to be at least twice the number of Canon cameras stocked. She also wants to stock at least 4 Canon cameras. Assume that the store makes a profit of $40 on a Kodak camera and a profit of $55 on a Canon camera.

a) List the constraints.

b) Determine the objective function for maximizing profit.

c) Graph the set of constraints.

d) Determine the vertices of the feasible region.

e) How many cameras of each brand should the manager stock to maximize the store's profit?

f) Determine the maximum profit.

18. MODELING - *On Wheels* The Boards and Blades Company manufactures skateboards and in-line skates. The company can produce a maximum of 20 skateboards and pairs of in-line skates per day. It makes a profit of $25 on a skateboard and a profit of $20 on a pair of in-line skates. The company's planners want to make at least 3 skateboards but not more than 6 skateboards per day. To keep customers happy, they must make at least 2 pairs of in-line skates per day.

a) List the constraints.

b) Determine the objective function.

c) Graph the set of constraints.

d) Determine the vertices of the feasible region.

e) How many skateboards and pairs of in-line skates should be made to maximize the profit?

f) Find the maximum profit.

▲ Central Park, New York City, see Exercise 18

19. MODELING - *Paint Production* A paint supplier has two machines that produce both indoor paint and outdoor paint. To meet one of its contractual obligations, the company must produce at least 60 gal of indoor paint and 100 gal of outdoor paint. Machine I makes 3 gal of indoor paint and 10 gal of outdoor paint per hour. Machine II makes 4 gal of indoor paint and 5 gal of outdoor paint per hour. It costs $28 per hour to run machine I and $33 per hour to run machine II.

   a) List the constraints.

   b) Determine the objective function.

   c) Graph the set of constraints.

   d) Determine the vertices of the feasible region.

   e) How many hours should each machine be operated to fulfill the contract at a minimum cost?

   f) Determine the minimum cost.

CHALLENGE PROBLEMS/GROUP ACTIVITIES

20. MODELING - *Hot Dog Profits* To make one package of all-beef hot dogs, a manufacturer uses 1 lb of beef; to make one package of regular hot dogs, the manufacturer uses $\frac{1}{2}$ lb each of beef and pork. The profit on the all-beef hot dogs is 40 cents per pack and the profit on regular hot dogs is 30 cents per pack. If there are 200 lb of beef and 150 lb of pork available, how many packs of all-beef and regular hot dogs should the manufacturer make to maximize the profit? What is the profit?

21. MODELING - *Car Seats and Strollers* A company makes car seats and strollers. Each car seat and stroller passes through three processes: assembly, safety testing, and packaging. A car seat requires 1 hr in assembly, 2 hr in safety testing, and 1 hr in packaging. A stroller requires 3 hr in assembly, 1 hr in safety testing, and 1 hr in packaging. Employee work schedules allow for 24 hr per day for assembly, 16 hr per day for safety testing, and 10 hr per day for packaging. The profit for each car seat is $25, and the profit for each stroller is $35. How many units of each type should the company make per day to maximize the profit? What is the maximum profit?

22. MODELING - *Special Diet* A dietitian prepares a special diet using two food groups, *A* and *B*. Each ounce of food group *A* contains 3 units of vitamin C and 1 unit of vitamin D. Each ounce of food group *B* contains 1 unit of vitamin C and 2 units of vitamin D. The minimum daily requirements with this diet are at least 9 units of vitamin C and at least 8 units of vitamin D. Each ounce of food group *A* costs 50 cents, and each ounce of food group *B* costs 30 cents.

   a) List the constraints.

   b) Determine the objective function for minimizing cost.

   c) Graph the set of constraints.

   d) Determine the vertices of the feasible region.

   e) How many ounces of each food group should be used to meet the daily requirements and minimize the cost?

   f) Determine the minimum cost.

INTERNET/RESEARCH ACTIVITY

23. *Operations research* draws on several disciplines, including mathematics, probability theory, statistics, and economics. George B. Dantzig (see the Profile in Mathematics on page 459) was one of the key people in developing operations research. Write a paper on Dantzig and his contributions to operations research and linear programming.

CHAPTER 7 SUMMARY

IMPORTANT FACTS

SYSTEMS OF EQUATIONS

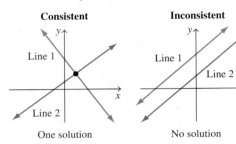

Consistent

Line 1

Line 2

One solution

Inconsistent

Line 1

Line 2

No solution

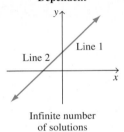

Dependent

Line 1

Line 2

Infinite number
of solutions

METHODS OF SOLVING SYSTEMS OF EQUATIONS

1. Graphing
2. Substitution
3. Addition (or elimination) method

MULTIPLICATIVE IDENTITY MATRIX

$$\begin{bmatrix} 1 & 0 \\ 0 & 1 \end{bmatrix}, \begin{bmatrix} 1 & 0 & 0 \\ 0 & 1 & 0 \\ 0 & 0 & 1 \end{bmatrix}, \dots$$

FUNDAMENTAL PRINCIPLE OF LINEAR PROGRAMMING
If the objective function $K = Ax + By$ is evaluated at each point in a feasible region, the maximum and minimum values of the equation occur at vertices of the region.

CHAPTER 7 REVIEW EXERCISES

7.1

In Exercises 1–4, solve the system of equations graphically. If the system does not have a single ordered pair as a solution, state whether the system is inconsistent or dependent.

1. $x = 2$
$y = -1$

2. $x + 2y = 4$
$2x - 2y = 2$

3. $x = 3$
$x + y = 5$

4. $x + 2y = 5$
$2x + 4y = 4$

In Exercises 5–8, determine without graphing whether the system of equations has exactly one solution, no solution, or an infinite number of solutions.

5. $y = \frac{1}{3}x + 5$
$3y - x = 15$

6. $2x + y = 4$
$y = -2x + 6$

7. $6y - 2x = 20$
$4y + 2x = 10$

8. $2x - 4y = 8$
$-2x + y = 6$

7.2

In Exercises 9–12, solve the system of equations by the substitution method. If the system does not have a single ordered pair as a solution, state whether the system is inconsistent or dependent.

9. $-x + y = -2$
$x + 2y = 5$

10. $x - 2y = 9$
$y = 2x - 3$

11. $2x - y = 4$
$3x - y = 2$

12. $3x + y = 1$
$3y = -9x - 4$

In Exercises 13–18, solve the system of equations by the addition method. If the system does not have a single ordered pair as a solution, state whether the system is inconsistent or dependent.

13. $x - 2y = 8$
$2x + y = 6$

14. $2x + y = 2$
$-3x - y = 5$

15. $x + y = 2$
$x + 3y = -2$

16. $4x - 8y = 16$
$x - 2y = 4$

17. $3x - 4y = 10$
$5x + 3y = 7$

18. $3x + 4y = 6$
$2x - 3y = 4$

7.3

Given $A = \begin{bmatrix} 1 & -3 \\ 2 & 4 \end{bmatrix}$ and $B = \begin{bmatrix} -2 & -5 \\ 6 & 3 \end{bmatrix}$, determine the following.

19. $A + B$

20. $A - B$

21. $2A$

22. $2A - 3B$

23. $A \times B$

24. $B \times A$

7.4

In Exercises 25–30, use an augmented matrix to solve the system of equations.

25. $x + 3y = 8$
$x + y = 4$

26. $-x + y = 4$
$x + 3y = 4$

27. $2x + y = 3$
$3x - y = 12$

28. $2x + 3y = 2$
$4x - 9y = 4$

29. $x + 3y = 3$
$3x - 2y = 2$

30. $3x - 6y = -9$
$4x + 5y = 14$

7.1–7.4

31. MODELING - *Borrowing Money* A company borrows $600,000 for 1 year to expand its product line. Some of the money was borrowed at a 4% simple interest rate, and the rest of the money was borrowed at a 6% simple interest rate. How much money was borrowed at each rate if the total annual interest was $29,000?

32. MODELING - *Chemistry* In chemistry class, Tom Northrup has an 80% acid solution and a 50% acid solution. How much of each solution should he mix to get 100 liters of a 75% acid solution?

33. MODELING - *Landscaping* The Garden Factory purchased 4 tons of topsoil and 3 tons of mulch for $1529. The next week the company purchased 2 tons of topsoil and 5 tons of mulch for $1405. Determine the price per ton for topsoil and the price per ton for mulch.

34. MODELING - *Cool Air* Emily Richelieu needs to purchase a new air conditioner for the office. Model 1600A costs $950 to purchase and $32 per month to operate. Model 6070B, a more efficient unit, costs $1275 to purchase and $22 per month to operate.

a) After how many months will the total cost of both units be equal?

b) Which model will be the more cost effective if the life of both units is guaranteed for 10 years?

35. MODELING - *Minimizing Parking Costs* The cost of parking in All-Day parking lot is $5 for the first hour and $0.50 for each additional hour. Sav-a-Lot parking lot costs $4.25 for the first hour and $0.75 for each additional hour.

a) In how many hours after the first hour would the total cost of parking at All-Day and Sav-a-Lot be the same?

b) If Mark McMahon needed to park his car for 5 hr, which parking lot would be less expensive?

7.5

In Exercises 36–39, graph the system of linear inequalities and indicate the solution set.

36. $y \le 3x - 1$
$y > -2x + 1$

37. $2x + y < 8$
$y \ge 2x - 1$

38. $x + 3y \le 6$
$2x - 7y \ge 14$

39. $x - y > 5$
$6x + 5y \le 30$

7.6

40. The set of constraints and profit formula for a linear programming problem are

$$2x + 3y \le 12$$
$$2x + y \le 8$$
$$x \ge 0$$
$$y \ge 0$$
$$P = 5x + 3y$$

a) Draw the graph of the constraints and determine the vertices of the feasible region.

b) Use the vertices to determine the maximum and minimum profit.

CHAPTER ⑦ TEST

1. From a graph, explain how you would identify a consistent system of equations, an inconsistent system of equations, and a dependent system of equations.

2. Solve the system of equations graphically.
$$y = 2x - 12$$
$$2x + 2y = -6$$

3. Determine without graphing whether the system of equations has exactly one solution, no solution, or an infinite number of solutions.
$$4x + 5y = 6$$
$$-3x + 5y = 13$$

Solve the system of equations by the method indicated.

4. $x + y = -1$
$2x + 3y = -5$
(substitution)

5. $y = 3x - 7$
$y = 5x - 3$
(substitution)

6. $x - y = 4$
$2x + y = -10$
(addition)

7. $4x + 3y = 5$
$2x + 4y = 10$
(addition)

8. $3x + 4y = 6$
$2x - 3y = 4$
(addition)

9. $x + 3y = 4$
$5x + 7y = 4$
(matrices)

In Exercises 10–12, for $A = \begin{bmatrix} 2 & -5 \\ 1 & 3 \end{bmatrix}$ *and*
$B = \begin{bmatrix} -1 & -3 \\ 5 & 2 \end{bmatrix}$, *determine the following.*

10. $A + B$ 11. $A - 2B$ 12. $A \times B$

13. Graph the system of linear inequalities and indicate the solution set.
$$y < -2x + 2$$
$$y > 3x + 2$$

Solve Exercises 14 and 15 by using a system of equations.

14. **MODELING** - *Truck Rental* U-Haul charges a daily fee plus a mileage charge to rent a truck. Dorothy DiMento rented a truck with U-Haul and was charged $132 for 3 days rental and 150 miles driven. Elena

Dilai rented the same truck and was charged $142 for 2 days rental and 400 miles driven. Determine the daily fee and the mileage charge for renting this truck.

15. **MODELING** - *Checking Accounts* The charge for maintaining a checking account at Union Bank is $6 per month plus 10 cents for each check that is written. The charge at Citrus Bank is $2 per month and 20 cents per check.

a) How many checks would a customer have to write in a month for the total charges to be the same at both banks?

b) If Brent Pickett planned to write 14 checks per month, which bank would be the least expensive?

16. The set of constraints and profit formula for a linear programming problem are
$$x + 3y \le 6$$
$$4x + 3y \le 15$$
$$x \ge 0$$
$$y \ge 0$$
$$P = 6x + 4y$$

a) Draw the graph of the constraints and determine the vertices of the feasible region.

b) Use the vertices to determine the maximum and minimum profit.

G R O U P   P R O J E C T S

1. Make up three different systems of equations that have (1, 4) as a solution. Explain how you determined your systems.

LINEAR PROGRAMMING

2. **MODELING - *Profit from Bookcases*** The Bookholder Company manufactures two types of bookcases out of both oak and walnut. Model 01 requires 5 board feet of oak and 2 board feet of walnut. Model 02 requires 4 board feet of oak and 3 board feet of walnut. A profit of $75 is made on each Model 01 bookcase and a profit of $125 is made on each Model 02 bookcase. The company has a supply of 1000 board feet of oak and 600 board feet of walnut. The company has orders for 40 Model 01 bookcases and 50 Model 02 bookcases. These orders indicate the minimum number the company must manufacture of each model.

   a) Write the set of constraints.

   b) Write the objective function.

   c) Graph the set of constraints.

   d) Determine the number of bookcases of each type the company should manufacture in order to maximize profits.

   e) Determine the maximum profit.

CREATE YOUR OWN WORD PROBLEM

3. a) Write a word problem that can be solved by using a system of two equations with two unknowns.

   b) For the problem in part (a), write the system of equations and find the answer.

   c) Explain how you developed the problem in part (a).

CHAPTER 8

The Metric System

▲ Everywhere outside the United States you may see traffic signs given in metric units.

WHAT YOU WILL LEARN

- The advantages of using the metric system
- The basic units used in the metric system
- Conversions within the metric system
- Determining length, area, volume, mass, and temperature in the metric system
- Dimensional analysis and converting to and from the metric system

WHY IT IS IMPORTANT

When you leave the United States, whether you travel to Canada, Mexico, or most other places in the world, you may see metric measurements being used. Clothing sizes may be given in centimeters, gasoline may be sold in liters, and speed limit signs may be given in kilometers per hour. Each day in the United States we see and use metric measurements. For example, soda is sold in liters, medicines are measured in milligrams, and tire sizes are given in millimeters. An understanding of the metric system will help you both at home and when you travel outside the United States.

CHAPTER 12

Probability

▲ Probability is involved in all games of chance, including lotteries.

WHAT YOU WILL LEARN

- Empirical probability and theoretical probability
- Compound probability, conditional probability, and binomial probability
- Odds against an event and odds in favor of an event
- Expected value
- Tree diagrams
- Mutually exclusive events and independent events
- The counting principle, permutations, and combinations

WHY IT IS IMPORTANT

Each year, millions of Americans play lotteries. If you play a lottery, your hope is to beat the odds and be the person with the winning numbers. Not satisfied with leaving things to chance, mathematicians of the sixteenth, seventeenth, and eighteenth centuries invented the study of probability to determine the likelihood of an event such as winning the lottery.

   Although the rules of probability were first applied to gaming, they have many other applications. The cost of your car insurance, the weather forecast, the expected number of people who will attend an outdoor concert if it is raining all involve probability. In this chapter, we will learn many of the important concepts of probability that can help us make informed decisions in our lives.

12.1   THE NATURE OF PROBABILITY

▲ We can determine the probability of an event, such as the probability of someone purchasing a rock CD, based on actual observations.

On Monday morning before a music store opens, the manager reviews sales from the previous week. She notices that more rock compact discs (CDs) were sold than any other type of CD. Based on sales from the previous week, she can determine the probability that the first CD sold on Monday morning will be a rock CD. In this section, we will introduce several definitions that are important to the understanding of the probability of an event. We will also learn how to calculate the probability of an event based on actual observations from an experiment.

History

Probability is used in many areas, including public finance, medicine, insurance, elections, manufacturing, educational tests and measurements, genetics, weather forecasting, investments, opinion polls, the natural sciences, and games of chance. The study of probability originated from the study of games of chance. Archaeologists have found artifacts used in games of chance in Egypt dating from about 3000 B.C.

Mathematical problems relating to games of chance were studied by a number of mathematicians of the Renaissance. Italy's Girolamo Cardano (1501–1576) in his *Liber de Ludo Aleae* (book on the games of chance) presents one of the first systematic computations of probabilities. Although it is basically a gambler's manual, many consider it the first book ever written on probability. A short time later, two French mathematicians, Blaise Pascal (1623–1662) and Pierre de Fermat (1601–1665), worked together studying "the geometry of the die." In 1657, Dutch mathematician Christian Huygens (1629–1695) published *De Ratiociniis in Luno Aleae* (on ratiocination in dice games), which contained the first documented reference to the concept of mathematical expectation (see Section 12.4). Swiss mathematician Jacob Bernoulli (1654–1705), whom many consider the founder of probability theory, is said to have fused pure mathematics with the empirical methods used in statistical experiments. The works of Pierre-Simon de Laplace (1749–1827) dominated probability throughout the nineteenth century.

The Nature of Probability

Before we discuss the meaning of the word *probability* and learn how to calculate probabilities, we must introduce a few definitions.

> An **experiment** is a controlled operation that yields a set of results.

The process by which medical researchers administer experimental drugs to patients to determine their reaction is one type of experiment.

> The possible results of an experiment are called its **outcomes**.

For example, the possible outcomes from administering an experimental drug may be a favorable reaction, no reaction, or an adverse reaction.

A die (one of a pair of dice) contains six surfaces, called faces. Each face contains a unique number of dots, from 1 to 6. The sum of the dots on opposite surfaces is 7.

An **event** is a subcollection of the outcomes of an experiment.

For example, when a die is rolled, the event of rolling a number greater than 2 can be satisfied by any one of four outcomes: 3, 4, 5, or 6. The event of rolling a 5 can be satisfied by only one outcome, the 5 itself. The event of rolling an even number can be satisfied by any of three outcomes: 2, 4, or 6.

Probability is classified as either *empirical* (experimental) or *theoretical* (mathematical). *Empirical probability* is the relative frequency of occurrence of an event and is determined by actual observations of an experiment. *Theoretical probability* is determined through a study of the possible *outcomes* that can occur for the given experiment. We will indicate the probability of an event E by $P(E)$, which is read "P of E."

Empirical Probability

In this section, we will briefly discuss empirical probability. The emphasis in the remaining sections is on theoretical probability. Following is the formula for computing empirical probability, or relative frequency.

EMPIRICAL PROBABILITY (RELATIVE FREQUENCY)

$$P(E) = \frac{\text{number of times event } E \text{ has occurred}}{\text{total number of times the experiment has been performed}}$$

The probability of an event, whether empirical or theoretical, is always a number between 0 and 1, inclusive, and may be expressed as a decimal number or a fraction. An empirical probability of 0 indicates that the event has never occurred. An empirical probability of 1 indicates that the event has always occurred.

EXAMPLE ❶ *Heads Up!*

In 100 tosses of a fair coin, 44 landed heads up. Find the empirical probability of the coin landing heads up.

SOLUTION Let E be the event that the coin lands heads up. Then

$$P(E) = \frac{44}{100} = 0.44$$

EXAMPLE ❷ *Weight Reduction*

A pharmaceutical company is testing a drug that is supposed to help with weight reduction. The drug is given to 500 individuals with the following outcomes.

Weight reduced	Weight unchanged	Weight increased
379	62	59

If this drug is given to an individual, find the empirical probability that the person's weight is (a) reduced, (b) unchanged, (c) increased.

SOLUTION

a) Let E be the event that the weight is reduced.

$$P(E) = \frac{379}{500} = 0.758$$

b) Let E be the event that the weight is unchanged.

$$P(E) = \frac{62}{500} = 0.124$$

c) Let E be the event that the weight is increased.

$$P(E) = \frac{59}{500} = 0.118$$

Empirical probability is used when probabilities cannot be theoretically calculated. For example, life insurance companies use empirical probabilities to determine the chance of an individual in a certain profession, with certain risk factors, living to age 65.

Empirical Probability in Genetics

Using empirical probability, Gregor Mendel (1822–1884) developed the laws of heredity by crossbreeding different types of "pure" pea plants and observing the relative frequencies of the resulting offspring. These laws became the foundation for the study of genetics. For example, when he crossbred a pure yellow pea plant and a pure green pea plant, the resulting offspring (the first generation) were always yellow; see Fig. 12.1(a). When he crossbred a pure round-seeded pea plant and a pure wrinkled-seeded pea plant, the resulting offspring (the first generation) were always round; see Fig. 12.1(b).

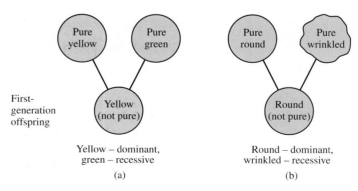

Figure 12.1

Mendel called traits such as yellow color and round seeds *dominant* because they overcame or "dominated" the other trait. He labeled the green color and the wrinkled traits *recessive*.

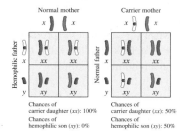
Mendel then crossbred the offspring of the first generation. The resulting second-generation offspring had both the dominant and the recessive traits of their grandparents; see Fig. 12.2(a) and (b). What's more, these traits always appeared in approximately a 3 to 1 ratio of dominant to recessive.

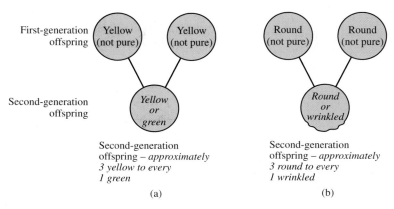

Figure 12.2

Table 12.1 lists some of the actual results of Mendel's experiments with pea plants. Note that the ratio of dominant trait to recessive trait in the second-generation offspring is about 3 to 1 for each experiment. The empirical probability of the dominant trait has also been calculated. How would you find the empirical probability of the recessive trait?

Table 12.1 Second-Generation Offspring

Dominant Trait	Number with Dominant Trait	Recessive Trait	Number with Recessive Trait	Ratio of Dominant to Recessive	P (Dominant Trait)
Yellow seeds	6022	Green seeds	2001	3.01 to 1	$\frac{6022}{8023} \approx 0.75$
Round seeds	5474	Wrinkled seeds	1850	2.96 to 1	$\frac{5474}{7324} \approx 0.75$

From his work, Mendel concluded that the sex cells (now called gametes) of the pure yellow (dominant) pea plant carried some factor that caused the offspring to be yellow and that the gametes of the green variety had a variant factor that "induced the development of green plants." In 1909, Danish geneticist W. Johannsen called these factors "genes." Mendel's work led to the understanding that each pea plant contains two genes for color, one that comes from the mother and the other from the father. If the two genes are alike—for instance, both for yellow plants or both for green plants—the plant will be that color. If the genes for color are different, the plant will grow the color of the dominant gene. Thus, if one parent contributes a gene for the plant to be yellow (dominant) and the other parent contributes a gene for the plant to be green (recessive), the plant will be yellow.

"The laws of probability, so true in general, so fallacious in particular."

Edward Gibbon, 1796

The Law of Large Numbers

Most of us accept that if a "fair coin" is tossed many, many times, it will land heads up approximately half of the time. Intuitively, we can guess that the probability that a fair coin will land heads up is $\frac{1}{2}$. Does that mean that if a coin is tossed twice, it will land heads up exactly once? If a fair coin is tossed 10 times, will there necessarily be five heads? The answer is clearly no. What, then, does it mean when we state that the probability that a fair coin will land heads up is $\frac{1}{2}$? To answer this question, let's examine Table 12.2, which shows what may occur when a fair coin is tossed a given number of times.

Table 12.2

Number of Tosses	Expected Number of Heads	Actual Number of Heads Observed	Relative Frequency of Heads
10	5	4	$\frac{4}{10} = 0.4$
100	50	45	$\frac{45}{100} = 0.45$
1000	500	546	$\frac{546}{1000} = 0.546$
10,000	5000	4852	$\frac{4852}{10,000} = 0.4852$
100,000	50,000	49,770	$\frac{49,770}{100,000} = 0.49770$

The far right column of Table 12.2, the relative frequency of heads, is a ratio of the number of heads observed to the total number of tosses of the coin. The relative frequency is the empirical probability, as defined earlier. Note that as the number of tosses increases, the relative frequency of heads gets closer and closer to $\frac{1}{2}$, or 0.5, which is what we expect.

The nature of probability is summarized by the law of large numbers.

> The **law of large numbers** states that probability statements apply in practice to a large number of trials, not to a single trial. It is the relative frequency over the long run that is accurately predictable, not individual events or precise totals.

What does it mean to say that the probability of rolling a 2 on a die is $\frac{1}{6}$? It means that over the long run, on the average, one of every six rolls will result in a 2.

DID YOU KNOW?

Batting Averages

If Joe Mauer of the Minnesota Twins gets three hits in his first three at bats of the season, he is batting a thousand (1.000). Over the course of the 162 games of the season (with three or four at bats per game), however, his batting average will fall closer to 0.347 (his 2006 major league leading batting average). In 2006, out of 521 at bats, Mauer had 181 hits, an average above all other players' but much less than 1.000. His batting average is a relative frequency (or empirical probability) of hits to at bats. It is only the long-term average that we take seriously because it is based on the law of large numbers.

SECTION 12.1 EXERCISES

CONCEPT/WRITING EXERCISES

1. What is an experiment?

2. **a)** What are outcomes of an experiment?

   b) What is an event?

3. What is empirical probability, and how is empirical probability determined?

4. What are theoretical probabilities based on?

5. Explain in your own words the law of large numbers.

6. Explain in your own words why empirical probabilities are used in determining premiums for life insurance policies.

7. The theoretical probability of a coin landing heads up is $\frac{1}{2}$. Does this probability mean that if a coin is flipped two times, one flip will land heads up? If not, what does it mean?

8. To determine premiums, life insurance companies must compute the probable date of death. On the basis of a great deal of research, Mr. Duncan, age 36, is expected to live another 43.21 years. Does this determination mean that Mr. Duncan will live until he is 79.21 years old? If not, what does it mean?

9. **a)** Explain how you would find the empirical probability of rolling a 5 on a die.

   b) What do you believe is the empirical probability of rolling a 5?

   c) Determine the empirical probability of rolling a 5 by rolling a die 40 times.

10. The theoretical probability of rolling a 4 on a die is $\frac{1}{6}$. Does this probability mean that if a die is rolled six times one 4 will appear? If not, what does it mean?

PRACTICE THE SKILLS

11. *Flip a Coin* Flip a coin 50 times and record the results. Determine the empirical probability of flipping

a) a head.

b) a tail.

c) Does the probability of flipping a head appear to be the same as flipping a tail?

12. *Pair of Dice* Roll a pair of dice 60 times and record the sums. Determine the empirical probability of rolling a sum of

a) 2.

b) 7.

c) Does the probability of rolling a sum of 2 appear to be the same as the probability of rolling a sum of 7?

13. *Roll a Die* Roll a die 50 times and record the results. Determine the empirical probability of rolling

a) a 1.

b) a 4.

c) Does the probability of rolling a 1 appear to be the same as the probability of rolling a 4? Explain.

14. *Two Coins* Flip two coins 50 times and record the number of times exactly one head was obtained. Determine the empirical probability of flipping exactly one head.

PROBLEM SOLVING

15. *Birds at a Feeder* The last 30 birds that fed at the Haines' bird feeder were 14 finches, 10 cardinals, and 6 blue jays. Use this information to determine the empirical probability that the next bird to feed from the feeder is

a) a finch.   **b)** a cardinal.   **c)** a blue jay.

16. *Music Purchases* At the Virgin Music store in Times Square, 60 people entering the store were selected at random and were asked to choose their favorite type of music. Of the 60, 12 chose rock, 16 chose country, 8 chose classical, and 24 chose something other than rock, country, or classical. Determine the empirical probability that the next person entering the store favors

a) rock music.

b) country music.

c) something other than rock, country, or classical music.

17. *Veterinarian* In a given week, a veterinarian treated the following animals.

Animal	Number Treated
Dog	45
Cat	40
Bird	15
Rabbit	5

Determine the empirical probability that the next animal she treats is

a) a dog.

b) a cat.

c) a rabbit.

18. *Prader–Willi Syndrome* In a sample of 50,000 first-born babies, 5 were found to have Prader–Willi syndrome. Find the empirical probability that a family's first child will be born with this syndrome.

19. *Studying Abroad* The table at the top of the right-hand column shows the 10 most popular destinations for U.S. college students studying abroad for the 2003–2004 school year.

Destination	Number of Students
United Kingdom	32,237
Italy	21,922
Spain	20,080
France	13,718
Australia	11,418
Mexico	9293
Germany	5985
Ireland	5198
China	4737
Costa Rica	4510
Total	129,098

Source: Institute of International Education

If a student were selected at random from those who studied abroad in 2003–2004 at one of the destinations in the table, determine the empirical probability that the student studied in

a) China.   **b)** Italy.   **c)** Australia.

20. *Travel Web Sites* The following table shows the number of visitors, in millions, to the five most frequently visited travel web sites in November 2005.

Web Site	Number of Visitors
MapQuest	31,200,000
Expedia	14,200,000
Travelocity	11,200,000
Orbitz	10,900,000
Southwest Airlines	7,100,000
Total	74,600,000

Source: Nielsen/NetRatings

Assuming this trend continues, if a person chooses to visit only one of the listed web sites, determine the empirical probability the person will visit

a) Expedia.

b) Travelocity.

c) Southwest Airlines.

21. *Bird Flu* As of March 24, 2006, a total of 186 people had contracted the bird flu worldwide. The graph below shows the number of bird flu cases by country. If a person contracted the bird flu, determine the empirical probability that the person contracted it in

a) Indonesia.

b) Vietnam.

c) Turkey.

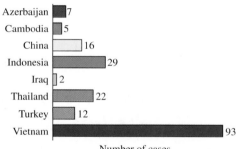

Bird Flu Cases by Country

Azerbaijan 7
Cambodia 5
China 16
Indonesia 29
Iraq 2
Thailand 22
Turkey 12
Vietnam 93

Number of cases

Sources: World Health Organization and Gannett News Service

22. *Grade Distribution* Mr. Doole's grade distribution over the past 3 years for a course in college algebra is shown in the chart below.

Grade	Number
A	43
B	182
C	260
D	90
F	62
I	8

If Sue Gilligan plans to take college algebra with Mr. Doole, determine the empirical probability that she receives a grade of

a) A.   b) C.   c) D or higher.

23. *Election* In an election for student council president at Russell Sage College, 80 students were polled and asked for whom they planned to vote. The table shows the results of the poll.

Candidate	Votes
Allison	22
Emily	18
Kimberly	20
Johanna	14
Other	6

If one student from Russell Sage College is selected at random, determine the empirical probability that the person planned to vote for

a) Allison.

b) Emily.

c) Kimberly.

d) Johanna.

e) Someone other than the four people listed above.

24. *U.S. Foreign-Born Workers* In 2004, there were 20 million foreign-born workers in the United States. The circle graph below shows the occupations of those workers.

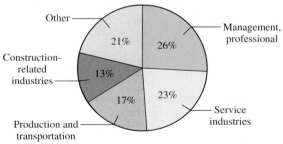

Occupations of Foreign-Born Workers in the United States

Other
Management, professional 26%
21%
Construction-related industries 13%
Service industries 23%
17%
Production and transportation

Source: Knight-Ridder

If one foreign-born worker is selected at random, determine the empirical probability the person's occupation is in

a) the service industries.

b) construction-related industries.

c) management or is a professional.

25. *Hitting a Bull's-Eye* The pattern of hits shown on the target resulted from a marksman firing 20 rounds. For a single shot,

a) determine the empirical probability that the marksman hits the 50-point bull's-eye (the center of the target).

b) determine the empirical probability that the marksman does not hit the bull's-eye.

c) determine the empirical probability that the marksman scores at least 20 points.

d) determine the empirical probability that the marksman does not score any points (the area outside the large circle).

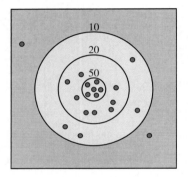

26. *Rock Toss* Jim Handy finds an irregularly shaped five-sided rock. He labels each side and tosses the rock 100 times. The results of his tosses are shown in the table. Determine the empirical probability that the rock will land on side 4 if tossed again.

Side	1	2	3	4	5
Frequency	32	18	15	13	22

27. *Cell Biology Experiment* An experimental serum was injected into 500 guinea pigs. Initially, 150 of the guinea pigs had circular cells, 250 had elliptical cells, and 100 had irregularly shaped cells. After the serum was injected, none of the guinea pigs with circular cells were affected, 50 with elliptical cells were affected, and all those with irregular cells were affected. Determine the empirical probability that a guinea pig with (a) circular cells, (b) elliptical cells, and (c) irregular cells will be affected by injection of the serum.

28. *Baby Gender* In the United States, more male babies are born than female. In 2004, 2,104,661 males were born and 2,007,391 females were born. Determine the empirical probability of an individual being born

a) male.   b) female.

29. *Mendel's Experiment* In one of his experiments (see pages 726–727), Mendel crossbred nonpure purple flower pea plants. These purple pea plants had two traits for flowers, purple (dominant) and white (recessive). The result of this crossbreeding was 705 second-generation plants with purple flowers and 224 second-generation plants with white flowers. Determine the empirical probability of a second-generation plant having

a) white flowers.   b) purple flowers.

30. *Second-Generation Offspring* In another experiment, Mendel crossbred nonpure tall pea plants. As a result, the second-generation offspring were 787 tall plants and 277 short plants. Determine the empirical probability of a second-generation plant being

a) tall.   b) short.

CHALLENGE PROBLEM/GROUP ACTIVITY

31. a) *Design an Experiment* Which do you believe is used more frequently in a magazine or newspaper article, the word *a* or the word *the*?

b) Design an experiment to determine the empirical probabilities (or relative frequencies) of the words *a* and *the* appearing in a magazine or newspaper article.

c) Perform the experiment in part (b) and determine the empirical probabilities.

d) Which word, *a* or *the*, appears to occur more frequently?

RECREATIONAL MATHEMATICS

32. *Cola Preference* Can people selected at random distinguish Coke from Pepsi? Which do they prefer?

a) Design an experiment to determine the empirical probability that a person selected at random can select Coke when given samples of both Coke and Pepsi.

b) Perform the experiment in part (a) and determine the empirical probability.

c) Determine the empirical probability that a person selected at random will prefer Coke over Pepsi.

INTERNET/RESEARCH ACTIVITIES

33. Write a paper on how insurance companies use empirical probabilities in determining insurance premiums. An insurance agent may be able to direct you to a source of information.

34. Write a paper on how Gregor Mendel's use of empirical probability led to the development of the science of genetics. You may want to check with a biology professor to determine references to use.

12.2 THEORETICAL PROBABILITY

▲ We use probability to determine the likelihood of winning money at a casino.

Should you spend the money for a stamp to return a sweepstakes ticket? What are your chances of winning a lottery? If you go to a carnival, bazaar, or casino, which games provide the greatest chance of winning? These and similar questions can be answered once you have an understanding of theoretical probability that we will discuss in this section.

In the remainder of this chapter, the word probability will refer to theoretical probability.

Recall from Section 12.1 that the results of an experiment are called outcomes. When you roll a die and observe the number of points that face up, the possible outcomes are 1, 2, 3, 4, 5, and 6. It is equally likely that you will roll any one of the possible numbers.

> If each outcome of an experiment has the same chance of occurring as any other outcome, we say that the outcomes are **equally likely outcomes**.

Can you think of a second set of equally likely outcomes when a die is rolled? An odd number is as likely to be rolled as an even number. Therefore, odd and even numbers are another set of equally likely outcomes.

TIMELY TIP To be able to do the problems in this section and the remainder of the chapter, you must have a thorough understanding of fractions. If you have forgotten how to work with fractions, we strongly suggest that you review Section 5.3 before beginning this section.

If an event E has *equally likely outcomes*, the probability of event E, symbolized by $P(E)$, may be calculated with the following formula.

> **PROBABILITY**
>
> $$P(E) = \frac{\text{number of outcomes favorable to } E}{\text{total number of possible outcomes}}$$

Example 1 illustrates how to use this formula.

EXAMPLE ❶ *Finding Probabilities*

A die is rolled. Find the probability of rolling

a) a 3. b) an even number. c) a number greater than 2.

d) a 7. e) a number less than 7.

SOLUTION

a) There are six possible equally likely outcomes: 1, 2, 3, 4, 5, and 6. The event of rolling a 3 can occur in only one way.

$$P(3) = \frac{\text{number of outcomes that will result in a 3}}{\text{total number of possible outcomes}} = \frac{1}{6}$$

b) The event of rolling an even number can occur in three ways: 2, 4, or 6.

$$P(\text{even number}) = \frac{\text{number of outcomes that result in an even number}}{\text{total number of possible outcomes}}$$

$$= \frac{3}{6} = \frac{1}{2}$$

c) Four numbers are greater than 2, namely, 3, 4, 5 and 6.

$$P(\text{number greater than 2}) = \frac{4}{6} = \frac{2}{3}$$

d) No outcomes will result in a 7. Thus, the event cannot occur and the probability is 0.

$$P(7) = \frac{0}{6} = 0$$

e) All the outcomes 1 through 6 are less than 7. Thus, the event must occur and the probability is 1.

$$P(\text{number less than 7}) = \frac{6}{6} = 1$$

Four important facts about probability follow.

IMPORTANT FACTS

1. The probability of an event that cannot occur is 0.
2. The probability of an event that must occur is 1.
3. Every probability is a number between 0 and 1 inclusive; that is, $0 \leq P(E) \leq 1$.
4. The sum of the probabilities of all possible outcomes of an experiment is 1.

EXAMPLE ❷ *Choosing One Bird from a List*

The names of 15 birds and their food preferences are listed in Table 12.3 on page 735. Each of the 15 birds' names is listed on a slip of paper, and the 15 slips are placed in a bag. One slip is to be selected at random from the bag. Find the probability that the slip contains the name of

a) a finch (any type listed).

b) a bird that has a high attractiveness to cracked corn.

c) a bird that has a low attractiveness to peanut kernels, *and* a low attractiveness to cracked corn, *and* a high attractiveness to black-striped sunflower seeds.

d) a bird that has a high attractiveness to either peanut kernels *or* cracked corn (or both).

▲ Northern cardinal

Table 12.3 Birds and Their Food Preferences

Bird	Peanut Kernels	Cracked Corn	Black-Striped Sunflower Seeds
American goldfinch	L	L	H
Blue jay	H	M	H
Chickadee	M	L	H
Common grackle	M	H	H
Evening grosbeak	L	L	H
House finch	M	L	H
House sparrow	L	M	M
Mourning dove	L	M	M
Northern cardinal	L	L	H
Purple finch	L	L	H
Scrub jay	H	L	H
Song sparrow	L	L	M
Tufted titmouse	H	L	H
White-crowned sparrow	H	M	H
White-throated sparrow	H	H	H

Source: *How to Attract Birds* (Ortho Books)

Note: H = high attractiveness; M = medium attractiveness; L = low attractiveness.

SOLUTION

a) Three of the 15 birds listed are finches (American goldfinch, house finch, and purple finch).

$$P(\text{finch}) = \frac{3}{15} = \frac{1}{5}$$

b) Two of the 15 birds listed have a high attractiveness to cracked corn (common grackle and white-throated sparrow).

$$P(\text{high attractiveness to cracked corn}) = \frac{2}{15}$$

c) Reading across the rows reveals that 4 birds have a low attractiveness to peanut kernels, a low attractiveness to cracked corn, and a high attractiveness to black-striped sunflower seeds (American goldfinch, evening grosbeak, northern cardinal, and purple finch).

$$P\left(\begin{array}{c}\text{low attractiveness to peanuts, and low to}\\\text{corn, and high to black-striped sunflower seeds}\end{array}\right) = \frac{4}{15}$$

d) Six birds have a high attractiveness to either peanut kernels or to cracked corn (or both). They are the blue jay, common grackle, scrub jay, tufted titmouse, white-crowned sparrow, and white-throated sparrow.

$$P(\text{high attractiveness to peanut kernels or cracked corn}) = \frac{6}{15} = \frac{2}{5}$$

In any experiment, an event must either occur or not occur. *The sum of the probability that an event will occur and the probability that it will not occur is 1.* Thus, for any event A we conclude that

$$P(A) + P(\text{not } A) = 1$$

or

$$P(\text{not } A) = 1 - P(A)$$

For example, if the probability that event A will occur is $\frac{5}{12}$, the probability that event A will not occur is $1 - \frac{5}{12}$, or $\frac{7}{12}$. Similarly, if the probability that event A will not occur is 0.3, the probability that event A will occur is $1 - 0.3 = 0.7$, or $\frac{7}{10}$. We make use of this concept in Example 3.

EXAMPLE ❸ *Selecting One Card from a Deck*

A standard deck of 52 playing cards is shown in Figure 12.3. The deck consists of four suits: hearts, clubs, diamonds, and spades. Each suit has 13 cards, including numbered cards ace (1) through 10 and three picture (or face) cards, the jack, the queen, and the king. Hearts and diamonds are red cards; clubs and spades are black cards. There are 12 picture cards, consisting of 4 jacks, 4 queens, and 4 kings. One card is to be selected at random from the deck of cards. Find the probability that the card selected is

a) a 5.

b) not a 5.

c) a diamond.

d) a jack *or* queen *or* king (a picture card).

e) a heart *and* a club.

f) a card greater than 6 *and* less than 9.

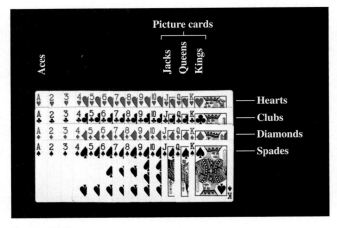

Figure 12.3

SOLUTION

a) There are four 5's in a deck of 52 cards.

$$P(5) = \frac{4}{52} = \frac{1}{13}$$

b) $P(\text{not a } 5) = 1 - P(5) = 1 - \dfrac{1}{13} = \dfrac{12}{13}$

This probability could also have been found by noting that there are 48 cards that are not 5's in a deck of 52 cards.

$$P(\text{not a } 5) = \dfrac{48}{52} = \dfrac{12}{13}$$

c) There are 13 diamonds in the deck.

$$P(\text{diamond}) = \dfrac{13}{52} = \dfrac{1}{4}$$

d) There are 4 jacks, 4 queens, and 4 kings, or a total of 12 picture cards.

$$P(\text{jack } or \text{ queen } or \text{ king}) = \dfrac{12}{52} = \dfrac{3}{13}$$

e) The word *and* means that *both* events must occur. Since it is not possible to select one card that is both a heart and a club, the probability is 0.

$$P(\text{heart and club}) = \dfrac{0}{52} = 0$$

f) The cards that are both greater than 6 and less than 9 are 7's and 8's. There are four 7's and four 8's, or a total of eight cards.

$$P(\text{greater than 6 } and \text{ less than 9}) = \dfrac{8}{52} = \dfrac{2}{13}$$

SECTION 12.2 EXERCISES

CONCEPT/WRITING EXERCISES

1. What are equally likely outcomes?

2. Explain in your own words how to find the theoretical probability of an event.

3. State the relationship that exists for $P(A)$ and $P(\text{not } A)$.

4. If the probability that an event occurs is $\frac{3}{7}$, determine the probability that the event does not occur.

5. If the probability that an event occurs is 0.7, determine the probability that the event does not occur.

6. If the probability that an event does not occur is 0.65, determine the probability that the event occurs.

7. If the probability that an event does not occur is $\frac{5}{12}$, determine the probability that the event occurs.

8. How many of each of the following are there in a standard deck of cards?

a) Total cards

b) Hearts

c) Red cards

d) Fives

e) Black cards

f) Picture cards

g) Aces

h) Queens

9. Using the definition of probability, explain in your own words why the probability of an event that must occur is 1.

10. Using the definition of probability, explain in your own words why the probability of an event that cannot occur is 0.

11. Between what two numbers (inclusively) will all probabilities lie?

12. What is the sum of all the probabilities of all possible outcomes of an experiment?

PRACTICE THE SKILLS

13. *Multiple-Choice Test* A multiple-choice test has five possible answers for each question.

    a) If you guess at an answer, what is the probability that you select the correct answer for one particular question?

    b) If you eliminate one of the five possible answers and guess from the remaining possibilities, what is the probability that you select the correct answer to that question?

14. *Remote Control* A TV remote control has keys for channels 0 through 9. If you select one key at random,

    a) what is the probability that you press channel 6?

    b) what is the probability that you press a key for an even number?

    c) what is the probability that you press a key for a number less than 7?

15. *Raffle* In a raffle where one number is chosen, determine the probability that you would win if you have a choice of 40 numbers to choose from. Explain your answer.

16. *Raffle* In a raffle where one number is chosen, determine the probability that you would win if you have a choice of 52 numbers to choose from. Explain your answer.

Select a Card In Exercises 17–26, one card is selected at random from a deck of cards. Determine the probability that the card selected is

17. a 5.

18. a 5 or a 7.

19. not a 5.

20. the five of diamonds.

21. a black card.

22. a diamond.

23. a red card or a black card.

24. a red card and a black card.

25. a card greater than 4 and less than 9.

26. a king and a club.

Spin the Spinner In Exercises 27–30, assume that the spinner cannot land on a line. Determine the probability that the spinner lands on (a) red, (b) green, (c) yellow, (d) blue.

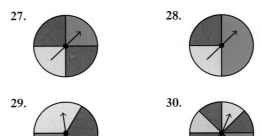

27.   28.

29.   30.

Picnic In Exercises 31–34, a cooler at a picnic contains 100 cans of soda covered by ice. There are 30 cans of cola, 40 cans of orange soda, 10 cans of ginger ale, and 20 cans of root beer. The cans are all the same size and shape. If one can is selected at random from the cooler, determine the probability that the soda selected is

31. root beer.

32. cola or orange soda.

33. cola, root beer, or orange soda.

34. ginger ale.

Wheel of Fortune In Exercises 35–38, use the small replica of the Wheel of Fortune.

If the wheel is spun at random, determine the probability of the sector indicated stopping under the pointer.

35. $600

36. A number greater than $700

37. Lose a turn or Bankrupt

38. $2500 or Surprise

Basketballs In Exercises 39–42, 30 basketballs (15 Spalding, 10 Wilson, and 5 other brand-name balls) are on a basketball court. Barry Wood closes his eyes and arbitrarily picks up a ball from the court. Determine the probability that the ball selected is

39. a Spalding.

40. a Wilson.

41. not a Wilson.

42. a Wilson or a Spalding.

Traffic Light In Exercises 43–46, a traffic light is red for 25 sec, yellow for 5 sec, and green for 55 sec. What is the probability that when you reach the light,

43. the light is green.

44. the light is yellow.

45. the light is not red.

46. the light is not green.

TENNESSEE In Exercises 47–52, each individual letter of the word TENNESSEE is placed on a piece of paper and all 9 pieces of paper are placed in a hat. If one letter is selected at random from the hat, determine the probability that

47. the letter *S* is selected.

48. the letter *S* is not selected.

49. a consonant is selected.

50. the letter *T* or *N* is selected.

51. the letter *W* is selected.

52. the letter *V* is not selected.

Hurricane Evacuees Following Hurricanes Katrina and Rita, many residents had to evacuate their homes. Some relocated in the same state, whereas others relocated to different states. In Exercises 53–56, use the following map, which shows the number of evacuees residing in each state and in the District of Columbia as of February 27, 2006.

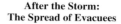
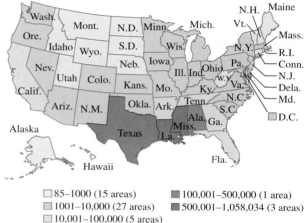

Source: Federal Emergency Management Agency

If 1 of the 51 areas illustrated on the map is selected at random, determine the probability that the area contained

53. between 500,001 and 1,058,034 residents who evacuated their homes.

54. between 10,001 and 100,000 residents who evacuated their homes.

55. between 1001 and 10,000 residents who evacuated their homes.

56. between 85 and 1000 residents who evacuated their homes.

Dart Board In Exercises 57–60, a dart is thrown randomly and sticks on the circular dart board with 26 partitions, as shown.

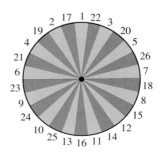

Assuming the dart cannot land on the black area or on a border between colors, determine the probability that the dart lands on

57. the area marked 15.

58. an orange area.

59. an area marked with a number greater than or equal to 22.

60. an area marked with a number greater than 6 and less than or equal to 9.

Car Dealership In Exercises 61–66, refer to the following table, which shows the type and manufacturer of vehicles at a specific car dealership.

	General Motors	Toyota	Total
Car	55	30	85
SUV	28	17	45
Total	83	47	130

If one person selects a vehicle at random from the dealership, determine the probability that the person selects

61. a car.

62. an SUV.

63. a vehicle manufactured by General Motors.

64. a vehicle manufactured by Toyota.

65. a car manufactured by General Motors.

66. an SUV manufactured by General Motors.

Stocking Peanut Butter In Exercises 67–72, refer to the following table, which contains information about a shopping cart full of peanut butter jars that must be stocked on a shelf.

Brand	Smooth	Chunky	Total
Peter Pan	10	6	16
Jif	7	5	12
Skippy	4	3	7
Other	2	1	3
Total	23	15	38

If a stock clerk selects one jar at random to place on the shelf, determine the probability he selects a jar of

67. Jif.

68. Skippy.

69. a chunky peanut butter.

70. a smooth peanut butter.

71. Peter Pan smooth peanut butter.

72. Jif chunky peanut butter.

Bean Bag Toss In Exercises 73–77, a bean bag is randomly thrown onto the square table top shown below and does not touch a line.

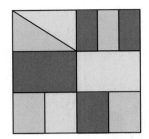

Determine the probability that the bean bag lands on

73. a red area.   **74.** a green area.

75. a yellow area.   **76.** a red or green area.

77. a yellow or green area.   **78.** a red or yellow area.

CHALLENGE PROBLEMS/GROUP ACTIVITIES

Before working Exercises 79 and 80, reread the material on genetics in Section 12.1.

79. *Genetics* Cystic fibrosis is an inherited disease that occurs in about 1 in every 2500 Caucasian births in North America and in about 1 in every 250,000 non-Caucasian births in North America. Let's denote the cystic fibrosis gene as *c* and a disease-free gene as *C*. Since the disease-free gene is dominant, only a person with *cc* genes will have the disease. A person who has *Cc* genes is a carrier of cystic fibrosis but does not actually have the disease. If one parent has *CC* genes and the other parent has *cc* genes, determine the probability that

   a) an offspring will inherit cystic fibrosis, that is, *cc* genes.

   b) an offspring will be a carrier of cystic fibrosis but not contract the disease.

80. *Genetics* Sickle-cell anemia is an inherited disease that occurs in about 1 in every 500 African-American births and about 1 in every 160,000 non-African-American births. Unlike cystic fibrosis, in which the cystic fibrosis gene is recessive, sickle-cell anemia is *codominant*. In other words, a person inheriting two sickle-cell genes will have sickle-cell anemia, whereas a person inheriting only one of the sickle-cell genes will have a mild version of sickle-cell anemia, called *sickle-cell trait*. Let's call the disease-free genes s_1 and the sickle cell gene s_2. If both parents have s_1s_2 genes, determine the probability that

a) an offspring will have sickle-cell anemia.

b) an offspring will have the sickle-cell trait.

c) an offspring will have neither sickle-cell anemia nor the sickle-cell trait.

In Exercises 81 and 82, the solutions involve material that we will discuss in later sections of the chapter. Try to solve them before reading ahead.

81. *Marbles* A bottle contains two red and two green marbles, and a second bottle also contains two red and two green marbles. If you select one marble at random from each bottle, determine the probability (to be discussed in Section 12.6) that you obtain

a) two red marbles.

b) two green marbles.

c) a red marble from the first bottle and a green marble from the second bottle.

82. *Birds* Consider Table 12.3 on page 735. Suppose you are told that one bird's name was selected at random from the birds listed and the bird selected has a low attractiveness to peanut kernels. Determine the probability (to be discussed in Section 12.7) that

a) the bird is a sparrow.

b) the bird has a high attractiveness to cracked corn.

c) the bird has a high attractiveness to black-striped sunflower seeds.

RECREATIONAL MATHEMATICS

83. *Dice* On a die, the sum of the dots on the opposite faces is seven. Two six-sided dice are placed together on top of one another, on a table, as shown in the figure below. The top and bottom faces of the bottom die and the bottom face of the top die cannot be seen. If you walk around the table, what is the sum of all the dots on all the visible faces of the dice?

INTERNET/RESEARCH ACTIVITY

84. On page 724, we briefly discuss Jacob Bernoulli. The Bernoulli family produced several prominent mathematicians, including Jacob I, Johann I, and Daniel. Write a paper on the Bernoulli family, indicating some of the accomplishments of each of the three Bernoullis named and their relationship to one another. Indicate which Bernoulli the Bernoulli numbers are named after, which Bernoulli the Bernoulli theorem in statistics is named after, and which Bernoulli the Bernoulli theorem of fluid dynamics is named after.

12.3 ODDS

The odds against winning the Fabulous Fortune lottery are about 2.6 million to 1. The odds against being audited by the IRS this year are about 47 to 1. The odds against the Chicago White Sox winning the World Series this year may be 6 to 1. We see the word *odds* daily in newspapers and magazines and often use it ourselves. Yet there is widespread misunderstanding of its meaning. In this section, we will explain the meaning of odds. We will also discuss how to determine odds against an event and how to determine odds in favor of an event.

▲ What are the odds against the Chicago White Sox winning the World Series this year?

Odds Against an Event

The odds given at horse races, at craps, and at all gambling games in Las Vegas and other casinos throughout the world are always *odds against* unless they are otherwise specified. The *odds against* an event is a ratio of the probability that the event will fail to occur (failure) to the probability that the event will occur (success). Thus, *to find odds you must first know or determine the probability of success and the probability of failure.*

$$\text{Odds against event} = \frac{P(\text{event fails to occur})}{P(\text{event occurs})} = \frac{P(\text{failure})}{P(\text{success})}$$

EXAMPLE ❶ *Rolling a 4*

Determine the odds against rolling a 4 on one roll of a die.

SOLUTION Before we can determine the odds, we must first determine the probability of rolling a 4 (success) and the probability of not rolling a 4 (failure). When a die is rolled there are six possible outcomes: 1, 2, 3, 4, 5, and 6.

$$P(\text{rolling a 4}) = \frac{1}{6} \qquad P(\text{failure to roll a 4}) = \frac{5}{6}$$

Now that we know the probabilities of success and failure, we can determine the odds against rolling a 4.

$$\text{Odds against rolling a 4} = \frac{P(\text{failure to roll a 4})}{P(\text{rolling a 4})}$$

$$= \frac{\dfrac{5}{6}}{\dfrac{1}{6}} = \frac{5}{6} \cdot \frac{6}{1} = \frac{5}{1}$$

The ratio $\frac{5}{1}$ is commonly written as 5 : 1 and is read "5 to 1." Thus, the odds against rolling a 4 are 5 to 1.   ●

TIMELY TIP The denominators of the probabilities in an odds problem will always divide out, as was shown in Example 1.

In Example 1, we considered the possible outcomes of the die: 1, 2, 3, 4, 5, 6. Over the long run, one of every six rolls will result in a 4, and five of every six rolls will result in a number other than 4. Therefore, if a person is gambling, for each dollar bet in favor of the rolling of a 4, $5 should be bet against the rolling of a 4 if the person is to break even. The person betting in favor of the rolling of a 4 will either lose $1 (if a number other than a 4 is rolled) or win $5 (if a 4 is rolled). The person betting against the rolling of a 4 will either win $1 (if a number other than a 4 is rolled) or lose $5 (if a 4 is rolled). If this game is played for a long enough period, each player theoretically will break even.

Example 2 involves a circle graph that contains percents; see Fig. 12.4 on page 743. Before we discuss Example 2, let us briefly discuss percents. Recall that probabilities are numbers between 0 and 1, inclusive. We can change a percent between 0% and 100% to a probability by writing the percent as a fraction or a decimal number. In Fig. 12.4, we see 51% in one of the sectors (or areas) of the circle. To change 51% to a probability, we can write $\frac{51}{100}$ or 0.51. Note that both the fraction and the decimal number are numbers between 0 and 1, inclusive.

EXAMPLE ❷ *Hours Worked per Week*

The circle graph in Figure 12.4 shows the percent of U.S. workers who work various hours per week. If one U.S. worker is selected at random, use the graph to determine the odds against the person working 35–39 hours per week.

Hours Worked per Week by U.S. Workers

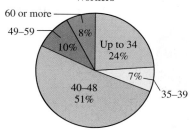

Source: *Statistical Abstract of the United States*

Figure 12.4

SOLUTION From the graph, we can determine that 7% of U.S. workers work 35–39 hours per week. When written as a probability, 7% is $\frac{7}{100}$. Therefore, the probability that a U.S. worker works 35–39 hours per week is $\frac{7}{100}$. The probability that a U.S. worker *does not* work 35–39 hours per week is $1 - \frac{7}{100} = \frac{93}{100}$.

$$\begin{aligned} \text{Odds against the person} \atop \text{working 35–39 hours per week} &= \frac{P(\text{person does not work 35–39 hours per week})}{P(\text{person works 35–39 hours per week})} \\ &= \frac{93/100}{7/100} \\ &= \frac{93}{100} \cdot \frac{100}{7} = \frac{93}{7}, \text{ or } 93:7 \end{aligned}$$

Thus, the odds against the person working 35–39 hours per week are $93:7$ ●

Odds in Favor of an Event

Although odds are generally given against an event, at times they may be given in favor of an event. The *odds in favor of* an event are expressed as a ratio of the probability that the event will occur to the probability that the event will fail to occur.

$$\text{Odds in favor of event} = \frac{P(\text{event occurs})}{P(\text{event fails to occur})} = \frac{P(\text{success})}{P(\text{failure})}$$

If the odds *against* an event are $a:b$, the odds *in favor of* the event are $b:a$.

EXAMPLE ❸ *Parents and Children Communicating*

A group of parents whose children attended Middlebury College were asked to identify the topic on which their child requested the most advice during the past year. The circle graph in Figure 12.5 on page 744 shows the parents' responses.

MATHEMATICS TODAY

Deal or No Deal

popular television show is the NBC game show *Deal or No Deal*. The rules are simple. A contestant chooses a briefcase from 26 briefcases. Inside each briefcase is a card indicating a specific, but unique, amount of money. As each round progresses, the contestant must either stay with the briefcase selected or make a "deal" with the "banker" to accept a cash offer in exchange for whatever dollar amount is in the chosen case. How does the banker know how much to offer, and when should the contestant accept or reject the banker's offer? *Deal or No Deal* is a repeated exercise in a branch of mathematics known as *decision theory*, in which the value of the *expected winnings* at any point in the game is the *mean* of the values contained in the unopened briefcases. To maximize the expected return without regard to risk, a contestant's optimal strategy is to reject the banker's offer if it is below the mean value of the amounts in the unrevealed briefcases. Typically, the banker's offer undervalues the remaining briefcases, especially at the start of the game. For further information, visit en.wikipedia.org/wiki/Deal_or_No_Deal. The Wikipedia article shows that many of the concepts presented in the probability and statistics chapters of this book may be used in deciding whether to accept or reject the banker's offer.

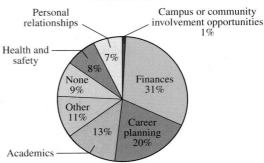

Parental Advice

Personal relationships — Campus or community involvement opportunities 1%

Health and safety

7%

None 9%

8%

Finances 31%

Other 11%

Career planning 20%

13%

Academics —

Source: 2006 Middlebury College survey

Figure 12.5

If one parent from those surveyed is selected at random, use the graph to determine

a) the odds against the parent saying that the child requested career planning advice.

b) the odds in favor of the parent saying that the child requested career planning advice.

SOLUTION

a) The graph shows that 20%, or $\frac{20}{100}$, of parents said that their child requested career planning advice. Thus, the probability that a child requested career planning advice is $\frac{20}{100}$. The probability that a child did not request career planning advice is therefore $1 - \frac{20}{100} = \frac{80}{100}$.

$$\begin{aligned} \text{Odds against a child having} &= \frac{P(\text{a child did not request career planning advice})}{P(\text{a child requested career planning advice})} \\ \text{requested career planning advice} \\ &= \frac{80/100}{20/100} = \frac{80}{100} \cdot \frac{100}{20} = \frac{80}{20} = \frac{4}{1} \text{ or } 4:1 \end{aligned}$$

Thus, the odds against parents saying that their child requested career planning advice are 4:1.

b) The odds in favor of parents saying that their child requested career planning advice are 1:4.

Finding Probabilities from Odds

When odds are given, either in favor of or against a particular event, it is possible to determine the probability that the event occurs and the probability that the event does not occur. The denominators of the probabilities are found by adding the numbers in the odds statement. The numerators of the probabilities are the numbers given in the odds statements.

EXAMPLE ❹ *Determining Probabilities from Odds*

The odds against Robin Murphy being admitted to the college of her choice are 9:2. Determine the probability that (a) Robin is admitted and (b) Robin is not admitted.

SOLUTION

a) We have been given odds against and have been asked to find probabilities.

$$\text{Odds against being admitted} = \frac{P(\text{fails to be admitted})}{P(\text{is admitted})}$$

Since the odds statement is $9:2$, the denominators of both the probability of success and the probability of failure must be $9 + 2$ or 11. To get the odds ratio of $9:2$, the probabilities must be $\frac{9}{11}$ and $\frac{2}{11}$. Since odds against is a ratio of failure to success, the $\frac{9}{11}$ and $\frac{2}{11}$ represent the probabilities of failure and success, respectively. Thus, the probability that Robin is admitted (success) is $\frac{2}{11}$.

b) The probability that Robin is not admitted (failure) is $\frac{9}{11}$. ●

Odds and probability statements are sometimes stated incorrectly. For example, consider the statement, "The odds of being selected to represent the district are 1 in 5." Odds are given using the word *to*, not *in*. Thus, there is a mistake in this statement. The correct statement might be, "The odds of being selected to represent the district are 1 to 5" or "The probability of being selected to represent the district is 1 in 5." Without additional information, it is not possible to tell which statement is the correct interpretation.

SECTION 12.3 EXERCISES

CONCEPT/WRITING EXERCISES

1. **a)** Explain how to determine the odds against an event.

   b) Explain how to determine the odds in favor of an event.

2. Explain the difference between the probability of an event and the odds in favor of an event.

3. Which odds are generally quoted, odds against or odds in favor?

4. Explain how to determine probabilities when you are given an odds statement.

5. The odds in favor of winning at Monopoly are $2:7$. Determine the odds against winning at Monopoly.

6. The odds against Fancy Frank winning the horse race are $8:3$. Determine the odds in favor of Fancy Frank winning.

7. If the odds against an event are $1:1$, what is the probability that the event will

   a) occur.

   b) fail to occur.

   Explain your answer.

8. If the probability an event will occur is $\frac{1}{2}$, determine

   a) the probability that the event will fail to occur.

   b) the odds against the event occurring.

   c) the odds in favor of the event occurring.

   Explain your answer.

PRACTICE THE SKILLS/PROBLEM SOLVING

9. *Dressing Up* Lalo Jaquez is going to wear a blue sportcoat and is trying to decide what tie he should wear with it. In his closet, he has 15 ties, 8 of which go well with the sportcoat. If Lalo selects one tie at random, determine

   a) the probability that it goes well with the sportcoat.

   b) the probability that it does not go well with the sportcoat.

   c) the odds against it going well with the sportcoat.

   d) the odds in favor of it going well with the sportcoat.

10. *Making a Donation* In her wallet, Anne Kelly has 12 bills. Six are $1 bills, two are $5 bills, three are $10 bills, and one is a $20 bill. She passes a volunteer seeking donations for the Salvation Army and decides to select one bill at random from her wallet and give it to the Salvation Army. Determine

   a) the probability that she selects a $5 bill.

   b) the probability that she does not select a $5 bill.

   c) the odds in favor of her selecting a $5 bill.

   d) the odds against her selecting a $5 bill.

Deal or No Deal In Exercises 11 and 12, consider the TV show Deal or No Deal. (See the Mathematics Today on page 744.) In the game show, there are 26 numbered cases, each indicating a cash prize ranging from 1 cent to $1,000,000. Contestants on the show have a series of choices to make, and each time they can either accept the cash offer made by the banker or select a case from the remaining cases. Assume that one of the remaining cases contains a $1,000,000 cash prize. Determine the odds against and the odds in favor of selecting the case containing the $1,000,000 cash prize if there are

11. seven cases remaining.

12. four cases remaining.

Toss a Die In Exercises 13–16, a die is tossed. Determine the odds against rolling

13. a 4.

14. an odd number.

15. a number less than 3.

16. a number greater than 4.

Deck of Cards In Exercises 17–20, a card is picked from a standard deck of cards. Determine the odds against and the odds in favor of selecting

17. a queen.

18. a heart.

19. a picture card.

20. a card greater than 5 (ace is low).

Spin the Spinner In Exercises 21–24, assume that the spinner cannot land on a line. Determine the odds against the spinner landing on the color red.

21.

22.

23.

24.

25. *Students* One person is selected at random from a class of 16 men and 14 women. Determine the odds against selecting

   a) a woman.

   b) a man.

26. *Lottery* One million tickets are sold for a lottery in which a single prize will be awarded.

   a) If you purchase a ticket, determine your odds against winning.

   b) If you purchase 10 tickets, determine your odds against winning.

Billiard Balls In Exercises 27–32, use the rack of 15 billiard balls shown.

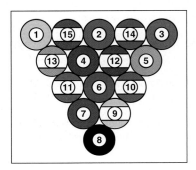

27. If one ball is selected at random, determine the odds against it containing a stripe. (Balls numbered 9 through 15 contain stripes.)

28. If one ball is selected at random, determine the odds in favor of it being a ball other than the 8 ball.

29. If one ball is selected at random, determine the odds in favor of it being an even-numbered ball.

30. If one ball is selected at random, determine the odds against it containing any red coloring (solid or striped).

31. If one ball is selected at random, determine the odds against it containing a number greater than or equal to 9.

32. If one ball is selected at random, determine the odds in favor of it containing two digits.

33. *NASCAR Winnings* The chart shows the winnings, in dollars, for the 10 highest-rated NASCAR drivers (according to point standings) for the 2005 season.

Driver	2005 Winnings
Tony Stewart	$6,987,530
Greg Biffle	$5,729,930
Carl Edwards	$4,889,990
Mark Martin	$5,994,350
Jimmie Johnson	$6,796,660
Ryan Newman	$5,578,110
Matt Kenseth	$5,790,770
Rusty Wallace	$4,868,980
Jeremy Mayfield	$4,566,910
Kurt Busch	$6,516,320

Source: www.NASCAR.com

If one of the drivers listed in the chart is selected at random, determine

a) the probability that the driver earned more than $6 million in 2005.

b) the odds against the driver earning more than $6 million in 2005.

▲ Tony Stewart

34. *Rolling a Special Die* A special die used in a game contains one dot on one side, two dots on two sides, and three dots on three sides. If the die is rolled, determine

a) the probability of rolling two dots.

b) the odds against rolling two dots.

35. *Medical Tests* The results of a medical test show that of 76 people selected at random who were given the test, 72 tested negative and 4 tested positive. Determine the odds against a person selected at random testing negative on the test. Explain how you determined your answer.

36. *A Red Marble* A box contains 9 red and 2 blue marbles. If you select one marble at random from the box, determine the odds against selecting a red marble. Explain how you determined your answer.

37. *Scholarship Award* The odds in favor of Wendy White winning a scholarship are 7 : 4. Determine the probability that

a) Wendy wins.

b) Wendy does not win.

38. *Chicken Wing Contest* The odds in favor of Boris Penzed winning the chicken wing eating contest are 3 : 8. Determine the probability that Boris will

a) win the contest.

b) not win the contest.

39. *Getting Promoted* The odds against Jason Judd getting promoted are 4 : 11. Determine the probability that Jason gets promoted.

40. *Winning a Race* The odds against Paul Phillips winning the 100 yard dash are 7 : 2. Determine the probability that

a) Paul wins.　　**b)** Paul does not win.

Playing Bingo When playing bingo, 75 balls are placed in a bin and balls are selected at random. Each ball is marked with a letter and number as indicated in the following chart.

B	I	N	G	O
1–15	16–30	31–45	46–60	61–75

For example, there are balls marked B1, B2, up to B15; I16, I17, up to I30; and so on (see photo). In Exercises 41–46, assuming one bingo ball is selected at random, determine

41. the probability that it contains the letter *G*.

42. the probability that it does not contain the letter *G*.

43. the odds in favor of it containing the letter *G*.

44. the odds against it containing the letter *G*.

45. the odds against it being *B*9.

46. the odds in favor of it being *B*9.

Blood Types In Exercises 47–52, the following circle graph shows the percent of Americans with the various types of blood.

Blood Types of Americans

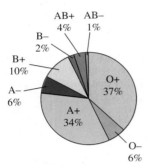

Source: 2003 Time Almanac

If one American is selected at random, use the graph to determine

47. the probability that the person has A+ blood.

48. the probability that the person has B− blood.

49. the odds against the person having A+ blood.

50. the odds in favor of the person having B− blood.

51. the odds in favor of the person having either O+ or O− blood.

52. the odds against the person having either A+ or O+ blood.

53. *Rock Concert* Suppose that the probability that a rock concert sells out is 0.9. Determine the odds against the concert selling out.

54. *High Blood Pressure* According to the U.S. Department of Health and Human Services, one in four Americans age 20 and older has high blood pressure. If an American who is age 20 or older is selected at random, determine the odds in favor of this person having high blood pressure.

55. *Bookcase Assembly* Suppose that the probability that all the parts needed to assemble a bookcase are included in the carton is $\frac{7}{8}$. Determine the odds in favor of the carton including all the needed parts.

56. *On-Time Flight Arrivals* A study of 175 airline flights in January 2006 showed that 138 of them arrived on time. If one of these flights was selected at random, determine

a) the probability that the flight arrived on time.

b) the odds against the flight arriving on time.

57. *Birth Defects* Birth defects affect 1 in 33 babies born in the United States each year.

a) What is the probability that a baby born in the United States will have a birth defect?

b) What are the odds against a baby born in the United States having a birth defect?

CHALLENGE PROBLEMS/GROUP ACTIVITIES

58. *Odds Against* Determine the odds against an even number or a number greater than 3 being rolled on a die.

59. *Horse Racing* Racetracks quote the approximate odds against each horse winning on a large board called a *tote board*. The odds quoted on a tote board for a race with five horses is as follows.

Horse Number	Odds
2	7:2
3	2:1
4	15:1
5	7:5
6	1:1

Determine the probability of each horse winning the race. (Do not be concerned that the sum of the probabilities is not 1.)

60. *Roulette* Turn to the roulette wheel illustrated on page 760. If the wheel is spun, determine

a) the probability that the ball lands on red.

b) the odds against the ball landing on red.

c) the probability that the ball lands on 0 or 00.

d) the odds in favor of the ball landing on 0 or 00.

RECREATIONAL MATHEMATICS

61. *Multiple Births* Multiple births make up about 3% of births per year in the United States. The following illustrates the number and type of multiple births in 2004.

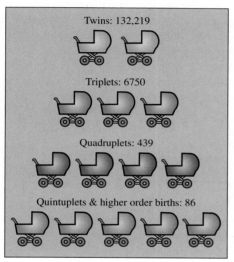

Multiple Births in the United States in 2004

Twins: 132,219

Triplets: 6750

Quadruplets: 439

Quintuplets & higher order births: 86

Source: National Center for Health Statistics

Using the above information, determine an estimate for the odds against a birth being a multiple birth in 2004.

INTERNET/RESEARCH ACTIVITIES

62. *State Lottery* Determine whether your state has a lottery. If so, do research and write a paper indicating

a) the probability of winning the grand prize.

b) the odds against winning the grand prize.

c) Explain, using real objects such as pennies or table tennis balls, what these odds actually mean.

63. *Casino Advantages* There are many types of games of chance to choose from at casinos. The house has the advantage in each game, but the advantages differ according to the game.

a) List the games available at a typical casino.

b) List those for which the house has the smallest advantage of winning.

c) List those for which the house has the greatest advantage of winning.

12.4 EXPECTED VALUE (EXPECTATION)

▲ Expected value can be used to determine the expected results of an experiment repeated many times.

Consider the following situation. Tim tells Barbara that he will give her $1 if she can roll an even number on a single die. If she fails to roll an even number, she must give Tim $1. Who would win money in the long run if this game were played many times? In this section, we will learn how to determine the expected results of an experiment over the long term.

Expected value, also called *expectation*, is often used to determine the expected results of an experiment or business venture *over the long term*. People use expectation to make important decisions in many different areas. For example, expectation is used in business to predict future profits of a new product. In the insurance industry, expectation is used to determine how much each insurance policy should cost for the company to make an overall profit. Expectation is also used to predict the expected gain or loss in games of chance such as the lottery, roulette, craps, and slot machines.

In the situation with Tim and Barbara, we would expect in the long run that half the time Tim would win $1 and half the time he would lose $1; therefore, Tim would break even. Mathematically, we could find Tim's expected gain or loss by the following procedure:

$$\text{Tim's expected gain or loss} = P\left(\begin{array}{c}\text{Tim}\\\text{wins}\end{array}\right) \cdot \left(\begin{array}{c}\text{amount}\\\text{Tim wins}\end{array}\right) + P\left(\begin{array}{c}\text{Tim}\\\text{loses}\end{array}\right) \cdot \left(\begin{array}{c}\text{amount}\\\text{Tim loses}\end{array}\right)$$

$$= \frac{1}{2}(\$1) + \frac{1}{2}(-\$1) = \$0$$

Note that the loss is written as a negative number. This procedure indicates that Tim has an expected gain or loss (or expected value) of $0. The expected value of zero indicates that he would indeed break even, as we had anticipated. Thus, the game is a *fair game*. If Tim's expected value were positive, it would indicate a gain; if negative, a loss.

The expected value, E, is calculated by multiplying the probability of an event occurring by the *net* amount gained or lost if the event occurs. If there are a number of different events and amounts to be considered, we use the following formula.

> ### EXPECTED VALUE
>
> $$E = P_1 \cdot A_1 + P_2 \cdot A_2 + P_3 \cdot A_3 + \cdots + P_n \cdot A_n$$

The symbol P_1 represents the probability that the first event will occur, and A_1 represents the net amount won or lost if the first event occurs. P_2 is the probability of the second event, and A_2 is the net amount won or lost if the second event occurs, and so on. The sum of these products of the probabilities and their respective amounts is the expected value. The expected value is the average (or mean) result that would be obtained if the experiment were performed a great many times.

EXAMPLE ❶ *A New Business Venture*

JetBlue Airways is considering adding a route to the city of Minneapolis, Minnesota. Before the company makes its decision as to whether or not to service Minneapolis, it needs to consider many factors, including potential profits and losses. Factors that may affect the company's profits and losses include the number of competing airlines, the potential number of customers, the overhead costs, and fees it must pay. After considerable research, the company estimates that if it serves Minneapolis, there is a 60% chance of making a $900,000 profit, a 10% chance of breaking even, and a 30% chance of losing $1,400,000. How much can JetBlue Airways "expect" to make on this new route?

SOLUTION The three amounts to be considered are a gain of $900,000, breaking even at $0, and a loss of $1,400,000. The probability of gaining $900,000 is 0.6, the probability of breaking even is 0.1, and the probability of losing $1,400,000 is 0.3.

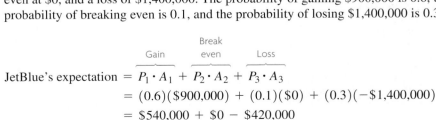

$$
\begin{aligned}
\text{JetBlue's expectation} &= \overbrace{P_1 \cdot A_1}^{\text{Gain}} + \overbrace{P_2 \cdot A_2}^{\substack{\text{Break}\\\text{even}}} + \overbrace{P_3 \cdot A_3}^{\text{Loss}} \\
&= (0.6)(\$900,000) + (0.1)(\$0) + (0.3)(-\$1,400,000) \\
&= \$540,000 + \$0 - \$420,000 \\
&= \$120,000
\end{aligned}
$$

JetBlue Airways has an expectation, or expected average gain, of $120,000 for adding this particular service. Thus, if the company opened routes like this one, with these particular probabilities and amounts, in the long run it would have an average gain of $120,000 per route. However, you must remember that there is a 30% chance that JetBlue will lose $1,400,000 on this *particular* route (or any particular route with these probabilities and amounts.)   ●

EXAMPLE ➋ *Test-Taking Strategy*

Maria is taking a multiple-choice exam in which there are five possible answers for each question. The instructions indicate that she will be awarded 2 points for each correct response, that she will lose $\frac{1}{2}$ point for each incorrect response, and that no points will be added or subtracted for answers left blank.

a) If Maria does not know the correct answer to a question, is it to her advantage or disadvantage to guess at an answer?

b) If she can eliminate one of the possible choices, is it to her advantage or disadvantage to guess at the answer?

SOLUTION

a) Let's determine the expected value if Maria guesses at an answer. Only one of five possible answers is correct.

$$P(\text{guesses correctly}) = \frac{1}{5} \qquad P(\text{guesses incorrectly}) = \frac{4}{5}$$

$$\text{Maria's expectation} = \overbrace{P_1 \cdot A_1}^{\substack{\text{Guesses}\\\text{correctly}}} + \overbrace{P_2 \cdot A_2}^{\substack{\text{Guesses}\\\text{incorrectly}}}$$

$$= \frac{1}{5}(2) + \frac{4}{5}\left(-\frac{1}{2}\right)$$

$$= \frac{2}{5} - \frac{2}{5} = 0$$

Thus, Maria's expectation is zero when she guesses. Therefore, over the long run she will neither gain nor lose points by guessing.

b) If Maria can eliminate one possible choice, one of four answers will be correct.

$$P(\text{guesses correctly}) = \frac{1}{4} \qquad P(\text{guesses incorrectly}) = \frac{3}{4}$$

$$\text{Maria's expectation} = \overbrace{P_1 \cdot A_1}^{\substack{\text{Guesses}\\\text{correctly}}} + \overbrace{P_2 \cdot A_2}^{\substack{\text{Guesses}\\\text{incorrectly}}}$$

$$= \frac{1}{4}(2) + \frac{3}{4}\left(-\frac{1}{2}\right)$$

$$= \frac{2}{4} - \frac{3}{8} = \frac{4}{8} - \frac{3}{8} = \frac{1}{8}$$

Since the expectation is a positive $\frac{1}{8}$, Maria will, on average, gain $\frac{1}{8}$ point each time she guesses when she can eliminate one possible choice.   ●

EXAMPLE ❸ *Selling Hot Dogs*

An outdoor hot dog vendor sells an average of 50 hot dogs per day in dry weather and an average of 15 per day in wet weather. If the weather in this area is wet 25% of the time, determine the expected (average) number of hot dogs sold per day.

SOLUTION The amounts in this example are the number of hot dogs sold. Since the weather is wet 25% of the time, it will be dry 100% − 25% = 75% of the time. When written as probabilities, 25% and 75% are 0.25 and 0.75, respectively.

$$E = P(\text{dry}) \cdot (\text{number sold}) + P(\text{wet}) \cdot (\text{number sold})$$
$$= 0.75(50) + 0.25(15) = 37.5 + 3.75 = 41.25$$

Thus, the average, or expected, number of hot dogs sold per day is 41.25.   ●

When we gave the expectation formula, we indicated that the amounts were the **net amounts**, which are the actual amounts gained or lost. Examples 4 and 5 illustrate how net amounts are used in two applications of expected value.

EXAMPLE ❹ *Winning a Door Prize*

When Josh Rosenberg attends a charity event, he is given a free ticket for the $50 door prize. A total of 100 tickets will be given out. Determine his expectation of winning the door prize.

SOLUTION The probability of winning the door prize is $\frac{1}{100}$ since Josh has 1 of 100 tickets. If he wins, his net or actual winnings will be $50 since he did not pay for the ticket. The probability that Josh loses is $\frac{99}{100}$. If Josh loses, the amount he loses is $0 because he did not pay for the ticket.

$$\text{Expectation} = P(\text{Josh wins}) \cdot (\text{amount won}) + P(\text{Josh loses}) \cdot (\text{amount lost})$$
$$= \frac{1}{100}(50) + \frac{99}{100}(0) = \frac{50}{100} = 0.50$$

Thus, Josh's expectation is $0.50, or 50 cents.   ●

Now we will consider a problem similar to Example 4, but this time we will assume that Josh must purchase the ticket for the door prize.

EXAMPLE ❺ *Winning a Door Prize*

When Josh Rosenberg attends a charity event, he is given the opportunity to purchase a ticket for the $50 door prize. The cost of the ticket is $2, and 100 tickets will be sold. Determine Josh's expectation if he purchases one ticket.

SOLUTION As in Example 4, Josh's probability of winning is $\frac{1}{100}$. However, if he does win, his actual or net winnings will be $48. The $48 is obtained by subtracting the cost of the ticket, $2, from the amount of the door prize, $50. There is also a probability of $\frac{99}{100}$ that Josh will not win the door prize. If he does not win the door prize, he has lost the $2 that he paid for the ticket. Therefore, we must consider two amounts when we determine Josh's expectation, winning $48 and losing $2.

$$\text{Expectation} = P(\text{Josh wins}) \cdot (\text{amount won}) + P(\text{Josh loses}) \cdot (\text{amount lost})$$
$$= \frac{1}{100}(48) + \frac{99}{100}(-2)$$

$$= \frac{48}{100} - \frac{198}{100} = -\frac{150}{100} = -1.50$$

Josh's expectation is $-\$1.50$ when he purchases one ticket.

In Example 5, we determined that Josh's expectation was $-\$1.50$ when he purchased one ticket. If he purchased two tickets, his expectation would be $2(-\$1.50)$, or $-\$3.00$. We could also compute Josh's expectation if he purchased two tickets as follows:

$$E = \frac{2}{100}(46) + \frac{98}{100}(-4) = -3.00$$

This answer, $-\$3.00$, checks with the answer obtained by multiplying the expectation for a single ticket by 2.

Let's look at one more example in which a person must pay for a chance to win a prize. In the following example, there will be more than two amounts to consider.

EXAMPLE 6 *Raffle Tickets*

One thousand raffle tickets are sold for $1 each. One grand prize of $500 and two consolation prizes of $100 will be awarded. The tickets are placed in a bin. The winning tickets will be selected from the bin. Assuming that the probability that any given ticket selected for the grand prize is $\frac{1}{1000}$ and the probability that any given ticket selected for a consolation prize is $\frac{2}{1000}$, determine

a) Irene Drew's expectation if she purchases one ticket.

b) Irene's expectation if she purchases five tickets.

SOLUTION

a) Three amounts are to be considered: the net gain in winning the grand prize, the net gain in winning one of the consolation prizes, and the loss of the cost of the ticket. If Irene wins the grand prize, her net gain is $499 ($500 minus $1 spent for the ticket). If Irene wins one of the consolation prizes, her net gain is $99 ($100 minus $1). The probability that Irene wins the grand prize is $\frac{1}{1000}$ and the probability that she wins a consolation prize is $\frac{2}{1000}$. The probability that she does not win a prize is $1 - \frac{1}{1000} - \frac{2}{1000} = \frac{997}{1000}$.

$$E = P_1 \cdot A_1 + P_2 \cdot A_2 + P_3 \cdot A_3$$

$$= \frac{1}{1000}(\$499) + \frac{2}{1000}(\$99) + \frac{997}{1000}(-\$1)$$

$$= \frac{499}{1000} + \frac{198}{1000} - \frac{997}{1000} = -\frac{300}{1000} = -0.30$$

Thus, Irene's expectation is $-\$0.30$ per ticket purchased.

b) On average, Irene loses 30 cents on each ticket purchased. On five tickets, her expectation is $(-\$0.30)(5)$, or $-\$1.50$.

TIMELY TIP In any expectation problem, the sum of the probabilities of all the events should always be 1. Note in Example 6 that the sum of the probabilities is $\frac{1}{1000} + \frac{2}{1000} + \frac{997}{1000} = \frac{1000}{1000} = 1$.

Fair Price

In Example 5, we determined that Josh's expectation was $-\$1.50$. Now let's determine how to find out how much should have been charged for a ticket so that his expectation would be $0. If Josh's expectation were to be $0, he could be expected to break even over the long run. Suppose that Josh paid 50 cents, or \$0.50, for the ticket. His expectation, if paying \$0.50 for the ticket, would be calculated as follows.

$$\text{Expectation} = P(\text{Josh wins}) \cdot (\text{amount won}) + P(\text{Josh loses}) \cdot (\text{amount lost})$$

$$= \frac{1}{100}(49.50) + \frac{99}{100}(-\$0.50)$$

$$= \frac{49.50}{100} - \frac{49.50}{100} = 0$$

Thus, if Josh paid 50 cents per ticket, his expectation would be $0. The 50 cents, in this case, is called the fair price of the ticket. The *fair price* is the amount to be paid that will result in an expected value of $0. The fair price may be found by adding the *cost to play* to the *expected value*.

> **Fair price** = expected value + cost to play

In Example 5, the cost to play was $2 and the expected value was determined to be $-\$1.50$. The fair price for a ticket in Example 5 may be found as follows.

$$\text{Fair price} = \text{expected value} + \text{cost to play}$$

$$= -1.50 + 2.00 = 0.50$$

We obtained a fair price of \$0.50. If the tickets were sold for the fair price of \$0.50 each, Josh's expectation would be $0, as shown above. Can you now find the fair price that Irene should pay for a raffle ticket in Example 6? In Example 6, the cost of a ticket was $1 and we determined that the expected value was $-\$0.30$.

$$\text{Fair price} = \text{expected value} + \text{cost to play}$$

$$= -\$0.30 + \$1.00 = \$0.70$$

Thus, the fair price for a ticket in Example 6 is \$0.70, or 70 cents. Verify for yourself now that if the tickets were sold for \$0.70, the expectation would be \$0.00.

EXAMPLE ⑦ *Expectation and Fair Price*

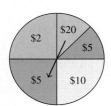

Suppose that you are playing a game in which you spin the pointer shown in the figure in the margin and you are awarded the amount shown under the pointer. If it costs $8 to play the game, determine

a) the expectation of a person who plays the game.

b) the fair price to play the game.

SOLUTION

a) There are four numbers on which the pointer can land: 2, 5, 10, and 20. The following chart shows the probability of the pointer landing on each number and the actual amount won or lost if the pointer lands on that number. The probabilities are obtained using the areas of the circle. The amounts won or lost are determined by subtracting the cost to play, $8, from each indicated amount.

Amount Shown on Wheel	$2	$5	$10	$20
Probability	$\frac{1}{4}$	$\frac{3}{8}$	$\frac{1}{4}$	$\frac{1}{8}$
Amount Won or Lost	$-$6	$-$3	$2	$12

Notice that the sum of the probabilities is $\frac{1}{4} + \frac{3}{8} + \frac{1}{4} + \frac{1}{8} = 1$, which shows that all possible outcomes have been considered.

Now let's find the expectation. There are four amounts to consider.

$$\text{Expectation} = P(\text{lands on \$2}) \cdot (\text{amount}) + P(\text{lands on \$5}) \cdot (\text{amount})$$
$$+ P(\text{lands on \$10}) \cdot (\text{amount}) + P(\text{lands on \$20}) \cdot (\text{amount})$$
$$= \frac{1}{4}(-6) + \frac{3}{8}(-3) + \frac{1}{4}(2) + \frac{1}{8}(12)$$
$$= -\frac{6}{4} - \frac{9}{8} + \frac{2}{4} + \frac{12}{8}$$
$$= -\frac{12}{8} - \frac{9}{8} + \frac{4}{8} + \frac{12}{8} = -\frac{5}{8} = -\$0.625$$

Thus, the expectation is $-\$0.625$.

b) Fair price = expectation + cost to play

$$= -\$0.625 + \$8 = \$7.375$$

Thus, the fair price to play the game is about $7.38.   ●

SECTION 12.4   EXERCISES

CONCEPT/WRITING EXERCISES

1. What does the expected value of an experiment or business venture represent?

2. a) What does an expected value of 0 mean?

   b) What does a negative expected value mean?

   c) What does a positive expected value mean?

3. What is meant by the fair price of a game of chance?

4. Write the formula used to find the expected value of an experiment with

   a) two possible outcomes.

   b) three possible outcomes.

5. If the expected value and cost to play are known for a particular game of chance, explain how you can determine the fair price to pay to play that game of chance.

6. Is the fair price to pay for a game of chance the same as the expected value of that game of chance? Explain your answer.

7. If a particular game costs $1.50 to play and the expectation for the game is $-\$1.00$, what is the fair price to pay to play the game? Explain how you determined your answer.

8. If a particular game cost $3.00 to play and the expectation for the game is $-\$2.00$, what is the fair price to pay to play the game? Explain how you determined your answer.

PRACTICE THE SKILLS/PROBLEM SOLVING

9. *Three Tickets* On a $1 lottery ticket, Marty Smith's expected value is $-$0.40$. What is Marty's expected value if he purchases three lottery tickets?

10. *Expected Value* If on a $1 bet, Paul Goldstein's expected value is $0.30, what is Paul's expected value on a $5 bet?

11. *Expected Attendance* For an outdoor concert of the Los Angeles Philharmonic Orchestra at the Hollywood Bowl, concert organizers estimate that 14,000 people will attend if it is not raining. If it is raining, concert organizers estimate that 8400 people will attend. On the day of the concert, meteorologists predict a 70% chance of rain. Determine the expected number of people who will attend this concert.

▲ The Hollywood Bowl

12. *A New Business* In a proposed business venture, Stephanie Morrison estimates that there is a 60% chance she will make $80,000 and a 40% chance she will lose $20,000. Determine Stephanie's expected value.

13. *Basketball* Candace Parker is a star player for the University of Tennessee Volunteers women's basketball team. She has injured her ankle, and it is doubtful that she will be able to play in an upcoming game. If Candace can play, the coach estimates that the Volunteers will score 78 points. If Candace is not able to play, the coach estimates that they will score 62 points. The team doctor estimates that there is a 50% chance Candace will play. Determine the number of points the team can expect to score.

▲ Candace Parker (left) and Brittany Hunter

14. *Career Fair Attendance* For a Nursing and Allied Health Care Career Fair, organizers estimate that 50 people will attend if it does not rain and 65 will attend if it rains. The weather forecast indicates that there is a 40% chance it will not rain and a 60% chance it will rain on the day of the career fair. Determine the expected number of people who will attend the fair.

15. *TV Shows* The NBC television network is scheduling its fall lineup of shows. For the Thursday night 8 P.M. slot, NBC has selected the show *Heroes*. If its rival network CBS schedules the show *CSI: Crime Scene Investigation* during the same time slot, NBC estimates that *Heroes* will get 1.2 million viewers. However, if CBS schedules the show *The Unit* during that time slot, NBC estimates that *Heroes* will get 1.6 million viewers. NBC believes that the probability that CBS will show *CSI* is 0.4 and the probability that CBS will show *The Unit* is 0.6. Determine the expected number of viewers for the show *Heroes*.

16. *Seattle Greenery* In July in Seattle, the grass grows $\frac{1}{2}$ in. a day on a sunny day and $\frac{1}{4}$ in. a day on a cloudy day. In Seattle in July, 75% of the days are sunny and 25% are cloudy.

   a) Determine the expected amount of grass growth on a typical day in July in Seattle.

   b) Determine the expected total grass growth in the month of July in Seattle.

17. *Investment Club* The Triple L investment club is considering purchasing a certain stock. After considerable research, the club members determine that there is a 60% chance of making $10,000, a 10% chance of breaking even, and a 30% chance of losing $7200. Determine the expectation of this purchase.

18. *Clothing Sale* At a special clothing sale at the Crescent Oaks Country Club, after the cashier rings up your purchase, you select a slip of paper from a box. The slip of paper indicates the dollar amount, either $5 or $10, that is deducted from your purchase price. The probability of selecting a slip indicating $5 is $\frac{7}{10}$, and the probability of selecting a slip indicating $10 is $\frac{3}{10}$. If your original purchase before you select the slip of paper is $200, determine

   a) the expected dollar amount to be deducted from your purchase.

   b) the expected dollar amount you will pay for your purchase.

19. *Fortune Cookies* At the Royal Dragon Chinese restaurant, a slip in the fortune cookies indicates a dollar amount that will be subtracted from your total bill. A bag of 10 fortune cookies is given to you from which you will select one. If seven fortune cookies contain "$1 off," two contain "$2 off," and one contains "$5 off," determine the expectation of a selection.

20. **Pick a Card** Mike and Dave play the following game. Mike picks a card from a deck of cards. If he selects a heart, Dave gives him $5. If not, he gives Dave $2.

a) Determine Mike's expectation.

b) Determine Dave's expectation.

21. **Roll a Die** Alyssa and Gabriel play the following game. Alyssa rolls a die. If she rolls a 1, 2, or 3, Gabriel gives Alyssa $3. If Alyssa rolls a 4 or 5, Gabriel gives Alyssa $2. However, if Alyssa rolls a 6, she gives Gabriel $14.

a) Determine Alyssa's expectation.

b) Determine Gabriel's expectation.

22. **Blue Chips and Red Chips** A bag contains 3 blue chips and 2 red chips. Chi and Dolly play the following game. Chi selects one chip at random from the bag. If Chi selects a blue chip, Dolly gives Chi $5. If Chi selects a red chip, Chi gives Dolly $8.

a) Determine Chi's expectation.

b) Determine Dolly's expectation.

23. **Multiple-Choice Test** A multiple-choice exam has five possible answers for each question. For each correct answer, you are awarded 5 points. For each incorrect answer, 1 point is subtracted from your score. For answers left blank, no points are added or subtracted.

a) If you do not know the correct answer to a particular question, is it to your advantage to guess? Explain.

b) If you do not know the correct answer but can eliminate one possible choice, is it to your advantage to guess? Explain.

24. **Multiple-Choice Test** A multiple-choice exam has four possible answers for each question. For each correct answer, you are awarded 5 points. For each incorrect answer, 2 points are subtracted from your score. For answers left blank, no points are added or subtracted.

a) If you do not know the correct answer to a particular question, is it to your advantage to guess? Explain.

b) If you do not know the correct answer but can eliminate one possible choice, is it to your advantage to guess? Explain.

25. **Raffle Tickets** Five hundred raffle tickets are sold for $2 each. One prize of $400 is to be awarded.

a) Raul Mondesi purchases one ticket. Determine his expected value.

b) Determine the fair price of a ticket.

26. **Raffle Tickets** One thousand raffle tickets are sold for $1 each. One prize of $800 is to be awarded.

a) Rena Condos purchases one ticket. Determine her expected value.

b) Determine the fair price of a ticket.

27. **Raffle Tickets** Two thousand raffle tickets are sold for $3.00 each. Three prizes will be awarded: one for $1000 and two for $500. Assume that the probability that any given ticket is selected for the $1000 prize is $\frac{1}{2000}$ and the probability that any given ticket is selected for the $500 prize is $\frac{2}{2000}$. Jeremy Sharp purchases one of these tickets.

a) Determine his expected value.

b) Determine the fair price of a ticket.

28. **Raffle Tickets** Ten thousand raffle tickets are sold for $5 each. Four prizes will be awarded: one for $5000, one for $2500, and two for $1000. Assume that the probability that any given ticket is selected for the $5000 prize is $\frac{1}{10,000}$, the probability that any given ticket is selected for the $2500 prize is $\frac{1}{10,000}$, and the probability that any given ticket is selected for a $1000 prize is $\frac{2}{10,000}$. Sidhardt purchases one of these tickets.

a) Determine his expected value.

b) Determine the fair price of a ticket.

Spinners In Exercises 29 and 30, assume that a person spins the pointer and is awarded the amount indicated by the pointer. Determine the person's expectation.

29.

30.

Spinners *In Exercises 31 and 32, assume that a person spins the pointer and is awarded the amount indicated if the pointer points to a positive number but must pay the amount indicated if the pointer points to a negative number. Determine the person's expectation if the person plays the game.*

31.

32.

Selecting an Envelope *In Exercises 33–36, a person randomly selects one of the five envelopes shown below. Each envelope contains a check that the person gets to keep. Determine the person's expectation if the checks in the envelopes are as follows.*

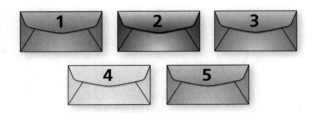

33. Two envelopes contain a $500 check, and three envelopes contain a $1000 check.

34. Four envelopes contain a $1000 check, and one envelope contains a $5000 check.

35. The five envelopes contain checks for $100, $200, $300, $400, and $1000, respectively.

36. Two envelopes contain a check for $600, two envelopes contain a check for $2000, and one envelope contains a check for $5000.

Spinners *In Exercises 37–40, assume that a person spins the pointer and is awarded the amount indicated by the pointer. If it costs $2 to play the game, determine*

a) *the expectation of a person who plays the game.*

b) *the fair price to play the game.*

37.

38.

39.

40.

Selecting an Envelope *In Exercises 41–44, a person randomly selects one of the four envelopes shown below. Each envelope contains a check that the person gets to keep. However, before the person can select an envelope, he or she must pay $10 to play. For the value of the checks indicated in the exercises, determine*

a) *the expectation for a person who plays.*

b) *the fair price to play.*

41. Two envelopes contain a $5 check, and two envelopes contain a $20 check.

42. Three envelopes contain a $15 check, and one envelope contains a $0 check.

43. The checks in the envelopes are for $0, $1, $5, and $10, respectively.

44. The checks in the envelopes are for $2, $2, $10, and $400, respectively.

45. *Reaching Base Safely* Based on his past baseball history, Jim Devias has a 17% chance of reaching first base safely, a 10% chance of hitting a double, a 2% chance of hitting a triple, an 8% chance of hitting a home run, and a 63% chance of making an out at his next at bat. Determine Jim's expected number of bases for his next at bat.

46. *Life Insurance* According to Bristol Mutual Life Insurance's mortality table, the probability that a 20-year-old woman will survive 1 year is 0.994 and the probability that she will die within 1 year is 0.006. If a 20-year-old woman buys a $10,000 1-year policy for $100, what is Bristol Mutual's expected gain or loss?

47. *Choosing a Colored Chip* In a box, there are a total of 10 chips. The chips are orange, green, and yellow, as shown below.

If you select an orange chip, you get 4 points, a green chip 3 points, and a yellow chip 1 point. If you select one chip at random, determine the expected number of points you will get.

48. *Choosing a Colored Chip* Repeat Exercise 47 but assume that an orange chip is worth 5 points, a green chip 2 points, and a yellow chip −3 points (3 points are taken away).

49. *Employee Hiring* The academic vice president at Brookdale Community College has requested that new academic programs be added to the college curriculum. If the college's Board of Trustees approves the new programs, the college will hire 75 new employees. If the new programs are not approved, the college will hire only 20 new employees. If the probability that the new programs will be approved is 0.65, what is the expected number of new employees to be hired by Brookdale Community College? Round your answer to the nearest whole number of employees.

50. *Completing a Project* A mechanical contractor is preparing for a construction project. He determines that if he completes the project on schedule, his net profit will be $450,000. If he completes the project between 0 and 3 months late, his net profit decreases to $120,000. If he completes the project more than 3 months late, his net loss is $275,000. The probability that he completes the project on schedule is 0.6, the probability that he completes the project between 0 and 3 months late is 0.3, and the probability that he completes the project more than 3 months late is 0.1. Determine his expected gain or loss for this project.

51. *New Store* Dunkin' Donuts is opening a new store. The company estimates that there is a 75% chance the store will have a profit of $10,000, a 10% chance the store will break even, and a 15% chance the store will lose $2000. Determine the expected gain or loss for this store.

52. *China Cabinet* The owner of an antique store estimates that there is a 40% chance she will make $2000 when she sells an antique china cabinet, a 50% chance she will make $750 when she sells the cabinet, and a 10% chance she will break even when she sells the cabinet. Determine the expected amount she will make when she sells the cabinet.

53. *Rolling a Die* A die is rolled many times, and the points facing up are recorded. Determine the expected (average) number of points facing up over the long run.

54. *Lawsuit* Don Vello is considering bringing a lawsuit against the Dummote Chemical Company. His lawyer estimates that there is a 70% chance Don will make $40,000, a 10% chance Don will break even, and a 20% chance they will lose the case and Don will need to pay $30,000 in legal fees. Estimate Don's expected gain or loss if he proceeds with the lawsuit.

55. *Road Service* On a clear day in Boston, the Automobile Association of American (AAA) makes an average of 110 service calls for motorist assistance, on a rainy day it makes an average of 160 service calls, and on a snowy day it makes an average of 210 service calls. If the weather in Boston is clear 200 days of the year, rainy 100 days of the year, and snowy 65 days of the year, determine the expected number of service calls made by the AAA in a given day.

56. *Real Estate* The expenses for Jorge Estrada, a real estate agent, to list, advertise, and attempt to sell a house are $1000. If Jorge succeeds in selling the house, he will receive a commission of 6% of the sales price. If an agent with a different company sells the house, Jorge still receives 3% of the sales price. If the house is unsold after 3 months, Jorge loses the listing and receives nothing. Suppose that the probability that he sells a $100,000 house is 0.2, the probability that another agent sells the house is 0.5, and the probability that the house is unsold after 3 months is 0.3. Determine Jorge's expectation if he accepts this house for listing. Should Jorge list the house? Explain.

Dart Board In Exercises 57 and 58, assume that you are blindfolded and throw a dart at the dart board shown on the top of page 760. Assume that your dart sticks in the dart board, and not on a line.

a) *Determine the probabilities that the dart lands on $1, $10, $20, and $100, respectively.*

b) *If you win the amount of money indicated by the section of the board where the dart lands, determine your expectation when you throw the dart.*

c) *If the game is to be fair, how much should you pay to play?*

57.

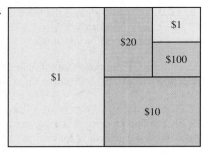

58.

CHALLENGE PROBLEMS/GROUP ACTIVITIES

59. *Term Life Insurance* An insurance company will pay the face value of a term life insurance policy if the insured person dies during the term of the policy. For how much should an insurance company sell a 10-year term policy with a face value of $40,000 to a 30-year-old man for the company to make a profit? The probability of a 30-year-old man living to age 40 is 0.97. Explain your answer. Remember that the customer pays for the insurance before the policy becomes effective.

60. *Lottery Ticket* Is it possible to determine your expectation when you purchase a lottery ticket? Explain.

Roulette In Exercises 61 and 62, use the roulette wheel illustrated. A roulette wheel typically contains slots with num- bers 1–36 and slots marked 0 and 00. A ball is spun on the wheel and comes to rest in one of the 38 slots. Eighteen numbers are colored red, and 18 numbers are colored black. The 0 and 00 are colored green. If you bet on one particular number and the ball lands on that number, the house pays off odds of 35 to 1. If you bet on a red number or black number and win, the house pays 1 to 1 (even money).

61. Determine the expected value of betting $1 on a particular number.

62. Determine the expected value of betting $1 on red.

RECREATIONAL MATHEMATICS

63. *Wheel of Fortune* The following is a miniature version of the Wheel of Fortune. When Dave Salem spins the wheel, he is awarded the amount on the wheel indicated by the pointer. If the wheel points to Bankrupt, he loses the total amount he has accumulated and also loses his turn. Assume that the wheel stops on a position at random and that each position is equally likely to occur.

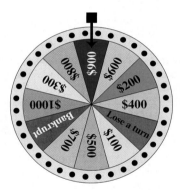

a) Determine Mr. Salem's expectation when he spins the wheel at the start of the game (he has no money to lose if he lands on Bankrupt).

b) If Mr. Salem presently has a balance of $1800, determine his expectation when he spins the wheel.

12.5 TREE DIAGRAMS

▲ We can use a tree diagram to illustrate the possible arrangements of boys and girls in a family with three children.

Suppose that a couple plans to have three children. What is the probability that the couple will have exactly two boys? What is the probability that the couple will have at least one girl? We stated earlier that the possible results of an experiment are called its outcomes. To solve probability problems such as the ones above, it is helpful if we are able to determine all the possible outcomes of an experiment. In this section, we will illustrate how the counting principle can be used to determine the number of outcomes of an experiment. We will also illustrate how tree diagrams can be used to determine all the possible outcomes of an experiment.

Now we will introduce the counting principle.

COUNTING PRINCIPLE
If a first experiment can be performed in M distinct ways and a second experiment can be performed in N distinct ways, then the two experiments in that specific order can be performed in $M \cdot N$ distinct ways.

If we wanted to find the number of possible outcomes when a coin is tossed and a die is rolled, we could reason that the coin has two possible outcomes, heads and tails. The die has six possible outcomes: 1, 2, 3, 4, 5, and 6. Thus, the two experiments together have $2 \cdot 6$, or 12, possible outcomes.

A list of all the possible outcomes of an experiment is called a *sample space*. Each individual outcome in the sample space is called a *sample point*. *Tree diagrams* are helpful in determining sample spaces.

A tree diagram illustrating all the possible outcomes when a coin is tossed and a die is rolled (see Fig. 12.6) has two initial branches, one for each possible outcome of the coin. Each of these branches will have six branches emerging from them, one for each possible outcome of the die. That will give a total of 12 branches, the same number of possible outcomes found by using the counting principle. We can obtain the sample space by listing all the possible combinations of branches. Note that this sample space consists of 12 sample points.

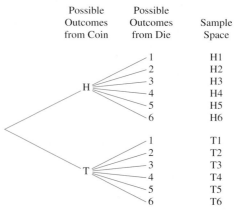

Figure 12.6

Example 1 uses the phrase "without replacement." This phrase tells us that once an item is selected, it cannot be selected again, making it impossible to select the same item twice.

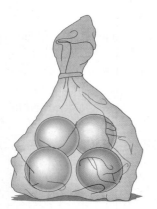

Figure 12.7

┌ **EXAMPLE ❶**   *Selecting Balls without Replacement*

Two balls are to be selected *without replacement* from a bag that contains one red, one blue, one green, and one orange ball (see Fig. 12.7).

a) Use the counting principle to determine the number of points in the sample space.

b) Construct a tree diagram and list the sample space.

c) Determine the probability that one orange ball is selected.

d) Determine the probability that a green ball followed by a red ball is selected.

SOLUTION

a) The first selection may be any one of the four balls. Once the first ball is selected, only three balls remain for the second selection. Thus, there are $4 \cdot 3$, or 12, sample points in the sample space.

b) The first ball selected can be red, blue, green, or orange. Since this experiment is done without replacement, the same colored ball cannot be selected twice. For example, if the first ball selected is red, the second ball selected must be either blue, green, or orange. The tree diagram and sample space are shown in Fig. 12.8. The sample space contains 12 points. That result checks with the answer obtained in part (a) using the counting principle.

First Selection	Second Selection	Sample Space
R	B	RB
	G	RG
	O	RO
B	R	BR
	G	BG
	O	BO
G	R	GR
	B	GB
	O	GO
O	R	OR
	B	OB
	G	OG

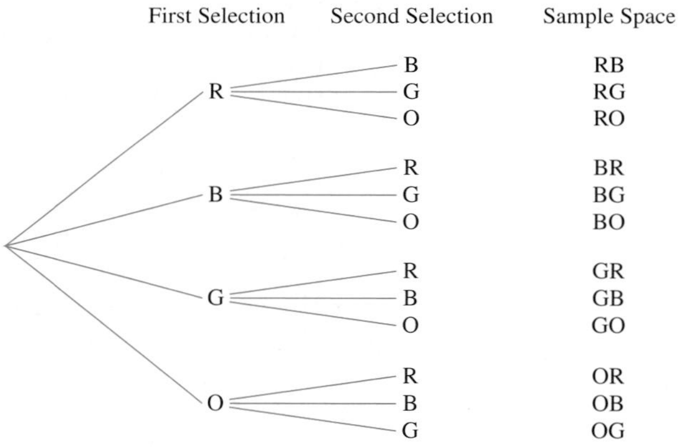

Figure 12.8

c) If we know the sample space, we can compute probabilities using the formula

$$P(E) = \frac{\text{number of outcomes favorable to } E}{\text{total number of outcomes}}$$

The total number of outcomes will be the number of points in the sample space. From Fig. 12.8, we determine that there are 12 possible outcomes. Six outcomes have one orange ball: RO, BO, GO, OR, OB, and OG.

$$P(\text{one orange ball is selected}) = \frac{6}{12} = \frac{1}{2}$$

d) One possible outcome meets the criteria of a green ball followed by a red ball: GR.

$$P(\text{green followed by red}) = \frac{1}{12}$$

The counting principle can be extended to any number of experiments, as illustrated in Example 2.

EXAMPLE ❷ *Lunch Choices*

At Theresa's Restaurant, each lunch special consists of a sandwich, a beverage, and a dessert. The sandwich choices are roast beef (r) or ham (h). The beverage choices are coffee (c), tea (t), or soda (s). The dessert choices are ice cream (i) or apple pie (p).

a) Use the counting principle to determine the number of different lunch specials offered by the restaurant.

b) Construct a tree diagram and list the sample space.

c) If a customer randomly selects one of the lunch specials, determine the probability that both a roast beef sandwich and ice cream are selected.

d) If a customer randomly selects one of the lunch specials, determine the probability that neither tea nor apple pie is selected.

SOLUTION

a) There are 2 choices for a sandwich, 3 choices for a beverage and 2 choices for dessert. Using the counting principle, we can determine that there are $2 \cdot 3 \cdot 2$ or 12 different lunch specials.

b) The tree diagram illustrating the 12 lunch specials is given in Fig. 12.9.

Sandwich	Beverage	Dessert	Sample Space
r	c	i	rci
		p	rcp
	t	i	rti
		p	rtp
	s	i	rsi
		p	rsp
h	c	i	hci
		p	hcp
	t	i	hti
		p	htp
	s	i	hsi
		p	hsp

Figure 12.9

c) Of the 12 lunch specials, 3 contain both a roast beef sandwich and ice cream (rci, rti, rsi).

$$P(\text{roast beef and ice cream are selected}) = \frac{3}{12} = \frac{1}{4}$$

d) Of the 12 lunch specials, 4 contain neither tea nor apple pie (rci, rsi, hci, hsi).

$$P(\text{neither tea nor ice cream are selected}) = \frac{4}{12} = \frac{1}{3}$$

EXAMPLE 3 *Selecting Ticket Winners*

A radio station has two tickets to give away to a Beyoncé concert. It held a contest and narrowed the possible recipients down to four people: Christine (C), Mike Hammer (MH), Mike Levine (ML), and Phyllis (P). The names of two of these four people will be selected at random from a hat and the two people selected will be awarded the tickets.

a) Use the counting principle to determine the number of points in the sample space.

b) Construct a tree diagram and list the sample space.

c) Determine the probability that Christine is selected.

d) Determine the probability that neither Mike Hammer nor Mike Levine is selected.

e) Determine the probability that at least one Mike is selected.

▲ Beyoncé

SOLUTION

a) The first selection may be any one of the four people; see Fig. 12.10. Once the first person is selected, only three people remain for the second selection. Thus, there are 4 · 3 or 12 sample points in the sample space.

b)
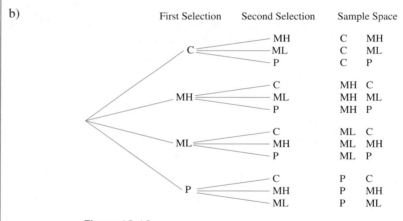
Figure 12.10

c) Of the 12 points in the sample space, 6 have Christine. They are C MH, C ML, C P, MH C, ML C, and P C.

$$P(\text{Christine is selected}) = \frac{6}{12} = \frac{1}{2}$$

d) Of the 12 points in the sample space, two have neither Mike. They are C P and P C.

$$P(\text{neither Mike selected}) = \frac{2}{12} = \frac{1}{6}$$

e) At least one Mike means that one or more Mikes are selected. There are 10 points in the sample space with at least one Mike (all those except C P and P C).

$$P(\text{at least one Mike is selected}) = \frac{10}{12} = \frac{5}{6}$$ ●

In Example 3, if you add the probability of no Mike being selected with the probability of at least one Mike being selected, you get $\frac{1}{6} + \frac{5}{6}$, or 1. In any probability problem, if E is a specific event, then either E happens at least one time or it does not happen at all. Thus, $P(E$ happening at least once$) + P(E$ does not happen$) = 1$, which leads to the following rule.

$$P(\text{event happening at least once}) = 1 - P(\text{event does not happen})$$

For example, suppose that the probability of not getting any red flowers from the seeds that are planted is $\frac{2}{7}$. Then the probability of getting at least one red flower from the seeds that are planted is $1 - \frac{2}{7} = \frac{5}{7}$. We will use this rule in later sections.

In all the tree diagrams in this section, the outcomes were always equally likely; that is, each outcome had the same probability of occurrence. Consider a rock that has 4 faces such that each face has a different surface area and the rock is not uniform in density (see Fig. 12.11). When the rock is dropped, the probability that the rock lands on face 1 will not be the same as the probability that the rock lands on face 2. In fact, the probabilities that the rock lands on face 1, face 2, face 3, and face 4 may all be different. Therefore, the outcomes of the rock landing on face 1, face 2, face 3, and face 4 are not equally likely outcomes. Because the outcomes are not equally likely and we are not given additional information, we cannot determine the theoretical probability of the rock landing on each individual face. However, we can still determine the sample space indicating the faces that the rock may land on when the rock is dropped twice. The tree diagram and sample space are shown in Fig. 12.12.

Figure 12.11

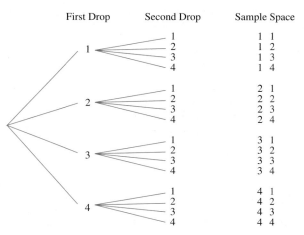

Figure 12.12

Since the outcomes are not equally likely, the probability of each of the 16 sample points in the sample space occurring cannot be determined. If the outcomes were equally likely, then each of the 16 points in the sample space would have a probability of $\frac{1}{16}$. See Exercises 29 and 30, which deal with outcomes that are not equally likely.

SECTION 12.5 EXERCISES

CONCEPT/WRITING EXERCISES

1. Explain the counting principle.

2. a) What is a sample space?

   b) What is a sample point?

3. If a first experiment can be performed in two distinct ways and a second experiment can be performed in seven distinct ways, how many possible ways can the two experiments be performed? Explain your answer.

4. In your own words, describe how to construct a tree diagram.

5. A problem states that two selections are made "without replacement." Explain what that means.

6. One experiment has five equally likely outcomes, and a second experiment has three equally likely outcomes. How many sample points will be in the sample space when the two experiments are performed one after the other?

PRACTICE THE SKILLS

7. *Selecting States* If two states are selected at random from the 50 U.S. states, use the counting principle to determine the number of possible outcomes if the states are selected

   a) with replacement.

   b) without replacement.

8. *Selecting Dates* If two dates are selected at random from the 365 days of the year, use the counting principle to determine the number of possible outcomes if the dates are selected

   a) with replacement.

   b) without replacement.

9. *Selecting Lightbulbs* A bag contains seven lightbulbs, all the same size and equally likely to be selected. Each lightbulb

is a different brand. If you select three lightbulbs at random, use the counting principle to determine how many points will be in the sample space if the lightbulbs are selected

   a) with replacement.

   b) without replacement.

10. *Remote Control* Your television remote control has buttons for digits 0–9. If you press two buttons, how many numbers are possible if

   a) the same button may be pressed twice.

   b) the same button may not be pressed twice.

In Exercises 11–28, use the counting principle to determine the answer to part (a). Assume that each event is equally likely to occur.

11. *Coin Toss* Two coins are tossed.

   a) Determine the number of points in the sample space.

   b) Construct a tree diagram and list the sample space.

   Determine the probability that

   c) no heads are tossed.

   d) exactly one head is tossed.

   e) two heads are tossed.

12. *Boys and Girls* A couple plans to have two children.

   a) Determine the number of points in the sample space of the possible arrangements of boys and girls.

   b) Construct a tree diagram and list the sample space.

Assuming that boys and girls are equally likely, determine the probability that the couple has

c) two girls.

d) at least one girl.

e) a girl and then a boy.

13. *Cards* A box contains three cards. On one card there is a sun, on another card there is a question mark, and on the third card there is an apple.

Two cards are to be selected at random with replacement.

a) Determine the number of points in the sample space.

b) Construct a tree diagram and list the sample space.

Determine the probability that

c) two apples are selected.

d) a sun and then a question mark are selected.

e) at least one apple is selected.

14. *Cards* Repeat Exercise 13 but assume that the cards are drawn without replacement.

15. *Marble Selection* A hat contains four marbles: 1 yellow, 1 red, 1 blue, and 1 green. Two marbles are to be selected at random without replacement from the hat.

a) Determine the number of points in the sample space.

b) Construct a tree diagram and list the sample space.

Determine the probability of selecting

c) exactly 1 red marble.

d) at least 1 marble that is not red.

e) no green marbles.

16. *Three Coins* Three coins are tossed.

a) Determine the number of points in the sample space.

b) Construct a tree diagram and list the sample space.

Determine the probability that

c) no heads are tossed.

d) exactly one head is tossed.

e) three heads are tossed.

17. *Paint Choices* The Flotterons plan to purchase paint for the walls and paint for the trim in their living room. They will select one color for the walls and one color for the trim from the following colors.

Walls	Trim
Sable	Alabaster
Java	White
Chocolate	Oyster

a) Determine the number of points in the sample space.

b) Construct a tree diagram and list the sample space.

Determine the probability that they select

c) Java.

d) Java and oyster.

e) paint other than java.

18. *Pet Shop* A pet shop is selling a calico cat, a Siamese cat, a Persian cat, and a Himalayan cat. The Chens are going to select two cats to bring home as pets.

a) Determine the number of points in the sample space.

b) Construct a tree diagram and list the sample space.

Determine the probability that they select

c) the Persian cat.

d) the Persian cat and the calico cat.

e) cats other than the Persian cat.

PROBLEM SOLVING

19. *Rolling Dice* Two dice are rolled.

   a) Determine the number of points in the sample space.

   b) Construct a tree diagram and list the sample space.

   Determine the probability that

   c) a double (a 1, 1 or 2, 2, etc.) is rolled.

   d) a sum of 7 is rolled.

   e) a sum of 2 is rolled.

   f) Are you as likely to roll a sum of 2 as you are of rolling a sum of 7? Explain your answer.

20. *Voting* At a homeowners' association meeting, a board member can vote yes, vote no, or abstain on a motion. There are three motions on which a board member must vote.

   a) Determine the number of points in the sample space.

   b) Construct a tree diagram and determine the sample space.

   Determine the probability that a board member votes

   c) no, yes, no in that order.

   d) yes on exactly two of the motions.

   e) yes on at least one motion.

21. *Gift Cards* Three different people are to be selected at random, and each will be given one gift card. There is one card from Home Depot, one from Best Buy, and one from Red Lobster. The first person selected gets to choose one of the cards. The second person selected gets to choose between the two remaining cards. The third person selected gets the third card.

   a) Determine the number of points in the sample space.

   b) Construct a tree diagram and determine the sample space.

   Determine the probability that

   c) the Best Buy card is selected first.

   d) the Home Depot card is selected first and the Red Lobster card is selected last.

   e) The cards are selected in this order: Best Buy, Red Lobster, Home Depot.

22. *Shopping* Susan Forman has to purchase a box of cereal, a bottle of soda, and a can of vegetables. The types of cereal, soda, and vegetables she is considering are shown below.

   Cereal: Rice Krispies, Frosted Flakes, Honeycomb
   Soda: orange, black cherry, ginger ale
   Vegetables: peas, carrots

   a) Determine the number of points in the sample space.

   b) Construct a tree diagram and determine the sample space.

   Determine the probability that she selects

   c) Honeycomb for the cereal.

   d) Rice Krispies and ginger ale.

   e) a soda other than black cherry.

23. *Apartment Options* Don Cater plans to rent an apartment from Rustic Village Apartments. The following chart displays information regarding the possible number of bedrooms, bathrooms, and other features from which he can choose. For his apartment, Don will select the number of bedrooms, number of bathrooms, and one other feature.

Bedrooms	Bathrooms	Other Features
1	1	Fireplace
2	2	Hardwood floors
3		Balcony

   a) Determine the number of points in the sample space.

   b) Construct a tree diagram and determine the sample space.

   Determine the probability that Don selects

   c) a two-bedroom apartment.

   d) a two-bedroom apartment with a fireplace.

   e) an apartment without a balcony.

24. *A New Computer* You visit Computer City to purchase a new computer system. You are going to purchase a computer, printer, and monitor from among the following brands.

Computer	Printer	Monitor
Compaq	Hewlett-Packard	Omega
IBM	Epson	Toshiba
Gateway		
Dell		

a) Determine the number of points in the sample space.

b) Construct a tree diagram and determine the sample space.

Determine the probability of selecting

c) a Gateway computer.

d) a Hewlett-Packard printer.

e) a Gateway computer and a Hewlett-Packard printer.

25. *Buying Appliances* Mr. and Mrs. Miller just moved into a new home and need to purchase kitchen appliances. The chart below shows the brands of appliances they are considering.

Refrigerator	Stove	Dishwasher
General Electric	General Electric	General Electric
Kenmore	Frigidaire	KitchenAid
Maytag	Roper	Whirlpool

The Millers are going to purchase a refrigerator, a stove, and a dishwasher.

a) Determine the number of points in the sample space.

b) Construct a tree diagram and determine the sample space.

Determine the probability that they select

c) General Electric for all three appliances.

d) no General Electric appliances.

e) at least one General Electric appliance.

26. *Literature Choices* You decide to take a Literature course. A requirement for the course is that you must read one classic book, one nonfiction book, and one science fiction book from the list below.

Classic	Nonfiction	Science Fiction
A Farewell to Arms (F)	*John Adams* (J)	*War of the Worlds* (W)
The Grapes of Wrath (G)	*Band of Brothers* (B)	*Dune* (D)
Tom Sawyer (T)		
Moby-Dick (M)		

a) Determine the number of points in the sample space.

b) Construct a tree diagram and determine the sample space.

Determine the probability that

c) *John Adams* is selected.

d) either *A Farewell to Arms* or *Moby-Dick* is selected.

e) *Moby-Dick* is not selected.

27. *Personal Characteristics* An individual can be classified as male or female with red, brown, black, or blond hair and with brown, blue, or green eyes.

a) How many different classifications are possible (for example, male, red-headed, blue-eyed)?

b) Construct a tree diagram to determine the sample space.

c) If each outcome is equally likely, determine the probability that the individual will be a male with black hair and blue eyes.

d) Determine the probability that the individual will be a female with blond hair.

28. *Mendel Revisited* A pea plant must have exactly one of each of the following pairs of traits: short (*s*) or tall (*t*); round (*r*) or wrinkled (*w*) seeds; yellow (*y*) or green (*g*) peas; and white (*wh*) or purple (*p*) flowers (for example, short, wrinkled, green pea with white flowers).

a) How many different classifications of pea plants are possible?

b) Use a tree diagram to determine all the classifications possible.

c) If each characteristic is equally likely, find the probability that the pea plant will have round peas.

d) Determine the probability that the pea plant will be short, have wrinkled seeds, have yellow seeds, and have purple flowers.

CHALLENGE PROBLEMS/GROUP ACTIVITIES

29. *Three Chips* Suppose that a bag contains one white chip and two red chips. Two chips are going to be selected at random from the bag *with replacement*.

a) What is the probability of selecting a white chip from the bag on the first selection?

b) What is the probability of selecting a red chip from the bag on the first selection?

c) Are the outcomes of selecting a white chip and selecting a red chip on the first selection equally likely? Explain.

d) The sample space when two chips are selected from the bag with replacement is ww, wr, rw, rr. Do you believe that the probability of selecting ww is greater than, equal to, or less than the probability of selecting rr? Explain.

30. *Thumbtacks* A thumbtack is dropped on a concrete floor. Assume that the thumbtack can only land point up (u) or point down (d), as shown in the figure below.

If two thumbtacks are dropped, one after the other, the tree diagram below can be used to show the possible outcomes.

First Thumbtack	Second Thumbtack	Sample Space
u	u	u u
	d	u d
d	u	d u
	d	d d

a) Do you believe that the outcomes of the thumbtack landing point up and the thumbtack landing point down are equally likely? Explain.

b) List the sample points in the sample space of this experiment.

c) Do you believe that the probability that both thumbtacks land point up (*uu*) is the same as the probability that both thumbtacks land point down (*dd*)? Explain.

d) Can you compute the theoretical probability of a thumbtack landing point up and the theoretical probability of a thumbtack landing point down? Explain.

e) Obtain a box of thumbtacks and drop the thumbtacks out of the box with care. Determine the empirical probability of a thumbtack landing point up when dropped and the empirical probability of a thumbtack landing point down when dropped.

RECREATIONAL MATHEMATICS

31. *Ties* All my ties are red except two. All my ties are blue except two. All my ties are brown except two. How many ties do I have?

32. *Rock Faces* An experiment consists of 3 parts: flipping a coin, tossing a rock, and rolling a die. If the sample space consists of 60 sample points, determine the number of faces on the rock.

12.6 *OR* AND *AND* PROBLEMS

▲ What is the probability that you select a movie that is a comedy or a movie rated PG?

Suppose you go to Blockbuster Video to rent a movie. You are overwhelmed with the number of movie choices, so you decide to randomly select a movie from the list of the top 100 rentals. What is the probability that you select a comedy *or* a movie rated PG? If you decide to randomly select two movies, what is the probability that the first movie selected is a comedy *and* the second movie selected is a drama? In this section, we will learn how to solve probability problems containing the words *or* and probability problems containing the word *and*.

In Section 12.5, we showed how to work probability problems by constructing sample spaces. Often it is inconvenient or too time consuming to solve a problem by first constructing a sample space. For example, if an experiment consists of selecting two cards with replacement from a deck of 52 cards, there would be $52 \cdot 52$ or 2704 points in the sample space. Trying to list all these sample points could take hours. In this section, we learn how to solve *compound probability* problems that contain the words *and* or *or* without constructing a sample space.

Or Problems

The *or probability problem* requires obtaining a "successful" outcome for *at least one* of the given events. For example, suppose that we roll one die and we are interested in finding the probability of rolling an even number *or* a number greater than 4. For this situation, rolling either a 2, 4, or 6 (an even number) or a 5 or 6 (a number greater than 4) would be considered successful. Note that the number 6 satisfies both criteria. Since 4 of the 6 numbers meet the criteria (the 2, 4, 5, and 6), the probability of rolling an even number *or* a number greater than 4 is $\frac{4}{6}$ or $\frac{2}{3}$.

A formula for finding the probability of event A or event B, symbolized $P(A \text{ or } B)$, follows.

$$P(A \text{ or } B) = P(A) + P(B) - P(A \text{ and } B)$$

Since we add (and subtract) probabilities to find $P(A \text{ or } B)$, this formula is sometimes referred to as the *addition formula*. We explain the use of the *or* formula in Example 1.

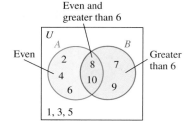

Figure 12.13

⌐EXAMPLE ❶ *Using the Addition Formula*

Each of the numbers 1, 2, 3, 4, 5, 6, 7, 8, 9, and 10 is written on a separate piece of paper. The 10 pieces of paper are then placed in a hat, and one piece is randomly selected. Determine the probability that the piece of paper selected contains an even number or a number greater than 6.

SOLUTION We are asked to find the probability that the number selected is *even* or is *greater than 6.* Let's use set A to represent the statement "the number is even" and set B to represent the statement "the number is greater than 6." Figure 12.13 is a Venn diagram, as introduced in Chapter 2, with sets *A* (even) and *B* (greater than 6). There are a total of 10 numbers, of which five are even (2, 4, 6, 8, and 10). Thus, the probability of selecting an even number is $\frac{5}{10}$. Four numbers are greater than 6: the 7, 8, 9, and 10. Thus, the probability of selecting a number greater than 6 is $\frac{4}{10}$. Two numbers are both even and greater than 6: the 8 and 10. Thus, the probability of selecting a number that is both even and greater than 6 is $\frac{2}{10}$.

If we substitute the appropriate statements for *A* and *B* in the formula, we obtain

$$P(A \text{ or } B) = P(A) + P(B) - P(A \text{ and } B)$$

$$P\left(\begin{array}{c}\text{even or}\\\text{greater than 6}\end{array}\right) = P(\text{even}) + P\left(\begin{array}{c}\text{greater}\\\text{than 6}\end{array}\right) - P\left(\begin{array}{c}\text{even and}\\\text{greater than 6}\end{array}\right)$$

$$= \frac{5}{10} + \frac{4}{10} - \frac{2}{10}$$

$$= \frac{7}{10}$$

Thus, the probability of selecting an even number or a number greater than 6 is $\frac{7}{10}$. The seven numbers that are even or greater than 6 are 2, 4, 6, 7, 8, 9, and 10.   ●

Example 1 illustrates that when finding the probability of *A* or *B*, we add the probabilities of events *A* and *B* and then subtract the probability of both events occurring simultaneously.

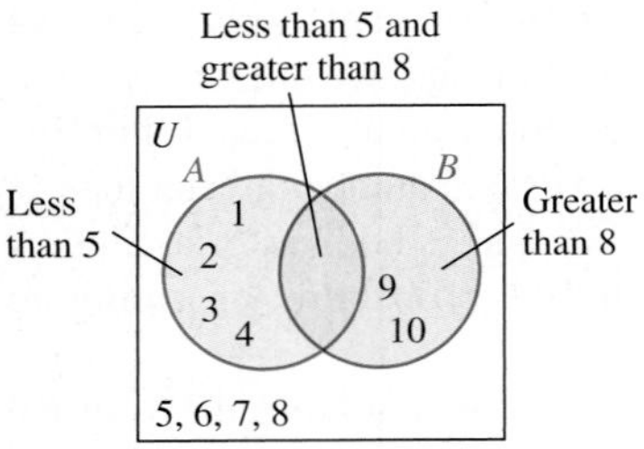

EXAMPLE ❷   *Using the Addition Formula*

Consider the same sample space, the numbers 1 through 10, as in Example 1. If one piece of paper is selected, determine the probability that it contains a number less than 5 or a number greater than 8.

SOLUTION Let *A* represent the statement "the number is less than 5" and *B* represent the statement "the number is greater than 8." A Venn diagram illustrating these statements is shown in Fig. 12.14.

$$P(\text{number is less than 5}) = \frac{4}{10}$$

$$P(\text{number is greater than 8}) = \frac{2}{10}$$

Since there are no numbers that are *both* less than 5 and greater than 8, *P*(number is less than 5 and greater than 8) = 0. Therefore,

$$P\left(\begin{array}{c}\text{number is}\\\text{less than 5}\\\text{or greater}\\\text{than 8}\end{array}\right) = P\left(\begin{array}{c}\text{number is}\\\text{less than 5}\end{array}\right) + P\left(\begin{array}{c}\text{number is}\\\text{greater than 8}\end{array}\right) - P\left(\begin{array}{c}\text{number is}\\\text{less than 5}\\\text{and greater}\\\text{than 8}\end{array}\right)$$

$$= \frac{4}{10} + \frac{2}{10} - 0 = \frac{6}{10} = \frac{3}{5}$$

Thus, the probability of selecting a number less than 5 or greater than 8 is $\frac{3}{5}$. The six numbers that are less than 5 or greater than 8 are 1, 2, 3, 4, 9, and 10.   ●

Figure 12.14

In Example 2, it is impossible to select a number that is both less than 5 *and* greater than 8 when only one number is to be selected. Events such as these are said to be *mutually exclusive.*

> Two events A and B are **mutually exclusive** if it is impossible for both events to occur simultaneously.

If events A and B are mutually exclusive, then $P(A \text{ and } B) = 0$ and the addition formula simplifies to $P(A \text{ or } B) = P(A) + P(B)$.

EXAMPLE ❸ *Probability of A or B*

One card is selected from a standard deck of playing cards. Determine whether the following pairs of events are mutually exclusive and find $P(A \text{ or } B)$.
a) A = an ace, B = a jack
b) A = an ace, B = a heart
c) A = a red card, B = a black card
d) A = a picture card, B = a red card

SOLUTION

a) There are four aces and four jacks in a standard deck of 52 cards. It is impossible to select both an ace and a jack when only one card is selected. Therefore, these events are mutually exclusive.

$$P(\text{ace or jack}) = P(\text{ace}) + P(\text{jack}) = \frac{4}{52} + \frac{4}{52} = \frac{8}{52} = \frac{2}{13}$$

b) There are 4 aces and 13 hearts in a standard deck of 52 cards. One card, the ace of hearts, is both an ace and a heart. Therefore, these events are not mutually exclusive.

$$P(\text{ace}) = \frac{4}{52} \qquad P(\text{heart}) = \frac{13}{52} \qquad P(\text{ace and heart}) = \frac{1}{52}$$

$$P(\text{ace or heart}) = P(\text{ace}) + P(\text{heart}) - P(\text{ace and heart})$$

$$= \frac{4}{52} + \frac{13}{52} - \frac{1}{52}$$

$$= \frac{16}{52} = \frac{4}{13}$$

The ace of hearts is both an ace and a heart.

c) There are 26 red cards and 26 black cards in a standard deck of 52 cards. It is impossible to select one card that is both a red card and a black card. Therefore, the events are mutually exclusive.

$$P(\text{red or black}) = P(\text{red}) + P(\text{black})$$

$$= \frac{26}{52} + \frac{26}{52} = \frac{52}{52} = 1$$

Since $P(\text{red or black}) = 1$, a red card or a black card must be selected.

d) There are 12 picture cards in a standard deck of 52 cards. Six of the 12 picture cards are red (the jacks, queens, and kings of hearts and diamonds). Thus, selecting a picture card and a red card are not mutually exclusive.

$$P\left(\begin{array}{c}\text{picture card}\\\text{or red card}\end{array}\right) = P\left(\begin{array}{c}\text{picture}\\\text{card}\end{array}\right) + P\left(\begin{array}{c}\text{red}\\\text{card}\end{array}\right) - P\left(\begin{array}{c}\text{picture card}\\\text{and red card}\end{array}\right)$$

$$= \frac{12}{52} + \frac{26}{52} - \frac{6}{52}$$

$$= \frac{32}{52} = \frac{8}{13}$$

And Problems

A second type of probability problem is the *and probability problem*, which requires obtaining a favorable outcome in *each* of the given events. For example, suppose that *two* cards are to be selected from a deck of cards and we are interested in the probability of selecting two aces (one ace *and* then a second ace). Only if *both* cards selected are aces would this experiment be considered successful. A formula for finding the probability of events A and B, symbolized $P(A \text{ and } B)$, follows.

$$P(A \text{ and } B) = P(A) \cdot P(B)$$

Since we multiply to find $P(A \text{ and } B)$, this formula is sometimes referred to as the *multiplication formula*. When using the multiplication formula, we **always assume that event A has occurred when calculating $P(B)$** because we are determining the probability of obtaining a favorable outcome in both of the given events.*

Unless we specify otherwise, $P(A \text{ and } B)$ indicates that we are determining the probability that event A occurs *and then* event B occurs (in that order). Consider a bag that contains three chips: 1 red chip, 1 blue chip, and 1 green chip. Suppose that two chips are selected from the bag with replacement. The tree diagram and sample space for the experiment are shown in Fig. 12.15. There are nine possible outcomes for the two selections, as indicated in the sample space.

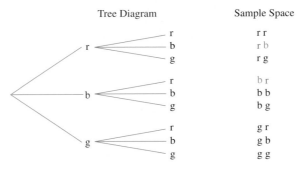

Figure 12.15

---

*$P(B)$, assuming that event A has occurred, may be denoted $P(B \mid A)$, which is read "the probability of B, given A." We will discuss this type of probability (conditional probability) further in Section 12.7.

Note that the probability of selecting a red chip followed by a blue chip (rb), indicated by P(red and blue), is $\frac{1}{9}$. The probability of selecting a red chip and a blue chip, in any order (rb or br), is $\frac{2}{9}$. In this section, when we ask for $P(A$ and $B)$, it means the probability of event A occurring *and then* event B occurring, in that order.

┌─ EXAMPLE ❹ *An Experiment with Replacement*

Two cards are to be selected *with replacement* from a deck of cards. Determine the probability that two queens will be selected.

SOLUTION Since the deck of 52 cards contains four queens, the probability of selecting a queen on the first draw is $\frac{4}{52}$. The card selected is then returned to the deck. Therefore, the probability of selecting a queen on the second draw remains $\frac{4}{52}$.

If we let A represent the selection of the first queen and B represent the selection of the second queen, the formula may be written as follows.

$$P(A \text{ and } B) = P(A) \cdot P(B)$$
$$P(2 \text{ queens}) = P(\text{queen } 1 \text{ } and \text{ queen } 2) = P(\text{queen } 1) \cdot P(\text{queen } 2)$$
$$= \frac{4}{52} \cdot \frac{4}{52}$$
$$= \frac{1}{13} \cdot \frac{1}{13} = \frac{1}{169}$$

┌─ EXAMPLE ❺ *An Experiment without Replacement*

Two cards are to be selected *without replacement* from a deck of cards. Determine the probability that two queens will be selected.

SOLUTION This example is similar to Example 4. However, this time we are doing the experiment without replacing the first card selected to the deck before selecting the second card.

The probability of selecting a queen on the first draw is $\frac{4}{52}$. When calculating the probability of selecting the second queen, we must assume that the first queen has been selected. Once this first queen has been selected, only 51 cards, including 3 queens, remain in the deck. The probability of selecting a queen on the second draw becomes $\frac{3}{51}$. The probability of selecting two queens without replacement is

$$P(2 \text{ queens}) = P(\text{queen } 1) \cdot P(\text{queen } 2)$$
$$= \frac{4}{52} \cdot \frac{3}{51}$$
$$= \frac{1}{13} \cdot \frac{1}{17} = \frac{1}{221}$$

Now we introduce *independent events*.

Event A and event B are **independent events** if the occurrence of either event in no way affects the probability of occurrence of the other event.

Rolling dice and tossing coins are examples of independent events. In Example 4, the events are independent since the first card was returned to the deck. The probability of selecting a queen on the second draw was not affected by the first selection. The events in Example 5 are not independent since the probability of the selection of the second queen was affected by removing the first queen selected from the deck. Such events are called *dependent events. Experiments done with replacement will result in independent events, and those done without replacement will result in dependent events.*

EXAMPLE ⑥ *Independent or Dependent Events?*

One hundred people attended a charity benefit to raise money for cancer research. Three people in attendance will be selected at random without replacement, and each will be awarded one door prize. Are the events of selecting the three people who will be awarded the door prize independent or dependent events?

SOLUTION The events are dependent since each time one person is selected, it changes the probability of the next person being selected. In the first selection, the probability that a specific individual is selected is $\frac{1}{100}$. If that person is not selected first, the probability that the specific person is selected second changes to $\frac{1}{99}$. In general, in any experiment in which two or more items are selected *without replacement*, the events will be dependent.

The multiplication formula may be extended to more than two events, as illustrated in Example 7.

EXAMPLE ⑦ *Drug Reaction*

A new medicine was given to a sample of 25 of Dr. Cleary's patients with flu symptoms. Of the total, 19 patients reacted favorably, 2 reacted unfavorably, and 4 were unaffected. Three of these patients are selected at random. Determine the probability of each of the following.

a) All three reacted favorably.
b) The first patient reacted favorably, the second patient reacted unfavorably, and the third patient was unaffected.
c) No patient reacted favorably.
d) At least one patient reacted favorably.

SOLUTION Each time a patient is selected, the number of patients remaining decreases by one.

a) The probability that the first patient reacted favorably is $\frac{19}{25}$. If the first patient reacted favorably, of the 24 remaining patients only 18 are left who reacted favorably. The probability of selecting a second patient who reacted favorably is $\frac{18}{24}$. If the second patient reacted favorably, only 17 patients are left who reacted favorably. The probability of selecting a third patient who reacted favorably is $\frac{17}{23}$.

$$P\begin{pmatrix}\text{three patients}\\\text{reacted}\\\text{favorably}\end{pmatrix} = P\begin{pmatrix}\text{first patient}\\\text{reacted}\\\text{favorably}\end{pmatrix} \cdot P\begin{pmatrix}\text{second patient}\\\text{reacted}\\\text{favorably}\end{pmatrix} \cdot P\begin{pmatrix}\text{third patient}\\\text{reacted}\\\text{favorably}\end{pmatrix}$$

$$= \frac{19}{25} \cdot \frac{18}{24} \cdot \frac{17}{23} = \frac{969}{2300}$$

b) The probability that the first patient reacted favorably is $\frac{19}{25}$. Once a patient is selected, there are only 24 patients remaining. Two of the remaining 24 patients reacted unfavorably. Thus, the probability that the second patient reacted unfavorably is $\frac{2}{24}$. After the second patient is selected, there are 23 remaining patients, of which 4 were unaffected. The probability that the third patient was unaffected is therefore $\frac{4}{23}$.

$$P\begin{pmatrix} \text{first patient reacted favorably, the} \\ \text{second patient reacted unfavorably, and} \\ \text{the third patient was unaffected} \end{pmatrix}$$

$$= P\begin{pmatrix} \text{first patient} \\ \text{reacted} \\ \text{favorably} \end{pmatrix} \cdot P\begin{pmatrix} \text{second patient} \\ \text{reacted} \\ \text{unfavorably} \end{pmatrix} \cdot P\begin{pmatrix} \text{third patient} \\ \text{was} \\ \text{unaffected} \end{pmatrix}$$

$$= \frac{19}{25} \cdot \frac{2}{24} \cdot \frac{4}{23} = \frac{19}{1725}$$

c) If none of the patients reacted favorably, the patients either reacted unfavorably or were unaffected. Six patients did not react favorably (2 reacted unfavorably and 4 were unaffected). The probability that the first patient selected did not react favorably is $\frac{6}{25}$. After the first patient is selected, 5 of the remaining 24 patients did not react favorably. After the second patient is selected, 4 of the remaining 23 patients did not react favorably.

$$P\begin{pmatrix} \text{none} \\ \text{reacted} \\ \text{favorably} \end{pmatrix} = P\begin{pmatrix} \text{first patient} \\ \text{did not react} \\ \text{favorably} \end{pmatrix} \cdot P\begin{pmatrix} \text{second patient} \\ \text{did not react} \\ \text{favorably} \end{pmatrix} \cdot P\begin{pmatrix} \text{third patient} \\ \text{did not react} \\ \text{favorably} \end{pmatrix}$$

$$= \frac{6}{25} \cdot \frac{5}{24} \cdot \frac{4}{23} = \frac{1}{115}$$

d) In Section 12.5, we learned that

$$P(\text{event happening at least once}) = 1 - P(\text{event does not happen})$$

In part (c), we found that the probability of selecting three patients none of whom reacted favorably was $\frac{1}{115}$. Therefore, the probability that at least one of the patients selected reacted favorably can be found as follows.

$$P\begin{pmatrix} \text{at least one of the three} \\ \text{patients reacted favorably} \end{pmatrix} = 1 - P\begin{pmatrix} \text{none of the three} \\ \text{patients reacted favorably} \end{pmatrix}$$

$$= 1 - \frac{1}{115} = \frac{115}{115} - \frac{1}{115} = \frac{114}{115} \qquad \bullet$$

TIMELY TIP

Which formula to use
It is sometimes difficult to determine when to use the *or* formula and when to use the *and* formula. The following information may be helpful in deciding which formula to use.

Continued on next page

Continued from previous page

Or formula

Or problems will almost always contain the word *or* in the statement of the problem. For example, determine the probability of selecting a heart *or* a 6. *Or* problems in this book generally involve only *one* selection. For example, "one card is selected" or "one die is rolled."

And formula

And problems often do *not* use the word *and* in the statement of the problem. For example, "determine the probability that both cards selected are red" or "determine the probability that none of those selected is a banana" are both *and*-type problems. *And* problems in this book will generally involve *more than one* selection. For example, the problem may read "two cards are selected" or "three coins are flipped."

SECTION 12.6 EXERCISES

CONCEPT/WRITING EXERCISES

1. **a)** In $P(A$ or $B)$, what does the word *or* indicate?

   b) In $P(A$ and $B)$, what does the word *and* indicate?

2. **a)** Give the formula for $P(A$ or $B)$.

   b) In your own words, explain how to determine $P(A$ or $B)$ with the formula.

3. **a)** What are mutually exclusive events? Give an example.

   b) How do you calculate $P(A$ or $B)$ when A and B are mutually exclusive?

4. **a)** Give the formula for $P(A$ and $B)$.

   b) In your own words, explain how to determine $P(A$ and $B)$ with the formula.

5. When finding $P(B)$ using the formula $P(A$ and $B)$, what do we always assume?

6. **a)** What are independent events? Give an example.

   b) What are dependent events? Give an example.

7. A family is selected at random. Let event A be the mother likes classical music. Let event B be the daughter likes classical music.

   a) Are events A and B mutually exclusive? Explain.

   b) Are they independent events? Explain.

8. A family is selected at random. Let event A be the father likes to cook. Let event B be the mother likes to golf.

   a) Are events A and B mutually exclusive? Explain.

   b) Are they independent events? Explain.

9. If events A and B are mutually exclusive, explain why the formula $P(A$ or $B) = P(A) + P(B) - P(A$ and $B)$ can be simplified to $P(A$ or $B) = P(A) + P(B)$.

10. **a)** Write a problem that you would use the *or formula* to solve. Solve the problem and give the answer.

    b) Write a problem that you would use the *and formula* to solve. Solve the problem and give the answer.

PRACTICE THE SKILLS

In Exercises 11–14, determine the indicated probability.

11. If $P(A) = 0.6$, $P(B) = 0.4$, and $P(A$ and $B) = 0.3$, determine $P(A$ or $B)$.

12. If $P(A$ or $B) = 0.9$, $P(A) = 0.7$, and $P(B) = 0.5$, determine $P(A$ and $B)$.

13. If $P(A$ or $B) = 0.7$, $P(A) = 0.6$, and $P(A$ and $B) = 0.3$, determine $P(B)$.

14. If $P(A$ or $B) = 0.6$, $P(B) = 0.3$, and $P(A$ and $B) = 0.1$, determine $P(A)$.

15. *Exam Preparation* Professor Connell is in charge of a program to prepare students for a high school equivalency exam. Records show that the probability that a student in the program needs help in mathematics is 0.7, the probability that a student needs help in English is 0.6, and the probability that a student needs help in both mathematics and English is 0.55. Determine the probability that a student in the program needs help in mathematics or English.

16. *Car Repair* The manager at Arango Automotive has found that the probability that a car brought into the shop requires an oil change is 0.6, the probability that a car brought into the shop requires brake repair is 0.4, and the probability that a car requires both an oil change and brake repair is 0.2. For a car brought into the shop, determine the probability that the car will require an oil change or brake repair.

Roll a Die In Exercises 17–20, a single die is rolled one time. Determine the probability of rolling

17. a 2 or 5.

18. an odd number or a number greater than 4.

19. a number greater than 4 or less than 2.

20. a number greater than 3 or less than 5.

Select One Card In Exercises 21–26, one card is selected from a deck of playing cards. Determine the probability of selecting

21. an ace or a 2.

22. a jack or a club.

23. a picture card or a red card.

24. a club or a red card.

25. a card less than 8 or a club. (*Note:* The ace is considered a low card.)

26. a card greater than 9 or a black card.

PROBLEM SOLVING

Select Two Cards In Exercises 27–34, a board game uses the deck of 20 cards shown.

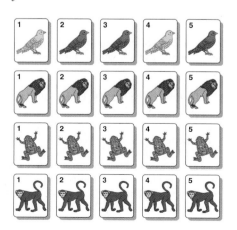

Two cards are selected at random from this deck. Determine the probability of the following

    a) *with replacement.*

    b) *without replacement.*

27. They both show monkeys.

28. They both show the number 3.

29. The first shows a lion, and the second shows a bird.

30. The first shows a 2, and the second shows a 4.

31. The first shows a red bird, and the second shows a monkey.

32. They both show even numbers.

33. Neither shows an even number.

34. The first shows a lion, and the second shows a red bird.

Select One Card In the deck of cards used in Exercises 27–34, if one card is drawn, determine the probability that the card shows

35. a frog or an even number.

36. a yellow bird or a number greater than 4.

37. a lion or a 5.

38. a red bird or an even number.

Two Spins In Exercises 39–48, assume that the pointer cannot land on the line and that each spin is independent. If the pointer in Fig. 12.16 is spun twice, determine the probability that the pointer lands on

39. red on both spins.   **40.** red and then yellow.

Figure 12.16

Two Spins If the pointer in Fig. 12.17 is spun twice, determine the probability that the pointer lands on

41. green and then red.   **42.** red on both spins.

Figure 12.17

Two Spins If the pointer in Fig. 12.18 is spun twice, determine the probability that the pointer lands on

43. red on both spins.

44. a color other than green on both spins.

Figure 12.18

Two Spins In Exercises 45–48, assume that the pointer in Fig. 12.16 on page 779 is spun and then the pointer in Fig. 12.17 is spun. Determine the probability of the pointers landing on

45. red on both spins.

46. yellow on the first spin and red on the second spin.

47. a color other than red on both spins.

48. yellow on the first spin and a color other than yellow on the second spin.

Selecting an Envelope In Exercises 49–56, consider the colored envelopes shown below.

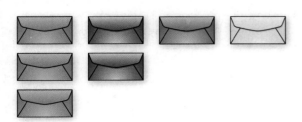

If one of the envelopes is selected at random, determine the probability that

49. a green or a red envelope is selected.

50. an envelope other than a blue envelope is selected.

If two envelopes are selected at random, with replacement, determine the probability that

51. both are red envelopes.

52. the first is a blue envelope and the second is a yellow envelope.

If three envelopes are selected at random, without replacement, determine the probability that

53. they are all red envelopes.

54. none is a red envelope.

55. the first is a red envelope, the second is a blue envelope, and the third is a blue envelope.

56. the first is a red envelope, the second is a green envelope, and the third is a red envelope.

Having a Family In Exercises 57–60, a couple has three children. Assuming independence and that the probability of a boy is $\frac{1}{2}$, determine the probability that

57. all three children are girls.

58. all three children are boys.

59. the youngest child is a boy and the two older children are girls.

60. the youngest child is a girl, the middle child is a boy, and the oldest child is a girl.

61. a) *Five Children* The Martinos plan to have five children. Determine the probability that all their children will be boys. (Assume that $P(\text{boy}) = \frac{1}{2}$ and assume independence.)

b) If their first four children are boys and Mrs. Martino is expecting another child, what is the probability that the fifth child will be a boy?

62. a) *The Probability of a Girl* The Bronsons plan to have eight children. Determine the probability that all their children will be girls. (Assume that $P(\text{girl}) = \frac{1}{2}$ and assume independence.)

b) If their first seven children are girls and Mrs. Bronson is expecting another child, what is the probability that the eighth child will be a girl?

Golf Balls Angel Sanchez has seven golf balls in one pocket of his golf bag: 4 Titleist balls, 2 Top Flite balls, and 1 Pinnacle ball. In Exercises 63–66, two balls will be selected at random. Determine the probability of selecting each of the following

a) *with replacement.*

b) *without replacement.*

63. a Titleist ball and then a Pinnacle ball

64. no Top Flite balls

65. at least one Top Flite ball

66. two Pinnacle balls

Health Insurance A sample of 50 people yielded the following information about their health insurance.

Number of People	Type of Insurance
24	Managed care plan
19	Traditional insurance
7	No insurance

Two people who provided information for the table were selected at random, without replacement. Determine the probability that

67. neither had traditional insurance.

68. they both had a managed care plan.

69. at least one had traditional insurance.

70. the first had traditional insurance and the second had a managed care plan.

Landscaping A sample of 40 homeowners who recently hired a landscaping service yielded the following information about their landscaper.

Number of Homeowners	Would You Recommend Your Landscaper to a Friend
23	Yes
7	No
10	Not sure

Three homeowners who provided information for the table were selected at random. Determine the probability that

71. they would all recommend their landscaper.

72. the first would not recommend the landscaper, but the second and third would recommend their landscapers.

73. the first two would not recommend their landscapers, and the third is not sure if he or she would recommend the landscaper.

74. the first would recommend his or her landscaper, but the second and third would not recommend their landscaper.

A New Medicine In Exercises 75–78, a new medicine was given to a sample of 100 hospital patients. Of the total, 70 patients reacted favorably, 10 reacted unfavorably, and 20 were unaffected by the drug. Assume that this sample is representative of the entire population. If this medicine is given to Mr. and Mrs. Rivera and their son Carlos, what is the probability of each of the following? (Assume independence.)

75. Mrs. Rivera reacts favorably.

76. Mr. and Mrs. Rivera react favorably, and Carlos is unaffected.

77. All three react favorably.

78. No one reacts favorably.

Multiple-Choice Exam In Exercises 79–84, each question of a five-question multiple-choice exam has four possible answers. Gurshawn Salk picks an answer at random for each question. Determine the probability that he selects the correct answer on

79. any one question.

80. only the first question.

81. only the third and fourth questions.

82. all five questions.

83. none of the questions.

84. at least one of the questions.

A Slot Machine In Exercises 85–88, consider a slot machine.

Most people who play slot machines end up losing money because the machines are designed to favor the casino (the house). There are 22 positions on each reel. Assume that the following is a list of the number of symbols of each type on each of the three reels and each symbol has the same chance of occurring (which is not the case; see the Did You Know? on page 777).

Pictures on Reels		Reels 1	2	3
Cherries	🍒	2	5	4
Oranges	🍊	5	4	5
Plums	⬤	6	4	4
Bells	🔔	3	4	4
Melons	⬤	3	2	3
Bars	BAR	2	2	1
7s	7	1	1	1

For this slot machine, assuming that the wheels are independent, determine the probability of obtaining

85. an orange on the first reel.

86. bells on all three reels.

87. no bars.

88. three 7's.

Two Wheels In Exercises 89–92, suppose that you spin the following double wheel.

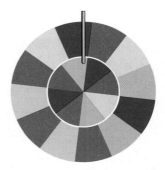

Assuming that the wheels are independent and each outcome is equally likely, determine the probability that you get

89. blue on both wheels.

90. red on the outer wheel and blue on the inner wheel.

91. red on neither wheel.

92. red on at least one wheel.

Hitting a Target In Exercises 93–96, the probability that a heat-seeking torpedo will hit its target is 0.4. If the first torpedo hits its target, the probability that the second torpedo will hit the target increases to 0.9 because of the extra heat generated by the first explosion. If two heat-seeking torpedoes are fired at a target, determine the probability that

93. neither hits the target.

94. the first hits the target and the second misses the target.

95. both hit the target.

96. the first misses the target and the second hits the target.

97. *Polygenetic Afflictions* Certain birth defects and syndromes are *polygenetic* in nature. Typically, the chance that an offspring will be born with a polygenetic affliction is small. However, once an offspring is born with the affliction, the probability that future offspring of the same parents will be born with the same affliction increases. Let's assume that the probability of a child being born with affliction A is 0.001. If a child is born with this affliction, the probability of a future child being born with the same affliction becomes 0.04.

a) Are the events of the births of two children in the same family with affliction *A* independent? Explain.

b) A couple plans to have one child. Determine the probability that the child will be born with this affliction.

A couple plans to have two children. Use the information provided to determine the probability that

c) both children will be born with the affliction.

d) the first will be born with the affliction and the second will not.

e) the first will not be born with the affliction and the second will.

f) neither will be born with the affliction.

98. *Lottery Ticket* In a bin are an equal number of balls marked with the digits 0, 1, 2, 3, . . . , 9. Three balls are to be selected from the bin, one after the other, at random with replacement to make the winning three-digit lottery number. Ms. Jones has a lottery ticket with a three-digit number in the range 000 to 999. Determine the probability that Ms. Jones's number is the winning number.

Chance of an Audit In Exercises 99–102, assume that 36 in every 1000 people in the $31,850–$77,100 income bracket are audited yearly. Assuming that the returns to be audited are selected at random and each year's selections are independent of the previous year's selections, determine the probability that a person in this income bracket will be audited

99. this year.

100. the next two years in succession.

101. this year but not next year.

102. neither this year nor next year.

CHALLENGE PROBLEMS/GROUP ACTIVITIES

103. *Picking Chips* A bag contains five red chips, three blue chips, and two yellow chips. Two chips are selected from the bag without replacement. Determine the probability that two chips of the same color are selected.

104. *Peso Coins* Ron has ten coins from Mexico: three 1-peso coins, one 2-peso coin, two 5-peso coins, one 10-peso coin, and three 20-peso coins. He selects two coins at random without replacement. Assuming that each coin is equally likely to be selected, determine the probability that Ron selects at least one 1-peso coin.

105. *A Fair Game?* Two playing cards are dealt to you from a well-shuffled standard deck of 52 cards. If either card is a diamond or if both are diamonds, you win; otherwise, you lose. Determine whether this game favors you, is fair, or favors the dealer. Explain your answer.

106. *Picture Card Probability* You have three cards: an ace, a king, and a queen. A friend shuffles the cards, selects two of them at random, and discards the third. You ask your friend to show you a picture card, and she turns over the king. What is the probability that she also has the queen?

RECREATIONAL MATHEMATICS

A Different Die For Exercises 107–110, consider a six-sided die that has 1 dot on one side, 2 dots on two sides, and 3 dots on three sides.

If the die is rolled twice, determine the probability of rolling

107. two 2's.

108. two 3's.

If the die is rolled only once, determine the probability of rolling

109. an even number or a number less than 3.

110. an odd number or a number greater than 1.

INTERNET/RESEARCH ACTIVITY

111. Girolamo Cardano (1501–1576) wrote *Liber de Ludo Aleae*, which is considered to be the first book on probability. Cardano had a number of different vocations. Do research and write a paper on the life and accomplishments of Girolamo Cardano.

12.7   CONDITIONAL PROBABILITY

▲ We use conditional probability to determine the probability of selecting a second rotten apple from a basket, given that the first apple selected is rotten.

A basket of 125 apples contains six rotten apples. Suppose that you are asked to randomly select two apples, without replacement, from the basket. What is the probability that both apples you select are rotten? The probability of selecting a rotten apple on the first selection is $\frac{6}{125}$. The probability of selecting a second rotten apple is $\frac{5}{124}$ since we assume that a rotten apple was removed from the basket with the first selection. Since the probability of selecting a second rotten apple is affected by the first rotten apple being selected, these two events are *dependent*. Probability problems involving dependent events can be solved by using conditional probability. In this section, we will discuss conditional probability problems.

In Section 12.6, we learned when two events are *dependent*, the occurrence of the first event, A, affected the probability of the second event, B, occurring. When we calculated $P(A \text{ and } B)$, when we determined the probability of event B, we assumed that event A occurred. That is, we calculated the probability of event B, given event A. The probability of event B, given event A is called a *conditional probability*. The definition of conditional probability follows.

> **CONDITIONAL PROBABILITY**
> In general, the probability of event E_2 occurring, given that an event E_1 has happened (or will happen; the time relationship does not matter), is called a **conditional probability** and is written $P(E_2 \mid E_1)$.

The symbol $P(E_2 \mid E_1)$, read "the probability of E_2, given E_1," represents the probability of E_2 occurring, assuming that E_1 has already occurred (or will occur).

EXAMPLE ❶   *Using Conditional Probability*

A single card is selected from a deck of cards. Determine the probability it is a club, given that it is black.

SOLUTION   We are told that the card is black. Thus, only 26 cards are possible, of which 13 are clubs. Therefore,

$$P(\text{club} \mid \text{black}) \text{ or } P(\text{C} \mid \text{B}) = \frac{13}{26} = \frac{1}{2}$$

EXAMPLE ❷   *Girls in a Family*

A family has two children. Assuming that boys and girls are equally likely, determine the probability that the family has

a) two girls.
b) two girls if you know that at least one of the children is a girl.
c) two girls given that the older child is a girl.

SOLUTION

a) To determine the probability that the family has two girls, we can determine the sample space of a family with two children. Then, from the sample space we can determine the probability that both children are girls. The sample space of two children can be determined by a tree diagram (see Fig. 12.19).

1st Child	2nd Child	Sample Space
B	B	BB
	G	BG
G	B	GB
	G	GG

Figure 12.19

There are four possible equally likely outcomes: BB, BG, GB, and GG. Only one of the outcomes has two girls, GG. Thus,

$$P(2 \text{ girls}) = \frac{1}{4}$$

b) We are given that at least one of the children is a girl. Therefore, for this example the sample space is BG, GB, GG. Since there are three possibilities, of which only one has two girls, GG,

$$P(\text{both girls} \mid \text{at least one is a girl}) = \frac{1}{3}$$

c) If the older child is a girl, the sample space reduces to GB, GG. Thus,

$$P(\text{both girls} \mid \text{older child is a girl}) = \frac{1}{2}$$

A number of formulas can be used to find conditional probabilities. The one we will use follows.

CONDITIONAL PROBABILITY
For any two events, E_1 and E_2,

$$P(E_2 \mid E_1) = \frac{n(E_1 \text{ and } E_2)}{n(E_1)}$$

In the formula, $n(E_1 \text{ and } E_2)$ represents the number of sample points common to both event 1 and event 2, and $n(E_1)$ is the number of sample points in event E_1, the given event. Since the intersection of E_1 and E_2, symbolized $E_1 \cap E_2$, represents the sample points common to both E_1 and E_2, the formula can also be expressed as

$$P(E_2 \mid E_1) = \frac{n(E_1 \cap E_2)}{n(E_1)}$$

Figure 12.20 on page 786 is helpful in explaining conditional probability.

$E_1 \cap E_2$

Figure 12.20

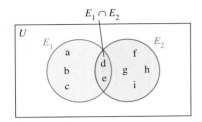
Here, the number of elements in E_1 is five, the number of elements in E_2 is six, and the number of elements in both E_1 and E_2, or $E_1 \cap E_2$, is two.

$$P(E_2 \mid E_1) = \frac{n(E_1 \text{ and } E_2)}{n(E_1)} = \frac{2}{5}$$

Thus, for this situation, the probability of selecting an element from E_2, given that the element is in E_1, is $\frac{2}{5}$.

EXAMPLE ❸ *Using the Conditional Probability Formula*

Two hundred patients who either had hip surgery or knee surgery were asked whether they were satisfied, dissatisfied, or neutral regarding the results of their surgery. The responses are given in the table below.

Surgery	Satisfied	Dissatisfied	Total
Knee	70	25	95
Hip	90	15	105
Total	160	40	200

If one person from the 200 patients surveyed is selected at random, determine the probability that the person

a) was satisfied with the results of the surgery.

b) was satisfied with the results of the surgery, given that the person had knee surgery.

c) was dissatisfied with the results of the surgery, given that the person had hip surgery.

d) had hip surgery, given that the person was dissatisfied with the results of the surgery.

SOLUTION

a) The total number of patients is 200, of which 160 were satisfied with the results of the surgery.

$$P(\text{satisfied with the results of the surgery}) = \frac{160}{200} = \frac{4}{5}$$

b) We are given that the person had knee surgery. Thus, we have a conditional probability problem. Let E_1 be the given information "the person had knee surgery." Let E_2 be "the person was satisfied with the results of the surgery." We are being asked to determine $P(E_2 \mid E_1)$. The number of people who had knee surgery, $n(E_1)$, is 95. The number of people who had knee surgery and were satisfied with the results of the surgery, $n(E_1 \text{ and } E_2)$, is 70. Thus,

$$P(E_2 \mid E_1) = \frac{n(E_1 \text{ and } E_2)}{n(E_1)} = \frac{70}{95} = \frac{14}{19}$$

c) We are given that the person had hip surgery. Thus, this example is a conditional probability problem. Let E_1 be the given information "the person had hip surgery." Let E_2 be "the person was dissatisfied with the results of the surgery." We are asked to find $P(E_2 \mid E_1)$. The number of people who had hip surgery, $n(E_1)$, is 105.

The number of people who had hip surgery and were dissatisfied with the results of the surgery, $n(E_1$ and $E_2)$, is 15. Thus,

$$P(E_2 \mid E_1) = \frac{n(E_1 \text{ and } E_2)}{n(E_1)} = \frac{15}{105} = \frac{1}{7}$$

d) We are given that the person was dissatisfied with the results of the surgery. Thus, we have a conditional probability problem. Let E_1 be the given information "the person was dissatisfied with the results of the surgery." Let E_2 be "the person had hip surgery." We are asked to determine $P(E_2 \mid E_1)$. The number of people who were dissatisfied with the results of the surgery, $n(E_1)$, is 40. The number of people who were dissatisfied with the results of the surgery and had hip surgery, $n(E_1$ and $E_2)$, is 15. Thus,

$$P(E_2 \mid E_1) = \frac{n(E_1 \text{ and } E_2)}{n(E_1)} = \frac{15}{40} = \frac{3}{8}$$ •

In many of the examples, we used the words *given that*. Other words may be used instead. For example, in Example 3(b), the question could have been worded "was satisfied with their surgery *if* the person had knee surgery."

SECTION 12.7 EXERCISES

CONCEPT/WRITING EXERCISES

1. What does the notation $P(E_2 \mid E_1)$ mean?

2. Give the formula for $P(E_2 \mid E_1)$.

3. If $n(E_1 \cap E_2) = 4$ and $n(E_1) = 12$, determine $P(E_2 \mid E_1)$.

4. If $n(E_1 \cap E_2) = 5$ and $n(E_1) = 22$, determine $P(E_2 \mid E_1)$.

PRACTICE THE SKILLS

Select a Circle *In Exercises 5–10, consider the circles shown.*

Assume that one circle is selected at random and each circle is equally likely to be selected. Determine the probability of selecting

5. a 5, given that the circle is orange.

6. a 3, given that the circle is yellow.

7. an even number, given that the circle is not orange.

8. a number less than 2, given that the number is less than 5.

9. a red number, given that the circle is orange.

10. a number greater than 3, given that the circle is yellow.

Select a Number *In Exercises 11–16, consider the following figures.*

Assume that one number from 1 to 7 is equally likely to be selected at random. Each number corresponds to one of the seven figures shown. Determine the probability of selecting

11. a circle, given that an odd number is selected.

12. a circle, given that a number greater than or equal to 5 is selected.

13. a red figure, given that an even number is selected.

14. a red or a blue figure, given that an even number is selected.

15. a circle or square, given that a number less than 4 is selected.

16. a circle, given that an even number is selected.

Spin the Wheel In Exercises 17–24, consider the following wheel.

If the wheel is spun and each section is equally likely to stop under the pointer, determine the probability that the pointer lands on

17. a four, given that the color is purple.

18. an even number, given that the color is red.

19. purple, given that the number is odd.

20. a number greater than 6, given that the color is red.

21. a number greater than 4, given that the color is purple.

22. an even number, given that the color is red or purple.

23. gold, given that the number is greater than 5.

24. gold, given that the number is greater than 10.

Money from a Hat In Exercises 25–28, assume that a hat contains four bills: a \$1 bill, a \$5 bill, a \$10 bill, and a \$20 bill. Two bills are to be selected at random with replacement. Construct a sample space as was done in Example 2 and determine the probability that

25. both bills are \$1 bills.

26. both bills are \$1 bills if the first selected is a \$1 bill.

27. both bills are \$5 bills if at least one of the bills is a \$5 bill.

28. both bills have a value greater than a \$5 bill if the second bill is a \$10 bill.

▲ See Exercises 25–28

Two Dice In Exercises 29–34, two dice are rolled one after the other. Construct a sample space and determine the probability that the sum of the dots on the dice total

29. 6.

30. 6 if the first die is a 1.

31. 6 if the first die is a 3.

32. an even number if the second die is a 2.

33. a number greater than 7 if the second die is a 5.

34. a 7 or 11 if the first die is a 5.

PROBLEM SOLVING

Costliest Hurricanes In Exercises 35–40, use the following information concerning the nine costliest hurricanes to strike the U.S. mainland.

Hurricane	Category	Damage (billions of dollars)
Katrina (2005)	4	80.0
Andrew (1992)	5	26.5
Charlie (2004)	4	15.0
Wilma (2005)	3	14.4
Ivan (2004)	3	14.2
Rita (2005)	3	9.4
Frances (2004)	2	8.9
Hugo (1989)	4	7.0
Jeanne (2004)	3	6.9

Source: National Oceanic and Atmospheric Administration

If one hurricane from the list is selected at random, determine the probability that it

35. was a category 4.

36. had damages of at least \$16 billion.

37. had damages of at least $20 billion, given that it was a category 4.

38. had damages of at least $10 billion, given that it was a category 3.

39. was a category 5, given that it had damages of at least $25 billion.

40. was a category 3, given that it had damages of at least $10 billion.

E-Z Pass In Exercises 41–46, use the following table, which shows the number of cars and trucks that used the Pennsylvania Turnpike on a particular day. The number of cars and trucks that used, and did not use, the E-Z Pass on that same day was also recorded.

E-Z Pass	Cars	Trucks	Total
Used	527	316	843
Did not use	935	683	1618
Total	1462	999	2461

If one of these vehicles is selected at random, determine the probability (as a decimal number rounded to four decimal places) that the

41. vehicle was a car.

42. vehicle used the E-Z Pass.

43. vehicle used the E-Z Pass, given that the vehicle was a car.

44. vehicle used the E-Z Pass, given that the vehicle was a truck.

45. vehicle was a car, given that the vehicle used the E-Z Pass.

46. vehicle was a truck, given that the vehicle used the E-Z Pass.

Sales Effectiveness In Exercises 47–52 use the following information. Sales representatives at a car dealership were split into two groups. One group used an aggressive approach to sell a customer a new automobile. The other group used a passive approach. The following table summarizes the records for 650 customers.

Approach	Sale	No Sale	Total
Aggressive	100	250	350
Passive	220	80	300
Total	320	330	650

If one of these customers is selected at random, determine the probability

47. that the aggressive approach was used.

48. of a sale.

49. of no sale, given that the passive approach was used.

50. of a sale, given that the aggressive approach was used.

51. of a sale, given that the passive approach was used.

52. of no sale, given that the aggressive approach was used.

Age Distribution For Exercises 53–58, use the following information concerning the age distribution of U.S. residents, based on 2005 population data. The data are rounded to the nearest million people.

Age	Male	Female	Total
0–14	31	30	61
15–64	99	99	198
65 years or over	15	21	36
Total	145	150	295

Source: *The World Factbook*, January 2006.

If one of these individuals is selected at random, determine the probability that the person is

53. male.

54. 15–64 years old.

55. 15–64 years old, given that the person is female.

56. 65 years or over, given that the person is female.

57. female, given that the person is 0–14 years old.

58. male, given that the person is 15–64 years old.

Quality Control In Exercises 59–64, Sally Horsefall, a quality control inspector, is checking a sample of light bulbs for defects. The following table summarizes her findings.

Wattage	Good	Defective	Total
20	80	15	95
50	100	5	105
100	120	10	130
Total	300	30	330

If one of these lightbulbs is selected at random, determine the probability that the lightbulb is

59. good.

60. good, given that it is 50 watts.

61. defective, given that it is 20 watts.

62. good, given that it is 100 watts.

63. good, given that it is 50 or 100 watts.

64. defective, given that it is not 50 watts.

News Survey In Exercises 65–70, 270 individuals are asked which evening news they watch most often. The results are summarized as follows.

Viewers	ABC	NBC	CBS	Other	Total
Men	30	20	40	55	145
Women	50	10	20	45	125
Total	80	30	60	100	270

If one of these individuals is selected at random, determine the probability that the person watches

65. ABC or NBC.

66. ABC, given that the individual is a woman.

67. ABC or NBC, given that the individual is a man.

68. a station other than CBS, given that the individual is a woman.

69. a station other than ABC, NBC, or CBS, given that the individual is a man.

70. NBC or CBS, given that the individual is a woman.

▲ Katie Couric, *CBS Evening News*

CHALLENGE PROBLEMS/GROUP ACTIVITIES

Mutual Fund Holdings Use the following information in Exercises 71–74. Mutual funds often hold many stocks. Each stock may be classified as a value stock, a growth stock, or a blend of the two. The stock may also be categorized by how large the company is. It may be classified as a large company stock, medium company stock, or small company stock. A selected mutual fund contains 200 stocks as illustrated in the following chart.

	Value	Blend	Growth	
	28	23	42	Large
	19	15	18	Medium
	26	12	17	Small

Equity Investment Style

If one stock is selected at random from the mutual fund, determine the probability that it is

71. a large company stock.

72. a value stock.

73. a blend, given that it is a medium company stock.

74. a large company stock, given that it is a blend stock.

75. Consider the Venn diagram below. The numbers in the regions of the circle indicate the number of items that belong to that region. For example, 60 items are in set *A* but not in set *B*.

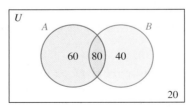

Determine **a)** $n(A)$ **b)** $n(B)$ **c)** $P(A)$ **d)** $P(B)$

Use the formula on page 785 to determine

e) $P(A \mid B)$.

f) $P(B \mid A)$.

g) Explain why $P(A \mid B) \neq P(A) \cdot P(B)$.

76. A formula we gave for conditional probability is

$$P(E_2 \mid E_1) = \frac{n(E_1 \text{ and } E_2)}{n(E_1)}$$

This formula may be derived from the formula

$$P(E_2 \mid E_1) = \frac{P(E_1 \text{ and } E_2)}{P(E_1)}$$

Can you explain why? [*Hint:* Consider what happens to the denominators of $P(E_1 \text{ and } E_2)$ and $P(E_1)$ when they are expressed as fractions and the fractions are divided out.]

77. Given that $P(A) = 0.3$, $P(B) = 0.5$, and $P(A \text{ and } B) = 0.15$, use the formula

$$P(E_2 \mid E_1) = \frac{P(E_1 \text{ and } E_2)}{P(E_1)}$$

to determine

a) $P(A \mid B)$.

b) $P(B \mid A)$.

c) Are A and B independent? Explain.

RECREATIONAL MATHEMATICS

In Exercises 78–83, suppose that each circle is equally likely to be selected. One circle is selected at random.

Determine the probability indicated.

78. $P(\text{green circle} \mid + \text{obtained})$

79. $P(+ \mid \text{orange circle obtained})$

80. $P(\text{yellow circle} \mid - \text{obtained})$

81. $P(\text{green} + \mid + \text{obtained})$

82. $P(\text{green or orange circle} \mid \text{green} + \text{obtained})$

83. $P(\text{orange circle with green} + \mid + \text{obtained})$

12.8 THE COUNTING PRINCIPLE AND PERMUTATIONS

▲ In how many different ways can five televisions be displayed?

You are a manager at an electronics store and want to display five different plasma televisions on the showroom floor. In how many different ways can you display the five televisions? In this section, we will learn how to determine the number of different ordered arrangements of a set of objects. We will also discuss how we can use the counting principle to determine the number of distinct ways two or more experiments can be performed.

The Counting Principle

In Section 12.5, we introduced the counting principle, which is repeated here for your convenience.

COUNTING PRINCIPLE
If a first experiment can be performed in M distinct ways and a second experiment can be performed in N distinct ways, then the two experiments in that specific order can be performed in $M \cdot N$ distinct ways.

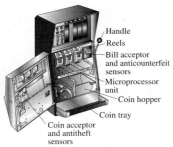
The counting principle is illustrated in Examples 1 and 2.

EXAMPLE ❶ *Counting Principle: Passwords*

A password used to gain access to a computer account is to consist of two lower-case letters followed by four digits. Determine how many different passwords are possible if

a) repetition of letters and digits is permitted.

b) repetition of letters and digits is not permitted.

c) the first letter must be a vowel (*a, e, i, o, u*) and the first digit cannot be a 0, and repetition of letters and digits is not permitted.

SOLUTION There are 26 letters and 10 digits (0–9). We have six positions to fill, as indicated.

$$\overline{L}\ \overline{L}\ \overline{D}\ \overline{D}\ \overline{D}\ \overline{D}$$

a) Since repetition is permitted, there are 26 possible choices for both the first and second positions. There are 10 possible choices for the third, fourth, fifth, and sixth positions.

$$\frac{26}{L}\ \frac{26}{L}\ \frac{10}{D}\ \frac{10}{D}\ \frac{10}{D}\ \frac{10}{D}$$

Since $26 \cdot 26 \cdot 10 \cdot 10 \cdot 10 \cdot 10 = 6{,}760{,}000$, there are 6,760,000 different possible arrangements.

b) There are 26 possibilities for the first position. Since repetition of letters is not permitted, there are only 25 possibilities for the second position. The same reasoning is used when determining the number of digits for positions 3 through 6.

$$\frac{26}{L}\ \frac{25}{L}\ \frac{10}{D}\ \frac{9}{D}\ \frac{8}{D}\ \frac{7}{D}$$

Since $26 \cdot 25 \cdot 10 \cdot 9 \cdot 8 \cdot 7 = 3{,}276{,}000$, there are 3,276,000 different possible arrangements.

c) Since the first letter must be an *a, e, i, o,* or *u,* there are five possible choices for the first position. The second position can be filled by any of the letters except for the vowel selected for the first position. Therefore, there are 25 possibilities for the second position.

   Since the first digit cannot be a 0, there are nine possibilities for the third position. The fourth position can be filled by any digit except the one selected for the third position. Thus, there are nine possibilities for the fourth position. Since the fifth position cannot be filled by any of the two digits previously used, there are eight possibilities for the fifth position. The last position can be filled by any of the seven remaining digits.

$$\frac{5}{L}\ \frac{25}{L}\ \frac{9}{D}\ \frac{9}{D}\ \frac{8}{D}\ \frac{7}{D}$$

Since $5 \cdot 25 \cdot 9 \cdot 9 \cdot 8 \cdot 7 = 567{,}000$, there are 567,000 different arrangements that meet the conditions specified.

┌─ EXAMPLE ❷ *Counting Principle: T-Shirt Colors*

At Old Navy, a supply of solid-colored T-shirts has just been received. The T-shirts come in the following colors: green, blue, white, yellow, and red. Billy Bragg, the floor manager, decides to display one of each color T-shirt in a row on a shelf.

a) In how many different ways can he display the five different color T-shirts on a shelf?

b) If he wants to place the blue T-shirt in the middle, in how many different ways can he arrange the T-shirts?

c) If Billy wants the white T-shirt to be the first T-shirt and the blue T-shirt to be the last T-shirt, in how many different ways can he arrange the T-shirts?

SOLUTION

a) There are five positions to fill, using the five colors. In the first position, on the left, he can use any one of the five colors. In the second position, he can use any of the four remaining colors. In the third position, he can use any of the three remaining colors, and so on. The number of distinct possible arrangements is

$$\underline{5} \cdot \underline{4} \cdot \underline{3} \cdot \underline{2} \cdot \underline{1} = 120$$

b) We begin by satisfying the specified requirements stated. In this case, the blue T-shirt must be placed in the middle. Therefore, there is only one possibility for the middle position.

$$\_\_\_ \underline{1} \_\_\_$$

For the first position, there are now four possibilities. For the second position, there will be three possibilities. For the fourth position, there will be two possibilities. Finally, in the last position, there is only one possibility.

$$\underline{4} \cdot \underline{3} \cdot \underline{1} \cdot \underline{2} \cdot \underline{1} = 24$$

Thus, under the condition stated, there are 24 different possible arrangements.

c) For the first T-shirt, there is only one possibility, the white T-shirt. For the last T-shirt, there is only one possibility, the blue T-shirt.

$$\underline{1} \_\_\_\_ \underline{1}$$

The second position can be filled by any of the three remaining T-shirts. The third position can be filled by any of the two remaining T-shirts. There is only one T-shirt left for the fourth position. Thus, the number of possible arrangements is

$$\underline{1} \cdot \underline{3} \cdot \underline{2} \cdot \underline{1} \cdot \underline{1} = 6$$

There are only six possible arrangements that satisfy the given conditions.   ●

Permutations

Now we introduce the definition of a permutation.

A **permutation** is any *ordered arrangement* of a given set of objects.

Curly   Moe   Larry

"Larry, Curly, Moe" and "Curly, Moe, Larry" represent two different ordered arrangements or two different permutations of the same three names. In Example 2(a), there are 120 different ordered arrangements, or permutations, of the five colored T-shirts. In Example 2(b), there are 24 different ordered arrangements, or permutations possible, if the blue T-shirt must be displayed in the middle.

When determining the number of permutations possible, we assume that repetition of an item is not permitted. To help you understand and visualize permutations, we illustrate the various permutations possible when a triangle, rectangle, and circle are to be placed in a line, see Figure 12.21.

Six Permutations

Figure 12.21

For this set of three shapes, six different arrangements, or six permutations, are possible. We can obtain the number of permutations by using the counting principle. For the first position, there are three choices. There are then two choices for the second position, and only one choice is left for the third position.

$$\text{Number of permutations} = 3 \cdot 2 \cdot 1 = 6$$

The product $3 \cdot 2 \cdot 1$ is referred to as 3 factorial, and is written 3!. Thus,

$$3! = 3 \cdot 2 \cdot 1 = 6$$

NUMBER OF PERMUTATIONS
The number of permutations of n distinct items is n factorial, symbolized $n!$, where

$$n! = n(n - 1)(n - 2) \cdots (3)(2)(1)$$

It is important to note that 0! is defined to be 1. Many calculators have the ability to determine factorials. Often to determine factorials you need to press the $\boxed{\text{2nd}}$ or $\boxed{\text{INV}}$ key. Read your calculator manual to determine how to find factorials on your calculator.

┌─ **EXAMPLE ❸** *Children in Line*

In how many different ways can seven children be arranged in a line?

SOLUTION Since there are seven children, the number of permutations is 7!.

$$7! = 7 \cdot 6 \cdot 5 \cdot 4 \cdot 3 \cdot 2 \cdot 1 = 5040$$

The seven children can be arranged in 5040 different ways.   ●

Example 4 illustrates how to use the counting principle to determine the number of permutations possible when only a part of the total number of items is to be selected and arranged.

Some of the many
permutations
of 3 of the 5 letters

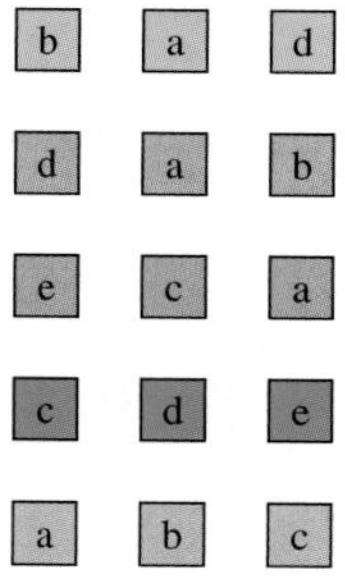

b	a	d
d	a	b
e	c	a
c	d	e
a	b	c

Figure 12.22

┌ **EXAMPLE ④** *Permutations of Three Out of Five Letters*

Consider the five letters a, b, c, d, e. In how many distinct ways can three letters be
selected and arranged if repetition is not allowed?

SOLUTION We are asked to select and arrange only three of the five possible letters. Figure 12.22 shows some possibilities. Using the counting principle, we find
that there are five possible letters for the first choice, four possible letters for the
second choice, and three possible letters for the third choice:

$$5 \cdot 4 \cdot 3 = 60$$

Thus, there are 60 different possible ordered arrangements, or permutations. On the
left, we show 5 of the 60 possible permutations.   ●

In Example 4, we determined the number of different ways in which we could select and arrange three of the five items. We can indicate that result by using the notation $_5P_3$. The notation $_5P_3$ is read "the number of permutations of five items taken
three at a time." The notation $_nP_r$ is read "the number of permutations of n items taken
r at a time."

We use the counting principle below to evaluate $_8P_4$, $_9P_3$, and $_{10}P_5$. Note the relationship between the number preceding the P, the number following the P, and the
last number in the product.

$$\overset{\text{One more than } 8 - 4}{\downarrow}$$
$$_8P_4 = 8 \cdot 7 \cdot 6 \cdot 5$$

$$\overset{\text{One more than } 9 - 3}{\downarrow}$$
$$_9P_3 = 9 \cdot 8 \cdot 7$$

$$\overset{\text{One more than } 10 - 5}{\downarrow}$$
$$_{10}P_5 = 10 \cdot 9 \cdot 8 \cdot 7 \cdot 6$$

To evaluate $_nP_r$, we begin with n and form a product of r consecutive descending factors. For example, to evaluate $_{10}P_5$, we start with 10 and form a product of five consecutive descending factors (see the preceding illustration).

In general, the number of permutations of n items taken r at a time, $_nP_r$, may be
found by the formula

$$\overset{\text{One more than } n - r}{\downarrow}$$
$$_nP_r = n(n - 1)(n - 2) \cdots (n - r + 1)$$

Therefore, when evaluating $_{20}P_{15}$, we would find the product of consecutive decreasing
integers from 20 to $(20 - 15 + 1)$ or 6, which is written as $20 \cdot 19 \cdot 18 \cdot 17 \cdot \cdots \cdot 6$.

Now let's develop an alternative formula that we can use to find the number of
permutations possible when r objects are selected from n objects:

$$_nP_r = n(n - 1)(n - 2) \cdots (n - r + 1)$$

Now multiply the expression on the right side of the equals sign by $\dfrac{(n - r)!}{(n - r)!}$,
which is equivalent to multiplying the expression by 1.

$$_nP_r = n(n - 1)(n - 2) \cdots (n - r + 1) \times \frac{(n - r)!}{(n - r)!}$$

For example,

$$_{10}P_5 = 10 \cdot 9 \cdot \cdots \cdot 6 \times \frac{5!}{5!}$$

or

$$_{10}P_5 = \frac{10 \cdot 9 \cdot \cdots \cdot 6 \times 5!}{5!}$$

Since $(n - r)!$ means $(n - r)(n - r - 1) \cdots (3)(2)(1)$, the expression for $_nP_r$ can be rewritten as

$$_nP_r = \frac{n(n - 1)(n - 2) \cdots (n - r + 1)\overbrace{(n - r)(n - r - 1) \cdots (3)(2)(1)}^{(n - r)!}}{(n - r)!}$$

Since the numerator of this expression is $n!$, we can write

$$_nP_r = \frac{n!}{(n - r)!}$$

For example,

$$_{10}P_5 = \frac{10!}{(10 - 5)!}$$

> The number of permutations possible when r objects are selected from n objects is found by the **permutation formula**
>
> $$_nP_r = \frac{n!}{(n - r)!}$$

In Example 4, we found that when selecting three of five letters, there were 60 permutations. We can obtain the same result using the permutation formula:

$$_5P_3 = \frac{5!}{(5 - 3)!} = \frac{5!}{2!} = \frac{5 \cdot 4 \cdot 3 \cdot \cancel{2 \cdot 1}}{\cancel{2 \cdot 1}} = 60$$

┌─ **EXAMPLE ⑤** *Using the Permutation Formula*

You are among eight people forming a skiing club. Collectively, you decide to put each person's name in a hat and to randomly select a president, a vice president, and a secretary. How many different arrangements or permutations of officers are possible?

SOLUTION There are eight people, $n = 8$, of which three are to be selected; thus, $r = 3$.

$$_8P_3 = \frac{8!}{(8 - 3)!} = \frac{8!}{5!} = \frac{8 \cdot 7 \cdot 6 \cdot \cancel{5 \cdot 4 \cdot 3 \cdot 2 \cdot 1}}{\cancel{5 \cdot 4 \cdot 3 \cdot 2 \cdot 1}} = 336$$

Thus, with eight people there can be 336 different arrangements for president, vice president, and secretary. ●

In Example 5, the fraction

$$\frac{8 \cdot 7 \cdot 6 \cdot \cancel{5} \cdot \cancel{4} \cdot \cancel{3} \cdot \cancel{2} \cdot \cancel{1}}{\cancel{5} \cdot \cancel{4} \cdot \cancel{3} \cdot \cancel{2} \cdot \cancel{1}} = 336$$

can be also expressed as

$$\frac{8 \cdot 7 \cdot 6 \cdot 5!}{5!} = 336$$

The solution to Example 5, like other permutation problems, can also be obtained using the counting principle.

EXAMPLE 6

The Prince George County bicycle club has 10 different routes members wish to travel exactly once, but they only have 6 specific dates for their trips. In how many ways can the different routes be assigned to the dates scheduled for their trips?

SOLUTION There are 10 possible routes but only 6 specific dates scheduled for the trips. Since traveling route A on day 1 and traveling route B on day 2 is different than traveling route B on day 1 and traveling route A on day 2, we have a permutation problem. There are 10 possible routes; thus, $n = 10$. There are 6 routes that are going to be selected and assigned to different days; thus, $r = 6$. Now we calculate the number of different permutations of selecting and arranging the dates for 6 out of 10 possible routes.

$$_{10}P_6 = \frac{10!}{(10-6)!} = \frac{10!}{4!} = \frac{10 \cdot 9 \cdot 8 \cdot 7 \cdot 6 \cdot 5 \cdot \cancel{4!}}{\cancel{4!}} = 151{,}200$$

There are 151,200 different ways that 6 routes can be selected and scheduled from the 10 possible routes.   ●

Example 6 could also be worked using the counting principle because we are discussing an *ordered arrangement* (a permutation) that is done *without replacement*. For the first date scheduled, there are 10 possible outcomes. For the second date selected, there are 9 possible outcomes. By continuing this process we would determine that the number of possible outcomes for the 6 different trips is $10 \cdot 9 \cdot 8 \cdot 7 \cdot 6 \cdot 5 = 151{,}200$.

We have worked permutation problems (selecting and arranging, without replacement, r items out of n *distinct* items) by using the counting principle and using the permutation formula. When you are given a permutation problem, unless specified by your instructor, you may use either technique to determine its solution.

Permutations of Duplicate Items

So far, all the examples we have discussed in this section have involved arrangements with distinct items. Now we will consider permutation problems in which some of the items to be arranged are duplicates. For example, the name BOB contains three letters, of which the two Bs are duplicates. How many permutations of the letters in the name BOB are possible? If the two Bs were distinguishable (one red and the other blue), there would be six permutations.

BOB   BBO   OBB

BOB   BBO   OBB

However, if the Bs are not distinguishable (replacing all colored Bs with black print), we see that there are only three permutations.

BOB   BBO   OBB

The number of permutations of the letters in BOB can be computed as

$$\frac{3!}{2!} = \frac{3 \cdot 2 \cdot 1}{2 \cdot 1} = 3$$

where 3! represents the number of permutations of three letters, assuming that none are duplicates, and 2! represents the number of ways the two items that are duplicates can be arranged (**BB** or **BB**). In general, we have the following rule.

PERMUTATIONS OF DUPLICATE OBJECTS

The number of distinct permutations of n objects where n_1 of the objects are identical, n_2 of the objects are identical, ..., n_r of the objects are identical is found by the formula

$$\frac{n!}{n_1! n_2! \cdots n_r!}$$

EXAMPLE **7** *Duplicate Letters*

In how many different ways can the letters of the word "TALLAHASSEE" be arranged?

SOLUTION Of the 11 letters, three are A's, two are S's, two are L's and two are E's. The number of possible arrangements is

$$\frac{11!}{3!2!2!2!} = \frac{11 \cdot 10 \cdot 9 \cdot 8 \cdot 7 \cdot 6 \cdot 5 \cdot 4 \cdot 3 \cdot 2 \cdot 1}{3 \cdot 2 \cdot 1 \cdot 2 \cdot 1 \cdot 2 \cdot 1 \cdot 2 \cdot 1} = 11 \cdot 10 \cdot 9 \cdot 7 \cdot 6 \cdot 5 \cdot 4 = 831,600$$

There are 831,600 different possible arrangements of the letters in the word "TALLAHASSEE." ●

TECHNOLOGY TIP Many scientific calculators and all graphing calculators have the ability to evaluate permutations. Read your calculator's instruction manual to determine the procedure to follow to evaluate permutations.

To evaluate $_{10}P_6$ on a TI-83 Plus or a TI-84 Plus calculator, enter the number 10. Then press the MATH key. Use the right arrow key to scroll over to PRB, which stands for probability. Then scroll down to $_nP_r$. Press the ENTER key. You should now see 10 $_nP_r$ on your screen. Next press 6. Press the ENTER key again. The answer will be 151,200, which agrees with our answer in Example 6.

SECTION 12.8 EXERCISES

CONCEPT/WRITING EXERCISES

1. In your own words, state the counting principle.

2. In your own words, describe a permutation.

3. a) Give the formula for the number of permutations of n distinct items.

   b) Give the formula for the number of permutations of n objects when $n_1, n_2, \ldots, n_r$ of the objects are identical.

4. In your own words, explain how to find $n!$ for any positive integer n.

5. How do you read $_nP_r$? When you evaluate $_nP_r$, what does the outcome represent?

6. Does $_1P_1 = {}_1P_0$? Explain.

7. Give the formula for the number of permutations when r objects are selected from n objects.

8. a) Explain how to calculate $\frac{500!}{499!}$ without a calculator.

   b) Evaluate $\frac{500!}{499!}$.

PRACTICE THE SKILLS

In Exercises 9–20, evaluate the expression.

9. $4!$

10. $7!$

11. $_7P_2$

12. $_5P_2$

13. $0!$

14. $_6P_4$

15. $_8P_0$

16. $_6P_0$

17. $_9P_4$

18. $_3P_3$

19. $_8P_3$

20. $_{10}P_6$

PROBLEM SOLVING

21. **ATM Codes** To use an automated teller machine, you generally must enter a four-digit code, using the digits 0–9. How many four-digit codes are possible if repetition of digits is permitted?

22. **Vice Presidents** The board of a pharmaceutical company has nine members. One board member will be selected as vice president of marketing, and a different board member will be selected as vice president of research. How many different arrangements of the two vice presidents are possible?

23. **Passwords** Assume that a password to log onto a computer account is to consist of three letters followed by two digits. Determine the number of possible passwords if

a) repetition is not permitted.

b) repetition is permitted.

24. **Passwords** Assume that a password to log onto a computer account is to consist of any four digits or letters (repetition is permitted). Determine the number of passwords possible if

a) the letters are not case sensitive (that is, a lowercase letter is treated the same as an uppercase letter).

b) the letters are case sensitive (that is, an uppercase letter is considered different than the same lowercase letter).

25. **Car Door Locks** Some doors on cars can be opened by pressing the correct sequence of buttons. A display of the five buttons by the door handle of a car follows.*

The correct sequence of five buttons must be pressed to unlock the door.

a) If the same button may be pressed consecutively, how many possible ways can the five buttons be pressed (repetition is permitted)?

b) If five buttons are pressed at random, determine the probability that a sequence that unlocks the door will be entered.

26. **Social Security Numbers** A social security number consists of nine digits. How many different social security numbers are possible if repetition of digits is permitted?

27. **License Plate** A license plate is to have five uppercase letters or digits. Determine the number of license plates possible if repetition is permitted and if any position can contain either a letter or digit with the exception that the first position cannot contain the letter O or the number 0.

---

*On most cars, although each key lists two numbers, the key acts as a single number. Therefore, if your code is 1, 6, 8, 5, 3, the code 2, 5, 7, 6, 4 will also open the lock.

28. *Winning the Trifecta* The trifecta at most racetracks consists of selecting the first-, second-, and third-place finishers in a particular race in their proper order. If there are seven entries in the trifecta race, how many tickets must you purchase to guarantee a win?

29. *Choosing Classes* Kai Lu plans to enroll in four classes: sociology, chemistry, economics, and humanities. There are seven sociology classes, four chemistry classes, three economics classes, and four humanities classes that fit his schedule. How many different ways can he select his four classes?

30. *Geometric Shapes* Consider the five figures shown.

In how many different ways can the figures be arranged

a) from left to right?

b) from top to bottom if placed one under the other?

c) from left to right if the triangle is to be placed on the far right?

d) from left to right if the circle is to be placed on the far left and the triangle is to be placed on the far right?

31. *Arranging Pictures* The six pictures shown are to be placed side by side along a wall.

In how many ways can they be arranged from left to right if

a) they can be arranged in any order?

b) the bird must be on the far left?

c) the bird must be on the far left and the giraffe must be next to the bird?

d) a four-legged animal must be on the far right?

32. *Nursing Positions* There are 15 candidates for three nursing positions available at Community General Hospital. One position is for the day supervisor. The second position is for the evening supervisor. The third position is for the night supervisor. If all 15 candidates are equally qualified for the three positions, in how many different ways can the three positions be filled?

▲ See Exercise 32

33. *Club Officers* If a club consists of 10 members, how many different arrangements of president, vice-president, and secretary are possible?

34. *ISBN Codes* Each book registered in the Library of Congress must have an ISBN code number. For an ISBN number of the form D-DD-DDDDDD-D, where D represents a digit from 0–9, how many different ISBN numbers are possible if repetition of digits is allowed? (See research activity Exercise 72 on page 802.)

35. *Wedding Reception* At the reception line of a wedding, the bride, the groom, the best man, the maid of honor, the four ushers, and the four bridesmaids must line up to receive the guests.

a) If these individuals can line up in any order, how many arrangements are possible?

b) If the groom must be the last in line and the bride must be next to the groom, and the others can line up in any order, how many arrangements are possible?

c) If the groom is to be last in line, the bride next to the groom, and males and females are to alternate, how many arrangements are possible?

36. *Disc Jockey* A disc jockey has 9 songs to play. Five are slow songs, and 4 are fast songs. Each song is to be played only once. In how many ways can the disc jockey play the 9 songs if

a) the songs can be played in any order.

b) the first song must be a slow song and the last song must be a slow song.

c) the first two songs must be fast songs.

Letter Codes In Exercises 37–40, an identification code is to consist of three letters followed by four digits. How many different codes are possible if

37. repetition is not permitted?

38. repetition is permitted?

39. repetition of letters is permitted, repetition of numbers is not permitted, and the first three entries must all be the same letter?

40. the first letter must be an *A, B, C,* or *D* and repetition is not permitted?

License Plates In Exercises 41–44, a license plate is to consist of three digits followed by two uppercase letters. Determine the number of different license plates possible if

41. repetition of numbers and letters is permitted.

42. repetition of numbers and letters is not permitted.

43. the first and second digits must be odd, and repetition is not permitted.

44. the first digit cannot be zero, and repetition is not permitted.

45. *Possible Phone Numbers* A telephone number consists of seven digits with the restriction that the first digit cannot be 0 or 1.

   a) How many distinct telephone numbers are possible?

   b) How many distinct telephone numbers are possible with three-digit area codes preceding the seven-digit number, where the first digit of the area code is not 0 or 1?

   c) With the increasing use of cell phones and paging systems, our society is beginning to run out of usable phone numbers. Various phone companies are developing phone numbers that use 11 digits instead of 7. How many distinct phone numbers can be made with 11 digits assuming that the area code remains three digits and the first digit of the area code and the phone number cannot be 0 or 1?

46. *Granola Bars* Mrs. Williams and her four children go shopping at a local grocery store. Each of the children will be allowed to select one box of granola bars. On the store's shelf there are 12 boxes of granola bars, and each box contains a different type of bar. In how many ways can the selections be made?

47. *Track Meet* A track meet has 15 participants for the 100-meter event. The 6 participants with the fastest speeds will be listed, in the order of their speed, on the leader board. How many different ways are there for the names to be listed?

48. *History Test* In one question on a history test, a student is asked to match 10 dates with 10 events; each date can only be matched with 1 event. In how many different ways can this question be answered?

49. *Color Permutations* Determine the number of permutations of the colors in the spectrum that follows.

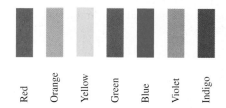

Red Orange Yellow Green Blue Violet Indigo

50. *Drive-Through at a Bank* A bank has three drive-through stations. Assuming that each is equally likely to be selected by customers, in how many different ways can the next six drivers select a station?

51. *Computer Systems* At a computer store, a customer is considering 5 different computers, 4 different monitors, 7 different printers, and 2 different scanners. Assuming that each of the components is compatible with one another and that one of each is to be selected, determine the number of different computer systems possible.

52. *Selecting Furniture* The Johnsons just moved into their new home and are selecting furniture for the family room. They are considering 5 different sofas, 2 different chairs, and 6 different tables. They plan to select one item from each category. Determine the number of different ways they can select the furniture.

53. Determine the number of permutations of the letters of the word "EDUCATION."

54. Determine the number of permutations of the letters of the word "SELECTION."

55. In how many ways can the letters in the word "DIFFERENCE" be arranged?

56. In how many ways can the letters in the word "MISSISSIPPI" be arranged?

57. In how many ways can the digits in the number 9,876,678 be arranged?

58. In how many ways can the digits of the number 2,142,332 be arranged?

59. *Flag Messages* Five different colored flags will be placed on a pole, one beneath another. The arrangement of the colors indicates the message. How many messages are possible if five flags are to be selected from nine different colored flags?

60. *Multiple-Choice Test* Keri Kershaw is taking a 12-question multiple-choice exam. Each question has three possible answers, (a), (b), and (c). In how many possible ways can Keri answer the questions?

61. *Batting Order* In how many ways can the manager of a National League baseball team arrange his batting order of nine players if

  a) the pitcher must bat last?

  b) there are no restrictions?

62. *Painting Exhibit* Five Monet paintings are to be displayed in a museum.

  a) In how many different ways can they be arranged if they must be next to one another?

  b) In how many different ways can they be displayed if a specific one is to be in the middle?

▲ *The Water Lily Pond, Pink Harmony,* 1900 by Claude Monet

CHALLENGE PROBLEMS/GROUP ACTIVITIES

63. *Car Keys* Door keys for a certain automobile are made from a blank key on which five cuts are made. Each cut may be one of five different depths.

  a) How many different keys can be made?

  b) If 400,000 of these automobiles are made such that each of the keys determined in part (a) opens the same number of cars, find how many cars can be opened by a specific key.

  c) If one of these cars is selected at random, what is the probability that the key selected at random will unlock the door?

64. *Voting* On a ballot, each committee member is asked to rank three of eight candidates for recommendation for promotion, giving first, second, and third choices (no ties). What is the minimum number of ballots that must be cast to guarantee that at least two ballots are the same?

65. *Scrabble* Nancy Lin, who is playing Scrabble with Dale Grey, has seven different letters. She decides to test each five-letter permutation before her next move. If each permutation takes 5 sec, how long will it take Nancy to check all the permutations?

66. *Scrabble* In Exercise 65, assume, of Nancy's seven letters, that three are identical and two are identical. How long will it take Nancy to try all different permutations of her seven letters?

67. Does $_nP_r = {_nP_{(n-r)}}$ for all whole numbers, where $n \geq r$? Explain.

RECREATIONAL MATHEMATICS

68. *Stations* There are eight bus stations from town A to town B. How many different single tickets must be printed so that a passenger may purchase a ticket from any station to any other station?

A o—o—o—o—o—o—o—o B

69. *Bus Loop* How many tickets with different points of origin and destination can be sold on a bus line that travels a loop with 25 stops?

Jumbles Many newspapers contain Jumble puzzles, where the letters of a word are given out of order. In Exercises 70 and 71, determine

  a) *the number of possible arrangements of the letters given.*

  b) *the word.*

70. HEICOC

71. ROSEGOC

INTERNET/RESEARCH ACTIVITY

72. When a book is published, it is assigned a 10-digit code number called the International Standard Book Number (ISBN). Do research and write a report on how this coding system works.

12.9 COMBINATIONS

▲ We can use combinations to determine how many different committees of three people can be selected from 25 people.

The members of the student senate at Austin Community College want to select three of their 25 members to attend a meeting with the faculty senate. In how many different ways can three members of the student senate be selected? If Frank, Sue, and Joe are the three students selected, does it make a difference which student was selected first, which student was selected second, or which student was selected third? For this example, the order of the selection of the students does not matter because the same set of students would attend the meeting. In this section, we will learn how to determine the number of combinations when the order of the selection of the items is not important to the final outcome.

When the order of the selection of the items is important to the final outcome, the problem is a permutation problem. When the order of the selection of the items is unimportant to the final outcome, the problem is a *combination* problem.

Recall from Section 12.8 that permutations are *ordered* arrangements. For example, a, b, c and b, c, a are two different permutations because the ordering of the three letters is different. The letters a, b, c and b, c, a represent the same combination of letters because the *same letters* are used in each set. However, the letters a, b, c and a, b, d represent two different combinations of letters because the letters contained in each set are different.

> A **combination** is a distinct group (or set) of objects without regard to their arrangement.

EXAMPLE ❶ *Permutation or Combination*

Determine whether the situation represents a permutation or combination problem.
a) A group of five friends, Arline, Inez, Judy, Dan, and Eunice, are forming a club. The group will elect a president and a treasurer. In how many different ways can the president and treasurer be selected?
b) Of the five individuals named, two will be attending a meeting together. In how many different ways can they do so?

SOLUTION

a) Since the president's position is different from the treasurer's position, we have a permutation problem. Judy as president with Dan as treasurer is different from Dan as president with Judy as treasurer. The order of the selection is important.
b) Since the order in which the two individuals selected to attend the meeting is not important, we have a combination problem. There is no difference if Judy is selected and then Dan is selected, or if Dan is selected and then Judy is selected. ●

In Section 12.8, you learned that $_nP_r$ represents the number of permutations when r items are selected from n distinct items. *Similarly, $_nC_r$ represents the number of combinations when r items are selected from n distinct items.*

Consider the set of elements $\{a, b, c, d, e\}$. The number of permutations of two letters from the set is represented as $_5P_2$, and the number of combinations of two letters from the set is represented as $_5C_2$. Twenty permutations of two letters and 10 combinations of two letters are possible from these five letters. Thus, $_5P_2 = 20$ and $_5C_2 = 10$, as shown.

Permutations	**Combinations**
$ab, ba, ac, ca, ad, da, ae, ea, bc, cb,$ $bd, db, be, eb, cd, dc, ce, ec, de, ed$ $\Big\}$ 20	$ab, ac, ad, ae, bc,$ bd, be, cd, ce, de $\Big\}$ 10

When discussing both combination and permutation problems, we always assume that the experiment is performed without replacement. That is why duplicate letters such as *aa* or *bb* are not included in the preceding example.

Note that from one combination of two letters, two permutations can be formed. For example, the combination *ab* gives the permutations *ab* and *ba*, or twice as many permutations as combinations. Thus, for this example we may write

$$_5P_2 = 2 \cdot (_5C_2)$$

Since $2 = 2!$, we may write

$$_5P_2 = 2!(_5C_2)$$

If we repeated this same process for comparing the number of permutations in $_nP_r$ with the number of combinations in $_nC_r$, we would find that

$$_nP_r = r!(_nC_r)$$

Dividing both sides of the equation by $r!$ gives

$$_nC_r = \frac{_nP_r}{r!}$$

Since $_nP_r = \dfrac{n!}{(n-r)!}$, the combination formula may be expressed as

$$_nC_r = \frac{n!/(n-r)!}{r!} = \frac{n!}{(n-r)!r!}$$

> The number of combinations possible when *r* objects are selected from *n* objects is found by the **combination formula**
>
> $$_nC_r = \frac{n!}{(n-r)!r!}$$

EXAMPLE ❷ *Exam Question Selection*

An exam consists of six questions. Any four may be selected for answering. In how many ways can this selection be made?

SOLUTION This problem is a combination problem because the order in which the four questions are answered does not matter.

$$_6C_4 = \frac{6!}{(6-4)!4!} = \frac{6!}{2!4!} = \frac{\overset{3}{\cancel{6}} \cdot 5 \cdot \cancel{4 \cdot 3 \cdot 2 \cdot 1}}{2 \cdot 1 \cdot \cancel{4 \cdot 3 \cdot 2 \cdot 1}} = 15$$

There are 15 different ways that four of the six questions can be selected. ●

TECHNOLOGY TIP Many scientific calculators and all graphing calculators have the ability to evaluate combinations. Read your calculator's instruction manual to determine the procedure to follow to evaluate combinations.

To evaluate $_6C_4$ on a TI-83 Plus or TI-84 Plus calculator, enter the number 6. Then press the MATH key. Use the right arrow key to scroll over to PRB, which stands for probability. Then scroll down to $_nC_r$. Press the ENTER key. You should now see $6\,_nC_r$ on your screen. Next press 4. Press the ENTER key again. The answer will be 15, which agrees with our answer displayed in Example 2.

EXAMPLE ❸ *Floral Arrangements*

Jan Funkhauser has 10 different cut flowers from which she will choose 6 to use in a floral arrangement. How many different ways can she do so?

SOLUTION This problem is a combination problem because the order in which the 6 flowers are selected is unimportant. There are a total of 10 different flowers, so $n = 10$. Six flowers are to be selected, so $r = 6$.

$$_{10}C_6 = \frac{10!}{(10-6)!6!} = \frac{10!}{4!6!} = \frac{10 \cdot 9 \cdot 8 \cdot 7 \cdot \cancel{6 \cdot 5 \cdot 4 \cdot 3 \cdot 2 \cdot 1}}{4 \cdot 3 \cdot 2 \cdot 1 \cdot \cancel{6 \cdot 5 \cdot 4 \cdot 3 \cdot 2 \cdot 1}} = 210$$

Thus, there are 210 different ways Jan can choose 6 cut flowers from a group of 10 cut flowers.

EXAMPLE ❹ *Dinner Combinations*

At the Royal Dynasty Chinese restaurant, dinner for eight people consists of 3 items from column A, 4 items from column B, and 3 items from column C. If columns A, B, and C have 5, 7, and 6 items, respectively, how many different dinner combinations are possible?

SOLUTION For column A, 3 of 5 items must be selected, which can be represented as $_5C_3$. For column B, 4 of 7 items must be selected, which can be represented as $_7C_4$. For column C, 3 of 6 items must be selected, or $_6C_3$.

$$_5C_3 = 10 \qquad _7C_4 = 35 \quad \text{and} \quad _6C_3 = 20$$

Using the counting principle, we can determine the total number of dinner combinations by multiplying the number of choices from columns A, B, and C:

$$\text{Total number of dinner choices} = {_5C_3} \cdot {_7C_4} \cdot {_6C_3}$$
$$= 10 \cdot 35 \cdot 20 = 7000$$

Therefore, 7000 different combinations are possible under these conditions.

We have presented various counting methods, including the counting principle, permutations, and combinations. You often need to decide which method to use to solve a problem. Table 12.4 on page 806 may help you in selecting the procedure to use.

DID YOU KNOW?

Poker versus Bridge

A nice bridge hand

In popular card games, there is such a variety of possible combinations of cards that a player rarely gets the same hand twice. The total number of different 5-card poker hands using a standard deck of 52 cards is 2,598,960, and for 13-card bridge hands this number increases to 635,013,559,600.

Table 12.4 Summary of Counting Methods

Counting Principle: If a first experiment can be performed in M distinct ways and a second experiment can be performed in N distinct ways, then the two experiments in that specific order can be performed in $M \cdot N$ distinct ways. The counting principle may be used with or without repetition of items. It is used when determining the number of different ways that two or more experiments can occur. It is also used when there are specific placement requirements, such as the first digit must be a 0 or 1.	Determining the Number of Ways of Selecting r Items from n Items Repetition not permitted.	
	Permutations	**Combinations**
	Permutations are used when order is important. For example, a, b, c and b, c, a are two different permutations of the same three letters. $$_nP_r = \frac{n!}{(n-r)!}$$ Problems solved with the permutation formula may also be solved by using the counting principle.	Combinations are used when order is not important. For example, a, b, c and b, c, a are the same combination of three letters. But $a, b, c,$ and a, b, d are two different combinations of three letters. $$_nC_r = \frac{n!}{(n-r)!r!}$$

SECTION 12.9 EXERCISES

CONCEPT/WRITING EXERCISES

1. In your own words, explain what is meant by a combination.

2. What does $_nC_r$ mean?

3. Give the formula for finding $_nC_r$.

4. What is the relationship between $_nC_r$ and $_nP_r$?

5. In your own words, explain the difference between a permutation and a combination.

6. Assume that you have seven different objects and that you are going to select four without replacement. Will there be more combinations or more permutations of the four items? Explain.

PRACTICE THE SKILLS

In Exercises 7–20, evaluate the expression.

7. $_4C_2$

8. $_8C_3$

9. a) $_6C_4$ b) $_6P_4$

10. a) $_8C_2$ b) $_8P_2$

11. a) $_8C_0$ b) $_8P_0$

12. a) $_{12}C_8$ b) $_{12}P_8$

13. a) $_{10}C_3$ b) $_{10}P_3$

14. a) $_5C_5$ b) $_5P_5$

15. $\dfrac{_5C_3}{_5P_3}$

16. $\dfrac{_7C_2}{_7P_2}$

17. $\dfrac{_9C_4}{_9C_2}$

18. $\dfrac{_6C_6}{_8C_0}$

19. $\dfrac{_9P_5}{_{10}C_4}$

20. $\dfrac{_7P_0}{_7C_0}$

PROBLEM SOLVING

21. *Attending a Conference* The Sarasota City Council plans to send 2 of its 8 members to a conference in Hawaii. How many different ways can the 2 members be selected?

22. *Banana Split* An ice-cream parlor has 20 different flavors. Cynthia orders a banana split and has to select 3 different flavors. How many different selections are possible?

23. *Test Essays* A student must select and answer four of five essay questions on a test. In how many ways can she do so?

24. *Software Packages* During a special promotion at CompUSA, a customer purchasing a computer and a printer is given the choice of 2 free software packages. If there are 9 different software packages from which to select, how many different ways can the 2 packages be selected?

25. *Scholarships* A scholarship committee has received 8 applications for a $500 scholarship. The committee has decided to select 3 of the 8 candidates for further consideration. In how ways can the committee do so?

26. *Attending Plays* While visiting New York City, the Nygens want to attend 3 plays out of 10 plays they would like to see. In how many ways can they do so?

▲ Theater district, New York City

27. *Taxi Ride* A group of 7 people wants to use taxis to go to a local restaurant. When the first taxi arrives, the group decides that 4 people should get into the taxi. In how many ways can that be done?

28. *Plants* Mary Robinson purchased a package of 24 different plants, but she only needed 20 plants for planting. In how many ways can she select the 20 plants from the package to be planted?

29. *Entertainers* Ruth Eckerd Hall must select 8 of 12 possible entertainers for its summer schedule. In how many ways can that be done?

30. *CD Purchase* Neo Anderson wants to purchase six different CDs but only has enough money to purchase four. In how many ways can he select four of six CDs for purchase?

31. *Posters* Matthew Abbott has eight posters he would like to hang on the wall of his bedroom, but his wall is only wide enough to hang four posters. In how many ways can Matthew select the four posters to hang on his bedroom wall?

32. *Washers and Dryers* Sears has nine different washing machines in stock and six different clothes dryers in stock. The manager wants to place three of the nine washing machines and two of the six clothes dryers on sale. In how many ways can the manager select the items to be listed as sale items?

33. *Quinella Bet* A quinella bet consists of selecting the first- and second-place winners, in any order, in a particular event. For example, suppose you select a 2–5 quinella. If 2 wins and 5 finishes second, or if 5 wins and 2 finishes second, you win. Mr. Smith goes to a jai alai match. In the match, 8 jai alai teams compete. How many quinella tickets must Mr. Smith purchase to guarantee a win?

▲ Jai alai game

34. *Test Question* On an English test, Tito Ramirez must write an essay for three of the five questions in Part 1 and four of the six questions in Part 2. How many different combinations of questions can he answer?

35. *Plasma and LCD TVs* A television/stereo store has 12 different plasma televisions and 8 different LCD televisions in stock. The store's manager wishes to place 3 plasma televisions and 2 LCD televisions on sale. In how many ways can that be done?

36. *Medical Research* At a medical research center, an experimental drug is to be given to 16 people, 8 men and 8 women. If 14 men and 11 women have volunteered to be given the drug, in how many ways can the researcher choose the 16 people to be given the drug?

37. *Dinner Party* Sue Less is having a dinner party. She has 10 different bottles of red wine and 8 different bottles of white wine on her wine rack. She wants to select 4 bottles of red wine and 2 bottles of white wine to serve at her party. In how many ways can she do so?

38. *Forming a Committee* The Webster Town Board is forming a committee to explore ways to improve public safety in the town. The committee will consist of 4 representatives from the town board and 3 representatives from a citizens advisory board. If there are 7 town board members and 5 citizens advisory board members from which to choose, how many different ways can the committee be formed?

39. *Selecting Soda* Angel Ramirez is sent to the store to get 5 different bottles of regular soda and 3 different bottles of diet soda. If there are 10 different types of regular sodas and 7 different types of diet sodas to choose from, how many different choices does Angel have?

40. *Constructing a Test* A teacher is constructing a mathematics test consisting of 10 questions. She has a pool of 28 questions, which are classified by level of difficulty as follows: 6 difficult questions, 10 average questions, and 12 easy questions. How many different 10-question tests can she construct from the pool of 28 questions if her test is to have 3 difficult, 4 average, and 3 easy questions?

41. *Selecting Mutual Funds* Joe Chang recently graduated from college and now has a job that provides a retirement investment plan. Joe wants to diversify his investments, so he wants to invest in four stock mutual funds and two bond mutual funds. If he has a choice of eight stock mutual funds and five bond mutual funds, how many different selections of mutual funds does he have?

42. *Door Prize* As part of a door prize, Mary McCarty won three tickets to a baseball game and three tickets to a theater performance. She decided to give all the tickets to friends. For the baseball game she is considering six different friends, and for the theater she is considering eight different friends. In how many ways can she distribute the tickets?

43. *New Breakfast Cereals* General Mills is testing 6 oat cereals, 5 wheat cereals, and 4 rice cereals. If it plans to market 3 of the oat cereals, 2 of the wheat cereals, and 2 of the rice cereals, how many different combinations are possible?

44. *Catering Service* A catering service is making up trays of hors d'oeuvres. The hors d'oeuvres are categorized as inexpensive, average, and expensive. If the client must select three of the eight inexpensive, five of the nine average, and two of the four expensive hors d'oeuvres, how many different choices are possible?

CHALLENGE PROBLEMS/GROUP ACTIVITIES

45. *Test Answers* Consider a 10-question test in which each question can be answered either correctly or incorrectly.

a) How many different ways are there to answer the questions so that eight are correct and two are incorrect?

b) How many different ways are there to answer the questions so that at least eight are correct?

46. a) *A Dinner Toast* Four people at dinner make a toast. If each person is to tap glasses with each other person one at a time, how many taps will take place?

b) Repeat part (a) with five people.

c) How many taps will there be if there are n people at the dinner table?

47. *Pascal's Triangle* The notation $_nC_r$ may be written $\binom{n}{r}$.

a) Use this notation to evaluate each of the combinations in the following array. Form a triangle of the results, similar to the one given, by placing the answer to each combination in the same relative position in the triangle.

$$\binom{0}{0}$$

$$\binom{1}{0} \qquad \binom{1}{1}$$

$$\binom{2}{0} \qquad \binom{2}{1} \qquad \binom{2}{2}$$

$$\binom{3}{0} \qquad \binom{3}{1} \qquad \binom{3}{2} \qquad \binom{3}{3}$$

$$\binom{4}{0} \qquad \binom{4}{1} \qquad \binom{4}{2} \qquad \binom{4}{3} \qquad \binom{4}{4}$$

b) Using the number pattern in part (a), find the next row of numbers of the triangle (known as *Pascal's triangle*).

48. *Lottery Combinations* Determine the number of combinations possible in a state lottery where you must select

a) 6 of 46 numbers.

b) 6 of 47 numbers.

c) 6 of 48 numbers.

d) 6 of 49 numbers.

e) Does the number of combinations increase by the same amount going from part (a) to part (b) as from part (b) to part (c)?

49. a) *Table Seating Arrangements* How many distinct ways can four people be seated in a row?

   b) How many distinct ways can four people be seated at a circular table?

50. Show that $_nC_r = {_nC_{(n-r)}}$.

51. *Forming a Committee* A group of 15 people wants to form a committee consisting of a chair, vice chair, and three additional members. How many different committees can be formed?

RECREATIONAL MATHEMATICS

52. a) *Combination Lock* To open a combination lock, you must know the lock's three-number sequence in its proper order. Repetition of numbers is permitted. Why is this lock more like a permutation lock than a combination lock? Why is it not a true permutation problem?

   b) Assuming that a combination lock has 40 numbers, determine how many different three-number

arrangements are possible if repetition of numbers is allowed.

   c) Answer the question in part (b) if repetition is not allowed.

INTERNET/RESEARCH ACTIVITY

53. The area of mathematics called combinatorics is the science of counting. Do research and write a paper on combinatorics and its many applications.

12.10 SOLVING PROBABILITY PROBLEMS BY USING COMBINATIONS

▲ What is the probability of selecting two picture cards from a standard deck of 52 cards when the two cards are selected without replacement?

Suppose that we want to find the probability of selecting two picture cards (jacks, queens, or kings) when two cards are selected, without replacement, from a standard deck of cards. In Section 12.6, we used the *and* probability formula to solve this type of probability problem. In this section, we will learn another way to solve this type of probability problem by using combinations.

Using the *and* formula for the above example, we could reason as follows:

$$P(2 \text{ picture cards}) = P(\text{first picture card}) \cdot P(\text{second picture card})$$
$$= \frac{12}{52} \cdot \frac{11}{51} = \frac{132}{2652} \quad \text{or} \quad \frac{11}{221}$$

Since the order of the two picture cards selected is not important to the final answer, this problem can be considered a combination probability problem.

We can also find the probability of selecting two picture cards, using combinations, by finding the number of possible successful outcomes (selecting two picture cards) and dividing that answer by the total number of possible outcomes (selecting any two cards).

The number of ways in which two picture cards can be selected from the 12 picture cards in a deck is $_{12}C_2$, or

$$_{12}C_2 = \frac{12!}{(12-2)!2!} = \frac{\overset{6}{\cancel{12}} \cdot 11 \cdot \cancel{10!}}{\cancel{10!} \cdot 2 \cdot 1} = 66$$

The number of ways in which two cards can be selected from a deck of 52 cards is $_{52}C_2$, or

$$_{52}C_2 = \frac{52!}{(52-2)!2!} = \frac{52 \cdot 51 \cdot \overset{26}{\cancel{50!}}}{\cancel{50!} \cdot \cancel{2} \cdot 1} = 1326$$

Thus,

$$P(\text{selecting 2 picture cards}) = \frac{_{12}C_2}{_{52}C_2} = \frac{66}{1326} = \frac{11}{221}$$

Note that the same answer is obtained with either method. To give you more exposure to counting techniques, we will work the problems in this section using combinations.

EXAMPLE ❶ Committee of Three Women

A club consists of four men and five women. Three members are to be selected at random to form a committee. What is the probability that the committee will consist of three women?

SOLUTION The order in which the three members are selected is not important. Therefore, we may work this problem using combinations.

$$P\left(\begin{array}{c}\text{committee consists} \\ \text{of 3 women}\end{array}\right) = \frac{\text{number of possible committees with 3 women}}{\text{total number of possible 3-member committees}}$$

Since there is a total of 5 women, the number of possible committees with three women is $_5C_3 = 10$. Since there is a total of 9 people, the total number of possible three-member committees is $_9C_3 = 84$.

$$P(\text{committee consists of 3 women}) = \frac{10}{84} = \frac{5}{42}$$

The probability of randomly selecting a committee with three women is $\frac{5}{42}$. ●

EXAMPLE ❷ A Heart Flush

A flush in the game of poker is five cards of the same suit (5 hearts, 5 diamonds, 5 clubs, or 5 spades). If you are dealt a five-card hand, find the probability that you will be dealt a heart flush.

SOLUTION The order in which the five hearts are dealt is not important. Therefore, we may work this problem using combinations.

$$P(\text{heart flush}) = \frac{\text{number of possible 5-card heart flushes}}{\text{total number of possible 5-card hands}}$$

Since there are 13 hearts in a deck of cards, the number of possible five-card heart flush hands is $_{13}C_5 = 1287$. The total number of possible five-card hands in a deck of 52 cards is $_{52}C_5 = 2,598,960$.

$$P(\text{heart flush}) = \frac{_{13}C_5}{_{52}C_5} = \frac{1287}{2,598,960} = \frac{33}{66,640}$$

The probability of being dealt a heart flush is $\frac{33}{66,640}$, or ≈ 0.000495. ●

EXAMPLE ❸ *Employment Assignments*

A temporary employment agency has six men and five women who wish to be assigned for the day. One employer has requested four employees for security guard positions, and the second employer has requested three employees for moving furniture in an office building. If we assume that each of the potential employees has the same chance of being selected and being assigned at random and that only seven employees will be assigned, find the probability that

a) three men will be selected for moving furniture.

b) three men will be selected for moving furniture and four women will be selected for security guard positions.

SOLUTION

a) $P\left(\begin{array}{c} \text{3 men selected} \\ \text{for moving furniture} \end{array}\right) = \dfrac{\left(\begin{array}{c} \text{number of possible combinations} \\ \text{of 3 men selected} \end{array}\right)}{\left(\begin{array}{c} \text{total number of possible combinations} \\ \text{for selecting 3 people} \end{array}\right)}$

The number of possible combinations with 3 men is $_6C_3$. The total number of possible selections of 3 people is $_{11}C_3$.

$$P\left(\begin{array}{c} \text{3 men selected} \\ \text{for moving furniture} \end{array}\right) = \frac{_6C_3}{_{11}C_3} = \frac{20}{165} = \frac{4}{33}$$

Thus, the probability that 3 men are selected is $\frac{4}{33}$.

b) The number of ways of selecting 3 men out of 6 is $_6C_3$, and the number of ways of selecting 4 women out of 5 is $_5C_4$. The total number of possible selections when 7 people are selected from 11 is $_{11}C_7$. Since both the 3 men *and* the 4 women must be selected, the probability is calculated as follows:

$$P\left(\begin{array}{c} \text{3 men and} \\ \text{4 women selected} \end{array}\right) = \frac{\left(\begin{array}{c} \text{number of combinations} \\ \text{of 3 men selected} \end{array}\right) \cdot \left(\begin{array}{c} \text{number of combinations} \\ \text{of 4 women selected} \end{array}\right)}{\left(\begin{array}{c} \text{total number of possible combinations} \\ \text{for selecting 7 people} \end{array}\right)}$$

$$= \frac{_6C_3 \cdot _5C_4}{_{11}C_7} = \frac{20 \cdot 5}{330} = \frac{100}{330} = \frac{10}{33}$$

Thus, the probability is $\frac{10}{33}$.   ●

EXAMPLE ❹ *New Breakfast Cereals*

Kellogg's is testing 12 new cereals for possible production. They are testing 3 oat cereals, 4 wheat cereals, and 5 rice cereals. If we assume that each of the 12 cereals has the same chance of being selected and 4 new cereals will be produced, find the probability that

a) no wheat cereals are selected.

b) at least 1 wheat cereal is selected.

c) 2 wheat cereals and 2 rice cereals are selected.

SOLUTION

a) If no wheat cereals are to be selected, then only oat and rice cereals must be selected. Eight cereals are oat or rice. Thus, the number of ways that 4 oat or rice cereals may be selected from the 8 possible oat or rice cereals is $_8C_4$. The total number of possible selections is $_{12}C_4$.

$$P(\text{no wheat cereals}) = \frac{_8C_4}{_{12}C_4} = \frac{70}{495} = \frac{14}{99}$$

b) When 4 cereals are selected, the choice must contain either no wheat cereal or at least 1 wheat cereal. Since one of these outcomes must occur, the sum of the probabilities must be 1, or

$$P(\text{no wheat cereal}) + P(\text{at least 1 wheat cereal}) = 1$$

Therefore,

$$P(\text{at least 1 wheat cereal}) = 1 - P(\text{no wheat cereal})$$
$$= 1 - \frac{14}{99} = \frac{99}{99} - \frac{14}{99} = \frac{85}{99}$$

Note that the probability of selecting no wheat cereals, $\frac{14}{99}$, was found in part (a).

c) The number of ways of selecting 2 wheat cereals out of 4 wheat cereals is $_4C_2$, which equals 6. The number of ways of selecting 2 rice cereals out of 5 rice cereals is $_5C_2$, which equals 10. The total number of possible selections when 4 cereals are selected from the 12 choices is $_{12}C_4$ which equals 495. Since both the 2 wheat *and* the 2 rice cereals must be selected, the probability is calculated as follows.

$$P(\text{2 wheat and 2 rice}) = \frac{_4C_2 \cdot {_5C_2}}{_{12}C_4} = \frac{6 \cdot 10}{495} = \frac{60}{495} = \frac{4}{33}$$ ●

EXAMPLE ⑤ *Rare Coins*

Conner Shanahan's rare coin collection is made up of 8 silver dollars, 7 quarters, and 5 dimes. Conner plans to sell 8 of his 20 coins to finance part of his college education. If he selects the coins at random, what is the probability that 3 silver dollars, 2 quarters, and 3 dimes are selected?

SOLUTION   The number of ways that Conner can select 3 out of 8 silver dollars is $_8C_3$. The number of ways he can select 2 out of 7 quarters is $_7C_2$. The number of ways he can select 3 out of 5 dimes is $_5C_3$. He will select 8 coins from a total of 20 coins. The number of ways he can do so is $_{20}C_8$. The probability that Conner selects 3 silver dollars, 2 quarters, and 3 dimes is calculated as follows.

$$P(\text{3 silver dollars, 2 quarters, and 3 dimes}) = \frac{_8C_3 \cdot {_7C_2} \cdot {_5C_3}}{_{20}C_8}$$
$$= \frac{56 \cdot 21 \cdot 10}{125{,}970} = \frac{11{,}760}{125{,}970} = \frac{392}{4199}$$ ●

SECTION 12.10 EXERCISES

CONCEPT/WRITING EXERCISES

In Exercises 1–8, set up the problem as if it were to be solved, but do not solve. Assume that each problem is to be done without replacement. Explain why you set up the exercises as you did.

1. Eight red balls and four blue balls are in a bag. If four balls from the bag are to be selected at random, determine the probability of selecting four red balls.

2. A class consists of 19 girls and 15 boys. If 12 of the students are to be selected at random, determine the probability that they are all girls.

3. Three letters are to be selected at random from the English alphabet of 26 letters. Determine the probability that 3 vowels (a, e, i, o, u) are selected.

4. Determine the probability of being dealt 3 aces from a standard deck of 52 cards when 3 cards are dealt.

5. A dog breeder has 15 puppies for sale, of which 8 are yellow Labrador retrievers. If 5 puppies are selected at random, determine the probability they are all yellow Labrador retrievers.

6. Of 80 people attending a dance, 28 have a college degree. If 4 people at the dance are selected at random, determine the probability that each of the 4 has a college degree.

7. A basket of 50 golf balls contains 22 Nike balls. If 8 balls are selected at random from the basket, determine the probability that *none* of those selected is a Nike ball.

8. A class of 16 people contains 4 people whose birthday is in October. If 3 people from the class are selected at random, determine the probability that *none* of those selected has an October birthday.

PRACTICE THE SKILLS/PROBLEM SOLVING

In Exercises 9–18, the problems are to be done without replacement. Use combinations to determine probabilities.

9. *Green and Red Balls* A bag contains four red balls and five green balls. You plan to select three balls at random. Determine the probability of selecting three green balls.

10. *Selecting Lightbulbs* A box contains 4 defective and 6 good lightbulbs. If two lightbulbs are to be selected at random from the box, determine the probability that both lightbulbs are defective.

11. *Flu Serum* A doctor has five doses of flu protection serum left. He has six women and eight men who want the medication. If the names of five of these people are selected at random, determine the probability that five men's names are selected.

12. *Bills of Four Denominations* Duc Tran's wallet contains 8 bills of the following denominations: four $5 bills, two $10 bills, one $20 bill, and one $50 bill. If Duc selects two bills at random, determine the probability that he selects two $5 bills.

13. *Selecting Digits* Each of the digits 0–9 is written on a slip of paper, and the slips are placed in a hat. If three slips of paper are selected at random, determine the probability that the three numbers selected are greater than 4.

14. *Selecting Books* Barnes and Noble has 20 different books listed on its clearance list. Twelve books are listed as mystery, and 8 are listed as romance. If 4 books are selected at random from the list, determine the probability that they are all mystery books.

15. **Gift Certificates** The sales department at Atwell Studios consists of three people, the manufacturing department consists of six people, and the accounting department consists of two people. Three people will be selected at random from these people and will be given gift certificates to Sweet Tomatoes, a local restaurant. Determine the probability that two of those selected will be from the manufacturing department and one will be from the accounting department.

16. **Faculty-Student Committee** A committee of four is to be randomly selected from a group of seven teachers and eight students. Determine the probability that the committee will consist of two teachers and two students.

17. **Winning the Grand Prize** A lottery consists of 46 numbers. You select 6 numbers, and if they match the 6 numbers selected by the lottery commission, you win the grand prize. Determine the probability of winning the grand prize.

18. **Red Cards** You are dealt 5 cards from a standard deck of 52 cards. Determine the probability that you are dealt 5 red cards.

TV Game Show *In Exercises 19–22, a television game show has five doors, of which the contestant must pick two. Behind two of the doors are expensive cars, and behind the other three doors are consolation prizes. The contestant gets to keep the items behind the two doors she selects. Determine the probability that the contestant wins*

19. no cars.

20. both cars.

21. at least one car.

22. exactly one car.

Baseball *In Exercises 23–26, assume that a particular professional baseball team has 10 pitchers, 6 infielders, and 9 other players. If 3 players' names are selected at random, determine the probability that*

23. all 3 are infielders.

24. none of the three is a pitcher.

25. 2 are pitchers and 1 is an infielder.

26. 1 is a pitcher and 2 are players other than pitchers and infielders.

▲ See Exercises 23–26

Car Rental *In Exercises 27–30, a car rental agency has 10 midsized and 15 compact cars on its lot, from which 6 will be selected. Assuming that each car is equally likely to be selected and the cars are selected at random, determine the probability (as a decimal number rounded to four decimal places) that the cars selected consist of*

27. all midsized cars.

28. 2 midsized cars and 4 compact cars.

29. 3 midsized cars and 3 compact cars.

30. at least 1 compact car.

Airline Routes *In Exercises 31–34, an airline is given permission to fly 4 new routes of its choice. The airline is considering 12 new routes: 4 routes in Florida, 5 routes in California, and 3 routes in Texas. If the airline selects the 4 new routes at random from the 12 possibilities, determine the probability that*

31. 2 are in Florida and 2 are in Texas.

32. 3 are in California and 1 is in Florida.

33. 1 is in Florida, 1 is in California, and 2 are in Texas.

34. at least one is in Texas.

Theater *In Exercises 35–38, five men and six women are going to be assigned to a specific row of seats in a theater. If the 11 tickets for the numbered seats are given out at random, determine the probability that*

35. five women are given the first five seats next to the center aisle.

36. at least one woman is in one of the first five seats.

37. exactly one woman is in one of the first five seats.

38. three women are seated in the first three seats and two men are seated in the next two seats.

39. *Working Overtime* Of 24 employees at Lowe's home improvement store, 10 work as cashiers and 14 stock shelves. If 3 of the 24 employees are selected at random to work overtime, determine the probability that all 3 are cashiers.

40. *Poker Probability* A full house in poker consists of three of one kind and two of another kind in a five-card hand. For example, if a hand contains three kings and two 5's, it is a full house. If 5 cards are dealt at random from a standard deck of 52 cards, without replacement, determine the probability of getting three kings and two 5's.

41. *A Royal Flush* A royal flush consists of an ace, king, queen, jack, and 10 all in the same suit. If 7 cards are dealt at random from a standard deck of 52 cards, determine the probability of getting a

   a) royal flush in spades.

   b) royal flush in any suit.

42. *Restaurant Staff* The staff of a restaurant consists of 25 people, including 8 waiters, 12 waitresses, and 5 cooks. For Mother's Day, a total of 9 people will need to be selected to work. If the selections are made at random, determine the probability that 3 waiters, 4 waitresses, and 2 cooks will be selected.

43. *"Dead Man's Hand"* A pair of aces and a pair of 8's is often known as a "dead man's hand." (See the Did You Know? on page 810.)

   a) Determine the probability of being dealt a dead man's hand (any two aces, any two 8's, and one other card that is not an ace or an 8) when 5 cards are dealt, without replacement, from a standard deck of 52 cards.

   b) The actual cards "Wild Bill" Hickok was holding when he was shot were the aces of spades and clubs, the 8's of spades and clubs, and the 9 of diamonds. If you are dealt five cards without replacement, determine the probability of being dealt this exact hand.

CHALLENGE PROBLEMS/GROUP ACTIVITIES

44. *Alternate Seating* If three men and three women are to be assigned at random to six seats in a row at a theater, determine the probability that they will alternate by gender.

45. *Selecting Officers* A club consists of 15 people including Ali, Kendra, Ted, Alice, Marie, Dan, Linda, and Frank. From the 15 members, a president, vice president, and treasurer will be selected at random. An advisory committee of 5 other individuals will also be selected at random.

   a) Determine the probability that Ali is selected president, Kendra is selected vice president, Ted is selected treasurer, and the other 5 individuals named form the advisory committee.

   b) Determine the probability that 3 of the 8 individuals named are selected for the three officers' positions and the other 5 are selected for the advisory board.

46. *A Marked Deck* A number is written with a magic marker on each card of a deck of 52 cards. The number 1 is put on the first card, 2 on the second, and so on. The cards are then shuffled and cut. What is the probability that the top 4 cards will be in ascending order? (For example, the top card is 12, the second 22, the third 41, and the fourth 51.)

RECREATIONAL MATHEMATICS

47. *Hair* When the Isle of Flume took its most recent census, the population was 100,002 people. Nobody on the isle has more than 100,001 hairs on his or her head. Determine the probability that at least two people have exactly the same number of hairs on their head.

12.11 BINOMIAL PROBABILITY FORMULA

Suppose that you are a waiter at a restaurant and have learned from past experience that 80% of your customers leave a tip. If you wait on 6 customers, what is the probability that all 6 customers will leave a tip? If you wait on 8 customers, what is the probability that at least 5 of them will leave you a tip? In this section, we will learn how to use the binomial probability formula to answer these and similar questions.

▲ We can use the binomial formula to determine the probability that selected customers waited on will leave a tip.

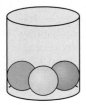

Figure 12.23

Suppose that a basket contains three identical balls, except for their color. One is red, one is blue, and one is yellow (Fig. 12.23). Suppose further that we are going to select three balls *with replacement* from the basket. We can determine specific probabilities by examining the tree diagram shown in Fig. 12.24. Note that 27 different selections are possible, as indicated in the sample space.

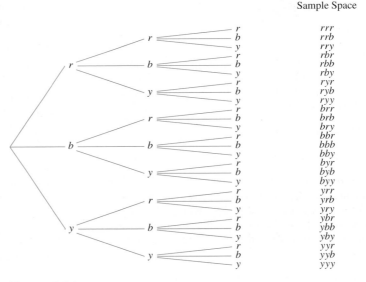

Figure 12.24

Our three selections may yield 0, 1, 2, or 3 red balls. We can determine the probability of selecting exactly 0, 1, 2, or 3 red balls by using the sample space. To determine the probability of selecting 0 red balls, we count those outcomes that do not contain a red ball. There are 8 of them (*bbb*, *bby*, *byb*, *byy*, *ybb*, *yby*, *yyb*, *yyy*). Thus, the probability of obtaining exactly 0 red balls is 8/27. We determine the probability of selecting exactly 1 red ball by counting the sample points that contain exactly 1 red ball. There are 12 of them. Thus, the probability is $\frac{12}{27}$, or $\frac{4}{9}$.

We can determine the probability of selecting exactly 2 red balls and exactly 3 red balls in a similar manner. The probabilities of selecting exactly 0, 1, 2, and 3 red balls are illustrated in Table 12.5 on page 817.

Table 12.5 A Probability Distribution for Three Balls Selected with Replacement

Number of Red Balls Selected, (x)	Probability of Selecting the Number of Red Balls, P(x)
0	$\dfrac{8}{27}$
1	$\dfrac{12}{27}$
2	$\dfrac{6}{27}$
3	$\dfrac{1}{27}$
	Sum $= \dfrac{27}{27} = 1$

Note that the sum of the probabilities is 1. This table is an example of a *probability distribution*, which shows the probabilities associated with each specific outcome of an experiment. *In a probability distribution, every possible outcome must be listed and the sum of the probabilities must be 1.*

Let us specifically consider the probability of selecting 1 red ball in 3 selections. We see from Table 12.5 that this probability is $\frac{12}{27}$, or $\frac{4}{9}$. Can we determine this probability without developing a tree diagram? The answer is yes.

Suppose that we consider selecting a red ball success, S, and selecting a non–red ball failure, F. Furthermore, suppose that we let p represent the probability of success and q the probability of failure on any trial. Then $p = \frac{1}{3}$ and $q = \frac{2}{3}$. We can obtain 1 success in three selections in the following ways:

$$\text{SFF} \qquad \text{FSF} \qquad \text{FFS}$$

We can compute the probabilities of each of these outcomes using the multiplication formula because each of the selections is independent.

$$P(\text{SFF}) = P(\text{S}) \cdot P(\text{F}) \cdot P(\text{F}) = p \cdot q \cdot q = pq^2 = \frac{1}{3}\left(\frac{2}{3}\right)^2 = \frac{4}{27}$$

$$P(\text{FSF}) = P(\text{F}) \cdot P(\text{S}) \cdot P(\text{F}) = q \cdot p \cdot q = pq^2 = \frac{1}{3}\left(\frac{2}{3}\right)^2 = \frac{4}{27}$$

$$P(\text{FFS}) = P(\text{F}) \cdot P(\text{F}) \cdot P(\text{S}) = q \cdot q \cdot p = pq^2 = \frac{1}{3}\left(\frac{2}{3}\right)^2 = \frac{4}{27}$$

$$\text{Sum} = \frac{12}{27} = \frac{4}{9}$$

We obtained an answer of $\frac{4}{9}$, the same answer that was obtained using the tree diagram. Note that each of the 3 sets of outcomes above has 1 success and 2 failures. Rather than listing all the possibilities containing 1 success and 2 failures, we can use the combination formula to determine the number of possible combinations of 1 success in 3 trials. To do so, evaluate $_3C_1$.

$$_3C_1 = \frac{3!}{(3-1)!1!} = \frac{3 \cdot 2 \cdot 1}{2 \cdot 1 \cdot 1} = 3$$

Number of trials   Number of successes

Thus, we see that there are 3 ways the 1 success could occur in 3 trials. To compute the probability of 1 success in 3 trials, we can multiply the probability of success in any one trial, $p \cdot q^2$, by the number of ways the 1 success can be arranged among the 3 trials, $_3C_1$. Thus, the probability of selecting 1 red ball, $P(1)$, in 3 trials may be found as follows.

$$P(1) = (_3C_1)p^1q^2 = 3\left(\frac{1}{3}\right)\left(\frac{2}{3}\right)^2 = \frac{12}{27} = \frac{4}{9}$$

The binomial probability formula, which we introduce shortly, explains how to obtain expressions like $P(1) = (_3C_1)p^1q^2$ and is very useful in finding certain types of probabilities.

To use the binomial probability formula, the following three conditions must hold.

TO USE THE BINOMIAL PROBABILITY FORMULA

1. There are n repeated independent trials.
2. Each trial has two possible outcomes, *success* and *failure.*
3. For each trial, the probability of success (and failure) remains the same.

Before going further, let's discuss why we can use the binomial probability formula to find the probability of selecting a specific number of red balls when three balls are selected with replacement. First, since each trial is performed *with replacement*, the three trials are independent of each other. Second, we may consider selecting a red ball as success and selecting any ball of another color as failure. Third, for each selection, the probability of success (selecting a red ball) is $\frac{1}{3}$ and the probability of failure (selecting a ball of another color) is $\frac{2}{3}$. Now let's discuss the binomial probability formula.

BINOMIAL PROBABILITY FORMULA

The probability of obtaining exactly x successes, $P(x)$, in n independent trials is given by

$$P(x) = (_nC_x)p^xq^{n-x}$$

where p is the probability of success on a single trial and q is the probability of failure on a single trial.

In the formula, p will be a number between 0 and 1, inclusive, and $q = 1 - p$. Therefore, if $p = 0.2$, then $q = 1 - 0.2 = 0.8$. If $p = \frac{3}{5}$, then $q = 1 - \frac{3}{5} = \frac{2}{5}$. Note that $p + q = 1$ and the values of p and q remain the same for each independent trial. The combination $_nC_x$ is called the *binomial coefficient.*

In Example 1, we use the binomial probability formula to solve the same problem we recently solved by using a tree diagram.

EXAMPLE ❶ Selecting Colored Balls with Replacement

A basket contains 3 balls: 1 red, 1 blue, and 1 yellow. Three balls are going to be selected with replacement from the basket. Find the probability that

a) no red balls are selected.

b) exactly 1 red ball is selected.

c) exactly 2 red balls are selected.

d) exactly 3 red balls are selected.

SOLUTION

a) We will consider selecting a red ball a success and selecting a ball of any other color a failure. Since only 1 of the 3 balls is red, the probability of success on any single trial, p, is $\frac{1}{3}$. The probability of failure on any single trial, q, is $1 - \frac{1}{3} = \frac{2}{3}$. We are finding the probability of selecting 0 red balls, or 0 successes. Since x represents the number of successes, we let $x = 0$. There are 3 independent selections (or trials), so $n = 3$. In our calculations, we will need to evaluate $\left(\frac{1}{3}\right)^0$. Note that any nonzero number raised to a power of 0 is 1. Thus, $\left(\frac{1}{3}\right)^0 = 1$. We determine the probability of 0 successes, or $P(0)$, as follows.

$$P(x) = (_nC_x)p^x q^{n-x}$$

$$P(0) = (_3C_0)\left(\frac{1}{3}\right)^0 \left(\frac{2}{3}\right)^{3-0}$$

$$= (1)(1)\left(\frac{2}{3}\right)^3$$

$$= \left(\frac{2}{3}\right)^3 = \frac{8}{27}$$

b) We are finding the probability of obtaining exactly 1 red ball or exactly 1 success in 3 independent selections. Thus, $x = 1$ and $n = 3$. We find the probability of exactly 1 success, or $P(1)$, as follows.

$$P(x) = (_nC_x)p^x q^{n-x}$$

$$P(1) = (_3C_1)\left(\frac{1}{3}\right)^1 \left(\frac{2}{3}\right)^{3-1}$$

$$= 3\left(\frac{1}{3}\right)\left(\frac{2}{3}\right)^2$$

$$= 3\left(\frac{1}{3}\right)\left(\frac{4}{9}\right) = \frac{4}{9}$$

c) We are finding the probability of selecting exactly 2 red balls in 3 independent trials. Thus, $x = 2$ and $n = 3$. We find $P(2)$ as follows.

$$P(x) = (_nC_x)p^x q^{n-x}$$

$$P(2) = {}_3C_2\left(\frac{1}{3}\right)^2 \left(\frac{2}{3}\right)^{3-2}$$

$$= 3\left(\frac{1}{3}\right)^2 \left(\frac{2}{3}\right)^1$$

$$= 3\left(\frac{1}{9}\right)\left(\frac{2}{3}\right) = \frac{2}{9}$$

d) We are finding the probability of selecting exactly 3 red balls in 3 independent trials. Thus, $x = 3$ and $n = 3$. We find $P(3)$ as follows.

$$P(x) = (_nC_x)p^x q^{n-x}$$
$$P(3) = (_3C_3)\left(\frac{1}{3}\right)^3\left(\frac{2}{3}\right)^{3-3}$$
$$= 1\left(\frac{1}{3}\right)^3\left(\frac{2}{3}\right)^0$$
$$= 1\left(\frac{1}{27}\right)(1) = \frac{1}{27}$$

All the probabilities obtained in Example 1 agree with the answers obtained by using the tree diagram. Whenever you obtain a value for $P(x)$, you should obtain a value between 0 and 1, inclusive. If you obtain a value greater than 1, you have made a mistake.

EXAMPLE ❷ *Quality Control for Flashlights*

A manufacturer of flashlights knows that 0.4% of the flashlights produced by the company are defective.

a) Write the binomial probability formula that would be used to determine the probability that exactly x out of n flashlights produced are defective.

b) Write the binomial probability formula that would be used to find the probability that exactly 3 flashlights of 75 produced will be defective. Do not evaluate.

SOLUTION

a) We want to find the probability that exactly x flashlights are defective where selecting a defective flashlight is considered success. The probability, P, that an individual flashlight is defective is 0.4%, or 0.004 in decimal form. The probability that a flashlight is not defective, q, is $1 - 0.004$, or 0.996. The general formula for finding the probability that exactly x out of n flashlights produced are defective is

$$P(x) = (_nC_x)p^x q^{n-x}$$

Substituting 0.004 for p and 0.996 for q, we obtain the formula

$$P(x) = (_nC_x)(0.004)^x(0.996)^{n-x}$$

b) We want to determine the probability that exactly 3 flashlights out of 75 produced are defective. Thus, $x = 3$ and $n = 75$. Substituting these values into the formula in part (a) gives

$$P(3) = (_{75}C_3)(0.004)^3(0.996)^{75-3}$$
$$= (_{75}C_3)(0.004)^3(0.996)^{72}$$

The answer may be obtained using a scientific calculator.

EXAMPLE ❸   *Weather Forecast Accuracy*

The local weatherperson has been accurate in her temperature forecast on 80% of the days. Find the probability that she is accurate

a) exactly 3 of the next 5 days.

b) exactly 4 of the next 4 days.

SOLUTION

a) We want to find the probability that the forecaster is successful (or accurate) exactly 3 of the next 5 days. Thus, $x = 3$ and $n = 5$. The probability of success on any one day, p, is 80%, or 0.8. The probability of failure, q, is $1 - 0.8 = 0.2$. Substituting these values into the binomial probability formula yields

$$P(x) = (_nC_x)p^x q^{n-x}$$
$$P(3) = (_5C_3)(0.8)^3(0.2)^{5-3}$$
$$= 10(0.8)^3(0.2)^2$$
$$= 10(0.512)(0.04)$$
$$= 0.2048$$

Thus, the probability that she is accurate in exactly 3 of the next 5 days is 0.2048.

b) We want to find the probability that she is accurate in each of the next 4 days. Thus, $x = 4$ and $n = 4$. We wish to find $P(4)$.

$$P(x) = (_nC_x)p^x q^{n-x}$$
$$P(4) = (_4C_4)(0.8)^4(0.2)^{4-4}$$
$$= 1(0.8)^4(0.2)^0$$
$$= 1(0.4096)(1)$$
$$= 0.4096$$

TECHNOLOGY TIP   Now would be a good time to spend a few minutes learning how to evaluate expressions such as $(0.8)^3(0.2)^2$ using your calculator. Read the instruction manual that comes with your calculator to learn the procedure to follow to evaluate exponential expressions. Many scientific calculators have keys for evaluating factorials, and some can be used to evaluate permutations and combinations. Check to see if your calculator can be used to evaluate factorials, permutations, and combinations. Also, check with your instructor to see if these features on your calculator can be used on exams.

EXAMPLE ❹   *Planting Trees*

The probability that a tree planted by a landscaping company will survive is 0.8. Determine the probability that

a) none of four trees planted will survive.

b) at least one of four trees planted will survive.

SOLUTION

a) Success is a tree survives. Thus, $p = 0.8$ and $q = 1 - p = 1 - 0.8 = 0.2$.
   We want to find the probability of 0 successes in 4 trials. Thus, $x = 0$ and $n = 4$.
   We find the probability of 0 successes, or $P(0)$, as follows.

$$P(x) = ({}_nC_x)p^x q^{n-x}$$
$$P(0) = ({}_4C_0)(0.8)^0(0.2)^{4-0}$$
$$= 1(1)(0.2)^4$$
$$= 1(1)(0.0016)$$
$$= 0.0016$$

Thus, the probability that none of the four trees planted will survive is 0.0016.

b) The probability that at least one tree of the four trees planted will survive can be
   found by subtracting from 1 the probability that none of the four trees survives.
   We worked problems of this type in earlier sections of the chapter, including
   Sections 12.6 and 12.10.
       In part (a), we determined the probability that none of the four trees planted
   survives is 0.0016. Thus,

$$P(\text{at least one tree planted will survive}) = 1 - P\left(\begin{array}{c}\text{none of the four trees}\\\text{planted will survive}\end{array}\right)$$
$$= 1 - 0.0016$$
$$= 0.9984$$

SECTION 12.11 EXERCISES

CONCEPT/WRITING EXERCISES

1. What is a probability distribution?

2. What are the three requirements that must be met to use
   the binomial probability formula?

3. Write the binomial probability formula.

4. a) In the binomial probability formula, what do p and q
      represent?

   b) If $p = 0.7$, what is the value of q?

   c) If $p = 0.25$, what is the value of q?

PRACTICE THE SKILLS

*In Exercises 5–10, assume that each of the n trials is inde-
pendent and that p is the probability of success on a given
trial. Use the binomial probability formula to find P(x).*

5. $n = 5, x = 3, p = 0.2$

6. $n = 3, x = 2, p = 0.6$

7. $n = 5, x = 2, p = 0.4$

8. $n = 3, x = 3, p = 0.8$

9. $n = 6, x = 0, p = 0.5$

10. $n = 5, x = 3, p = 0.4$

PROBLEM SOLVING

11. *A Dozen Eggs* An egg distributor determines that the prob-
    ability that any individual egg has a crack is 0.14.

    a) Write the binomial probability formula to determine the
       probability that exactly x eggs of n eggs are cracked.

    b) Write the binomial probability formula to determine the
       probability that exactly 2 eggs in a one-dozen egg car-
       ton are cracked. Do not evaluate.

12. *Getting Audited* The probability that a self-employed tax-payer will be audited by the Internal Revenue Service (IRS) is 0.0077.

   a) Write the binomial probability formula to determine the probability that exactly x out of n self-employed tax-payers selected at random will be audited by the IRS.

   b) Write the binomial probability formula to determine the probability that exactly 5 out of 20 self-employed taxpayers selected at random will be audited by the IRS. Do not evaluate.

In Exercises 13–21, use the binomial probability formula to answer the question. Round answers to five decimal places.

13. *Leaving a Tip* Thomas Zellner works as a waiter at Outback Steakhouse. He has learned from experience that 80% of customers who dine alone leave a tip. If Thomas waits on 6 customers dining alone, determine the probability that exactly 4 of them leave a tip.

14. *Traffic Tickets* In Georgia, the probability that a driver is actually given a ticket when he or she is pulled over for a traffic infraction by a member of the Georgia State Police is 0.6. If eight people who were pulled over are selected at random, determine the probability that exactly five of them were given tickets.

15. *Bank Loans* Records from a specific bank show that 70% of car loan applications are approved. If eight car loan applications from this bank are selected at random, determine the probability that exactly five of the applications are approved.

16. *Basketball* Jean Woody makes 80% of her free throws in a basketball game. Determine the probability that she makes exactly four of the next seven free throws.

17. *Dolphin Drug Care* When treated with the antibiotic resonocyllin, 92% of all dolphins are cured of a particular bacterial infection. If six dolphins with the particular bacterial infection are treated with resonocyllin, determine the probability that exactly four are cured.

18. *Manufacturing Lightbulbs* A quality control engineer at a GE lightbulb plant finds that 1% of its bulbs are defective.

Determine the probability that exactly two of the next six bulbs made are defective.

19. *Water Heaters* The probability that a specific brand of water heater produces the water temperature it is set to produce is $\frac{4}{5}$. Determine the probability that if five of these water heaters are selected at random, exactly four of them will produce the water temperature they are set to produce.

20. *TV Purchases* At a Circuit City store, $\frac{1}{4}$ of those purchasing color televisions purchase a large-screen TV. Determine the probability that

   a) none of the next four people who purchase a color television at Circuit City purchases a large-screen TV.

   b) at least one of the next four people who purchase a color television at Circuit City purchases a large-screen TV.

21. *Multiple-Choice Quiz* Edward Dunn has to take a five-question multiple-choice quiz in his sociology class. Each question has four choices for answers, of which only one is correct. Assuming that Edward guesses on all five questions, what is the probability that he will answer

   a) all five questions correctly.

   b) exactly three questions correctly.

   c) at least three questions correctly.

CHALLENGE PROBLEMS/GROUP ACTIVITIES

22. *Transportation to Work* In a random sample of 80 working mothers in Duluth, Minnesota, the following data indicating how they get to work were obtained.

Mode of Transportation	Number of Mothers
Car	40
Bus	20
Bike	16
Other	4

If this sample is representative of all working mothers in Duluth, determine the probability that exactly three of five working mothers selected at random

   a) take a car to work.

   b) take a bus to work.

23. *Selecting 6 Cards* Six cards are selected from a standard deck of playing cards with replacement. Determine the probability that

   a) exactly three picture cards are obtained.

   b) exactly two spades are obtained.

24. *Office Visit* The probability that a person visiting Dr. Guillermo Suarez's office is more than 60 years old is 0.7. Determine the probability that

a) exactly three of the next five people visiting the office are more than 60 years old.

b) at least three of the next five people visiting the office are more than 60 years old.

RECREATIONAL MATHEMATICS

25. *Aruba* The island of Aruba is well known for its beaches and predictable warm, sunny weather. In fact, Aruba's weather is so predictable that the daily newspapers don't even bother to print a forecast. Strangely enough, however, on New Year's Eve, as the islanders were counting down the last 10 sec of 2007, it began to rain. What is the probability, from 0 to 1, that 72 hr later the sun will be shining?

CHAPTER ⑫ SUMMARY

IMPORTANT FACTS

EMPIRICAL PROBABILITY

$$P(E) = \frac{\text{number of times event } E \text{ has occurred}}{\left(\begin{array}{c}\text{total number of times the}\\\text{experiment has been performed}\end{array}\right)}$$

THE LAW OF LARGE NUMBERS

Probability statements apply in practice to a large number of trials, not to a single trial. It is the relative frequency over the long run that is accurately predictable, not individual events or precise totals.

THEORETICAL PROBABILITY

$$P(E) = \frac{\text{number of outcomes favorable to } E}{\text{total number of possible outcomes}}$$

The probability of an event that cannot occur is 0. The probability of an event that must occur is 1. Every probability must be a number between 0 and 1 inclusively; that is

$$0 \le P(E) \le 1$$

The sum of the probabilities of all possible outcomes of an event is 1.

$$P(A) + P(\text{not } A) = 1$$

ODDS AGAINST AN EVENT

$$\text{Odds against} = \frac{P(\text{event fails to occur})}{P(\text{event occurs})} = \frac{P(\text{failure})}{P(\text{success})}$$

ODDS IN FAVOR OF AN EVENT

$$\text{Odds in favor} = \frac{P(\text{event occurs})}{P(\text{event fails to occur})} = \frac{P(\text{success})}{P(\text{failure})}$$

EXPECTED VALUE

$$E = P_1 A_1 + P_2 A_2 + P_3 A_3 + \cdots + P_n A_n$$

FAIR PRICE

$$\text{Fair price} = \text{expected value} + \text{cost to play}$$

COUNTING PRINCIPLE

If a first experiment can be performed in M distinct ways and a second experiment can be performed in N distinct ways, then the two experiments in that specific order can be performed in $M \cdot N$ distinct ways.

OR AND AND PROBLEMS

$$P(A \text{ or } B) = P(A) + P(B) - P(A \text{ and } B)$$
$$P(A \text{ and } B) = P(A) \cdot P(B)$$

CONDITIONAL PROBABILITY

$$P(E_2 \mid E_1) = \frac{n(E_1 \text{ and } E_2)}{n(E_1)}$$

The **number of permutations** of n items is $n!$.

$$n! = n(n-1)(n-2)\cdots(3)(2)(1)$$

PERMUTATION FORMULA

$$_nP_r = \frac{n!}{(n-r)!}$$

The number of different permutations of n objects where $n_1, n_2, \ldots, n_r$ of the objects are identical is

$$\frac{n!}{n_1! n_2! \cdots n_r!}$$

COMBINATION FORMULA

$$_nC_r = \frac{n!}{(n-r)! r!}$$

BINOMIAL PROBABILITY FORMULA

$$P(x) = (_nC_x) p^x q^{n-x}$$

CHAPTER ⑫ REVIEW EXERCISES

12.1–12.11

1. In your own words, explain the law of large numbers.

2. Explain how empirical probability can be used to determine whether a die is "loaded" (not a fair die).

3. *Cars* Of 40 people who purchase a vehicle at a car dealership, 8 purchased an SUV. Determine the empirical probability that the next person who purchases a vehicle from that car dealership purchases an SUV.

4. *Cards* Select a card from a deck of cards 40 times with replacement and compute the empirical probability of selecting a heart.

5. *Television News* In a small town, 200 people were asked whether they watched ABC, CBS, NBC, or Fox news. The results are indicated below.

Network	Number of People
ABC	80
CBS	30
NBC	55
Fox	35

Find the empirical probability that the next person selected at random from the town watches ABC news.

Digits In Exercises 6–9, each of the digits 0, 1, 2, 3, 4, 5, 6, 7, 8, 9 is written on a piece of paper and all the pieces of paper are placed in a hat. One number is selected at random. Determine the probability that the number selected is

6. even.

7. odd or greater than 5.

8. greater than 3 or less than 6.

9. even and greater than 6.

Cheese Preference In Exercises 10–13, a taste test is given to 50 customers at a supermarket. The customers are asked to taste 4 types of cheese and to list their favorite. The results are summarized at the top of the right column.

Type	Number of People
Cheddar	18
Colby jack	14
Muenster	11
Swiss	7

If one person who participated in the taste test is selected at random, determine the probability that the person's favorite was

10. colby jack.

11. muenster.

12. either cheddar or colby jack.

13. a cheese other than Swiss.

14. *Obesity* According to the U.S. Centers for Disease Control and Prevention, 31% of men in the United States are obese. If a man was selected at random, determine the odds

   a) against him being obese.

   b) in favor of him being obese.

15. *Vegetable Mix-up* Nicholas Delaney, a mischievous little boy, has removed labels on the eight cans of vegetables in the cabinet. Nicholas's father knows that there are three cans of corn, three cans of beans, and two cans of carrots. If the father selects and opens one can at random, determine the odds against his selecting a can of corn.

16. *Horseracing* The odds against Buttermilk winning the Triple Crown in horse racing are 82:3. Determine the probability that Buttermilk wins the Triple Crown.

17. *Coffee Shop Success* The probability that a new coffee shop will succeed at a given location is 0.7. Determine the odds in favor of the coffee shop succeeding.

18. *Raffle Tickets* One thousand raffle tickets are sold at $2 each. Three prizes of $200 and two prizes of $100 will be awarded. Assume that the probability that any given ticket is selected for a $200 prize is $\frac{3}{1000}$ and the probability that any given ticket is selected for a $100 prize is $\frac{2}{1000}$.

   a) Determine the expectation of a person who purchases a ticket.

   b) Determine the expectation of a person who purchases three tickets.

   c) Determine the fair price to pay for a ticket.

19. *Expectation of a Card* If Cameron selects a picture card from a standard deck of 52 cards, Lindsey will give him $9. If Cameron does not select a picture card, he must give Lindsey $3.

   a) Determine Cameron's expectation.

   b) Determine Lindsey's expectation.

   c) If Cameron plays this game 100 times, how much can he expect to lose or gain?

20. *Expected Attendance* If the day is sunny, 1000 people will attend the baseball game. If the day is cloudy, only 500 people will attend. If it rains, only 100 people will attend. The local meteorologist states that the probability of a sunny day is 0.4, of a cloudy day is 0.5, and of a rainy day is 0.1. Determine the number of people that are expected to attend.

21. *Club Officers* Tina, Jake, Gina, and Carla form a club. They plan to select a president and a vice president.

   a) Construct a tree diagram showing all the possible outcomes.

   b) List the sample space.

   c) Determine the probability that Gina is selected president and Jake is selected vice president.

22. *A Coin and a Number* A coin is flipped and then a number from 1 through 4 is selected at random from a bag.

   a) Construct a tree diagram showing all the possible outcomes.

   b) List the sample space.

   c) Determine the probability that a head is flipped and an odd number is selected.

   d) Determine the probability that a head is flipped or an odd number is selected.

Spinning Two Wheels *In Exercises 23–28, the outer and inner wheels are spun.*

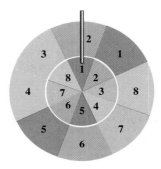

Assuming that the wheels are independent and the outcomes are equally likely, determine the probability of obtaining

23. even numbers on both wheels.

24. numbers greater than 5 on both wheels.

25. an odd number on the outer wheel and a number less than 6 on the inner wheel.

26. an even number or a number less than 6 on the outer wheel.

27. an even number or a color other than green on the inner wheel.

28. gold on the outer wheel and a color other than gold on the inner wheel.

Cereal Selection *In Exercises 29–32, assume that Mrs. Alexander is going to purchase 3 boxes of cereal at a convenience store. The store has 12 different boxes of cereal, including 5 different boxes made by General Mills, 4 different boxes made by Kellogg's, and 3 different boxes made by Post. If Mrs. Alexander selects 3 of these 12 boxes at random, determine the probability that she selects*

29. 3 boxes of General Mills.

30. no boxes of Kellogg's.

31. at least 1 box of Kellogg's.

32. boxes of General Mills, General Mills, and Post, in that order.

Spinner Probabilities *In Exercises 33–36, assume that the spinner cannot land on a line.*

If spun once, determine

33. the probability that the spinner lands on yellow.

34. the odds against and the odds in favor of the spinner landing on yellow.

35. You are awarded $5 if the spinner lands on red, $10 if it lands on yellow, and $20 if it lands on green. Determine your expected value.

36. If the spinner is spun twice, determine the probability that it lands on red and then green (assume independence).

Spinner Probabilities *In Exercises 37–40, assume that the spinner cannot land on a line.*

If spun once, determine

37. the probability that the spinner does not land on green.

38. the odds in favor of and the odds against the spinner landing on green.

39. A person wins $10 if the spinner lands on green, wins $5 if the spinner lands on red, and loses $20 if the spinner lands on yellow. Find the expectation of a person who plays this game.

40. If the spinner is spun three times, determine the probability that at least one spin lands on red.

Restaurant Service *In Exercises 41–44, use the results of a survey regarding the service at the Lobster House restaurant,* *which is summarized as follows.*

Meal	Service Rated Good	Service Rated Poor	Total
Lunch	65	10	75
Dinner	85	10	95
Total	150	20	170

If one person who completed the survey is selected at random, determine the probability that the person indicated that the

41. service was rated good.

42. service was rated good, given that the meal was dinner.

43. service was rated poor, given that the meal was lunch.

44. meal was dinner, given that the service was rated poor.

Neuroscience *In Exercises 45–48, assume that in a neuroscience course the students perform an experiment. Tests are given to determine if people are right brained, are left brained, or have no predominance. It is also recorded whether they are right handed or left handed. The following chart shows the results obtained.*

	Right Brained	Left Brained	No Predominance	Total
Right handed	40	130	60	230
Left handed	120	30	20	170
Total	160	160	80	400

If one person who completed the survey is selected at random, determine the probability the person selected is

45. right handed.

46. left brained, given that the person is left handed.

47. right handed, given that the person has no predominance.

48. right brained, given that the person is left handed.

49. Television Show Four contestants are on a television show. There are four different-colored rubber balls in a box, and each contestant gets to pick one from the box. Inside each ball is a slip of paper indicating the amount the contestant has won. The amounts are $10,000, $5000, $2000, and $1000.

   a) In how many different ways can the contestants select the balls?

   b) What is the expectation of a contestant?

50. *Spelling Bee* Five finalists remain in a high school spelling bee. Two will receive $50 each, two will receive $100 each, and one will receive $500. How many different arrangements of prizes are possible?

51. *Candy Selection* Mrs. Williams takes her 3 children shopping. Each of her children gets to select a different type of candy that only that child will eat. At the store, there are only 10 boxes of candy left and each is a different type. In how many ways can the 3 children select the candy?

52. *Astronaut Selection* Three of nine astronauts must be selected for a mission. One will be the captain, one will be the navigator, and one will perform scientific experiments. Assuming each of the nine astronauts can perform any of the tasks, in how many ways can a three-person crew be selected so that each person has a different assignment?

53. *Medicine* Dr. Goldberg has three doses of serum for influenza type A. Six patients in the office require the serum. In how many different ways could Dr. Goldberg dispense the serum?

54. *Dogsled* Ten of 15 huskies are to be selected to pull a dogsled.

   a) Assuming each of the nine astronauts can perform any of the tasks, in how many ways can this selection be made?

   b) How many different arrangements of the 10 huskies on a dogsled are possible?

55. *Mega Millions* The Big Game Mega Millions is a multistate lottery game offered in California, Georgia, Illinois, Maryland, Massachusetts, Michigan, New Jersey, New York, Ohio, Texas, Virginia, and Washington. To play, you select 5 numbers from 1 through 56 and 1 Big Money Ball number from 1 through 46. If you win the Big Game by matching all 6 numbers, your guaranteed minimum payoff is $10 million. If you match the 5 numbers but do not match the Big Money number, your guaranteed minimum payoff is $250,000.

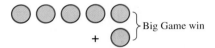

   a) What is the probability that you match the 5 numbers?

   b) What is the probability that you have a Big Game win?

56. *Parent-Teacher Committee* A committee of 7 is to be formed from 10 parents and 12 teachers. If the committee is to consist of 2 parents and 5 teachers, how many different committees are possible?

57. *Selecting Test Subjects* In a psychology research laboratory, one room contains eight men and another room contains five women. Three men and two women are to be selected at random to be given a psychological test. How many different combinations of these people are possible?

58. *Choosing Two Aces* Two cards are selected at random, without replacement, from a standard deck of 52 cards. Determine the probability that two aces are selected (use combinations).

Color Chips In Exercises 59–62, a bag contains five red chips, three white chips, and two blue chips. Three chips are to be selected at random, without replacement. Determine the probability that

59. all are red.

60. the first two are red and the third is blue.

61. the first is red, the second is white, and the third is blue.

62. at least one is red.

Magazines In Exercises 63–66, on a table in a doctor's office are six Newsweek *magazines, five* U.S. News and World Report *magazines, and three* Time *magazines. If Ramona Cleary randomly selects three magazines, determine the probability that*

63. three *U.S. News and World Report* magazines were selected.

64. two *Newsweek* magazines and one *Time* magazine were selected.

65. no *Newsweek* magazines were selected.

66. at least one *Newsweek* magazine was selected.

67. *New Homes* In the community of Spring Hill, 60% of the homes purchased cost more than $160,000.

    a) Write the binomial probability formula to determine the probability that exactly x of the next n homes purchased in Spring Hill cost more than $160,000.

    b) Write the binomial probability formula to determine the probability that exactly 75 of the next 100 home purchases cost more than $160,000.

68. *Long-Stemmed Roses* At the Floyd's Flower Shop, $\frac{1}{5}$ of people ordering flowers select long-stemmed roses. Determine the probability that exactly 3 of the next 5 customers ordering flowers select long-stemmed roses.

69. *Taking a Math Course* During any semester at City College, 60% of the students are taking a mathematics course. Determine the probability that of five students selected at random,

    a) none is taking a mathematics course this semester.

    b) at least one is taking a mathematics course this semester.

CHAPTER 12 TEST

1. *Deep-Sea Fishing* Of 40 people who went deep-sea fishing off the coast of Miami, 22 were fishing for tuna. Determine the empirical probability that the next person who goes deep-sea fishing off the coast of Miami will be fishing for tuna.

One Sheet of Paper In Exercises 2–5, each of the numbers 1–9 is written on a sheet of paper and the nine sheets of paper are placed in a hat. If one sheet of paper is selected at random from the hat, determine the probability that the number selected is

2. greater than 7.

3. odd.

4. even or greater than 4.

5. odd and greater than 4.

Two Sheets of Paper In Exercises 6–9, if two of the same nine sheets of paper mentioned at the left are selected, without replacement, from the hat, determine the probability that

6. both numbers are greater than 5.

7. both numbers are even.

8. the first number is odd and the second number is even.

9. neither of the numbers is greater than 6.

10. One card is selected at random from a standard deck of 52 cards. Determine the probability that the card selected is a red card or a picture card.

One Chip and One Die In Exercises 11–15, one colored chip—red, blue, or green—is selected at random and a die is rolled.

11. Use the counting principle to determine the number of sample points in the sample space.

12. Construct a tree diagram illustrating all the possible outcomes and list the sample space.

In Exercises 13–15, by observing the sample space of the chips and die, determine the probability of obtaining

13. the color green and the number 2.

14. the color red or the number 1.

15. a color other than red or an even number.

16. *Passwords* A personal password for an Internet brokerage account is to consist of a letter, followed by two digits, followed by two letters. Determine the number of personal codes possible if the first digit cannot be zero and repetition is permitted.

17. *Puppies* A litter of collie puppies consists of four males and five females. If one of the puppies is selected at random, determine the odds

a) against the puppy being male.

b) in favor of the puppy being female.

18. *Tennis Odds* The odds against Mark Ernsthausen winning the Saddlebrook Tennis Tournament are 7 : 2. What is the probability that Mark wins the tournament?

19. *Pick a Card* You get to select one card at random from a standard deck of 52 cards. If you pick a club, you win $8. If you pick a heart, you win $4. If you pick any other suit, you lose $6. Determine your expectation for this game.

20. *Cars and SUVs* The number of cars and the number of SUVs going through the toll gates of two bridges is recorded. The results are shown below.

Bridge	Cars	SUVs	Total
George Washington	120	106	226
Golden Gate	94	136	230
Total	214	242	456

▲ A toll booth at the Golden Gate bridge

If one of these vehicles going over the bridges is selected at random, determine the probability that

a) it is a car.

b) it is going over the Golden Gate Bridge.

c) it is an SUV, given that it is going over the Golden Gate Bridge.

d) it is going over the George Washington Bridge, given that it is a car.

21. *Awarding Prizes* Three of six people are to be selected and given small prizes. One will be given a book, one will be given a calculator, and one will be given a $10 bill. In how many different ways can these prizes be awarded?

Quality Control In Exercises 22 and 23, a bin contains a total of 20 batteries, of which 6 are defective. If you select 2 at random, without replacement, determine the probability that

22. none of the batteries is good.

23. at least one battery is good.

24. *Apples from a Bucket* Five green apples and seven red apples are in a bucket. Five apples are to be selected at random, without replacement. Determine the probability that two green apples and three red apples are selected.

25. *University Admission* The probability that a person is accepted for admission to a specific university is 0.3. Determine the probability that exactly three of the next five people who apply to the university get accepted.

G R O U P   P R O J E C T S

THE PROBABILITY OF AN EXACT MEASURED VALUE

1. Your car's speedometer indicates that you are traveling at 65 mph. What is the probability that you are traveling at *exactly* 65 mph? Explain your answer.

TAKING AN EXAM

2. A 10-question multiple-choice exam is given, and each question has five possible answers. Pascal Gonyo takes this exam and guesses at every question. Use the binomial probability formula to determine the probability (to 5 decimal places) that

   a) he gets exactly 2 questions correct.

   b) he gets no questions correct.

   c) he gets at least 1 question correct (use the information from part (b) to answer this part).

   d) he gets at least 9 questions correct.

   e) Without using the binomial probability formula, determine the probability that he gets exactly 2 questions correct.

   f) Compare your answers to parts (a) and (e). If they are not the same explain why.

KEYLESS ENTRY

3. Many cars have keyless entry. To open the lock, you may press a 5-digit code on a set of buttons like that illustrated. The code may include repeated digits like 11433 or 55512.

a) How many different 5-digit codes can be made using the 10 digits if repetition is permitted?

b) How many different ways are there of pressing 5 buttons if repetition is allowed?

c) A burglar is going to press 5 buttons at random, with repetition allowed. What is the probability that the burglar hits the sequence to open the door?

d) Suppose that each button had only one number associated with it as illustrated below. How many different 5-digit codes can be made with the 5 digits if repetition is permitted?

e) Using the buttons labeled 1–5, how many different ways are there to press 5 buttons if repetition is allowed?

f) A burglar is going to press 5 buttons of those labeled 1–5 at random with repetition allowed. Determine the probability that the burglar hits the sequence to open the door.

g) Is a burglar more likely, is he or she less likely, or does he or she have the same likelihood of pressing 5 buttons and opening the car door if the buttons are labeled as in the first illustration or as in the second illustration? Explain your answer.

h) Can you see any advantages in labeling the buttons as in the first illustration? Explain.*

---

*In actuality, in most cars that have key pads like that shown on the bottom left, each key acts as if it contains a single digit. For example, if your code is 7, 9, 5, 1, 3, the code 8, 0, 6, 2, 4 will unlock the door. The extra numbers, in effect, give the owner a false sense of security.

CHAPTER 13

Statistics

▲ Numbers are the foundation of all statistical information.

WHAT YOU WILL LEARN

- Sampling techniques
- Misuses of statistics
- Frequency distributions
- Histograms, frequency polygons, stem-and-leaf displays
- Mode, median, mean, and midrange
- Percentiles and quartiles
- Range and standard deviation
- z-scores and the normal distribution
- Correlation and regression

WHY IT IS IMPORTANT

Benjamin Disraeli (1804–1881), once prime minister of the United Kingdom, said that there are three kinds of lies: lies, damned lies, and statistics. Do numbers lie? Numbers are the foundation of all statistical information. The "lie" occurs when, either intentionally or carelessly, a number is used in such a way that leads us to an unjustified or incorrect conclusion. Numbers may not lie, but they can be manipulated and misinterpreted. This chapter will provide information that can help you recognize when statistical information is being manipulated and misinterpreted. It will also help you see the many valuable uses of statistics.

13.1 SAMPLING TECHNIQUES

▲ Statisticians have several different techniques with which they can collect numerical information.

According to Harris Interactive, 66% of American adults say that the costs for prescription drugs are unreasonably high. It would be very expensive for Harris Interactive to ask every American adult his or her opinion on the cost of prescription drugs. Instead, to collect this information the polling company may ask a subset of American adults. If it does not ask every American adult for his or her opinion, how do we know that Harris Interactive's results are accurate? In this section, we will discuss different techniques statisticians use to collect numerical information. We will also learn how statisticians can make accurate conclusions about the opinions of all American adults while only collecting information from a small portion of them.

The study of statistics was originally used by governments to manage large amounts of numerical information. The use of statistics has grown significantly and today is applied in all walks of life. Governments use statistics to estimate the amount of unemployment and the cost of living. In psychology and education, the statistical theory of tests and measurements has been developed to compare achievements of individuals from diverse places and backgrounds. Newspapers and magazines carry the results of different polls on topics ranging from the president's popularity to the number of cans of soda consumed. Statistics is used in scores of other professions; in fact, it is difficult to find any profession that does not depend on some aspect of statistics.

Before we discuss different techniques used to collect numerical information, we will first introduce a few important definitions. *Statistics* is the art and science of gathering, analyzing, and making inferences (predictions) from numerical information obtained in an experiment. The numerical information so obtained is referred to as *data*. Statistics is divided into two main branches: descriptive and inferential. *Descriptive statistics* is concerned with the collection, organization, and analysis of data. *Inferential statistics* is concerned with making generalizations or predictions from the data collected.

Probability and statistics are closely related. Someone in the field of probability is interested in computing the chance of occurrence of a particular event when all the possible outcomes are known. A statistician's interest lies in drawing conclusions about possible outcomes through observations of only a few particular events.

If a probability expert and a statistician find identical boxes, the probability expert might open the box, observe the contents, replace the cover, and proceed to compute the probability of randomly selecting a specific object from the box. The statistician might select a few items from the box without looking at the contents and make a prediction as to the total contents of the box.

The entire contents of the box constitute the *population*. A population consists of all items or people of interest. The statistician often uses a subset of the population, called a *sample*, to make predictions concerning the population. It is important to understand the difference between a population and a sample. A population includes *all* items of interest. A sample includes *some* of the items in the population.

When a statistician draws a conclusion from a sample, there is always the possibility that the conclusion is incorrect. For example, suppose that a jar contains 90 blue marbles and 10 red marbles, as shown in Fig. 13.1 on page 834. If the statistician selects a random sample of five marbles from the jar and they are all blue, he or she may

Figure 13.1

wrongly conclude that the jar contains all blue marbles. If the statistician takes a larger sample, say, 15 marbles, he or she is likely to select some red marbles. At that point, the statistician may make a prediction about the contents of the jar based on the sample selected. Of course, the most accurate result would occur if every object in the jar, the entire population, were observed. However, in most statistical experiments, observing the entire population is not practical.

Statisticians use samples instead of the entire population for two reasons: (a) it is often impossible to obtain data on an entire population, and (b) sampling is less expensive because collecting the data takes less time and effort. For example, suppose that you wanted to determine the number of each species of all the fish in a lake. To do so would be almost impossible without using a sample. If you did try to obtain this information from the entire population, the cost would be astronomical. Or suppose that you wanted to test soup cans for spoilage. If every can produced by the company was opened and tested, the company wouldn't have any product left to sell. Instead of testing the entire population of soup cans, a sample is selected. The results obtained from the sample of soup cans selected are used to make conclusions about the entire population of soup cans.

Later in this chapter we will discuss statistical measures such as the *mean* and the *standard deviation*. When statisticians calculate the mean and the standard deviation of the entire population, they use different symbols and formulas than when they calculate the mean and standard deviation of a sample. The following chart shows the symbols used to represent the mean and standard deviation of a sample and of a population. Note that the mean and standard deviation of a population are symbolized by Greek letters.

Measure	Sample	Population
Mean	$\overline{x}$ (read "*x* bar")	μ (mu)
Standard deviation	s	σ (sigma)

Unless otherwise indicated, in this book we will always assume that we are working with a sample and so we will use $\overline{x}$ and s. If you take a course in statistics, you will use all four symbols and different formulas for a sample and for a population.

Consider the task of determining the political strength of a certain candidate running in a national election. It is not possible for pollsters to ask each of the approximately 207 million eligible voters his or her preference of a candidate. Thus, pollsters must select and use a sample of the population to obtain their information.

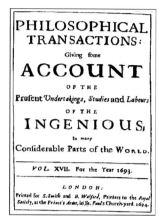
How large a sample do you think they use to make predictions about an upcoming national election? You might be surprised to learn that pollsters use only about 1600 registered voters in their national sample. How can a pollster using such a small percentage of the population make an accurate prediction?

The answer is that when pollsters select a sample, they use sophisticated statistical techniques to obtain an unbiased sample. An *unbiased sample* is one that is a small replica of the entire population with regard to income, education, gender, race, religion, political affiliation, age, and so on. The procedures statisticians use to obtain unbiased samples are quite complex. The following sampling techniques will give you a brief idea of how statisticians obtain unbiased samples.

Random Sampling

If a sample is drawn in such a way that each time an item is selected each item in the population has an equal chance of being drawn, the sample is said to be a *random sample*. When using a random sample, one combination of a specified number of items has the same probability of being selected as any other combination. When all the items in the population are similar with regard to the specific characteristic we are interested in, a random sample can be expected to produce satisfactory results. For example, consider a large container holding 300 tennis balls that are identical except for color. One-third of the balls are yellow, one-third are white, and one-third are green. If the balls can be thoroughly mixed between each draw of a tennis ball so that each ball has an equally likely chance of being selected, randomness is not difficult to achieve. However, if the objects or items are not all the same size, shape, or texture, it might be impossible to obtain a random sample by reaching into a container and selecting an object.

The best procedure for selecting a random sample is to use a random number generator or a table of random numbers. A random number generator is a device, usually a calculator or computer program, that produces a list of random numbers. A random number table is a collection of random digits in which each digit has an equal chance of appearing. To select a random sample, first assign a number to each element in the population. Numbers are usually assigned in order. Then select the number of random numbers needed, which is determined by the sample size. Each numbered element from the population that corresponds to a selected random number becomes part of the sample.

Systematic Sampling

When a sample is obtained by drawing every *n*th item on a list or production line, the sample is a *systematic sample*. The first item should be determined by using a random number.

It is important that the list from which a systematic sample is chosen include the entire population being studied. See the Did You Know? called "Don't Count Your Votes Until They're Cast" on page 836. Another problem that must be avoided when this method of sampling is used is the constantly recurring characteristic. For example, on an assembly line, every 10th item could be the work of robot X. If only every 10th item is checked for defects, the work of other robots doing the same job may not be checked and may be defective.

Cluster Sampling

A *cluster sample* is sometimes referred to as an *area sample* because it is frequently applied on a geographical basis. Essentially, the sampling consists of a random selection of groups of units. To select a cluster sample, we divide a geographic area into sections. Then we randomly select the sections or clusters. Either each member of the selected cluster is included in the sample or a random sample of the members of each cluster is used. For example, geographically we might randomly select city blocks to use as a sample unit. Then either every member of each selected city block would be used or a random sample from each selected city block would be used. Another example is to select x boxes of screws from a whole order, count the number of defective screws in the x boxes selected, and use this number to determine the expected number of defective screws in the whole order.

Stratified Sampling

When a population is divided into parts, called strata, for the purpose of drawing a sample, the procedure is known as *stratified sampling*. Stratified sampling involves dividing the population by characteristics called *stratifying factors* such as gender, race, religion, or income. When a population has varied characteristics, it is desirable to separate the population into classes with similar characteristics and then take a random sample from each stratum (or class). For example, we could separate the population of undergraduate college students into strata called freshmen, sophomores, juniors, and seniors.

The use of stratified sampling requires some knowledge of the population. For example, to obtain a cross section of voters in a city, we must know where various groups are located and the approximate number of voters in each location.

Convenience Sampling

A *convenience sample* uses data that are easily or readily obtained. Occasionally, data that are conveniently obtained may be all that is available. In some cases, some information is better than no information at all. Nevertheless, convenience sampling can be extremely biased. For example, suppose that a town wants to raise taxes to build a new elementary school. The local newspaper wants to obtain the opinion of some of the residents and sends a reporter to a senior citizens center. The first 10 people who exit the building are asked if they are in favor of raising taxes to build a new school. This sample could be biased against raising taxes for the new school. Most senior citizens would not have school-age children and may not be interested in paying increased taxes to build a new school. Although a convenience sample may be very easy to select, one must be very cautious when using the results obtained by this method.

EXAMPLE ❶ *Identifying Sampling Techniques*

Identify the sampling technique used to obtain a sample in the following. Explain your answer.

a) Every 20th car coming off an assembly line is checked for defects.
b) A \$50 gift certificate is given away at the Annual Bankers Convention. Tickets are placed in a bin, and the tickets are mixed up. Then the winning ticket is selected by a blindfolded person.

c) Children in a large city are classified based on the neighborhood school they attend. A random sample of five schools is selected. All the children from each selected school are included in the sample.

d) The first 50 people entering a zoo are asked if they support an increase in taxes to support a zoo expansion.

e) Students at Portland State University are classified according to their major. Then a random sample of 15 students from each major is selected.

SOLUTION

a) Systematic sampling. The sample is obtained by drawing every nth item. In this example, every 20th item on an assembly line is selected.

b) Random sampling. Every ticket has an equal chance of being selected.

c) Cluster sampling. A random sample of geographic areas is selected.

d) Convenience sampling. The sample is selected by picking data that are easily obtained.

e) Stratified sampling. The students are divided into strata based on their majors. Then random samples are selected from each strata.

SECTION 13.1 EXERCISES

CONCEPT/WRITING EXERCISES

1. Define *statistics* in your own words.

2. Explain the difference between descriptive and inferential statistics.

3. When you hear the word *statistics*, what specific words or ideas come to mind?

4. Attempt to list at least two professions in which no aspect of statistics is used.

5. Name five areas other than those mentioned in this section in which statistics is used.

6. Explain the difference between probability and statistics.

7. a) What is a population?

   b) What is a sample?

8. a) What is a random sample?

   b) How might a random sample be selected?

9. a) What is a systematic sample?

   b) How might a systematic sample be selected?

10. a) What is a convenience sample?

    b) How might a convenience sample be selected?

11. a) What is a cluster sample?

    b) How might a cluster sample be selected?

12. a) What is a stratified sample?

    b) How might a stratified sample be selected?

13. What is an unbiased sample?

14. *Family Size* The principal of an elementary school wishes to determine the "average" family size of the children who attend the school. To obtain a sample, the principal visits each room and selects the four students closest to each corner of the room. The principal asks each of these students how many people are in his or her family.

    a) Will this technique result in an unbiased sample? Explain your answer.

    b) If the sample is biased, will the average be greater than or less than the true family size? Explain.

PRACTICE THE SKILLS

Sampling Techniques In Exercises 15–24, identify the sampling technique used to obtain a sample. Explain your answer.

15. Faculty members at Cayuga Community College are classified according to the department in which they teach, and then random samples from each department are taken.

16. Every 10th iPod coming off an assembly line is checked for defects.

17. A state is divided into counties. A random sample of 12 counties is selected. A random sample from each of the 12 selected counties is selected.

18. A door prize is given away at a home improvement seminar. Tickets are placed in a bin, and the tickets are mixed up. Then a ticket is selected by a blindfolded person.

19. Every 17th person in line at a grocery store is asked his or her age.

20. The businesses in Iowa City are grouped according to type: medical, service, retail, manufacturing, financial, construction, restaurant, hotel, tourism, and other. A random sample of 10 businesses from each type is selected.

21. The first 25 students leaving the cafeteria are asked how many hours per week they work.

22. The Food and Drug Administration randomly selects five stores from each of four randomly selected sections of a large city and checks food items for freshness. These stores are used as a representative sample of the entire city.

23. Bingo balls in a bin are shaken, and then balls are selected from the bin.

24. The Student Senate at the University of North Carolina is electing a new president. The first 25 people leaving the library are asked for whom they will vote.

CHALLENGE PROBLEMS/GROUP ACTIVITIES

25. a) *Random Sampling* Select a topic and population of interest to which a random sampling technique can be applied to obtain data.

    b) Explain how you or your group would obtain a random sample for your population of interest.

    c) Actually obtain the sample by the procedure stated in part (b).

26. *Data from Questionnaire* Some subscribers of *Consumer Reports* respond to an annual questionnaire regarding their satisfaction with new appliances, cars, and other items. The information obtained from these questionnaires is then used as a sample from which frequency of repairs and other ratings are made by the magazine. Are the data obtained from these returned questionnaires representative of the entire population, or are they biased? Explain your answer.

RECREATIONAL MATHEMATICS

27. Statistically speaking, what is the most dangerous job in the United States?

28. Refer to the Did You Know? on page 775. Select a random sample of 30 people and see how many of the 30 people have the same birthday. (*Hint:* The probability of at least 2 of the 30 sharing the same birthday is greater than 0.5).

INTERNET/RESEARCH ACTIVITY

29. We have briefly introduced sampling techniques. Using statistics books and Internet websites as references, select one type of sampling technique (it may be one that we have not discussed in this section) and write a report on how statisticians obtain that type of sample. Also indicate when that type of sampling technique may be preferred. List two examples of when the sampling technique may be used.

13.2 THE MISUSES OF STATISTICS

▲ It is important to examine statistical statements about products before accepting the statements as fact.

Many of us may have seen an advertisement stating, "Four out of five dentists recommend sugarless gum for their patients who chew gum." Seeing an advertisement like this one may cause some of us to be a bit skeptical. Should we believe that sugarless chewing gum will not harm our teeth? Or should we investigate a bit further before buying that next pack of chewing gum? In this section, we will learn how to examine statistical statements before accepting them as fact.

Statistics, when used properly, is a valuable tool to society. However, many individuals, businesses, and advertising firms misuse statistics to their own advantage. You should examine statistical statements very carefully before accepting them as fact. You should ask yourself two questions: Was the sample used to gather the statistical data unbiased and of sufficient size? Is the statistical statement ambiguous; that is, can it be interpreted in more than one way?

Let's examine two advertisements. "Four out of five dentists recommend sugarless gum for their patients who chew gum." In this advertisement, we do not know the sample size and the number of times the experiment was performed to obtain the desired results. The advertisement does not mention that possibly only 1 out of 100 dentists recommended gum at all.

In a golf ball commercial, a "type A" ball is hit and a second ball is hit in the same manner. The type A ball travels farther. We are supposed to conclude that the type A is the better ball. The advertisement does not mention the number of times the experiment was previously performed or the results of the earlier experiments. Possible sources of bias include (1) wind speed and direction, (2) that no two swings are identical, and (3) that the ball may land on a rough or smooth surface.

Vague or ambiguous words also lead to statistical misuses or misinterpretations. The word *average* is one such culprit. There are at least four different "averages," some of which are discussed in Section 13.5. Each is calculated differently, and each may have a different value for the same sample. During contract negotiations, it is not uncommon for an employer to state publicly that the average salary of its employees is $45,000, whereas the employees' union states that the average is $40,000. Who is lying? Actually, both sides may be telling the truth. Each side will use the average that best suits its needs to present its case. Advertisers also use the average that most enhances their products. Consumers often misinterpret this average as the one with which they are most familiar.

Another vague word is *largest*. For example, ABC claims that it is the largest department store in the United States. Does that mean largest profit, largest sales, largest building, largest staff, largest acreage, or largest number of outlets?

Still another deceptive technique used in advertising is to state a claim from which the public may draw irrelevant conclusions. For example, a disinfectant manufacturer claims that its product killed 40,760 germs in a laboratory in 5 seconds. "To prevent colds, use disinfectant A." It may well be that the germs killed in the laboratory were not related to any type of cold germ. In another example, company C claims that its paper towels are heavier than its competition's towels. Therefore, they will hold more water. Is weight a measure of absorbency? A rock is heavier than a sponge, yet a sponge is more absorbent.

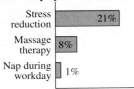
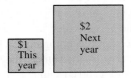

Figure 13.4

An insurance advertisement claims that in Duluth, Minnesota, 212 people switched to insurance company Z. One may conclude that this company is offering something special to attract these people. What may have been omitted from the advertisement is that 415 people in Duluth, Minnesota, dropped insurance company Z during the same period.

A foreign car manufacturer claims that 9 of every 10 of a popular-model car it sold in the United States during the previous 10 years were still on the road. From this statement, the public is to conclude that this foreign car is well manufactured and would last for many years. The commercial neglects to state that this model has been selling in the United States for only a few years. The manufacturer could just as well have stated that 9 of every 10 of these cars sold in the United States in the previous 100 years were still on the road.

Charts and graphs can also be misleading or deceptive. In Fig. 13.2, the two graphs show the performance of two stocks over a 6-month period. Based on the graphs, which stock would you purchase? Actually, the two graphs present identical information; the only difference is that the vertical scale of the graph for stock B has been exaggerated.

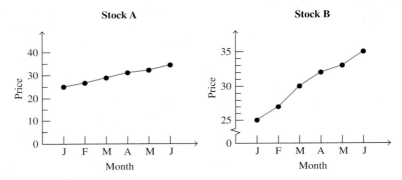

Figure 13.2

The two graphs in Fig. 13.3 show the same change. However, the graph in part (a) appears to show a greater increase than the graph in part (b), again because of a different scale.

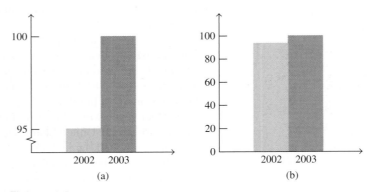

Figure 13.3

Consider a claim that if you invest $1, by next year you will have $2. This type of claim is sometimes misrepresented, as in Fig. 13.4. Actually, your investment has only doubled, but the area of the square on the right is four times that of the square on the left. By expressing the amounts as cubes (Fig. 13.5), you increase the volume eightfold.

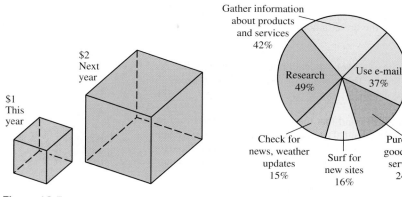

Figure 13.5   Figure 13.6

The graph in Fig. 13.6 is an example of a circle graph. We will discuss how to construct circle graphs in Section 13.4. In a circle graph, the total circle represents 100%. Therefore, the sum of the parts should add up to 100%. This graph is misleading since the sum of its parts is 183%. A graph other than a circle graph should have been used to display the top six reasons Americans say they use the Internet.

Despite the examples presented in this section, you should not be left with the impression that statistics is used solely for the purpose of misleading or cheating the consumer. As stated earlier, there are many important and necessary uses of statistics. Most statistical reports are accurate and useful. You should realize, however, the importance of being an aware consumer.

SECTION 13.2   EXERCISES

CONCEPT/WRITING EXERCISES

1. Find five advertisements or commercials that may be statistically misleading. Explain why each may be misleading.

2. The following circle graph appeared in a popular magazine in 2005. The graph shows various types of identity theft and the percent of victims of identity theft in 2004 that experienced these types of thefts. Is the graph misleading? Explain.

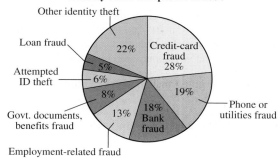

Source: Data from Federal Trade Commission. Image from *Newsweek*, July 4, 2005. © 2005.

PRACTICE THE SKILLS

Misinterpretations of Statistics In Exercises 3–16, discuss the statement or graph and tell what possible misuses or misinterpretations may exist.

3. In 2007, Liberty Travel received more requests for travel brochures to Hawaii than to Las Vegas. Therefore, in 2008, Liberty Travel sold more travel packages to Hawaii than to Las Vegas.

4. There are more empty spaces in the parking lot of Mama Mia's Italian restaurant than at Shanghi Chinese restaurant. Therefore, more people prefer Chinese food than Italian food.

5. Healthy Snacks cookies are fat free. So eat as many as you like and you will not gain weight.

6. Most accidents occur on Saturday night. That means that people do not drive carefully on Saturday night.

7. Morgan's is the largest department store in New York. So shop at Morgan's and save money.

8. Eighty percent of all automobile accidents occur within 10 miles of the driver's home. Therefore, it is safer to take long trips.

9. Arizona has the highest death rate for asthma in the United States. Therefore, it is unsafe to go to Arizona if you have asthma.

10. Thirty students said that they would recommend Professor Malone to a friend. Twenty students said that they would recommend Professor Wagner to a friend. Therefore, Professor Malone is a better teacher than Professor Wagner.

11. A steak is more expensive at Dino's Steak House than at Rick's Prime Rib House. Therefore, the quality of a steak at Dino's Steak House is better than the quality of a steak at Rick's Prime Rib House.

12. John Deere lawn tractors cost more than Toro lawn tractors. Therefore, John Deere lawn tractors will last longer than Toro lawn tractors.

13. The average depth of the pond is only 3 ft, so it is safe to go wading.

14. More men than women are involved in automobile accidents. Therefore, women are better drivers.

15. At West High School, half the students are below average in mathematics. Therefore, the school should receive more federal aid to raise student scores.

16. In 2007, more men than women applied for sales positions at Dick's Sporting Goods. Therefore, in 2007, more men than women were hired for sales positions at Dick's Sporting Goods.

17. **Number of Males to Females** The following table shows the number of males per 100 females in the U.S. for selected years.

Year	Number of males per 100 females
1980	94.5
1990	95.1
2000	96.3
2004	96.9

Source: U.S. Census Bureau

Draw a line graph that makes the increase in the number of males per 100 females for the years shown appear to be

a) small.   b) large.

18. **Four or More Years of College** The following table shows the percent of the U.S. population with a bachelor's degree or higher for selected years.

Year	Percent
1998	24.4
1999	25.2
2000	25.6
2001	26.1
2002	26.7
2003	27.2
2004	27.7

Source: U.S. Department of Education

Draw a line graph that makes the increase in the percent of U.S. population with a bachelor's degree or higher appear to be

a) small.   b) large.

First Marriage In Exercises 19 and 20, use the following table.

Median Age at First Marriage

Male		Female	
Year	Age	Year	Age
1998	26.7	1998	25.0
2000	26.8	2000	25.1
2002	26.9	2002	25.3
2004	27.1	2004	25.8

Source: U.S. Census Bureau

19. a) Draw a bar graph that appears to show a small increase in the median age at first marriage for males.

   b) Draw a bar graph that appears to show a large increase in the median age at first marriage for males.

20. a) Draw a bar graph that appears to show a small increase in the median age at first marriage for females.

   b) Draw a bar graph that appears to show a large increase in the median age at first marriage for females.

21. **Online Purchasing** The graph on the top of page 843 shows the percent of males and the percent of females surveyed who purchased clothing accessories online during the months from November 2006 to January 2007.

   a) Draw a bar graph that shows the entire scale from 0 to 10.

   b) Does the new graph give a different impression? Explain.

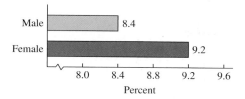

Percent of Survey Respondents Who Purchased Clothing Accessories Online, Nov. 2006–Jan. 2007

CHALLENGE PROBLEM/GROUP ACTIVITY

22. Consider the following graph, which shows the U.S. population in 2000 and the projected U.S. population in 2050.

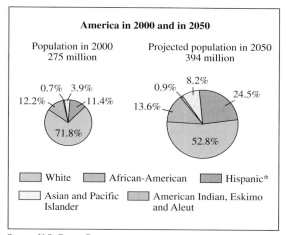

America in 2000 and in 2050

Population in 2000
275 million

Projected population in 2050
394 million

- White
- African-American
- Hispanic*
- Asian and Pacific Islander
- American Indian, Eskimo and Aleut

Source: U.S. Census Bureau

a) Compute the projected percent increase in population from 2000 to 2050 by using the formula given on page 649.

b) Measure the radius and then compute the area of the circle representing 2000. Use $A = \pi r^2$.

c) Repeat part (b) for the circle representing 2050.

d) Compute the percent increase in the size of the area of the circle from 2000 to 2050.

e) Are the circle graphs misleading? Explain your answer.

RECREATIONAL MATHEMATICS

23. What mathematical symbol can you place between 1 and 2 to obtain a number greater than 1 but less than 2?

INTERNET/RESEARCH ACTIVITY

24. Read the book *How to Lie with Statistics* by Darrell Huff and write a book report on it. Select three illustrations from the book that show how people manipulate statistics.

13.3 FREQUENCY DISTRIBUTIONS

▲ Organizing and summarizing data can make large sets of information more useful.

Suppose that you have a job waiting on tables in a restaurant. You decide to keep track of how much money you make each day from tips. After keeping a list of your tips each day for several months, you realize that you have a large set of data and want to condense your data into a more manageable form. In this section, we will learn a method to use to organize and summarize data.

It is not uncommon for statisticians and others to have to analyze thousands of pieces of data. A *piece of data* is a single response to an experiment. When the amount of data is large, it is usually advantageous to construct a frequency distribution. A *frequency distribution* is a listing of the observed values and the corresponding frequency of occurrence of each value. Example 1 shows how we construct a frequency distribution.

EXAMPLE ❶ *Frequency Distribution*

The number of children per family is recorded for 64 families surveyed. Construct a frequency distribution of the following data:

0	1	1	2	2	3	4	5
0	1	1	2	2	3	4	5
0	1	1	2	2	3	4	6
0	1	2	2	2	3	4	6
0	1	2	2	2	3	4	7
0	1	2	2	3	3	4	8
0	1	2	2	3	3	5	8
0	1	2	2	3	3	5	9

SOLUTION Listing the number of children (observed values) and the number of families (frequency) gives the following frequency distribution.

Number of Children (Observed Values)	Number of Families (Frequency)
0	8
1	11
2	18
3	11
4	6
5	4
6	2
7	1
8	2
9	1
	64

Eight families had no children, 11 families had one child, 18 families had two children, and so on. Note that the sum of the frequencies is equal to the original number of pieces of data, 64. ●

Often data are grouped in classes to provide information about the distribution that would be difficult to observe if the data were ungrouped. Graphs called *histograms* and *frequency polygons* can be made of grouped data, as will be explained in Section 13.4. These graphs also provide a great deal of useful information.

When data are grouped in classes, certain rules should be followed.

RULES FOR DATA GROUPED BY CLASSES

1. The classes should be of the same "width."

2. The classes should not overlap.

3. Each piece of data should belong to only one class.

In addition, it is often suggested that a frequency distribution should be constructed with 5 to 12 classes. If there are too few or too many classes, the distribution may become difficult to interpret. For example, if you use fewer than 5 classes, you risk losing too much information. If you use more than 12 classes, you may gain more detail but you risk losing clarity. Let the spread of the data be a guide in deciding the number of classes to use.

To understand these rules, let's consider a set of observed values that go from a low of 0 to a high of 26. Let's assume that the first class is arbitrarily selected to go from 0 through 4. Thus, any of the data with values of 0, 1, 2, 3, 4 would belong in this class. We say that the *class width* is 5 since there are five integral values that belong to the class. This first class ended with 4, so the second class must start with 5. If this class is to have a width of 5, at what value must it end? The answer is 9 (5, 6, 7, 8, 9). The second class is 5–9. Continuing in the same manner, we obtain the following set of classes.

Classes

Lower class limits $\left\{\begin{array}{c} 0-4 \\ 5-9 \\ 10-14 \\ 15-19 \\ 20-24 \\ 25-29 \end{array}\right\}$ Upper class limits

We need not go beyond the 25–29 class because the largest value we are considering is 26. The classes meet our three criteria: They have the same width, there is no overlap among the classes, and each of the values from a low of 0 to a high of 26 belongs to one and only one class.

The choice of the first class, 0–4, was arbitrary. If we wanted to have more classes or fewer classes, we would make the class widths smaller or larger, respectively.

The numbers 0, 5, 10, 15, 20, 25 are called the *lower class limits*, and the numbers 4, 9, 14, 19, 24, 29 are called the *upper class limits*. Each class has a width of 5. Note that the class width, 5, can be obtained by subtracting the first lower class limit from the second lower class limit: $5 - 0 = 5$. The difference between any two consecutive lower class or upper class limits is also 5.

EXAMPLE ❷ *A Frequency Distribution of Consumer Magazines*

Table 13.1 on the next page shows the 2005 circulation for the 48 leading U.S. consumer magazines (excluding *AARP Magazine* and *AARP Bulletin*, which are far ahead of the other magazines). The circulation is rounded to the nearest ten thousand. Construct a frequency distribution of the data, letting the first class be 157–241.

SOLUTION Forty-eight pieces of data are given in *descending order* from highest to lowest. We are given that the first class is 157–241. The second class must therefore start at 242. To find the class width, we subtract 157 (the lower class limit of the first class) from 242 (the lower class limit of the second class) to obtain a class width of 85. The upper class limit of the second class is found by

Table 13.1

Magazine	Circulation (ten thousands)
Reader's Digest	1001
Better Homes & Gardens	761
TV Guide	735
National Geographic	538
Good Housekeeping	466
Family Circle	429
Ladies' Home Journal	411
Woman's Day	409
TIME	403
People	369
AAA Westways	368
Prevention	335
Sports Illustrated	324
Newsweek	312
Cosmopolitan	301
Playboy	301
Via Magazine	275
Southern Living	274
Guideposts	263
American Legion	253
Maxim	250
AAA Going Places	248
Redbook	243
O, the Oprah Magazine	240
Glamour	240
AAA Living	240
Parents	205
Smithsonian	205
U.S. News & World Report	203
Seventeen	203
Money	199
Martha Stewart Living	197
Parenting	193
ESPN the Magazine	189
Real Simple	186
Game Informer	183
Family Fun	180
Men's Health	178
In Style	177
Entertainment Weekly	176
Country Living	174
Cooking Light	172
Endless Vacation	172
VFW Magazine	169
US Weekly	166
Shape	165
Golf Digest	160
Home & Away	157

Source: Audit Bureau of Circulations

adding the class width, 85, to the upper class limit of the first class, 241. Therefore, the upper class limit of the second class is $241 + 85 = 326$. Thus,

$$157-241 \quad \text{first class}$$
$$242-326 \quad \text{second class}$$

The other classes are found using a similar technique. They are 327–411, 412–496, 497–581, 582–666, 667–751, 752–836, 837–921, 922–1006. Since the highest value in the data is 1001, there is no need to go any further. Note that each two consecutive lower class limits differ by 85, as does each two consecutive upper class limits. There are 25 pieces of data in the 157–241 class. There are 11 pieces of data in the 242–326 class, 6 in the 327–411 class, 2 in the 412–496 class, 1 in the 497–581 class, 0 in the 582–666 class, 1 in the 667–751 class, 1 in the 752–836 class, 0 in the 837–921 class, and 1 in the 922–1006 class. The complete frequency distribution of the 10 classes is given below. The number of magazines totals 48, so we have included each piece of data.

Circulation	Number of Magazines (ten thousands)
157–241	25
242–326	11
327–411	6
412–496	2
497–581	1
582–666	0
667–751	1
752–836	1
837–921	0
922–1006	1
	48

The *modal class* of a frequency distribution is the class with the greatest frequency. In Example 2, the modal class is 157–241. The *midpoint of a class*, also called the *class mark*, is found by adding the lower and upper class limits and dividing the sum by 2. The midpoint of the first class in Example 2 is

$$\frac{157 + 241}{2} = \frac{398}{2} = 199$$

Note that the difference between successive class marks is the class width. The class mark of the second class can therefore be obtained by adding the class width, 85, to the class mark of the first class, 199. The sum is $199 + 85 = 284$. Note that $\frac{242 + 326}{2} = 284$, which checks with the class mark obtained by adding the class width to the first class mark.

DID YOU KNOW?

Cyberspace Is the Place to Be

Seattle, Washington

Do you remember the days when you were only able to access the Internet from your office, school, or home? With wireless Internet access, we can now connect to the Internet to share information and enjoy entertainment while we are on the go. Today, wireless hotspots, locations offering wireless access to the Internet, show up in diverse places such as coffee shops, parks, gas stations, bowling alleys, airports, and golf courses in addition to more traditional places such as colleges and hotels. According to a survey conducted by Intel in April 2005, the Seattle-Bellevue-Everett-Tacoma area was the most accessible wireless Internet area in the United States. Many websites, such as www.wififreespot.com, list worldwide locations that offer free wireless Internet access.

EXAMPLE ❸ *A Frequency Distribution of Family Income*

The following set of data represents the family income (in thousands of dollars, rounded to the nearest hundred) of 15 randomly selected families.

31.5	16.8	30.8	29.7	25.9
50.2	37.4	29.6	38.7	33.8
20.5	25.3	24.8	41.3	35.7

Construct a frequency distribution with a first class of 16.5–22.6.

SOLUTION First rearrange the data from lowest to highest so that the data will be easier to categorize.

16.8	25.3	29.7	33.8	38.7
20.5	25.9	30.8	35.7	41.3
24.8	29.6	31.5	37.4	50.2

The first class goes from 16.5 to 22.6. Since the data are in tenths, the class limits will also be given in tenths. The first class ends with 22.6; therefore, the second class must start with 22.7. The class width of the first class is $22.7 - 16.5$, or 6.2. The upper class limit of the second class must therefore be $22.6 + 6.2$, or 28.8. The frequency distribution is as follows.

Income ($1000)	Number of Families
16.5–22.6	2
22.7–28.8	3
28.9–35.0	5
35.1–41.2	3
41.3–47.4	1
47.5–53.6	$\frac{1}{15}$

Note in Example 3 that the class width is 6.2, the modal class is $28.9 - 35.0$, and the class mark of the first class is $(16.5 + 22.6)/2$, or 19.55.

SECTION 13.3 EXERCISES

CONCEPT/WRITING EXERCISES

1. What is a frequency distribution?

2. How can a class width be determined using class limits?

3. Suppose that the first class of a frequency distribution is 9–15.

   a) What is the width of this class?

   b) What is the second class?

   c) What is the lower class limit of the second class?

   d) What is the upper class limit of the second class?

4. Repeat Exercise 3 for a frequency distribution whose first class is 12–20.

5. What is the modal class of a frequency distribution?

6. What is another name for the midpoint of a class? How is the midpoint of a class determined?

PRACTICE THE SKILLS/PROBLEM SOLVING

In Exercises 7 and 8, use the frequency distribution to determine

    a) *the total number of observations.*
    b) *the width of each class.*
    c) *the midpoint of the second class.*
    d) *the modal class (or classes).*
    e) *the class limits of the next class if an additional class were to be added.*

7.

Class	Frequency
9–15	4
16–22	7
23–29	1
30–36	0
37–43	3
44–50	5

8.

Class	Frequency
40–49	7
50–59	5
60–69	3
70–79	2
80–89	7
90–99	1

9. *Visits to the Library* El Paso Community College is planning to expand its library. Forty students were asked how many times they visited the library during the previous semester. Their responses are given below. Construct a frequency distribution, letting each class have a width of 1 (as in Example 1).

0	1	1	3	4	5	7	8
0	1	2	3	5	5	7	8
0	1	2	3	5	5	7	9
1	1	2	3	5	6	8	10
1	1	3	4	5	6	8	10

10. *Hot Dog Sales* A hot dog vendor is interested in the number of hot dogs he sells each day at his hot dog cart. The number of hot dogs sold is indicated below for 32 consecutive days. Construct a frequency distribution, letting each class have a width of 1.

15	16	19	20	21	22	24	27
15	18	19	20	21	22	25	27
15	18	19	20	21	23	25	28
16	18	19	21	21	23	26	29

Note that there were no days in which the vendor sold 17 hot dogs. However, it is customary to include a missing value as an observed value and assign to it a frequency of 0.

▲ See Exercise 10

IQ Scores In Exercises 11–14, use the following data, which show the result of 50 sixth-grade I.Q. scores.

80	89	92	95	97	100	102	106	110	120
81	89	93	95	98	100	103	108	113	120
87	90	94	97	99	100	103	108	114	122
88	91	94	97	100	100	103	108	114	128
89	92	94	97	100	101	104	109	119	135

Use this data to construct a frequency distribution with a first class of

11. 78–86.

12. 80–88.

13. 80–90.

14. 80–92.

Placement Test Scores In Exercises 15–18, use the following data, which represent the English placement test scores of a sample of 30 students.

559	482	490	520	514
498	472	490	523	491
480	490	562	486	491
498	543	506	539	576
508	509	499	515	501
593	512	510	577	533

Use this data to construct a frequency distribution with a first class of

15. 472–492.

16. 470–486.

17. 472–487.

18. 472–496.

Magazine Circulation In Exercises 19–22, use the data given in Table 13.1 on page 846 to construct a frequency distribution with a first class (in ten thousands) of

19. 157–306.

20. 150–296.

21. 157–256.

22. 157–234.

City Population In Exercises 23–26, use the following data, which represent the population of the 20 most populous cities in the world in 2006, in millions of people (rounded to the nearest 100,000).

11.9	10.1	8.7	8.1	7.2
11.0	9.8	8.6	7.8	7.0
10.9	9.3	8.5	7.6	6.3
10.3	8.8	8.4	7.4	6.1

▲ Mumbai, India is the world's most populated city.

Use these data to construct a frequency distribution with a first class of

23. 6.0–6.9.

24. 5.5–6.4.

25. 5.5–6.5.

26. 6.0–6.4.

Residents in Poverty In Exercises 27–30, use the data in the following table.

Percent of U.S. Residents Living in Poverty in 2004, by State

State	Percent	State	Percent
AL	16.0	AR	16.4
AK	9.4	CA	13.2
AZ	13.9	CO	9.9
CT	9.1	NH	5.6
DE	8.2	NJ	8.3
FL	12.2	NM	17.3
GA	12.5	NY	14.6
HI	8.9	NC	15.1
ID	10.0	ND	9.7
IL	12.4	OH	11.3
IN	10.8	OK	11.8
IA	9.9	OR	12.1
KS	11.1	PA	10.9
KY	16.0	RI	11.5
LA	16.8	SC	13.8
ME	11.6	SD	13.0
MD	9.2	TN	15.0
MA	9.7	TX	16.7
MI	12.3	UT	9.5
MN	7.2	VT	8.2
MS	17.3	VA	9.7
MO	11.5	WA	12.0
MT	14.6	WV	15.8
NE	9.6	WI	11.0
NV	10.9	WY	9.9

Source: Bureau of the Census

Construct a frequency distribution with a first class of

27. 5.6–7.5.

28. 5.6–8.2.

29. 5.6–7.0.

30. 5.6–8.0.

RECREATIONAL MATHEMATICS

31. In what month do people take the least number of daily vitamins?

32. a) Count the number of F's in the sentence at the bottom of the Did You Know? on page 845.

  b) Can you explain why so many people count the number of F's incorrectly?

13.4 STATISTICAL GRAPHS

For a class research project, you are required to collect information and write a report about the percent of college students who work in retail, service, or other areas. How could you display this information in a way that is helpful to the reader of your report? In this section, we will introduce four types of graphs that can be used to display information.

▲ Graphs can be used to display numerical information.

Distractions at the Movies

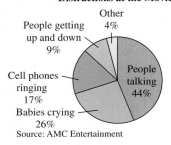

Source: AMC Entertainment

Figure 13.7

We will consider four types of graphs: the circle graph, the histogram, the frequency polygon, and the stem-and-leaf display.

Circle Graphs

Circle graphs (also known as pie charts) are often used to compare parts of one or more components of the whole to the whole. The circle graph in Fig. 13.7 shows what moviegoers say is the most annoying distraction during a movie. Since the total circle represents 100%, the sum of the percents of the sectors should be 100%, and it is.

In the next example, we will discuss how to construct a circle graph given a set of data.

┌ **EXAMPLE ❶** *Circus Performances*

Six hundred people who attended a Ringling Bros. and Barnum & Bailey circus were asked to indicate their favorite performance. The results are illustrated below.

Performance	Number of People
Tigers	230
Elephants	154
Acrobats	99
Jugglers	91
Other	26
	600

Use this information to construct a circle graph illustrating the percent of people whose favorite circus performance was tigers, elephants, acrobats, jugglers, and other performances.

SOLUTION Determine the measure of the central angle, as illustrated in the following table.

Performance	Number of People	Percent of Total (to the nearest tenth percent)	Measure of Central Angle
Tigers	230	$\frac{230}{600} \times 100 \approx 38.3\%$	$0.383 \times 360 = 137.9°$
Elephants	154	$\frac{154}{600} \times 100 \approx 25.7\%$	$0.257 \times 360 = 92.5°$
Acrobats	99	$\frac{99}{600} \times 100 \approx 16.5\%$	$0.165 \times 360 = 59.4°$
Jugglers	91	$\frac{91}{600} \times 100 \approx 15.2\%$	$0.152 \times 360 = 54.7°$
Other	26	$\frac{26}{600} \times 100 \approx 4.3\%$	$0.043 \times 360 = 15.5°$
Total	600	100.0%	360.0°

Favorite Performance at the Circus

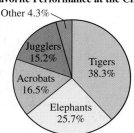

Figure 13.8

Now use a protractor (see Section 9.1, page 519) to construct a circle graph and label it properly, as illustrated in Fig. 13.8. The measure of the central angle for tigers is about 137.9°, for elephants it is about 92.5°, for acrobats it is about 59.4°, for jugglers it is about 54.7°, and for other performances it is about 15.5°. ●

> **TIMELY TIP** When computing values to construct a circle graph, if you round your values, the sum of the percents of the total may not exactly equal 100%, and the sum of the measures of the central angle may not exactly equal 360°.

Histograms and Frequency Polygons

Histograms and frequency polygons are statistical graphs used to illustrate frequency distributions. A *histogram* is a graph with observed values on its horizontal scale and frequencies on its vertical scale. A bar is constructed above each observed value (or class when classes are used), indicating the frequency of that value (or class). The horizontal scale need not start at zero, and the calibrations on the horizontal and vertical scales do not have to be the same. The vertical scale must start at zero. To accommodate large frequencies on the vertical scale, it may be necessary to break the scale. Because histograms and other bar graphs are easy to interpret visually, they are used a great deal in newspapers and magazines.

┌─ EXAMPLE ❷ *Construct a Histogram*

The frequency distribution developed in Example 1, Section 13.3 on page 844, is repeated here. Construct a histogram of this frequency distribution.

Number of Children (Observed Values)	Number of Families (Frequency)
0	8
1	11
2	18
3	11
4	6
5	4
6	2
7	1
8	2
9	1

SOLUTION The vertical scale must extend at least to the number 18 since that is the greatest recorded frequency. The horizontal scale must include the numbers 0–9, the number of children observed. Eight families have no children. We indicate that by constructing a bar above the number 0, centered at 0, on the horizontal scale extended up to 8 on the vertical scale (see Fig. 13.9 on page 852). Eleven families have one child, so we construct a bar extending to 11 above the number 1, centered at 1, on the horizontal scale. We continue this procedure for each observed value. Both the horizontal and vertical scales should be labeled, the bars should be the same width and centered at the observed value, and the histogram should have a title. In a histogram, the bars should always touch.

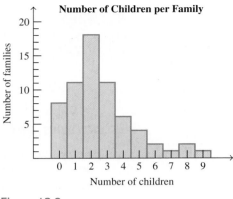

Figure 13.9

Frequency polygons are line graphs with scales the same as those of the histogram; that is, the horizontal scale indicates observed values and the vertical scale indicates frequency. To construct a frequency polygon, place a dot at the corresponding frequency above each of the observed values. Then connect the dots with straight-line segments. When constructing frequency polygons, always put in two additional class marks, one at the lower end and one at the upper end on the horizontal scale (values for these added class marks are not needed on the frequency polygon). Since the frequency at these added class marks is 0, the end points of the frequency polygon will always be on the horizontal scale.

┌ EXAMPLE ❸ *Construct a Frequency Polygon*

Construct a frequency polygon of the frequency distribution in Example 2.

SOLUTION Since eight families have no children, place a mark above the 0 at 8 on the vertical scale, as shown in Fig. 13.10. Because there are 11 families with one child, place a mark above the 1 on the horizontal scale at the 11 on the vertical scale, and so on. Connect the dots with straight-line segments and bring the end points of the graph down to the horizontal scale, as shown.

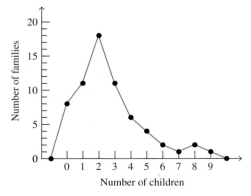

Figure 13.10

Table 13.2

Distance (miles)	Number of Workers
1–7	15
8–14	24
15–21	13
22–28	8
29–35	5
36–42	5

TIMELY TIP When constructing a histogram or frequency polygon, be sure to label both scales of the graph.

EXAMPLE ❹ Commuting Distances

The frequency distribution of the one-way commuting distances for 70 workers is listed in Table 13.2. Construct a histogram and then construct a frequency polygon.

SOLUTION The histogram can be constructed with either class limits or class marks (class midpoints) on the horizontal scale. Frequency polygons are constructed with class marks on the horizontal scale. Since we will construct a frequency polygon on the histogram, we will use class marks. Recall that class marks are found by adding the lower class limit and upper class limit and dividing the sum by 2. For the first class, the class mark is $\frac{1+7}{2}$, or 4. Since the class widths are seven units, the class marks will also differ by seven units (see Fig. 13.11).

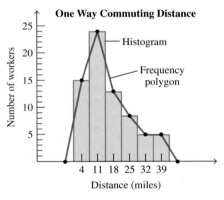

Figure 13.11

EXAMPLE ❺ Carry-on Luggage Weights

The histogram in Fig. 13.12 shows the weights of selected pieces of carry-on luggage at an airport. Construct the frequency distribution from the histogram in Fig. 13.12.

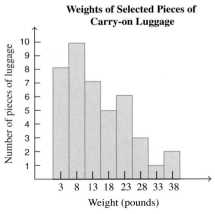

Figure 13.12

Table 13.3

Weight (pounds)	Number of Pieces of Luggage
1–5	8
6–10	10
11–15	7
16–20	5
21–25	6
26–30	3
31–35	1
36–40	2

> **SOLUTION** There are five units between class midpoints, so each class width must also be five units. Since three is the midpoint of the first class, there must be two units below and two units above it. The first class must be 1–5. The second class must therefore be 6–10. The frequency distribution is given in Table 13.3. •

Stem-and-Leaf Displays

Frequency distributions and histograms provide very useful tools to organize and summarize data. However, if the data are grouped, we cannot identify specific data values in a frequency distribution and in a histogram. For example, in Example 5, we know that there are eight pieces of luggage in the class of 1 to 5 pounds, but we don't know the specific weights of those eight pieces of luggage.

A *stem-and-leaf display* is a tool that organizes and groups the data while allowing us to see the actual values that make up the data. To construct a stem-and-leaf display each value is represented with two different groups of digits. The left group of digits is called the *stem*. The remaining group of digits on the right is called the *leaf*. There is no rule for the number of digits to be included in the stem. Usually the units digit is the leaf and the remaining digits are the stem. For example, the number 53 would be broken up into 5 and 3. The 5 would be the stem and the 3 would be the leaf. The number 417 would be broken up into 41 and 7. The 41 would be the stem and the 7 would be the leaf. The number 6, which can be represented as 06, would be broken up into 0 and 6. The stem would be the 0 and the leaf would be the 6. With a stem-and-leaf display, the stems are listed, in ascending order, to the left of a vertical line. Then we place each leaf to the right of its corresponding stem, to the right of the vertical line.* Example 6 illustrates this procedure.

┌ EXAMPLE ❻ *Stem-and-Leaf Display*

The table below indicates the ages of a sample of 20 guests who stayed at Captain Fairfield House Bed and Breakfast. Construct a stem-and-leaf display.

29	31	39	43	56
60	62	59	58	32
47	27	50	28	71
72	44	45	44	68

> **SOLUTION** By quickly glancing at the data, we can see the ages consist of two-digit numbers. Let's use the first digit, the tens digit, as our stem and the second digit, the units digit, as the leaf. For example, for an age of 62, the stem is 6 and the leaf is 2. Our values are numbers in the 20s, 30s, 40s, 50s, 60s, and 70s. Therefore, the stems will be 2, 3, 4, 5, 6, 7 as shown below.

```
2 │
3 │
4 │
5 │
6 │
7 │
```

---

*In stem-and-leaf displays, the leaves are sometimes listed from lowest digit to greatest digit, but that is not necessary.

Next we place each leaf on its stem. We will do so by placing the second digit of each value next to its stem, to the right of the vertical line. Our first value is 29. The 2 is the stem and the 9 is the leaf. Therefore, we place a 9 next to the stem of 2 and to the right of the vertical line.

$$2 \mid 9$$

The next value is 31. We will place a leaf of 1 next to the stem of 3.

$$\begin{array}{c|c} 2 & 9 \\ 3 & 1 \end{array}$$

The next value is 39. Therefore, we will place a leaf of 9 after the leaf of 1 that is next to the stem of 3.

$$\begin{array}{c|cc} 2 & 9 \\ 3 & 1 & 9 \end{array}$$

We continue this process until we have listed all the leaves on the display. The diagram below shows the stem-and-leaf display for the ages of the guests. In our display, we will also include a legend to indicate the values represented by the stems and leaves. For example, 5 | 6 represents 56.

5 | 6 represents 56

Stem	Leaves				
2	9	7	8		
3	1	9	2		
4	3	7	4	5	4
5	6	9	8	0	
6	0	2	8		
7	1	2			

Every piece of the original data can be seen in a stem-and-leaf display. From the above diagram, we can see that five of the guests' ages were in the 40s. Only two guests were older than 70. Note that the stem-and-leaf display gives the same visual impression as a sideways histogram.

SECTION 13.4 EXERCISES

CONCEPT/WRITING EXERCISES

1. In your own words, explain how to construct a circle graph from a table of values.

2. a) What is listed on the horizontal axis of a histogram and frequency polygon?

   b) What is listed on the vertical axis of a histogram and frequency polygon?

3. In your own words, explain how to construct a frequency polygon from a set of data.

4. In your own words, explain how to construct a histogram from a set of data.

5. a) In your own words, explain how to construct a frequency polygon from a histogram.

   b) Construct a frequency polygon from the histogram at the top of the next page.

Number of Textbooks Required

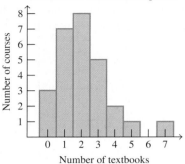

6. a) In your own words, explain how to construct a histogram from a frequency polygon.

b) Construct a histogram from the frequency polygon below.

Number of Sick Days Taken Last Year

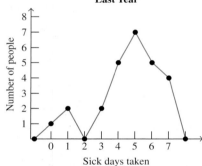

7. a) In your own words, explain how to construct a stem-and-leaf display.

b) Construct a frequency distribution, letting each class have a width of 1, from the following stem-and-leaf display.

4 | 5 represents 45

Stem Leaf

4 | 5 5 5 7 9
5 | 0 1 1

8. Construct a frequency distribution, letting each class have a width of 1, from the following stem-and-leaf display.

2 | 3 represents 23

Stem Leaf

1 | 7 8 7 9 6
2 | 3 1 2 2 5 5 4

PRACTICE THE SKILLS

9. *College Costs* The cost to attend Rochester Institute of Technology (RIT) for the 2005–2006 school year was $32,235. The following circle graph shows the percent of that cost for tuition, room, board, and student fees. Determine the cost, in dollars, for each category. Round answers to the nearest cent.

Cost to Attend Rochester Institute of Technology for 2005–2006

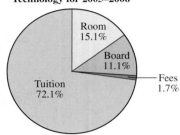

Source: RIT

10. *Bausch & Lomb Sales* The following circle graph shows the percent of Bausch & Lomb 2004 sales for the following categories: contact lenses, pharmaceuticals, lens care products, cataract/vitreoretinal, and refractive products. If the company's 2004 sales were $2.2 billion, determine their sales from each category.

Bausch & Lomb Sales, 2004

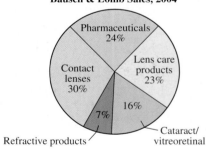

Source: Bausch & Lomb

11. *Eating at Fast-Food Restaurants* A sample of 600 people were asked which meal (breakfast, lunch, dinner, or a snack) they were most likely to eat at a fast-food restaurant. Their responses are given in the table below. Use this information to construct a circle graph illustrating the percent of people who gave each response. Round percents to the nearest tenth.

Meal	Number of Respondents
Breakfast	46
Lunch	293
Dinner	190
Snack	71

12. *Online Travel Websites* A sample of 500 travelers who used the Internet to book a trip were asked which travel website they used. Their responses are given in the table below. Use this information to construct a circle graph illustrating the percent of people who gave each response.

Online Travel Website	Number of Bookings
Travelocity	175
Expedia	125
Orbitz	85
Other	115

13. *Audition* The frequency distribution indicates the ages of a group of 50 dancers attending an audition.

Age	Number of People
17	2
18	6
19	8
20	9
21	5
22	10
23	7
24	3

a) Construct a histogram of the frequency distribution.

b) Construct a frequency polygon of the frequency distribution.

14. *Heights* The frequency distribution indicates the heights of 45 male high school seniors.

Height (in.)	Number of Males
64	2
65	6
66	7
67	9
68	10
69	6
70	3
71	0
72	2

a) Construct a histogram of the frequency distribution.

b) Construct a frequency polygon of the frequency distribution.

15. *DVDs* The frequency distribution indicates the number of DVDs owned by a sample of 40 people.

Number of DVDs	Number of People
6–13	4
14–21	5
22–29	10
30–37	11
38–45	6
46–53	3
54–61	1

a) Construct a histogram of the frequency distribution.

b) Construct a frequency polygon of the frequency distribution.

16. *Annual Salaries* The frequency distribution illustrates the annual salaries, in thousands of dollars, of the people in management positions at the X-Chek Corporation.

Salary (in $1000)	Number of People
35–40	3
41–46	6
47–52	9
53–58	8
59–64	7
65–70	6
71–76	4

a) Construct a histogram of the frequency distribution.

b) Construct a frequency polygon of the frequency distribution.

PROBLEM SOLVING

17. *Number of Televisions per Home* Use the histogram below to answer the following questions.

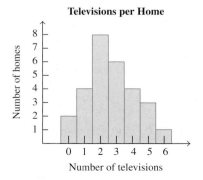

a) How many homes were included in the survey?

b) In how many homes were four televisions observed?

c) What is the modal class?

d) How many televisions were observed?

e) Construct a frequency distribution from this histogram.

18. *Car Insurance* Use the histogram below to answer the following questions.

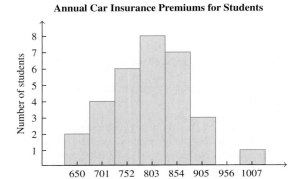

Annual Car Insurance Premiums for Students

a) How many students were surveyed?

b) What are the lower and upper class limits of the first and second classes?

c) How many students have an annual car insurance premium in the class with a class mark of $752?

d) What is the class mark of the modal class?

e) Construct a frequency distribution from this histogram. Use a first class of 625–675.

19. *Text Messages* Use the frequency polygon below to answer the following questions.

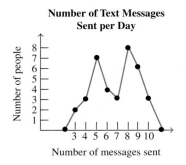

Number of Text Messages Sent per Day

a) How many people sent five text messages?

b) How many people sent six or fewer text messages?

c) How many people were included in the survey?

d) Construct a frequency distribution from the frequency polygon.

e) Construct a histogram from the frequency distribution in part (d).

20. *San Diego Zoo* Use the frequency polygon below to answer the following questions.

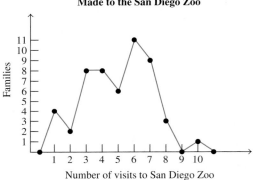

Number of Visits Selected Families Have Made to the San Diego Zoo

a) How many families visited the San Diego Zoo four times?

b) How many families visited the San Diego Zoo at least six times?

c) How many families were surveyed?

d) Construct a frequency distribution from the frequency polygon.

e) Construct a histogram from the frequency distribution in part (d).

21. Construct a histogram and a frequency polygon from the frequency distribution given in Exercise 7 of Section 13.3. See page 848.

22. Construct a histogram and a frequency polygon from the frequency distribution given in Exercise 8 of Section 13.3. See page 848.

23. *Jogging Distances* Twenty members of a health club who jog were asked how many miles they jog per week. The responses are as follows. Construct a stem-and-leaf display. For single digit data, use a stem of 0.

12	15	4	7	12	25	21
33	18	6	8	27	40	22
19	13	23	34	17	16	

24. *College Credits* Eighteen students in a geology class were asked how many college credits they had earned. The responses are as follows. Construct a stem-and-leaf display.

10	15	24	36	48	45
42	53	60	17	24	30
33	45	48	62	54	60

25. *Starting Salaries* Starting salaries (in thousands of dollars) for social workers with a bachelor of science degree and no experience are shown for a random sample of 25 different social workers.

27	28	29	31	33
28	28	29	31	33
28	28	30	32	33
28	29	30	32	34
28	29	30	32	34

a) Construct a frequency distribution. Let each class have a width of one.

b) Construct a histogram.

c) Construct a frequency polygon.

d) Construct a stem-and-leaf display.

26. *Visiting a Museum* The ages of a random sample of people visiting a museum are

20	23	25	30	32	35	39	44
21	23	26	30	33	35	40	45
21	24	27	30	34	35	40	45
22	24	28	31	34	37	40	46
23	25	28	31	34	38	42	47

a) Construct a frequency distribution with a first class of 20–24.

b) Construct a histogram.

c) Construct a frequency polygon.

d) Construct a stem-and-leaf display.

27. *Broadway Shows* The following table shows the number of performances for the 50 longest-running Broadway shows as of September 1, 2006.

Play	Performances
The Phantom of the Opera	7755*
Cats	7485
Les Miserables	6680
A Chorus Line	6137
Oh! Calcutta (revival)	5959
Beauty and the Beast	5080*
Rent	4301*
Miss Saigon	4092
Chicago (revival)	4080*
The Lion King	3633*
42nd Street	3486
Grease	3388
Fiddler on the Roof	3242
Life With Father	3224
Tobacco Road	3182
Hello, Dolly!	2844
My Fair Lady	2717
Annie	2377
Cabaret (revival)	2377
Man of La Mancha	2328
Abie's Irish Rose	2327
The Producers	2235*
Oklahoma!	2212
Smokey Joe's Café	2036
Mamma Mia!	2026*
Pippin	1944
South Pacific	1925
The Magic Show	1920
Aida	1852
Gemini	1819
Deathtrap	1793
Harvey	1775
Dancin'	1774

Table continued on next page

Table continued from privious page

Play	Performances
La Cage aux Folles	1761
Hair	1750
Hairspray	1685*
The Wiz	1672
Born Yesterday	1642
Crazy For You	1622
Ain't Misbehavin'	1604
The Best Little Whorehouse in Texas	1584
Mary, Mary	1572
Evita	1567
The Voice of the Turtle	1557
Jekyll & Hyde	1543
Barefoot in the Park	1530
Brighton Beach Memoirs	1530
42nd Street (revival)	1524
Dreamgirls	1521
Mame	1508

Source: League of American Theatres and Producers, Inc
*Still running as of September 1, 2006.

a) Construct a frequency distribution with a first class of 1508–2548.

b) Construct a histogram.

c) Construct a frequency polygon.

28. **U.S. Presidents** The ages of the 43 U.S. presidents at their first inauguration (as of 2007) are

```
57  57  49  52  50  42  54  55  64
61  61  64  56  47  51  51  56  46
57  54  50  46  55  56  60  61  54
57  68  48  54  55  55  62  52
58  51  65  49  54  51  43  69
```

a) Construct a frequency distribution with a first class of 42–47.

b) Construct a histogram.

c) Construct a frequency polygon.

CHALLENGE PROBLEMS/GROUP ACTIVITIES

29. a) *Birthdays* What do you believe a histogram of the months in which the students in your class were born (January is month 1 and December is month 12) would look like? Explain.

b) By asking, determine the month in which the students in your class were born (include yourself).

c) Construct a frequency distribution containing 12 classes.

d) Construct a histogram from the frequency distribution in part (c).

e) Construct a frequency polygon of the frequency distribution in part (c).

30. *Social Security Numbers* Repeat Exercise 29 for the last digit of the students' social security numbers. Include classes for the digits 0–9.

INTERNET/RESEARCH ACTIVITY

31. Over the years many changes have been made in the U.S. Social Security System.

a) Do research and determine the number of people receiving social security benefits for the years 1945, 1950, 1955, 1960, . . . , 2005. Then construct a frequency distribution and histogram of the data.

b) Determine the maximum amount that self-employed individuals had to pay into social security (the FICA tax) for the years 1945, 1950, 1955, 1960, . . . , 2005. Then construct a frequency distribution and a histogram of the data.

13.5 MEASURES OF CENTRAL TENDENCY

Most people have an intuitive idea of what is meant by an "average." The term is used daily in many familiar ways. "This car averages 19 miles per gallon," "The average test grade was 82," and "The average height of adult males is 5 feet 9 inches" are three examples. In this section, we will introduce four different averages and discuss the circumstances in which each average is used.

▲ An average is used to describe the fuel efficiency of a car.

Measures of Central Tendency

An *average* is a number that is representative of a group of data. There are at least four different averages: the mean, the median, the mode, and the midrange. Each is calculated differently and may yield different results for the same set of data. Each will result in a number near the center of the data; for this reason, averages are commonly referred to as *measures of central tendency*.

The *arithmetic mean*, or simply the *mean*, is symbolized either by $\bar{x}$ (read "x bar") or by the Greek letter mu, μ. The symbol $\bar{x}$ is used when the mean of a *sample* of the population is calculated. The symbol μ is used when the mean of the *entire population* is calculated. Unless otherwise indicated, we will assume that the data featured in this book represent samples; therefore, we will use $\bar{x}$ for the mean.

The Greek letter sigma, Σ, is used to indicate "summation." The notation Σx, read "the sum of x," is used to indicate the sum of all the data. For example, if there are five pieces of data, 4, 6, 1, 0, 5, then $\Sigma x = 4 + 6 + 1 + 0 + 5 = 16$.

Now we can discuss the procedure for determining the mean of a set of data.

> The **mean**, $\bar{x}$, is the sum of the data divided by the number of pieces of data. The formula for calculating the mean is
>
> $$\bar{x} = \frac{\Sigma x}{n}$$
>
> where Σx represents the sum of all the data and n represents the number of pieces of data.

The most common use of the word *average* is the mean.

EXAMPLE 1 Determine the Mean

Determine the mean age of a group of patients at a doctor's office if the ages of the individuals are 27, 18, 48, 34, and 48.

SOLUTION

$$\bar{x} = \frac{\Sigma x}{n} = \frac{27 + 18 + 48 + 34 + 48}{5} = \frac{175}{5} = 35$$

Therefore, the mean, $\bar{x}$, is 35 years. ●

The mean represents "the balancing point" of a set of data. For example, if a seesaw were pivoted at the mean and uniform weights were placed at points corresponding to the ages in Example 1, the seesaw would balance. Figure 13.13 shows the five ages given in Example 1 and the calculated mean.

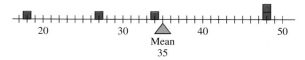

Figure 13.13

A second average is the *median*. To find the median of a set of data, *rank the data* from smallest to largest, or largest to smallest, and determine the value in the middle of the set of *ranked data*. This value will be the median.

> The **median** is the value in the middle of a set of *ranked data*.

EXAMPLE ② *Determine the Median*

Determine the median of the patients' ages in Example 1 on page 861.

SOLUTION Ranking the data from smallest to largest gives 18, 27, 34, 48, and 48. Since 34 is the value in the middle of this set of ranked data (two pieces of data above it and two pieces below it), 34 years is the median. ●

When there are an even number of pieces of data, the median is halfway between the two middle pieces. In this case, to find the median, add the two middle pieces and divide this sum by 2.

EXAMPLE ③ *Determine the Median of an Even Number of Pieces of Data*

Determine the median of the following sets of data.
a) 9, 14, 16, 17, 11, 16, 11, 12
b) 7, 8, 8, 8, 9, 10

SOLUTION

a) Ranking the data gives 9, 11, 11, 12, 14, 16, 16, 17. There are eight pieces of data. Therefore, the median will lie halfway between the two middle pieces, the 12 and the 14. The median is $\frac{12 + 14}{2}$, or $\frac{26}{2}$, or 13.

b) There are six pieces of data, and they are already ranked. Therefore, the median lies halfway between the two middle pieces. Both middle pieces are 8's. The median is $\frac{8 + 8}{2}$, or $\frac{16}{2}$, or 8. ●

> **TIMELY TIP** Data must be ranked before determining the median. A common error made when determining the median is neglecting to arrange the data in ascending (increasing) or in descending (decreasing) order.

A third average is the *mode*.

> The **mode** is the piece of data that occurs most frequently.

EXAMPLE ④ *Determine the Mode*

Determine the mode of the patients' ages in Example 1 on page 861.

SOLUTION The ages are 27, 18, 48, 34, and 48. The age 48 is the mode because it occurs twice and the other values occur only once. ●

If each piece of data occurs only once, the set of data has no mode. For example, the set of data 1, 2, 3, 4, 5 has no mode. If two values in a set of data occur more often than all the other data, we consider both these values as modes and say that the data

are **bimodal*** (which means two modes). For example, the set of data 1, 1, 2, 3, 3, 5 has two modes, 1 and 3.

The last average we will discuss is the midrange. The *midrange* is the value halfway between the lowest (L) and highest (H) values in a set of data. It is found by adding the lowest and highest values and dividing the sum by 2. A formula for finding the midrange follows.

$$\text{Midrange} = \frac{\text{lowest value} + \text{highest value}}{2}$$

EXAMPLE ❺ *Determine the Midrange*

Determine the midrange of the patients' ages given in Example 1 on page 861.

SOLUTION The ages of the patients are 27, 18, 48, 34, and 48. The lowest age is 18, and the highest age is 48.

$$\text{Midrange} = \frac{\text{lowest} + \text{highest}}{2} = \frac{18 + 48}{2} = \frac{66}{2} = 33 \text{ years}$$

The "average" of the ages 27, 18, 48, 34, 48 can be considered any one of the following values: 35 (mean), 34 (median), 48 (mode), or 33 (midrange). Which average do you feel is most representative of the ages? We will discuss this question later in this section.

EXAMPLE ❻ *Measures of Central Tendency*

The salaries of eight selected social workers rounded to the nearest thousand dollars are 40, 25, 28, 35, 42, 60, 60, and 73. For this set of data, determine the (a) mean, (b) median, (c) mode, and (d) midrange. Then (e) list the measures of central tendency from lowest to highest.

SOLUTION

a) $\bar{x} = \dfrac{\Sigma x}{n} = \dfrac{40 + 25 + 28 + 35 + 42 + 60 + 60 + 73}{8} = \dfrac{363}{8} = 45.375$

b) Ranking the data from the smallest to largest gives

$$25, 28, 35, 40, 42, 60, 60, 73$$

Since there are an even number of pieces of data, the median is halfway between 40 and 42. The median = (40 + 42)/2 = 82/2 = 41.

c) The mode is the piece of data that occurs most frequently. The mode is 60.

d) The midrange = (L + H)/2 = (25 + 73)/2 = 98/2 = 49.

e) The averages from lowest to highest are the median, mean, midrange, and mode. Their values are 41, 45.375, 49, and 60, respectively.

At this point, you should be able to calculate the four measures of central tendency: mean, median, mode, and midrange. Now let's examine the circumstances in which each is used.

---

*Some textbooks say that sets of data such as 1, 1, 2, 3, 3, 5 have no mode.

The mean is used when each piece of data is to be considered and "weighed" equally. It is the most commonly used average. It is the only average that can be affected by *any* change in the set of data; for this reason, it is the most sensitive of all the measures of central tendency (see Exercise 23).

Occasionally, one or more pieces of data may be much greater or much smaller than the rest of the data. When this situation occurs, these "extreme" values have the effect of increasing or decreasing the mean significantly so that the mean will not be representative of the set of data. Under these circumstances, the median should be used instead of the mean. The median is often used in describing average family incomes because a relatively small number of families have extremely large incomes. These few incomes would inflate the mean income, making it nonrepresentative of the millions of families in the population.

Consider a set of exam scores from a mathematics class: 0, 16, 19, 65, 65, 65, 68, 69, 70, 72, 73, 73, 75, 78, 80, 85, 88, 92. Which average would best represent these grades? The mean is 64.06. The median is 71. Since only 3 of the 18 scores fall below the mean, the mean would not be considered a good representative score. The median of 71 probably would be the better average to use.

The mode is the piece of data, if any, that occurs most frequently. Builders planning houses are interested in the most common family size. Retailers ordering shirts are interested in the most common shirt size. An individual purchasing a thermometer might choose one, from those on display, whose temperature reading is the most common reading among those on display. These examples illustrate how the mode may be used.

The midrange is sometimes used as the average when the item being studied is constantly fluctuating. Average daily temperature, used to compare temperatures in different areas, is calculated by adding the lowest and highest temperatures for the day and dividing the sum by 2. The midrange is actually the mean of the high value and the low value of a set of data. Occasionally, the midrange is used to estimate the mean since it is much easier to calculate.

Sometimes an average itself is of little value, and care must be taken in interpreting its meaning. For example, Jim is told that the average depth of Willow Pond is only 3 feet. He is not a good swimmer but decides that it is safe to go out a short distance in this shallow pond. After he is rescued, he exclaims, "I thought this pond was only 3 feet deep." Jim didn't realize that an average does not indicate extreme values or the spread of the values. The spread of data is discussed in Section 13.6.

Measures of Position

Measures of position are used to describe the position of a piece of data in relation to the rest of the data. If you took the Scholastic Aptitude Test (SAT) before applying to college, your score was described as a measure of position rather than a measure of central tendency. *Measures of position* are often used to make comparisons, such as comparing the scores of individuals from different populations, and are generally used when the amount of data is large.

Two measures of position are *percentiles* and *quartiles*. There are 99 percentiles dividing a set of data into 100 equal parts; see Fig. 13.14. For example, suppose that

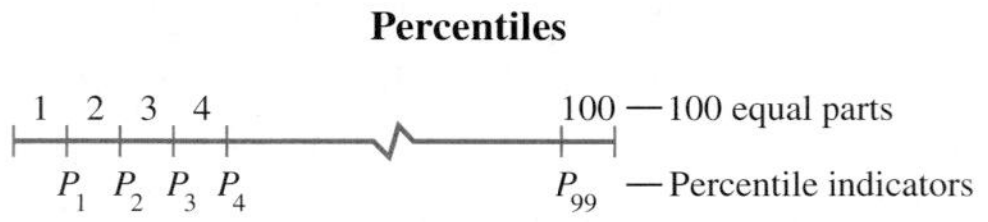

Figure 13.14

you scored 520 on the math portion of the SAT, and the score of 520 was reported to be in the 78th percentile of high school students. This wording *does not* mean that 78% of your answers were correct; it *does* mean that you outperformed about 78% of all those taking the exam. In general, a score in the nth percentile means that you outperformed about n% of the population who took the test and that $(100 - n)$% of the people taking the test performed better than you did.

┌─ EXAMPLE ❼ *English Achievement Test*

Kara Hopkins took an English achievement test to obtain college credit by exam for freshman English. Her score was at the 81st percentile. Explain what that means.

SOLUTION If a score is at the 81st percentile, it means that about 81% of the scores are below that score. Therefore, Kara scored better than about 81% of the students taking the exam. Also, about 19% of all students taking the exam scored higher than she did.   •

Quartiles are another measure of position. Quartiles divide data into four equal parts: The first quartile is the value that is higher than about $\frac{1}{4}$ or 25% of the population. It is the same as the 25th percentile. The second quartile is the value that is higher than about $\frac{1}{2}$ the population and is the same as the 50th percentile, or the median. The third quartile is the value that is higher than about $\frac{3}{4}$ of the population and is the same as the 75th percentile; see Fig. 13.15.

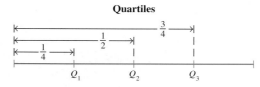

Figure 13.15

TO DETERMINE THE QUARTILES OF A SET OF DATA

1. List the data from smallest to largest.

2. Determine the median, or the 2nd quartile, of the set of data. If there is an odd number of pieces of data, the median is the middle value. If there is an even number of pieces of data, the median will be halfway between the two middle pieces of data.

3. The first quartile, Q_1, is the median of the lower half of the data; that is, Q_1 is the median of the data less than Q_2.

4. The third quartile, Q_3, is the median of the upper half of the data; that is, Q_3 is the median of the data greater than Q_2.

┌─ EXAMPLE ❽ *Finding Quartiles*

Electronics World is concerned about the high turnover of its sales staff. A survey was done to determine how long (in months) the sales staff had been in their current positions. The responses of 27 sales staff follow. Determine Q_1, Q_2, and Q_3.

$$
\begin{array}{ccccccccc}
25 & 3 & 7 & 15 & 31 & 36 & 17 & 21 & 2 \\
11 & 42 & 16 & 23 & 19 & 21 & 9 & 20 & 5 \\
8 & 12 & 27 & 14 & 39 & 24 & 18 & 6 & 10
\end{array}
$$

SOLUTION First we list the data from smallest to largest.

$$
\begin{array}{ccccccccc}
2 & 3 & 5 & 6 & 7 & 8 & 9 & 10 & 11 \\
12 & 14 & 15 & 16 & 17 & 18 & 19 & 20 & 21 \\
21 & 23 & 24 & 25 & 27 & 31 & 36 & 39 & 42
\end{array}
$$

Next we determine the median. Since there are 27 pieces of data, an odd number, the median will be the middle value. The middle value is 17, with 13 pieces of data less than 17 and 13 pieces of data greater than 17. Therefore, the median, Q_2, is 17, shown in red.

To find Q_1, the median of the lower half of the data, we need to find the median of the 13 pieces of data that are less than Q_2. The middle value of the lower half of the data is 9. There are 6 pieces of data less than 9 and 6 pieces of data greater than 9. Therefore, Q_1 is 9, shown in blue.

To find Q_3, the median of the upper half of the data, we need to find the median of the 13 pieces of data that are greater than 17, or Q_2. The middle value of the upper half of the data is 24. There are 6 pieces of data greater than 17 but less than 24 and 6 pieces of data greater than 24. Therefore, Q_3 is 24, shown in blue.   ●

TECHNOLOGY TIP Several computer software programs and calculators can be used to determine the mean of a set of data. These programs and calculators can also provide other types of statistical information that we will discuss in this chapter. We will provide the instructions for using a software program called Microsoft Excel as well as information on how to use Texas Instruments TI-83 Plus and TI-84 Plus graphing calculators. In the example, we will use the data from Example 1 on page 861, which represent the ages of patients in a doctor's office.

EXCEL

If you are new to Excel, first read the appendix on Excel in the back of the book. In our discussion, we will use the symbol > to indicate the next item to be selected from the list or menu of items.

Begin by entering the five pieces of data in column A. Press the Enter key after each piece of data is entered. Next select

Insert > Function . . . > Statistical > AVERAGE

Then click the ⬛OK⬛ box at the bottom. The program will then generate a gray box, where you need to enter the data. In the area to the right of **Number1**, you need to enter the data for which you want to find the mean. Since you have already entered the data in column A, rows 1 to 5, if A1:A5 is not already listed, you can enter A1:A5 in the area to the right of **Number1**. Then, at the bottom of the gray box, *Formula Results = 35* is displayed. The 35 is the mean of the set of data. If you then press the ⬛OK⬛ box, the mean will be displayed in the cell where the cursor was located.

If you do not want the mean displayed in a cell, press CANCEL . To find the median or mode you follow a similar procedure, except that instead of selecting AVERAGE you would select MEDIAN or MODE, respectively.

TI-83 PLUS AND TI-84 PLUS GRAPHING CALCULATORS

To enter the data, press STAT . Then highlight **1: Edit** and press the ENTER key. If any data are currently listed in column **L1**, move the cursor to the **L1** and press CLEAR and then the ENTER key. This step will eliminate all data from column **L1**. Now enter the data in column **L1**. After you enter each piece of data, press the ENTER key. After all the data has been entered, press STAT . Then highlight **CALC**. At this point, **1: 1−Var Stats** should be highlighted. Press the ENTER key twice. You will now see $\bar{x} = 35$. Thus, the mean is 35. Several other descriptive statistics that we will discuss shortly are also shown. If you scroll down, you will eventually see the values of Q_1, the median, and Q_3.

SECTION 13.5 EXERCISES

CONCEPT/WRITING EXERCISES

1. a) Describe the mean of a set of data and explain how to find it.

   b) Describe the median of a set of data and explain how to find it.

2. a) Describe the midrange of a set of data and explain how to find it.

   b) Describe the mode of a set of data and explain how to find it.

3. When might the median be the preferred average to use? Give an example.

4. When might the mode be the preferred average to use? Give an example.

5. When might the midrange be the preferred average to use? Give an example.

6. When might the mean be the preferred average to use? Give an example.

7. a) What symbol is used for the sample mean?

   b) What symbol is used for the population mean?

8. What is a set of *ranked data*?

9. Explain how to find the quartiles of a set of data.

10. a) What is another name for the 25th percentile?

    b) What is another name for the 50th percentile?

    c) What is another name for the 75th percentile?

PRACTICE THE SKILLS

In Exercises 11–20, determine the mean, median, mode, and midrange of the set of data. Round your answer to the nearest tenth.

11. 7, 8, 8, 10, 12, 12, 12, 23, 25

12. 10, 8, 11, 11, 11, 13, 15

13. 76, 82, 94, 55, 100, 52, 96

14. 4, 6, 10, 12, 10, 9, 365, 40, 37, 8

15. 1, 3, 5, 7, 9, 11, 13, 15

16. 40, 50, 30, 60, 90, 100, 140

17. 1, 7, 11, 27, 36, 14, 12, 9, 1

18. 1, 1, 1, 1, 4, 4, 4, 4, 6, 8, 10, 12, 15, 21

19. 6, 8, 12, 13, 11, 13, 15, 17

20. 5, 15, 5, 15, 5, 15

21. **Best-Seller List** The number of weeks the top 10 hard-cover fiction novels were on the best-seller list as of July 8, 2007, is 1, 5, 2, 2, 3, 4, 5, 3, 3, 7. Determine the mean, median, mode, and midrange.

22. **Daily Commission** The amount of money Steve Kilner collected in sales commission in each of seven days is $48, $67, $51, $25, $102, $61, $80. Determine the mean, median, mode, and midrange.

PROBLEM SOLVING

23. **Change in the Data** The mean is the "most sensitive" average because it is affected by any change in the data.

   a) Determine the mean, median, mode, and midrange for 1, 2, 3, 5, 5, 7, 11.

   b) Change the 7 to a 10 in part (a). Determine the mean, median, mode, and midrange.

   c) Which averages were affected by changing the 7 to a 10?

   d) Which averages will be affected by changing the 11 to a 10 in part (a)?

24. **Life Expectancy** In 2005, the National Center for Health Statistics indicated a record "average life expectancy" of 77.6 years for the total U.S. population. The average life expectancy for men was 74.8 years, and for women it was 80.1 years. Which "average" do you think the National Center for Health is using? Explain your answer.

25. **A Grade of B** To get a grade of B, a student must have a mean average of 80 or greater. Jim Condor has a mean average of 79 for 10 quizzes. He approaches his teacher and asks for a B, reasoning that he missed a B by only one point. What is wrong with Jim's reasoning?

26. **Employee Salaries** The salaries of 10 employees of a small company follow.

$28,000	$64,000
25,000	24,000
31,000	27,000
26,000	81,000
26,000	29,000

Determine the

a) mean.

b) median.

c) mode.

d) midrange.

e) If the employees wanted to demonstrate the need for a raise, which average would they use to show they are being underpaid: the mean or the median? Explain.

f) If the management did not want to give the employees a raise, which average would they use: the mean or the median? Explain.

27. **Passenger Traffic** The 10 U.S. airports with the most passenger arrivals and departures in 2005 are listed below.

Airport	Passenger Arrivals and Departures (millions of people)
Hartsfield Atlanta	85.9
Chicago O'Hare	75.5
Los Angeles	61.5
Dallas–Fort Worth	59.1
Las Vegas	44.3
Denver	43.3
Phoenix Sky Harbor	41.2
JFK–New York	40.6
Houston	39.7
Minneapolis–St. Paul	37.6

Source: Infoplease.com

Determine to the nearest tenth the

a) mean.

b) median.

c) mode.

d) midrange.

28. *Living Expenses* Bob Exler's monthly living expenses for 1 year are as follows:

$1000	$850	$1370	$1400
1900	850	1350	1250
1600	900	1110	1230

When appropriate, round your answer to the nearest cent. Determine the

a) mean.

b) median.

c) mode.

d) midrange.

29. *Amusement Park Attendance* The 10 amusement parks with the highest attendance in 2004 are listed below.

Park	Attendance (millions of people)
Magic Kingdom at Walt Disney World	15.1
Disneyland	13.4
Tokyo Disneyland	13.2
Tokyo Disney Sea	12.2
Disneyland Paris	10.2
Universal Studios Japan	9.9
Epcot at Walt Disney World	9.4
MGM Studios at Walt Disney World	8.3
Lotte World	8.0
Animal Kingdom at Walt Disney World	7.8

Source: Amusement Business

Determine to the nearest tenth the

a) mean.

b) median.

c) mode.

d) midrange.

30. *Exam Average* Malcolm Sander's mean average on five exams is 81. Determine the sum of his scores.

31. *Exam Average* Jeremy Urban's mean average on six exams is 92. Determine the sum of his scores.

32. *Creating a Data Set* Construct a set of five pieces of data in which the mode has a lower value than the median and the median has a lower value than the mean.

33. *Creating a Data Set* Construct a set of six pieces of data with a mean, median, and midrange of 75 and where no two pieces of data are the same.

34. *Creating a Data Set* Construct a set of six pieces of data with a mean of 84 and where no two pieces of data are the same.

35. *Water Park* For the 2007 season, 24,000 people visited the Blue Lagoon Water Park. The park was open 120 days for water activities. The highest number of visitors on a single day was 500. The lowest number of visitors on a single day was 50. Determine whether it is possible to find the following with the given information. Explain your answer.

a) the mean number of visitors per day.

b) the median number of visitors per day.

c) the mode number of visitors per day.

d) the midrange number of visitors per day.

36. *Determine a Necessary Grade* A mean average of 80 or greater for five exams is needed for a final grade of B in a course. Jorge Rivera's first four exam grades are 73, 69, 85, and 80. What grade does Jorge need on the fifth exam to get a B in the course?

37. *Grading Methods* A mean average of 60 on seven exams is needed to pass a course. On her first six exams, Sheryl Ward received grades of 51, 72, 80, 62, 57, and 69.

a) What grade must she receive on her last exam to pass the course?

b) An average of 70 is needed to get a C in the course. Is it possible for Sheryl to get a C? If so, what grade must she receive on the seventh exam?

c) If her lowest grade of the exams already taken is to be dropped, what grade must she receive on her last exam to pass the course?

d) If her lowest grade of the exams already taken is to be dropped, what grade must she receive on her last exam to get a C in the course?

38. Central Tendencies Which of the measures of central tendency *must* be an actual piece of data in the distribution? Explain.

39. Creating a Data Set Construct a set of six pieces of data such that if only one piece of data is changed, the mean, median, and mode will all change.

40. Changing One Piece of Data Consider the set of data 1, 1, 1, 2, 2, 2. If one 2 is changed to a 3, which of the following will change: mean, median, mode, midrange? Explain.

41. Changing One Piece of Data Is it possible to construct a set of six different pieces of data such that by changing only one piece of data you cause the mean, median, mode, and midrange to change? Explain.

42. Grocery Expenses The Taylor's have recorded their weekly grocery expenses for the past 12 weeks and determined that the mean weekly expense was $85.20. Later Mrs. Taylor discovered that 1 week's expense of $74 was incorrectly recorded as $47. What is the correct mean?

43. Percentiles For any set of data, what must be done to the data before percentiles can be determined?

44. Percentiles Josie Waverly scored in the 73rd percentile on the verbal part of her College Board test. What does that mean?

45. Percentiles When a national sample of heights of kindergarten children was taken, Kevin Geis was told that he was in the 35th percentile. Explain what that means.

46. Percentiles A union leader is told that, when all workers' salaries are considered, the first quartile is $20,750. Explain what that means.

47. Quartiles The prices of a gallon of the 21 top-rated exterior paints, as rated in the June 2006 issue of *Consumer Reports*, are as follows:

$15 $19 $19 $20 $22 $22 $24
$24 $24 $25 $25 $27 $29 $30
$32 $34 $34 $35 $36 $39 $42

Determine

a) Q_2.   **b)** Q_1.   **c)** Q_3.

48. Quartiles The prices of the 20 top-rated dishwashers, as rated in the February 2006 issue of *Consumer Reports*, are as follows:

$380 $430 $435 $460 $500
$500 $550 $580 $600 $600
$700 $800 $800 $800 $800
$830 $850 $880 $1100 $1550

Determine

a) Q_2.   **b)** Q_1.   **c)** Q_3.

49. The 50th Percentile Give the names of two other statistics that have the same value as the 50th percentile.

50. College Admissions Jonathan Burd took an admission test for the University of California and scored in the 85th percentile. The following year, Jonathan's sister Kendra took a similar admission test for the University of California and scored in the 90th percentile.

a) Is it possible to determine which of the two answered the higher percent of questions correctly on their respective exams? Explain your answer.

b) Is it possible to determine which of the two was in a better relative position with regard to their respective populations? Explain.

51. Employee Salaries The following statistics represent weekly salaries at the Midtown Construction Company:

Mean	$550	First quartile	$510
Median	$540	Third quartile	$575
Mode	$530	83rd percentile	$615

a) What is the most common salary?

b) What salary did half the employees' salaries surpass?

c) About what percent of employees' salaries surpassed $575?

d) About what percent of employees' salaries were less than $510?

e) About what percent of employees' salaries surpassed $615?

f) If the company has 100 employees, what is the total weekly salary of all employees?

CHALLENGE PROBLEMS/GROUP ACTIVITIES

52. The Mean of the Means Consider the following five sets of values.

i)   5   6   7   7   8   9   14
ii)   3   6   8   9
iii) 1   1   1   2   5
iv)   6   8   9   12   15
v)   50   51   55   60   80   100

a) Compute the mean of each of the five sets of data.

b) Compute the mean of the five means in part (a).

c) Find the mean of the 27 pieces of data.

d) Compare your answer in part (b) to your answer in part (c). Are the values the same? Does your answer make sense? Explain.

53. **Ruth versus Mantle** The tables below compare the batting performances for selected years for two well-known former baseball players, Babe Ruth and Mickey Mantle.

Babe Ruth
Boston Red Sox 1914–1919
New York Yankees 1920–1934

Year	At Bats	Hits	Pct.
1925	359	104	
1930	518	186	
1933	459	138	
1916	136	37	
1922	406	128	
Total	1878	593	

Mickey Mantle
New York Yankees 1951–1968

Year	At Bats	Hits	Pct.
1954	543	163	
1957	474	173	
1958	519	158	
1960	527	145	
1962	377	121	
Total	2440	760	

a) For each player, compute the batting average percent (pct.) for each year by dividing the number of hits by the number of at bats. Round to the nearest thousandth. Place the answers in the pct. column.

b) Going across each of the five horizontal lines (for example Ruth, 1925, vs. Mantle, 1954), compare the percents (pct.) and determine which is greater in each case.

c) For each player, compute the mean batting average percent for the 5 given years by dividing the total hits by the total at bats. Which is greater, Ruth's or Mantle's?

d) Based on your answer in part (b), does your answer in part (c) make sense? Explain.

e) Find the mean percent for each player by adding the five pcts. and dividing by 5. Which is greater, Ruth's or Mantle's?

f) Why do the answers obtained in parts (c) and (e) differ? Explain.

g) Who would you say has the better batting average percent for the 5 years selected? Explain.

54. **Employee Salaries** The following table gives the annual salary distribution for employees at Kulzer's Home Improvement.

Annual Salary	Number Receiving Salary
$100,000	1
85,000	2
24,000	6
21,000	4
18,000	5
17,000	7

Using the information provided in the table, determine the

a) mean annual salary.

b) median annual salary.

c) mode annual salary.

d) midrange annual salary.

e) Which is the best measure of central tendency for this set of data? Explain your answer.

Weighted Average Sometimes when we wish to find an average, we may wish to assign more importance, or weight, to some of the pieces of data. To calculate a weighted average,

we use the formula: weighted average $= \dfrac{\Sigma xw}{\Sigma w}$, where w is the

weight of the piece of data, x; Σxw is the sum of the products of each piece of data multiplied by its weight; and Σw is the sum of the weights. For example, suppose that students in a class need to submit a report that counts for 20% of their grade, they need to take a midterm exam that counts for 30% of their grade, and they need to take a final exam that counts for 50% of their grade. Suppose that a student got a 72 on the report, an 85 on the midterm exam, and a 93 on the final exam. To determine this student's weighted average, first find Σxw: $\Sigma xw = 72(0.20) + 85(0.30) + 93(0.50) = 86.4$. Next find Σw, the sum of the weights: $\Sigma w = 0.20 + 0.30 + 0.50 = 1.00$. Now determine the weighted average as follows.

$$\text{Weighted average} = \frac{\Sigma xw}{\Sigma w} = \frac{86.4}{1.00} = 86.4$$

Thus, the weighted average is 86.4. Note that Σw does not always have to be 1.00. In Exercises 55 and 56, use the weighted average formula.

55. **Course Average** Suppose that your final grade for a course is determined by a midterm exam and a final exam. The midterm exam is worth 40% of your grade, and the final exam is worth 60%. If your midterm exam grade is 84 and your final exam grade is 94, calculate your final average.

56. **Grade Point Average** In a four-point grade system, an A corresponds to 4.0 points, a B corresponds to 3.0 points, a C corresponds to 2.0 points, and a D corresponds to 1.0 points. No points are awarded for an F. Last semester, Tanya Reeves received a B in a four-credit hour course, an A in a three-credit hour course, a C in a three-credit hour course, and an A in another three-credit hour course. Grade point average (GPA) is calculated as a weighted average using the credit hours as weights and the number of points corresponding to the grade as pieces of data. Calculate

Tanya's GPA for the previous semester. (Round your answer to the nearest hundredth.)

RECREATIONAL MATHEMATICS

57. **Your Exam Average** a) Calculate the mean, median, mode, and midrange of your exam grades in your mathematics course.

b) Which measure of central tendency best represents your average grade?

c) Which measure of central tendency would you rather use as your average grade?

58. **Purchases** Matthew Riveria purchased some items at Staples each day for five days. The mode of the number of items Matthew purchased is higher than the median of the number of items he purchased. The median of the number of items Matthew purchased is higher than the mean of the number of items he purchased. He purchased at least two items but no more than seven items each day.

a) How many items did Matthew purchase each day? (*Note:* There is more than one correct answer.)

b) Determine the mean, median, and mode for your answer to part (a).

INTERNET/RESEARCH ACTIVITY

59. Two other measures of location that we did not mention in this section are *stanines* and *deciles*. Use statistics books, books on educational testing and measurements, and Internet websites to write a report on what stanines and deciles are and when percentiles, quartiles, stanines, and deciles are used.

13.6   MEASURES OF DISPERSION

▲ The average life span of an airplane engine may not be enough information to make a sound purchasing decision.

The measures of central tendency by themselves do not always give sufficient information to analyze a situation and make decisions. For example, two manufacturers of airplane engines are being considered for a contract. Manufacturer A's engines have an average (mean) life of 1000 hours of flying time before they fail. Manufacture B's engines have an average life of 950 hours of flying time before they fail. If you assume that both engines cost the same, which ones should be purchased? The average engine life may not be the most important factor. The fact that manufacturer A's engines have an average life of 1000 hours could mean that half will last about 500 hours and the other half will last about 1500 hours. If in fact all manufacturer B's engines have a life span of between 925 and 975 hours, then all of manufacturer B's engines are more consistent and reliable. This example illustrates the importance of knowing something about the *spread*, or *variability*, of the data. In this section, we will discuss two measures of variability or dispersion.

Measures of dispersion are used to indicate the *spread of the data*. The range and standard deviation* are the measures of dispersion that will be discussed in this book.

Range and Standard Deviation

The *range* is the difference between the highest and lowest values; it indicates the total spread of the data.

$$\textbf{Range} = \text{highest value} - \text{lowest value}$$

EXAMPLE 1 *Determine the Range*

The amount of carbohydrates, in grams, of 12 different soft drinks is given below. Determine the range of these data.

$$26, 27, 31, 35, 31, 29, 24, 26, 27, 25, 30, 31$$

SOLUTION Range = highest value − lowest value = 35 − 24 = 11. The range of the amounts of carbohydrates is 11 grams. ●

The second measure of dispersion we discuss in this section, the *standard deviation*, measures how much the data *differ from the mean*. It is symbolized either by the letter s or by the Greek letter sigma, σ.† The s is used when the standard deviation of a *sample* is calculated. The σ is used when the standard deviation of the entire *population* is calculated. Since we are assuming that all data presented in this section are for samples, we use s to represent the standard deviation (note, however, that on the height and weight charts on page 879, σ is used. Also, we will use σ in the next section when we determine standard scores.) The larger the spread of the data about the mean, the larger the standard deviation is. Consider the following two sets of data.

$$5, 8, 9, 10, 12, 13 \qquad 8, 9, 9, 10, 10, 11$$

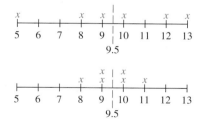

Figure 13.16

Both have a mean of 9.5. Which set of values on the whole do you believe differs less from the mean of 9.5? Figure 13.16 may make the answer more apparent. The scores in the second set of data are closer to the mean and therefore have a smaller standard deviation. You will soon be able to verify such relationships yourself.

Sometimes only a very small standard deviation is desirable or acceptable. Consider a cereal box that is to contain 8 oz of cereal. If the amount of cereal put into the boxes varies too much—sometimes underfilling, sometimes overfilling—the manufacturer will soon be in trouble with consumer groups and government agencies.

At other times, a larger spread of data is desirable or expected. For example, intelligence quotients (IQs) are expected to exhibit a considerable spread about the

---

Variance, another measure of dispersion, is the square of the standard deviation.

†Our alphabet uses both uppercase and lowercase letters, for example, *A* and *a*. The Greek alphabet also uses both uppercase and lowercase letters. The symbol Σ is the capital Greek letter sigma, and σ is the lowercase Greek letter sigma.

mean because everyone is different. The following procedure explains how we determine the standard deviation of a set of data.

TO DETERMINE THE STANDARD DEVIATION OF A SET OF DATA

1. Determine the mean of the set of data.
2. Make a chart having three columns:

   Data   Data $-$ Mean $(\text{Data} - \text{Mean})^2$

3. List the data vertically under the column marked Data.
4. Subtract the mean from each piece of data and place the difference in the Data $-$ Mean column.
5. Square the values obtained in the Data $-$ Mean column and record these values in the $(\text{Data} - \text{Mean})^2$ column.
6. Determine the sum of the values in the $(\text{Data} - \text{Mean})^2$ column.
7. Divide the sum obtained in step 6 by $n - 1$, where n is the number of pieces of data.*
8. Determine the square root of the number obtained in step 7. This number is the standard deviation of the set of data.

Example 2 illustrates the procedure to follow to determine the standard deviation of a set of data.

EXAMPLE ② *Determine the Standard Deviation*

A veterinarian in an animal hospital recorded the following life spans of selected Labrador retrievers (to the nearest year):

$$7, 9, 11, 15, 18, 12$$

Determine the standard deviation of the life spans.

SOLUTION First determine the mean:

$$\bar{x} = \frac{\Sigma x}{n} = \frac{7 + 9 + 11 + 15 + 18 + 12}{6} = \frac{72}{6} = 12$$

Next construct a table with three columns, as illustrated in Table 13.4, and list the data in the first column (it is often helpful to list the data in ascending or descending order). Complete the second column by subtracting the mean, 12 in this case, from each piece of data in the first column.

---

*To determine the standard deviation of a sample, divide the sum of $(\text{Data} - \text{Mean})^2$ column by $n - 1$. To find the standard deviation of a population, divide the sum by n. In this book, we assume that the set of data represents a sample and divide by $n - 1$. The quotient obtained in step 7 represents a measure of dispersion called the *variance*.

Table 13.4

Data	Data − Mean	(Data − Mean)^2
7	7 − 12 = −5	
9	9 − 12 = −3	
11	11 − 12 = −1	
12	12 − 12 = 0	
15	15 − 12 = 3	
18	18 − 12 = 6	
	0	

The sum of the values in the Data − Mean column should always be zero; if not, you have made an error. (If a rounded value of $\bar{x}$ is used, the sum of the values in the Data − Mean column will not always be exactly zero; however, the sum will be very close to zero.)

Next square the values in the second column and place the squares in the third column (Table 13.5).

Table 13.5

Data	Data − Mean	(Data − Mean)^2
7	−5	$(-5)^2 = (-5)(-5) = 25$
9	−3	$(-3)^2 = (-3)(-3) = 9$
11	−1	$(-1)^2 = (-1)(-1) = 1$
12	0	$(0)^2 = (0)(0) = 0$
15	3	$(3)^2 = (3)(3) = 9$
18	6	$(6)^2 = (6)(6) = 36$
	0	80

Add the squares in the third column. In this case, the sum is 80. Divide this sum by one less than the number of pieces of data $(n − 1)$. In this case, the number of pieces of data is 6. Therefore, we divide by 5 and get

$$\frac{80}{5} = 16*$$

Finally, take the square root of this number. Since $\sqrt{16} = 4$, the standard deviation, symbolized s, is 4.   ●

Now we will develop a formula for determining the standard deviation of a set of data. If we call the individual data x and the mean $\bar{x}$, we could write the three column heads Data, Data − Mean, and (Data − Mean)^2 in Table 13.4 as

$$x \qquad x - \bar{x} \qquad (x - \bar{x})^2$$

Let's follow the procedure we used to obtain the standard deviation in Example 2. We found the sum of the (Data − Mean)^2 column, which is the same as the sum of the $(x - \bar{x})^2$ column. We can represent the sum of the $(x - \bar{x})^2$ column by using the summation notation, $\Sigma(x - \bar{x})^2$. Thus, in Table 13.5, $\Sigma(x - \bar{x})^2 = 80$. We then divided this number by 1 less than the number of pieces of data, $n − 1$. Thus, we have

$$\frac{\Sigma(x - \bar{x})^2}{n - 1}$$

---

*16 is the variance, symbolized s^2, of this set of data.

Finally, we took the square root of this value to obtain the standard deviation.

> **Standard Deviation**
>
> $$s = \sqrt{\frac{\Sigma(x - \bar{x})^2}{n - 1}}$$

EXAMPLE ❸ *Determine the Standard Deviation of Stock Prices*

The following are the prices of nine stocks on the New York Stock Exchange. Determine the standard deviation of the prices.

$$\$17, \$28, \$32, \$36, \$50, \$52, \$66, \$74, \$104$$

SOLUTION The mean, $\bar{x}$, is

$$\bar{x} = \frac{\Sigma x}{n} = \frac{17 + 28 + 32 + 36 + 50 + 52 + 66 + 74 + 104}{9} = \frac{459}{9} = 51$$

The mean is $51.

Table 13.6

x	$x - \bar{x}$	$(x - \bar{x})^2$
17	-34	1156
28	-23	529
32	-19	361
36	-15	225
50	-1	1
52	1	1
66	15	225
74	23	529
104	53	2809
	0	5836

Table 13.6 shows us that $\Sigma(x - \bar{x})^2 = 5836$. Since there are nine pieces of data, $n - 1 = 9 - 1$, or 8.

$$s = \sqrt{\frac{\Sigma(x - \bar{x})^2}{n - 1}} = \sqrt{\frac{5836}{8}} = \sqrt{729.5} \approx 27.01$$

The standard deviation, to the nearest tenth, is $27.01. ●

Standard deviation will be used in Section 13.7 to find the percent of data between any two values in a normal curve. Standard deviations are also often used in determining norms for a population (see Exercise 31).

> **TECHNOLOGY TIP** In this Technology Tip, we will explain how to find the standard deviation using Excel as well as with the TI-83 Plus and TI-84 Plus graphing calculators. In our illustration, we will use the data from Example 3 on page 876, which represent the prices of nine stocks on the New York Stock Exchange.
>
> **EXCEL**
>
> The instructions used to determine the standard deviation are very similar to those used to determine the mean in the Technology Tip on pages 866–867 in Section 13.5. Please read that material now. Then enter the nine pieces of data in columns A1–A9 and press the Enter key. Now select the following:
>
> $$\text{Insert} > \text{Function} \ldots > \text{Statistical} > \text{STDEV}$$
>
> Then click the $\boxed{\text{OK}}$ box. The program will then generate a gray box where you need to enter the data. In the area to the right of **Number1** you need to enter the data for which you want to find the standard deviation. Since you have already entered the data in column A, rows 1 to 9, if A1:A9 is not already listed, you can enter A1:A9 in the area to the right of **Number1**. At the bottom of the gray box, *Formula Results* = 27.00925767, which is the standard deviation, is displayed. If you click OK, Excel will place the standard deviation in cell A10.
>
> **TI-83 PLUS AND TI-84 PLUS GRAPHING CALCULATORS**
>
> To find the standard deviation on Texas Instruments graphing calculators, follow the instructions for finding the mean in the Technology Tip on page 867 in Section 13.5. As explained there, press $\boxed{\text{STAT}}$ $\boxed{>}$ $\boxed{\text{EDIT}}$ $\boxed{>}$ $\boxed{\text{ENTER}}$. Remove existing data by highlighting **L1** and then pressing $\boxed{\text{CLEAR}}$ $\boxed{>}$ $\boxed{\text{ENTER}}$. Then enter the nine pieces of data, pressing the Enter key after each entry. Then press $\boxed{\text{STAT}}$ $\boxed{>}$ $\boxed{\text{CALC}}$ $\boxed{>}$ $\boxed{\text{ENTER}}$ $\boxed{>}$ $\boxed{\text{ENTER}}$. The fourth statistic down is $S_x = 27.00925767$. This value is the standard deviation.

SECTION 13.6 EXERCISES

CONCEPT/WRITING EXERCISES

1. Explain how to find the range of a set of data.

2. What does the standard deviation of a set of data measure?

3. Explain how to find the standard deviation of a set of data.

4. Why is measuring dispersion in observed data important?

5. What is the standard deviation of a set of data in which all the data values are the same? Explain.

6. What symbol is used to represent the sample standard deviation?

7. What symbol is used to represent the population standard deviation?

8. Can you think of any situations in which a large standard deviation may be desirable? Explain.

9. Can you think of any situations in which a small standard deviation may be desirable? Explain.

10. Without actually doing the calculations, decide which, if either, of the following two sets of data will have the greater standard deviation. Explain why.

    10, 13, 14, 15, 17, 21   16, 17, 17, 18, 18, 19

11. Without actually doing the calculations, decide which, if either, of the following two sets of data will have the greater standard deviation. Explain why.

    2, 4, 6, 8, 10   102, 104, 106, 108, 110

12. By studying the standard deviation formula, explain why the standard deviation of a set of data will always be greater than or equal to 0.

13. Patricia Wolff teaches two statistics classes, one in the morning and the other in the evening. On the midterm exam,

the morning class had a mean of 75.2 and a standard deviation of 5.7. The evening class had a mean of 75.2 and a standard deviation of 12.5.

a) How do the means compare?

b) If we compare the set of scores from the first class with those in the second class, how will the distributions of the two sets of scores compare? Explain.

14. Explain why the standard deviation is usually a better measure of dispersion than the range.

PRACTICE THE SKILLS

In Exercises 15–22, determine the range and standard deviation of the set of data. When appropriate, round standard deviations to the nearest hundredth.

15. 11, 9, 6, 12, 17

16. 15, 15, 19, 21, 13, 13

17. 130, 131, 132, 133, 134, 135, 136

18. 3, 7, 8, 12, 0, 9, 11, 12, 6, 2

19. 4, 8, 9, 11, 13, 15

20. 9, 9, 9, 9, 9, 9, 9

21. 7, 9, 7, 9, 9, 10, 12

22. 60, 58, 62, 67, 48, 51, 72, 70

23. *Toaster Ovens* Determine the range and standard deviation of the following prices of selected toaster ovens: $58, $58, $80, $75, $60, $75, $78, $48, $75, $53.

24. *Years until Retirement* Seven employees at a large company were asked the number of additional years they planned to work before retirement. Their responses were 10, 23, 28, 4, 1, 6, 12. Determine the range and standard deviation of the number of years.

25. *Fishing Poles* Determine the range and standard deviation of the following prices of selected fishing poles: $50, $120, $130, $60, $55, $75, $200, $110, $125, $175.

26. *Prescription Prices* The amount of money seven people spent on prescription medication in a year are as follows: $600, $100, $850, $350, $250, $140, $300. Determine the range and standard deviation of the amounts.

PROBLEM SOLVING

27. *Count Your Money* Six people were asked to determine the amount of money they were carrying, to the nearest dollar. The results were

$$\$32, \$60, \$14, \$25, \$5, \$68$$

a) Determine the range and standard deviation of the amounts.

b) Add $10 to each of the six amounts. How do you expect the range and standard deviation of the new set of data to change? Explain your answer.

c) Determine the range and standard deviation of the new set of data. Do the results agree with your answer to part (b)? If not, explain why.

28. a) *Adding to or Subtracting from Each Number* Pick any five numbers. Compute the mean and the standard deviation of this distribution.

b) Add 20 to each of the numbers in your original distribution and compute the mean and the standard deviation of this new distribution.

c) Subtract 5 from each number in your original distribution and compute the mean and standard deviation of this new distribution.

d) What conclusions can you draw about changes in the mean and the standard deviation when the same number is added to or subtracted from each piece of data in a distribution?

e) How will the mean and standard deviation of the numbers 8, 9, 10, 11, 12, 13, 14 differ from the mean and standard deviation of the numbers 648, 649, 650, 651, 652, 653, 654? Determine the mean and standard deviation of both sets of numbers.

29. a) *Multiplying Each Number* Pick any five numbers. Compute the mean and standard deviation of this distribution.

b) Multiply each number in your distribution by 3 and compute the mean and the standard deviation of this new distribution.

c) Multiply each number in your original distribution by 9 and compute the mean and the standard deviation of this new distribution.

d) What conclusions can you draw about changes in the mean and the standard deviation when each value in a distribution is multiplied by the same number?

e) The mean and standard deviation of the distribution 1, 3, 4, 4, 5, 7 are 4 and 2, respectively. Use the conclusion drawn in part (d) to determine the mean and standard deviation of the distribution

5, 15, 20, 20, 25, 35

30. *Waiting in Line* Consider the following illustrations of two bank-customer waiting systems.

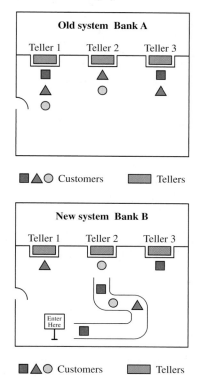

a) How would you expect the mean waiting time in Bank A to compare with the mean waiting time in Bank B? Explain your answer.

b) How would you expect the standard deviation of waiting times in Bank A to compare with the standard deviation of waiting times in Bank B? Explain your answer.

31. *Height and Weight Distribution* The chart shown on the right uses the symbol σ to represent the standard deviation. Note that 2σ represents the value that is two standard deviations above the mean; -2σ represents the value that is two standard deviations below the mean. The unshaded

areas, from two standard deviations below the mean to two standard deviations above the mean, are considered the normal range. For example, the average (mean) 8-year-old boy has a height of about 50 inches, but any heights between approximately 45 inches and 55 inches are considered normal for 8-year-old boys. Refer to the chart below to answer the following questions.

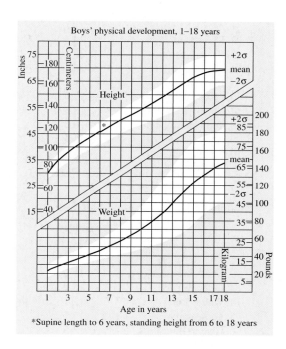

a) What happens to the standard deviation for weights of boys as the age of boys increases? What is the significance of this fact?

b) At age 16, what is the mean weight, in pounds, of boys?

c) What is the approximate standard deviation of boys' weights at age 16?

d) Determine the mean weight and normal range for boys at age 13.

e) Determine the mean height and normal range for boys at age 13.

f) Assuming that this chart was constructed so that approximately 95% of all boys are always in the normal range, determine what percentage of boys are not in the normal range.

CHALLENGE PROBLEMS/GROUP ACTIVITIES

32. *Athletes' Salaries* The following tables list the 10 highest-paid athletes in Major League Baseball and in the National Football League.

Major League Baseball (2006 Season)

Player	Salary (millions of dollars)
1. Alex Rodriguez	21.7
2. Derek Jeter	20.6
3. Jason Giambi	20.4
4. Jeff Bagwell	19.4
5. Barry Bonds	19.3
6. Mike Mussina	19.0
7. Manny Ramirez	18.3
8. Todd Helton	16.6
9. Andy Pettitte	16.4
10. Magglio Ordonez	16.2

Source: Major League Baseball Players Association

National Football League (2005 Season)

Player	Salary (millions of dollars)
1. Michael Vick	23.1
2. Matt Hasselbeck	19.0
3. Orlando Pace	18.0
4. Walter Jones	17.7
5. Tom Brady	15.7
6. Champ Bailey	13.5
7. Fred Smoot	12.3
8. Samari Rolle	12.0
9. Anthony Henry	11.6
10. Jonathan Ogden	10.7

Source: National Football League Players Association

a) Without doing any calculations, which do you believe is greater, the mean salary of the 10 baseball players or the mean salary of the 10 football players? Explain.

b) Without doing any calculations, which do you believe is greater, the standard deviation of the salary of the 10 baseball players or the standard deviation of the salary of the 10 football players? Explain.

c) Compute the mean salary of the 10 baseball players and the mean salary of the 10 football players and determine whether your answer in part (a) was correct.

d) Compute the standard deviation of the salary of the 10 baseball players and the standard deviation of the salary of the 10 football players and determine whether your answer in part (b) is correct. Round each mean to the nearest tenth to determine the standard deviation.

33. *Oil Change* Jiffy Lube has franchises in two different parts of the city. The number of oil changes made daily, for 25 days, is given below.

East Store					West Store				
33	59	27	30	42	38	46	38	38	30
19	42	25	22	32	38	38	37	39	31
43	27	57	37	52	39	36	40	37	47
40	67	38	44	43	30	34	42	45	29
15	31	49	41	35	31	46	28	45	48

a) Construct a frequency distribution for each store with a first class of 15–20.

b) Draw a histogram for each store.

c) Using the histogram, determine which store appears to have a greater mean, or do the means appear about the same? Explain.

d) Using the histogram, determine which store appears to have the greater standard deviation. Explain.

e) Calculate the mean for each store and determine whether your answer in part (c) was correct.

f) Calculate the standard deviation for each store and determine whether your answer in part (d) was correct.

RECREATIONAL MATHEMATICS

34. Calculate the range and standard deviation of your exam grades in this mathematics course. Round the mean to the nearest tenth to calculate the standard deviation.

35. Construct a set of five pieces of data with a mean, median, mode, and midrange of 6 and a standard deviation of 0.

INTERNET/RESEARCH ACTIVITY

36. Use a calculator with statistical function keys to find the mean and standard deviation of the salaries of the 10 Major League Baseball players and the 10 National Football League players in Exercise 32.

13.7 THE NORMAL CURVE

Suppose your mathematics teacher states that exam scores for the previous exam followed a bell-shaped distribution and that your score was 1.5 standard deviations above the mean. How does your exam grade compare with the exam grades of your classmates? What percent of students in your class had exam grades below your exam grade? In this section, we will discuss sets of data that form bell-shaped distributions and learn how to determine the percent of data that falls below a particular piece of data in the set of data.

▲ Some sets of data, such as exam grades, may form a bell-shaped distribution.

When examining data using a histogram, we can refer to the overall appearance of the histogram as the *shape* of the distribution of the data. Certain shapes of distributions of data are more common than others. In this section, we will illustrate and discuss a few of the more common ones. In each case, the vertical scale is the frequency and the horizontal scale is the observed values.

In a *rectangular distribution* (Fig. 13.17), all the observed values occur with the same frequency. If a die is rolled many times, we would expect the numbers 1–6 to occur with about the same frequency. The distribution representing the outcomes of the die is rectangular.

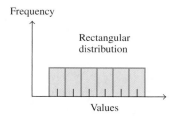

Figure 13.17

In *J-shaped distributions*, the frequency is either constantly increasing (Fig. 13.18a) or constantly decreasing (Fig. 13.18b). The number of hours studied per week by students may have a distribution like that in Fig. 13.18(b). The bars might represent (from left to right) 0–5 hours, 6–10 hours, 11–15 hours, and so on.

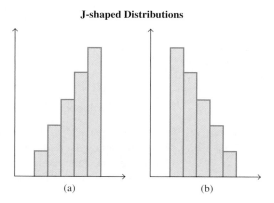

Figure 13.18

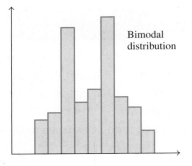

Figure 13.19

A *bimodal distribution* (Fig. 13.19) is one in which two nonadjacent values occur more frequently than any other values in a set of data. For example, if an equal number of men and women were weighed, the distribution of their weights would probably be bimodal, with one mode for the women's weights and the second for the men's weights. For a distribution to be considered bimodal, both modes need not have the same frequency but they must both have a frequency greater than the frequency of each of the other values in the distribution.

The life expectancy of lightbulbs has a bimodal distribution: a small peak very near 0 hours of life, resulting from the bulbs that burned out very quickly because of a manufacturing defect, and a much higher peak representing the nondefective bulbs. A bimodal frequency distribution generally means that you are dealing with two distinct populations, in this case, defective and nondefective lightbulbs.

Another distribution, called a *skewed distribution*, has more of a "tail" on one side than the other. A skewed distribution with a tail on the right (Fig. 13.20a) is said to be skewed to the right. If the tail is on the left (Fig. 13.20b), the distribution is referred to as skewed to the left.

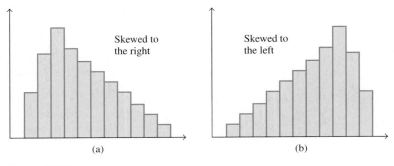

Figure 13.20

The number of children per family might be a distribution skewed to the right. Some families have no children, more families may have one child, the greatest percentage may have two children, fewer may have three children, still fewer may have four children, and so on.

Since few families have high incomes, distributions of family incomes might be skewed to the right.

Smoothing the histograms of the skewed distributions shown in Fig. 13.20 to form curves gives the curves illustrated in Fig. 13.21.

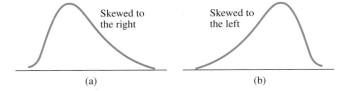

Figure 13.21

In Fig. 13.21(a), the greatest frequency appears on the left side of the curve and the frequency decreases from left to right. Since the mode is the value with the greatest frequency, the mode would appear on the left side of the curve.

Every value in the set of data is considered in determining the mean. The values on the far right side of the curve in Fig. 13.21(a) would tend to increase the value of the mean. Thus, the value of the mean would be farther to the right than the mode. The median

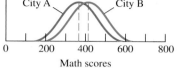
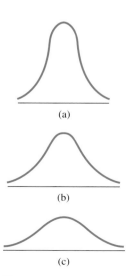

(a)

(b)

(c)

Figure 13.24

would be between the mode and the mean. The relationship between the mean, median, and mode for curves that are skewed to the right and left is given in Fig. 13.22.

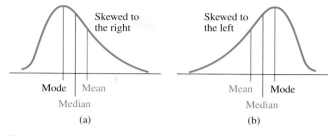

Skewed to the right

Skewed to the left

Mode | Mean
Median
(a)

Mean | Mode
Median
(b)

Figure 13.22

Normal Distributions

Each of these distributions is useful in describing sets of data. However, the most important distribution is the *normal* or *Gaussian distribution*, named for German mathematician Carl Friedrich Gauss. The histogram of a normal distribution is illustrated in Fig. 13.23.

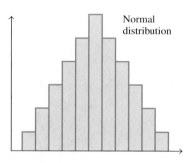

Normal distribution

Figure 13.23

The normal distribution is important because many sets of data are normally distributed or closely resemble a normal distribution. Such distributions include intelligence quotients, heights and weights of males, heights and weights of females, lengths of full-grown boa constrictors, weights of watermelons, wearout mileage of automobile brakes, and life spans of refrigerators, to name just a few.

The normal distribution is symmetric about the mean. If you were to fold the histogram of a normal distribution down the middle, the left side would fit the right side exactly. **In a normal distribution, the mean, median, and mode all have the same value.**

When the histogram of a normal distribution is smoothed to form a curve, the curve is bell-shaped. The bell may be high and narrow or short and wide. Each of the three curves in Fig. 13.24 represents a normal curve. Curve 13.24(a) has the smallest standard deviation (spread from the mean); curve 13.24(c) has the largest.

When we work with a distribution, we are working with an entire population. Therefore, when we discuss the normal distribution, we use μ for the mean and σ for the standard deviation.

Since the curve representing the normal distribution is symmetric, 50% of the data always falls above (to the right of) the mean and 50% of the data falls below (to the left of) the mean. In addition, every normal distribution has approximately 68% of the data between the value that is one standard deviation below the mean, $\mu - 1\sigma$, and the value that is one standard deviation above the mean, $\mu + 1\sigma$; see Fig. 13.25 on page 884.

Approximately 95% of the data falls between the value that is two standard deviations below the mean, $\mu - 2\sigma$, and the value that is two standard deviations above the mean, $\mu + 2\sigma$. Approximately 99.7% of the data falls between the value that is three standard deviations below the mean, $\mu - 3\sigma$, and the value that is three standard deviations above the mean, $\mu + 3\sigma$. These three percentages, 68%, 95%, and 99.7% are used in what is referred to as the Empirical Rule.

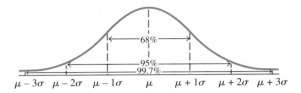

Figure 13.25

Thus, if a normal distribution has a mean of 100 and a standard deviation of 10, then approximately 68% of all the data falls between $100 - 10$ and $100 + 10$, or between 90 and 110. Approximately 95% of the data falls between $100 - 20$ and $100 + 20$, or between 80 and 120, and approximately 99.7% of the data falls between $100 - 30$ and $100 + 30$, or between 70 and 130.

The properties of a normal distribution are summarized as follows.

PROPERTIES OF A NORMAL DISTRIBUTION
- The graph of a normal distribution is called a normal curve.
- The normal curve is bell-shaped and symmetric about the mean.
- The mean, median, and mode of a normal distribution all have the same value and all occur at the center of the distribution.

EMPIRICAL RULE
In any normal distribution.

- Approximately 68% of all the data lies within one standard deviation of the mean (in both directions).
- Approximately 95% of all the data lies within two standard deviations of the mean (in both directions).
- Approximately 99.7% of all the data lies within three standard deviations of the mean (in both directions).

EXAMPLE ❶ *Applying the Empirical Rule*

Suppose that the weights of newborn infants are normally distributed. If approximately 2000 infants are born at Sarasota Memorial Hospital each year, determine the approximate number of infants who are expected to weigh

a) within one standard deviation of the mean.

b) within two standard deviations of the mean.

SOLUTION

a) By the empirical rule, about 68% of the infants weigh within one standard deviation of the mean. Since there are 2000 infants, the number of infants expected to weigh within one standard deviation of the mean is

$$68\% \times 2000 = 0.68 \times 2000 = 1360$$

Therefore, about 1360 infants are expected to weigh within one standard deviation of the mean.

b) By the empirical rule, about 95% of the infants weigh within two standard deviations of the mean. Since there are 2000 infants, the number of infants expected to weigh within two standard deviations of the mean is

$$95\% \times 2000 = 0.95 \times 2000 = 1900$$

Therefore, about 1900 infants are expected to weigh within two standard deviations of the mean. ●

z-Scores

Now we turn our attention to z-scores. We use *z-scores* (or *standard scores*) to determine how far, in terms of standard deviations, a given score is from the mean of the distribution. For example, a score that has a z-value of 1.5 indicates the score is 1.5 standard deviations above the mean. The standard or z-score is calculated as follows.

> The formula for finding **z-scores** or standard scores is
>
> $$z = \frac{\text{value of the piece of data} - \text{mean}}{\text{standard deviation}}$$

If we let x represent the value of the given piece of data, μ represent the mean, and σ represent the standard deviation, we can symbolize the z-score formula as

$$z = \frac{x - \mu}{\sigma}$$

In this book, the notation z_x represents the z-score, or standard score, of the value x. For example, if a normal distribution has a mean of 86 with a standard deviation of 12, a score of 110 has a standard or z-score of

$$z_{110} = \frac{110 - 86}{12} = \frac{24}{12} = 2$$

Therefore, a value of 110 in this distribution has a z-score of 2. The score of 110 is two standard deviations above the mean.

Data below the mean will always have negative z-scores; data above the mean will always have positive z-scores. The mean will always have a z-score of 0.

EXAMPLE ❷ *Finding z-Scores*

A normal distribution has a mean of 100 and a standard deviation of 10. Determine z-scores for the following values.

a) 110   b) 115   c) 100   d) 84

SOLUTION

a)
$$z = \frac{\text{value} - \text{mean}}{\text{standard deviation}}$$

$$z_{110} = \frac{110 - 100}{10} = \frac{10}{10} = 1$$

A score of 110 is one standard deviation above the mean.

b)
$$z_{115} = \frac{115 - 100}{10} = \frac{15}{10} = 1.5$$

A score of 115 is 1.5 standard deviations above the mean.

c)
$$z_{100} = \frac{100 - 100}{10} = \frac{0}{10} = 0$$

The mean always has a z-score of 0.

d)
$$z_{84} = \frac{84 - 100}{10} = \frac{-16}{10} = -1.6$$

A score of 84 is 1.6 standard deviations below the mean.   ●

If we are given any normal distribution with a known mean and standard deviation, it is possible through the use of Table 13.7 on pages 888 and 889 (the z-table) to determine the percent of data between any two given values. The total area under any normal curve is 1.00. Table 13.7 will be used to determine the cumulative area under the normal curve that lies to the *left of a specified z-value*. We will use Table 13.7(a) when we wish to determine area to the left of a *negative z-value*, and we will use Table 13.7(b) when we wish to determine area to the left of a *positive z-value*.

Example 3 illustrates the procedure to follow when using Table 13.7 to determine the area under the normal curve. When you are determining the area under the normal curve, it is often helpful to draw a picture and shade the area to be determined.

⌐EXAMPLE ❸ *Determining the Area under the Normal Curve*

Determine the area under the normal curve
a) to the left of $z = -1.00$.
b) to the left of $z = 1.19$.
c) to the right of $z = 1.19$.
d) between $z = -1.62$ and $z = 2.57$.

SOLUTION
a) To determine the area under the normal curve to the left of $z = -1.00$, as illustrated in Fig. 13.26, we use Table 13.7(a) since we are looking for an area to the left of a negative z-score. In the upper-left corner of the table, we see the letter z. The column under z gives the units and the tenths value for z. To locate the hundredths value of z, we use the column headings to the right of z. In this case, the hundredths value of $z = -1.00$ is 0, so we use the first column labeled .00. To determine the area to the left of $z = -1.00$, we use the row labeled -1.0 and move to the column labeled .00. The table entry, .1587, is circled in blue. Therefore, the total area to the left of $z = -1.00$ is 0.1587.

b) To determine the area under the normal curve to the left of $z = 1.19$ (Fig. 13.27), we use Table 13.7(b) since we are looking for an area to the left of a positive z-score. We first look for 1.1 in the column under z. Since the hundredths value of $z = 1.19$ is 9, we move to the column labeled .09. Using the row labeled 1.1

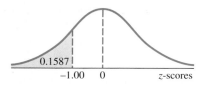

0.1587

−1.00   0   z-scores

Figure 13.26

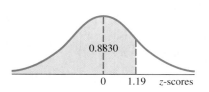

0.8830

0   1.19   z-scores

Figure 13.27

and the column labeled 0.09, the table entry is .8830, circled in pink. Therefore, the total area to the left of $z = 1.19$ is 0.8830.

c) To determine the area to the right of $z = 1.19$, we use the fact that the total area under the normal curve is 1. In part (b), we determined that the area to the left of $z = 1.19$ was 0.8830. To determine the area to the right of $z = 1.19$, we can subtract the area to the left of $z = 1.19$ from 1 (Fig. 13.28a). Therefore, the area to the right of $z = 1.19$ is $1 - 0.8830$, or 0.1170.

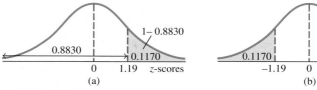

Figure 13.28

Another way to determine the area to the right of $z = 1.19$ is to use the fact that the normal curve is symmetric about the mean. Thus, the area to the left of a negative z-score is equal to the area to the right of a positive z-score. Therefore, the area to the left of $z = -1.19$ is equal to the area to the right of $z = 1.19$ (Fig. 13.28b). Using Table 13.7(a), we see that the area to the left of $z = -1.19$ is .1170. This value is circled in green in the table. Therefore, the area to the right of $z = 1.19$ is also .1170. This answer agrees with our answer obtained by subtracting the area to the left of $z = 1.19$ from 1.

d) To determine the area between two z-scores, we subtract the smaller area from the larger area (Fig. 13.29). Using Table 13.7(b), we see that the area to the left of $z = 2.57$ is .9949 (Fig. 13.29a). Using Table 13.7(a), we see that the area to the left of $z = -1.62$ is .0526 (Fig. 13.29b). Thus, the area between $z = -1.62$ and $z = 2.57$ is $0.9949 - 0.0526$, or 0.9423 (Fig. 13.29c).

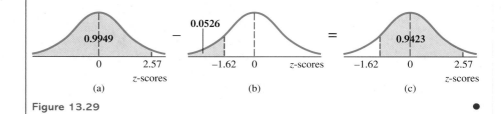

Figure 13.29

To change the area under the normal curve to a percent, multiply the area by 100%. In Example 3(a), we determined the area to the left of $z = -1.00$ to be 0.1587. To change this area to a percent, multiply 0.1587 by 100%.

$$0.1587 = 0.1587 \times 100\% = 15.87\%$$

Therefore 15.87% of the normal curve is less than a score that is one standard deviation below the mean.

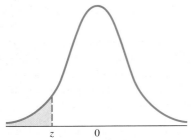

Table entry for z is the area to the left of z.

Table 13.7 Areas of a Standard Normal Distribution

(a) Table of Areas to the Left of z When z Is Negative

z	.00	.01	.02	.03	.04	.05	.06	.07	.08	.09
−3.4	.0003	.0003	.0003	.0003	.0003	.0003	.0003	.0003	.0003	.0002
−3.3	.0005	.0005	.0005	.0004	.0004	.0004	.0004	.0004	.0004	.0003
−3.2	.0007	.0007	.0006	.0006	.0006	.0006	.0006	.0005	.0005	.0005
−3.1	.0010	.0009	.0009	.0009	.0008	.0008	.0008	.0008	.0007	.0007
−3.0	.0013	.0013	.0013	.0012	.0012	.0011	.0011	.0011	.0010	.0010
−2.9	.0019	.0018	.0018	.0017	.0016	.0016	.0015	.0015	.0014	.0014
−2.8	.0026	.0025	.0024	.0023	.0023	.0022	.0021	.0021	.0020	.0019
−2.7	.0035	.0034	.0033	.0032	.0031	.0030	.0029	.0028	.0027	.0026
−2.6	.0047	.0045	.0044	.0043	.0041	.0040	.0039	.0038	.0037	.0036
−2.5	.0062	.0060	.0059	.0057	.0055	.0054	.0052	.0051	.0049	.0048
−2.4	.0082	.0080	.0078	.0075	.0073	.0071	.0069	.0068	.0066	.0064
−2.3	.0107	.0104	.0102	.0099	.0096	.0094	.0091	.0089	.0087	.0084
−2.2	.0139	.0136	.0132	.0129	.0125	.0122	.0119	.0116	.0113	.0110
−2.1	.0179	.0174	.0170	.0166	.0162	.0158	.0154	.0150	.0146	.0143
−2.0	.0228	.0222	.0217	.0212	.0207	.0202	.0197	.0192	.0188	.0183
−1.9	.0287	.0281	.0274	.0268	.0262	.0256	.0250	.0244	.0239	.0233
−1.8	.0359	.0351	.0344	.0336	.0329	.0322	.0314	.0307	.0301	.0294
−1.7	.0446	.0436	.0427	.0418	.0409	.0401	.0392	.0384	.0375	.0367
−1.6	.0548	.0537	.0526	.0516	.0505	.0495	.0485	.0475	.0465	.0455
−1.5	.0668	.0655	.0643	.0630	.0618	.0606	.0594	.0582	.0571	.0559
−1.4	.0808	.0793	.0778	.0764	.0749	.0735	.0721	.0708	.0694	.0681
−1.3	.0968	.0951	.0934	.0918	.0901	.0885	.0869	.0853	.0838	.0823
−1.2	.1151	.1131	.1112	.1093	.1075	.1056	.1038	.1020	.1003	.0985
−1.1	.1357	.1335	.1314	.1292	.1271	.1251	.1230	.1210	.1190	(.1170)
−1.0	(.1587)	.1562	.1539	.1515	.1492	.1469	.1446	.1423	.1401	.1379
−0.9	.1841	.1814	.1788	.1762	.1736	.1711	.1685	.1660	.1635	.1611
−0.8	.2119	.2090	.2061	.2033	.2005	.1977	.1949	.1922	.1894	.1867
−0.7	.2420	.2389	.2358	.2327	.2296	.2266	.2236	.2206	.2177	.2148
−0.6	.2743	.2709	.2676	.2643	.2611	.2578	.2546	.2514	.2483	.2451
−0.5	.3085	.3050	.3015	.2981	.2947	.2912	.2877	.2843	.2810	.2776
−0.4	.3446	.3409	.3372	.3336	.3300	.3264	.3228	.3192	.3156	.3121
−0.3	.3821	.3783	.3745	.3707	.3669	.3632	.3594	.3557	.3520	.3483
−0.2	.4207	.4168	.4129	.4090	.4052	.4013	.3974	.3936	.3897	.3859
−0.1	.4602	.4562	.4522	.4483	.4443	.4404	.4364	.4325	.4286	.4247
−0.0	.5000	.4960	.4920	.4880	.4840	.4801	.4761	.4721	.4681	.4641

For values of z less than −3.49, use 0.000 to approximate the area.

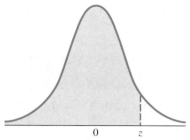

Table entry for z is the area to the left of z.

Areas of a Standard Normal Distribution (*continued*)

(b) Table of Areas to the Left of z When z Is Positive

z	.00	.01	.02	.03	.04	.05	.06	.07	.08	.09
0.0	.5000	.5040	.5080	.5120	.5160	.5199	.5239	.5279	.5319	.5359
0.1	.5398	.5438	.5478	.5517	.5557	.5596	.5636	.5675	.5714	.5753
0.2	.5793	.5832	.5871	.5910	.5948	.5987	.6026	.6064	.6103	.6141
0.3	.6179	.6217	.6255	.6293	.6331	.6368	.6406	.6443	.6480	.6517
0.4	.6554	.6591	.6628	.6664	.6700	.6736	.6772	.6808	.6844	.6879
0.5	.6915	.6950	.6985	.7019	.7054	.7088	.7123	.7157	.7190	.7224
0.6	.7257	.7291	.7324	.7357	.7389	.7422	.7454	.7486	.7517	.7549
0.7	.7580	.7611	.7642	.7673	.7704	.7734	.7764	.7794	.7823	.7852
0.8	.7881	.7910	.7939	.7967	.7995	.8023	.8051	.8078	.8106	.8133
0.9	.8159	.8186	.8212	.8238	.8264	.8289	.8315	.8340	.8365	.8389
1.0	.8413	.8438	.8461	.8485	.8508	.8531	.8554	.8577	.8599	.8621
1.1	.8643	.8665	.8686	.8708	.8729	.8749	.8770	.8790	.8810	.8830
1.2	.8849	.8869	.8888	.8907	.8925	.8944	.8962	.8980	.8997	.9015
1.3	.9032	.9049	.9066	.9082	.9099	.9115	.9131	.9147	.9162	.9177
1.4	.9192	.9207	.9222	.9236	.9251	.9265	.9279	.9292	.9306	.9319
1.5	.9332	.9345	.9357	.9370	.9382	.9394	.9406	.9418	.9429	.9441
1.6	.9452	.9463	.9474	.9484	.9495	.9505	.9515	.9525	.9535	.9545
1.7	.9554	.9564	.9573	.9582	.9591	.9599	.9608	.9616	.9625	.9633
1.8	.9641	.9649	.9656	.9664	.9671	.9678	.9686	.9693	.9699	.9706
1.9	.9713	.9719	.9726	.9732	.9738	.9744	.9750	.9756	.9761	.9767
2.0	.9772	.9778	.9783	.9788	.9793	.9798	.9803	.9808	.9812	.9817
2.1	.9821	.9826	.9830	.9834	.9838	.9842	.9846	.9850	.9854	.9857
2.2	.9861	.9864	.9868	.9871	.9875	.9878	.9881	.9884	.9887	.9890
2.3	.9893	.9896	.9898	.9901	.9904	.9906	.9909	.9911	.9913	.9916
2.4	.9918	.9920	.9922	.9925	.9927	.9929	.9931	.9932	.9934	.9936
2.5	.9938	.9940	.9941	.9943	.9945	.9946	.9948	.9949	.9951	.9952
2.6	.9953	.9955	.9956	.9957	.9959	.9960	.9961	.9962	.9963	.9964
2.7	.9965	.9966	.9967	.9968	.9969	.9970	.9971	.9972	.9973	.9974
2.8	.9974	.9975	.9976	.9977	.9977	.9978	.9979	.9979	.9980	.9981
2.9	.9981	.9982	.9982	.9983	.9984	.9984	.9985	.9985	.9986	.9986
3.0	.9987	.9987	.9987	.9988	.9988	.9989	.9989	.9989	.9990	.9990
3.1	.9990	.9991	.9991	.9991	.9992	.9992	.9992	.9992	.9993	.9993
3.2	.9993	.9993	.9994	.9994	.9994	.9994	.9994	.9995	.9995	.9995
3.3	.9995	.9995	.9995	.9996	.9996	.9996	.9996	.9996	.9996	.9997
3.4	.9997	.9997	.9997	.9997	.9997	.9997	.9997	.9997	.9997	.9998

For z values greater than 3.49, use 1.000 to approximate the area.

Below, we summarize the procedure to determine the percent of data for any interval under the normal curve.

TO DETERMINE THE PERCENT OF DATA BETWEEN ANY TWO VALUES

1. Draw a diagram of the normal curve, indicating the area or percent to be determined.

2. Use the formula $z = \dfrac{x - \mu}{\sigma}$ to convert the given values to z-scores. Indicate these z-scores on the diagram.

3. Look up the areas that correspond to the specified z-scores in Table 13.7.

   a) When determining the area to the left of a negative z-score, use Table 13.7(a).

   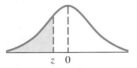

   b) When determining the area to the left of a positive z-score, use Table 13.7(b).

   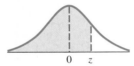

   c) When determining the area to the right of a z-score, subtract the percent of data to the left of the specified z-score from 100%.

   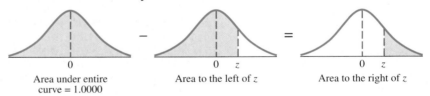

   Or, use the symmetry of a normal distribution.

   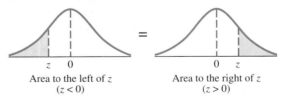

   d) When determining the area between two z-scores, subtract the smaller area from the larger area.

   In the figure below, we let z_1 represent the smaller z-score and z_2 represent the larger z-score.

   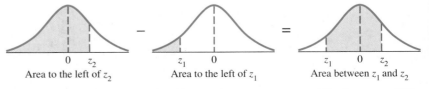

4. Change the areas you determined in step 3 to percents as explained on page 887.

EXAMPLE ❹ *IQ Scores*

Intelligence quotients (IQ scores) are normally distributed with a mean of 100 and a standard deviation of 15. Determine the percent of individuals with IQ scores

a) below 115.   b) below 130.

c) below 70.   d) between 70 and 115.

e) between 115 and 130.   f) above 122.5.

SOLUTION

a) We want to determine the area under the normal curve below the value of 115, as illustrated in Fig. 13.30(a). Converting 115 to a z-score yields a z-score of 1.00.

$$z_{115} = \frac{115 - 100}{15} = \frac{15}{15} = 1.00$$

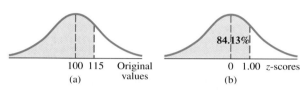

Figure 13.30

The percent of individuals with IQ scores below 115 is the same as the percent of data below a z-score of 1.00 (Fig. 13.30b). Since our z-score is positive, we use Table 13.7(b). From Table 13.7(b), we determine that the area to the left of a z-score of 1.00 is .8413. Therefore, 84.13% of all the IQ scores are below a z-score of 1.00. Thus, 84.13% of individuals have IQ scores below 115.

b) Begin by finding the z-score for 130.

$$z_{130} = \frac{130 - 100}{115} = \frac{30}{15} = 2.00$$

The percent of data below a z-score of 130 is the same as the percent of data below a z-score of 2.00 (Fig. 13.31). Using Table 13.7(b), we determine that the area to the left of a z-score of 2.00 is .9772. Therefore, 97.72% of the IQ scores are below a z-score of 2.00. Thus, 97.72% of all individuals have IQ scores below 130.

c) Begin by finding the z-score for 70.

$$z_{70} = \frac{70 - 100}{15} = \frac{-30}{15} = -2.00$$

The percent of data below a score of 70 is the same as the percent of data below a z-score of -2.00 (Fig. 13.32). Since our z-score is negative, we use Table 13.7(a). Using the table, we determine that the area to the left of $z = -2.00$ is .0228. Therefore, 2.28% of the data is below a z-score of -2.00. Thus, 2.28% of all individuals have IQ scores below 70.

d) In part (a), we determined that $z_{115} = 1.00$, and in part (c), we determined that $z_{70} = -2.00$. The percent of data below a z-score of 1.00 is 84.13% (Fig. 13.33a on page 892). The percent of data below a z-score of -2.00 is 2.28% (Fig. 13.33b). Since we want to find the percent of data between two z-scores, we subtract the smaller percent from the larger percent: $84.13\% - 2.28\% = 81.85\%$ (Fig. 13.33c). Thus, 81.85% of all individuals have IQ scores between 70 and 115.

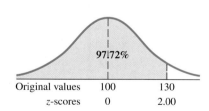

Figure 13.31

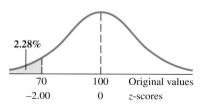

Figure 13.32

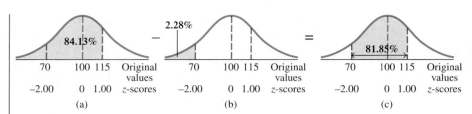

Figure 13.33

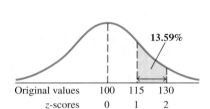

Figure 13.34

e) In part (a), we determined that $z_{115} = 1.00$, and in part (b), we determined $z_{130} = 2.00$. The percent of data below a z-score of 1.00 is 84.13%. The percent of data below a z-score of 2.00 is 97.72%. Since we want to find the percent of data between two z-scores, we subtract the smaller percent from the larger percent: $97.72\% - 84.13\% = 13.59\%$ (Fig. 13.34). Thus, 13.59% of all individuals have IQ scores between 115 and 130.

f) Begin by determining a z-score for 122.5.

$$z_{122.5} = \frac{122.5 - 100}{15} = \frac{22.5}{15} = 1.50$$

The percent of IQ scores above 122.5 is the same as the percent of data above $z = 1.50$ (Fig. 13.35). To determine the percent of data above $z = 1.50$, we can determine the percent of data below $z = 1.50$ and subtract this percent from 100%. In Table 13.7(b), we see that the area to the left of $z = 1.50$ is .9332. Therefore, 93.32% of the IQ scores are below $z = 1.50$. The percent of IQ scores above $z = 1.50$ are $100\% - 93.32\%$, or 6.68%. Thus, 6.68% of all IQ scores are greater than 122.5.

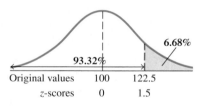

Figure 13.35

─**EXAMPLE ❺** *Horseback Rides*

Assume that the length of time for a horseback ride on the trail at Triple R Ranch is normally distributed with a mean of 3.2 hours and a standard deviation of 0.4 hour.

a) What percent of horseback rides last at least 3.2 hours?
b) What percent of horseback rides last less than 2.8 hours?
c) What percent of horseback rides are at least 3.7 hours?
d) What percent of horseback rides are between 2.8 hours and 4.0 hours?
e) In a random sample of 500 horseback rides at Triple R Ranch, how many are at least 3.7 hours?

SOLUTION

a) In a normal distribution, half the data are always above the mean. Since 3.2 hours is the mean, half, or 50%, of the horseback rides last at least 3.2 hours.
b) Convert 2.8 hours to a z-score.

$$z_{2.8} = \frac{2.8 - 3.2}{0.4} = -1.00$$

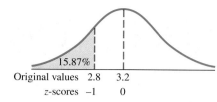

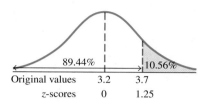

Figure 13.36

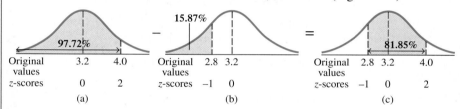

Figure 13.37

Use Table 13.7(a) to find the area of the normal curve that lies below a z-score of -1.00. The area to the left of $z = -1.00$ is 0.1587. Therefore, the percent of horseback rides that last less than 2.8 hours is 15.87% (Fig. 13.36).

c) At least 3.7 hours means greater than or equal to 3.7 hours. Therefore, we are seeking to find the percent of data to the right of 3.7 hours. Convert 3.7 hours to a z-score.

$$z_{3.7} = \frac{3.7 - 3.2}{0.4} = 1.25$$

From Table 13.7(b), we determine that the area to the left of $z = 1.25$ is .8944. Therefore, 89.44% of the data are below $z = 1.25$. The percent of data above $z = 1.25$ (or to the right of $z = 1.25$) is 100% $-$ 89.44%, or 10.56% (Fig. 13.37). Thus, 10.56% of horseback rides last at least 3.7 hours.

d) Convert 4.0 to a z-score.

$$z_{4.0} = \frac{4.0 - 3.2}{0.4} = 2.00$$

From Table 13.7(b), we determine that the area to the left of $z = 2.00$ is .9772 (Fig. 13.38a). Therefore the percent of data below a z-score of 2.00 is 97.72%. From part (b), we determined that $z_{28} = -1.00$ and that the percent of data below a z-score of -1.00 is 15.87% (Fig. 13.38b). To find the percent of data between a z-score of -1.00 and a z-score of 2.00, we subtract the smaller percent from the larger percent. Thus, the percent of horseback rides that last between 2.8 hours and 4.0 hours is 97.72% $-$ 15.87%, or 81.85% (Fig. 13.38c).

Figure 13.38

e) In part (c), we determined that 10.56% of all horseback rides last at least 3.7 hours. We now multiply 0.1056 times the number in the random sample, 500, to determine the number of horseback rides that last at least 3.7 hours. There are 0.1056 $\times$ 500 = 52.8, or approximately 53, horseback rides that last at least 3.7 hours. ●

TIMELY TIP Following is a summary of some important items presented in this section.

• The normal curve is symmetric about the mean.

• The area under the normal curve cannot be negative.

• A negative z-score indicates that the corresponding value in the original distribution is less than the mean.

• A positive z-score indicates that the corresponding value in the original distribution is greater than the mean.

• A z-score of 0 indicates that the corresponding value in the original distribution is the mean.

• Table 13.7 provides the area to the left of a specified z-score.

• When using Table 13.7 to determine the area to the left of a specified z-score, locate the units value and tenths value of your specified z-score under the column labeled z. Then move to the column containing the hundredths value of your specified z-score to obtain the area.

SECTION 13.7 EXERCISES

CONCEPT/WRITING EXERCISES

In Exercises 1–6, describe a

1. rectangular distribution.

2. J-shaped distribution.

3. bimodal distribution.

4. distribution that is skewed to the right.

5. distribution that is skewed to the left.

6. normal distribution.

7. What does a *z*-score measure?

8. Explain how to determine a *z*-score of a particular piece of data.

9. a) If a given piece of data has a negative *z*-score, is the given piece of data above the mean or below the mean?

   b) If a given piece of data has a positive *z*-score, is the given piece of data above the mean or below the mean?

10. What is the *z*-score of a value that is the mean of a set of data?

11. Consider the following normal curve, representing a normal distribution, with points *A*, *B*, and *C*. One of these points corresponds to μ, one point corresponds to $\mu + \sigma$, and one point corresponds to $\mu - 2\sigma$.

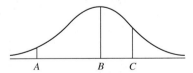

   a) Which point corresponds to μ?

   b) Which point corresponds to $\mu + \sigma$?

   c) Which point corresponds to $\mu - 2\sigma$?

12. Consider the following two normal curves.

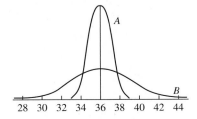

   a) Do these distributions have the same mean? If so, what is the mean?

   b) One of these curves corresponds to a normal distribution with $\sigma = 1$. The other curve corresponds to a normal distribution with $\sigma = 3$. Which curve, *A* or *B*, has $\sigma = 3$? Explain.

In Exercises 13–16, give an example of the type of distribution.

13. Rectangular

14. Skewed

15. J-shaped

16. Bimodal

For the distributions in Exercises 17–20, state whether you think the distribution would be normal, J-shaped, bimodal, rectangular, skewed left, or skewed right. Explain your answers.

17. The wearout mileage of automobile tires

18. The numbers resulting from tossing a die many times

19. The number of people per household in the United States

20. The heights of a sample of high school seniors, where there are an equal number of males and females

21. In a distribution that is skewed to the right, which has the greatest value: the mean, median, or mode? Which has the smallest value? Explain.

22. In a distribution skewed to the left, which has the greatest value: the mean, median, or mode? Which has the smallest value? Explain.

23. List three populations other than those given in the text that may be normally distributed.

24. List three populations other than those given in the text that may not be normally distributed.

25. In a normal distribution, what is the relationship between the mean, median, and mode?

26. In a normal distribution, approximately what percent of the data is between

    a) one standard deviation below the mean to one standard deviation above the mean?

    b) two standard deviations below the mean to two standard deviations above the mean?

    c) three standard deviations below the mean to three standard deviations above the mean?

PRACTICE THE SKILLS

In Exercises 27–38, use Table 13.7 on pages 888 and 889 to find the specified area.

27. Above the mean   **28.** Below the mean

29. Between two standard deviations below the mean and one standard deviation above the mean

30. Between 1.10 and 1.70 standard deviations above the mean

31. To the right of $z = 1.34$ **32.** To the left of $z = 1.62$

33. To the left of $z = -1.78$ **34.** To the right of $z = -1.78$

35. Between $z = -1.32$ and $z = -1.64$

36. To the left of $z = 1.84$

37. To the left of $z = -1.62$

38. To the left of $z = -0.92$

In Exercises 39–48, use Table 13.7 on pages 888 and 889 to determine the percent of data specified.

39. Less than $z = 0.71$ **40.** Less than $z = -0.82$

41. Between $z = -1.34$ and $z = 2.24$

42. Between $z = -2.18$ and $z = -1.90$

43. Greater than $z = -1.90$

44. Greater than $z = 2.66$

45. Less than $z = 1.96$

46. Between $z = -1.53$ and $z = -1.82$

47. Between $z = 0.72$ and $z = 2.14$

48. Between $z = -2.15$ and $z = 3.31$

PROBLEM SOLVING

Fitness Test Scores In Exercises 49 and 50, assume that the heights of 7-year-old children are normally distributed. The heights of 8 children are given in z-scores below.

Emily	0.9	Jason	0.0	Heather	−1.3	Juan	0.0
Sarah	1.7	Omar	−0.2	Carol	0.8	Kim	−1.2

49. a) Which of these children are taller than the mean?

    b) Which of these children are at the mean?

    c) Which of these children are shorter than the mean?

50. a) Which child is the tallest?

    b) Which child is the shortest?

Hours Worked by College Students In Exercises 51–54, assume that the number of hours college students spend working per week is normally distributed with a mean of 18 hours and standard deviation of 4 hours.

51. Determine the percent of college students who work at least 18 hours per week.

52. Determine the percent of college students who work between 14 and 26 hours per week.

53. Determine the percent of college students who work at least 23 hours per week.

54. In a random sample of 500 college students, how many work at least 23 hours per week?

SAT Scores In Exercises 55–60, assume that the mathematics scores on the Scholastic Aptitude Test (SAT) are normally distributed with a mean of 500 and a standard deviation of 100.

55. What percent of students who took the test have a mathematics score below 550?

56. What percent of students who took the test have a mathematics score above 650?

57. What percent of students who took the test have a mathematics score between 550 and 650?

58. What percent of students who took the test have a mathematics score below 300?

59. What percent of students who took the test have a mathematics score between 400 and 525?

60. What percent of students who took the test have a mathematics score above 380?

Vending Machine In Exercises 61–64, a vending machine is designed to dispense a mean of 7.6 oz of coffee into an 8 oz cup. If the standard deviation of the amount of coffee dispensed is 0.4 oz and the amount is normally distributed, find the percent of times the machine will

61. dispense from 7.4 oz to 7.7 oz.

62. dispense less than 7.0 oz.

63. dispense less than 7.7 oz.

64. result in the cup overflowing (therefore dispense more than 8 oz).

Automobile Speed In Exercises 65–70, assume that the speed of automobiles on an expressway during rush hour is normally distributed with a mean of 62 mph and a standard deviation of 5 mph.

65. What percent of cars are traveling faster than 62 mph?

66. What percent of cars are traveling between 58 mph and 66 mph?

67. What percent of cars are traveling slower than 56 mph?

68. What percent of cars are traveling faster than 70 mph?

69. If 200 cars are selected at random, how many will be traveling slower than 56 mph?

70. If 200 cars are selected at random, how many will be traveling faster than 70 mph?

Corn Flakes In Exercises 71–74, assume that the amount of corn flakes in a box is normally distributed with a mean of 16 oz and a standard deviation of 0.1 oz.

71. Determine the percent of boxes that will contain between 15.83 oz and 16.32 oz of corn flakes.

72. Determine the percent of boxes that will contain more than 16.16 oz of corn flakes.

73. If the manufacturer produces 300,000 boxes, how many of them will contain less than 15.83 oz of corn flakes?

74. If the manufacturer produces 300,000 boxes, how many of them will contain more than 16.16 oz of corn flakes?

Ages of Children at Day Care In Exercises 75–80, assume that the ages of children at Happy Times Day Care are normally distributed with a mean of 3.7 years and a standard deviation of 1.2 years.

75. What percent of the children are older than 3.1 years?

76. What percent of the children are between 2.5 and 4.3 years?

77. What percent of the children are older than 6.7 years?

78. What percent of the children are younger than 6.7 years?

79. If 120 children are enrolled at Happy Times Day Care, how many of them are older than 3.1 years?

80. If 120 children are enrolled at Happy Times Day Care, how many of them are between 2.5 and 4.3 years?

81. *Weight Loss* A weight-loss clinic guarantees that its new customers will lose at least 5 lb by the end of their first month of participation or their money will be refunded. If the weight loss of customers at the end of their first month is normally distributed, with a mean of 6.7 lb and a standard deviation of 0.81 lb, determine the percent of customers who will be able to claim a refund.

82. *Battery Warranty* The warranty on a car battery is 36 months. If the breakdown times of this battery are normally distributed with a mean of 46 months and a standard deviation of 8 months, determine the percent of batteries that can be expected to require repair or replacement under warranty.

83. *Coffee Machine* A vending machine that dispenses coffee does not appear to be working correctly. The machine rarely gives the proper amount of coffee. Some of the time the cup is underfilled, and some of the time the cup overflows. Does this variation indicate that the mean number of ounces dispensed has to be adjusted, or does it indicate that the standard deviation of the amount of coffee dispensed by the machine is too large? Explain your answer.

84. *Grading on a Normal Curve* Mr. Sanderson marks his class on a normal curve. Those with z-scores above 1.8 will receive an A, those between 1.8 and 1.1 will receive a B, those between 1.1 and −1.2 will receive a C, those between −1.2 and −1.9 will receive a D, and those under −1.9 will receive an F. Determine the percent of grades that will be A, B, C, D, and F.

▲ See Exercise 84

CHALLENGE PROBLEMS/GROUP ACTIVITIES

85. **Salesperson Promotion** The owner at Kim's Home Interiors is reviewing the sales records of two managers who are up for promotion, Katie and Stella, who work in different stores. At Katie's store, the mean sales have been $23,200 per month, with a standard deviation of $2170. At Stella's store, the mean sales have been $25,600 per month, with a standard deviation of $2300. Last month, Katie's store sales were $28,408 and Stella's store sales were $29,510. At both stores, the distribution of monthly sales is normal.

a) Convert last month's sales for Katie's store and for Stella's store to z-scores.

b) If one of the two were to be promoted based solely on the increase in sales last month, who should be promoted? Explain.

86. **Chebyshev's Theorem** How can you determine whether a distribution is approximately normal? A statistical theorem called *Chebyshev's theorem* states that the *minimum percent* of data between plus and minus K standard deviations from the mean ($K > 1$) in *any distribution* can be found by the formula

$$\text{Minimum percent} = 1 - \frac{1}{K^2}$$

Thus, for example, between ±2 standard deviations from the mean there will always be a minimum of 75% of data. This minimum percent applies to any distribution. For $K = 2$,

$$\text{Minimum percent} = 1 - \frac{1}{2^2}$$
$$= 1 - \frac{1}{4} = \frac{3}{4}, \quad \text{or} \quad 75\%$$

Likewise, between ±3 standard deviations from the mean there will always be a minimum of 89% of the data. For $K = 3$,

$$\text{Minimum percent} = 1 - \frac{1}{3^2}$$
$$= 1 - \frac{1}{9} = \frac{8}{9}, \quad \text{or} \quad 89\%$$

The following table lists the minimum percent of data in *any distribution* and the actual percent of data in *the normal distribution* between ±1.1, ±1.5, ±2.0, and ±2.5 standard deviations from the mean. The minimum percents of data in any distribution were calculated by using Chebyshev's theorem. The actual percents of data for the normal distribution were calculated by using the area given in the standard normal, or z, table.

	$K = 1.1$	$K = 1.5$	$K = 2$	$K = 2.5$
Minimum (for any distribution)	17.4%	55.6%	75%	84%
Normal distribution	72.9%	86.6%	95.4%	98.8%
Given distribution				

The third row of the chart has been left blank for you to fill in the percents when you reach part (e).

Consider the following 30 pieces of data obtained from a quiz.

1, 1, 1, 1, 2, 2, 2, 2, 3, 3, 4, 4, 4, 5, 6,
6, 6, 7, 7, 7, 7, 8, 8, 8, 8, 9, 9, 9, 10, 10

a) Determine the mean of the set of scores.

b) Determine the standard deviation of the set of scores.

c) Determine the values that correspond to 1.1, 1.5, 2, and 2.5 standard deviations above the mean. (For example, the value that corresponds to 1.5 standard deviations above the mean is $\mu + 1.5\sigma$.)

Then determine the values that correspond to 1.1, 1.5, 2, and 2.5 standard deviations below the mean. (For example, the value that corresponds to 1.5 standard deviations below the mean is $\mu - 1.5\sigma$.)

d) By observing the 30 pieces of data, determine the actual percent of quiz scores between

±1.1 standard deviations from the mean.

±1.5 standard deviations from the mean.

±2 standard deviations from the mean.

±2.5 standard deviations from the mean.

e) Place the percents found in part (d) in the third row of the chart.

f) Compare the percents in the third row of the chart with the minimum percents in the first row and the normal percents in the second row, and then make a judgment as to whether this set of 30 scores is approximately normally distributed. Explain your answer.

87. **Test Scores** Obtain a set of test scores from your instructor.

   a) Determine the mean, median, mode, and midrange of the test scores.

   b) Determine the range and standard deviation of the set of scores. (You may round the mean to the nearest tenth when finding the standard deviation.)

   c) Construct a frequency distribution of the set of scores. Select your first class so that there will be between 5 and 12 classes.

   d) Construct a histogram and frequency polygon of the frequency distribution in part (c).

   e) Does the histogram in part (d) appear to represent a normal distribution? Explain.

   f) Use the procedure explained in Exercise 86 to determine whether the set of scores approximates a normal distribution. Explain.

88. Determine a value of z such that $z \geq 0$ and 47.5% of the standard normal curve lies between 0 and the z-value.

89. Determine a value of z such that $z \leq 0$ and 38.1% of the standard normal curve lies between 0 and the z-value.

RECREATIONAL MATHEMATICS

90. Ask your instructor for the class mean and class standard deviation for one of the exams taken by your class. For that exam, calculate the z-score for your exam grade. How many standard deviations is your exam grade away from the mean?

91. If the mean score on a math quiz is 12.0 and 77% of the students in your class scored between 9.6 and 14.4, determine the standard deviation of the quiz scores.

INTERNET/RESEARCH ACTIVITY

92. In this project, you actually become the statistician.

   a) Select a project of interest to you in which data must be collected.

   b) Write a proposal and submit it to your instructor for approval. In the proposal, discuss the aims of your project and how you plan to gather the data to make your sample unbiased.

   c) After your proposal has been approved, gather 50 pieces of data by the method you proposed.

   d) Rank the data from smallest to largest.

   e) Compute the mean, median, mode, and midrange.

   f) Determine the range and standard deviation of the data. You may round the mean to the nearest tenth when computing the standard deviation.

   g) Construct a frequency distribution, histogram, frequency polygon, and stem-and-leaf display of your data. Select your first class so that there will be between 5 and 12 classes. Be sure to label your histogram and frequency polygon.

   h) Does your distribution appear to be normal? Explain your answer. Does it appear to be another type of distribution discussed? Explain.

   i) Determine whether your distribution is approximately normal by using the technique discussed in Exercise 86.

13.8 LINEAR CORRELATION AND REGRESSION

▲ You can predict the value of a car based on the age of the car.

Do you believe that there is a relationship between the time a person studied for an exam and the exam grade received? Is there a relationship between the age of a car and the value of the car? Can we predict the value of a car based on the age of the car? In this section, we will learn how to determine whether there is a relationship between two quantities and, if so, how strong that relationship is. We will also learn how to determine the equation of the line that best describes the relationship between two quantities.

In this section, we discuss two important statistical topics: correlation and regression. *Correlation* is used to determine whether there is a relationship between two quantities and, if so, how strong the relationship is. *Regression* is used to determine the equation that relates the two quantities. Although there are other types of correlation and regression, in this section we discuss only linear correlation and linear regression. We begin by discussing linear correlation.

Linear Correlation

The *linear correlation coefficient*, r, is a unitless measure that describes the strength of the linear relationship between two variables. A positive value of r, or a positive correlation, means that as one variable increases, the other variable also increases. A negative value of r, or a negative correlation, means that as one variable increases, the other variable decreases. The correlation coefficient, r, will always be a value between -1 and 1 inclusive. A value of 1 indicates the strongest possible positive correlation, a value of -1 indicates the strongest possible negative correlation, and a value of 0 indicates no correlation (Fig. 13.39).

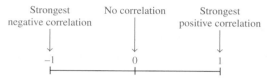

Figure 13.39

A visual aid used with correlation is the *scatter diagram*, a plot of data points. To help understand how to construct a scatter diagram, consider the following data from Egan Electronics. During a 6-day period, Egan Electronics kept daily records of the number of assembly line workers absent and the number of defective parts produced. The information is provided in the following chart.

Day	1	2	3	4	5	6
Number of workers absent	3	5	0	1	2	6
Number of defective parts	15	22	7	12	20	30

For each of the 6 days, two pieces of data are provided: number of workers absent and number of defective parts. We call the set of data *bivariate data*. Often when we have a set of bivariate data, we can control one of the quantities. We generally denote the quantity that can be controlled, the *independent variable*, x. The other variable, the *dependent variable*, is denoted as y. In this problem, we will assume that the number of defective parts produced is affected by the number of workers absent. Therefore, we will call the number of workers absent x and the number of defective parts produced y. When we plot bivariate data, the independent variable is marked on the horizontal axis and the dependent variable is marked on the vertical axis. Therefore, for this problem, number of workers absent is marked on the horizontal axis and number of defective parts is marked on the vertical axis. If we plot the six pieces of bivariate data in the Cartesian coordinate system, we get a scatter diagram, as shown in Fig. 13.40.

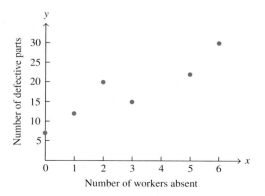

Figure 13.40

The figure shows that, generally, the more workers that are absent, the more defective parts are produced.

In Fig. 13.41, we show some scatter diagrams and indicate the corresponding strength of correlation between the quantities on the horizontal and vertical axes.

Earlier, we mentioned that r will always be a value between -1 and 1 inclusive. A value of $r = 1$ is obtained only when every point of the bivariate data on a scatter diagram lies in a straight line and the line is increasing from left to right (see Fig. 13.41a). In other words, the line has a positive slope, as discussed in Section 6.6.

A value of $r = -1$ will be obtained only when every point of the bivariate data on a scatter diagram lies in a straight line and the line is decreasing from left to right (see Fig. 13.41e). In other words, the line has a negative slope.

The value of r is a measure of how far a set of points varies from a straight line. The greater the spread, the weaker the correlation and the closer the value of r is to 0. Figure 13.41 shows that the more the points diverge from a straight line, the weaker the correlation becomes.

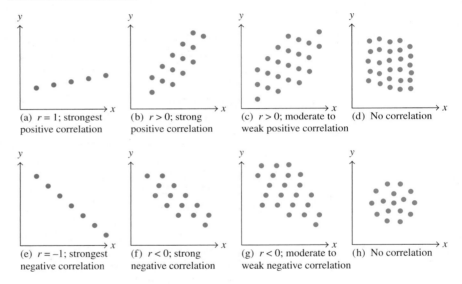

(a) $r = 1$; strongest positive correlation (b) $r > 0$; strong positive correlation (c) $r > 0$; moderate to weak positive correlation (d) No correlation

(e) $r = -1$; strongest negative correlation (f) $r < 0$; strong negative correlation (g) $r < 0$; moderate to weak negative correlation (h) No correlation

Figure 13.41

The following formula is used to calculate r.

LINEAR CORRELATION COEFFICIENT
The formula to calculate the **correlation coefficient, r,** is as follows.

$$r = \frac{n(\Sigma xy) - (\Sigma x)(\Sigma y)}{\sqrt{n(\Sigma x^2) - (\Sigma x)^2}\sqrt{n(\Sigma y^2) - (\Sigma y)^2}}$$

To determine the correlation coefficient, r, and the equation of the line of best fit (to be discussed shortly), a statistical calculator may be used. On the statistical calculator, you enter the ordered pairs, (x, y) and press the appropriate keys. At the end of this section, we indicate the procedure to follow to use the computer software spreadsheet program, Microsoft Excel, and the TI-83 Plus or the TI-84 Plus calculators to determine the correlation coefficient.

In Example 1, we show how to determine r for a set of bivariate data without the use of a statistical calculator. We will use the same set of bivariate data given on page 899 that was used to make the scatter diagram in Fig. 13.40.

EXAMPLE ❶ *Number of Absences versus Number of Defective Parts*

Egan Electronics provided the following daily records about the number of assembly line workers absent and the number of defective parts produced for 6 days. Determine the correlation coefficient between the number of workers absent and the number of defective parts produced.

Day		1	2	3	4	5	6
Number of workers absent		3	5	0	1	2	6
Number of defective parts		15	22	7	12	20	30

SOLUTION We plotted this set of data on the scatter diagram in Figure 13.40. We will call the number of workers absent x. We will call the number of defective parts produced y. We list the values of x and y and calculate the necessary sums: Σx, Σy, Σxy, Σx^2, Σy^2. We determine the values in the column labeled x^2 by squaring the x's (multiplying the x's by themselves). We determine the values in the column labeled y^2 by squaring the y's. We determine the values in the column labeled xy by multiplying each x value by its corresponding y value.

Number of Workers Absent	Number of Defective Parts			
x	y	x^2	y^2	xy
3	15	9	225	45
5	22	25	484	110
0	7	0	49	0
1	12	1	144	12
2	20	4	400	40
6	30	36	900	180
17	106	75	2202	387

Thus, $\Sigma x = 17$, $\Sigma y = 106$, $\Sigma x^2 = 75$, $\Sigma y^2 = 2202$, and $\Sigma xy = 387$. In the formula for r, we use both $(\Sigma x)^2$ and Σx^2. Note that $(\Sigma x)^2 = (17)^2 = 289$ and that $\Sigma x^2 = 75$. Similarly, $(\Sigma y)^2 = (106)^2 = 11{,}236$ and $\Sigma y^2 = 2202$.

The n in the formula represents the number of pieces of bivariate data. Here $n = 6$. Now let's determine r.

$$r = \frac{n(\Sigma xy) - (\Sigma x)(\Sigma y)}{\sqrt{n(\Sigma x^2) - (\Sigma x)^2}\sqrt{n(\Sigma y^2) - (\Sigma y)^2}}$$

$$= \frac{6(387) - (17)(106)}{\sqrt{6(75) - (17)^2}\sqrt{6(2202) - (106)^2}}$$

$$= \frac{2322 - 1802}{\sqrt{6(75) - 289}\sqrt{6(2202) - 11{,}236}}$$

$$= \frac{520}{\sqrt{450 - 289}\sqrt{13{,}212 - 11{,}236}}$$

$$= \frac{520}{\sqrt{161}\sqrt{1976}} \approx 0.922$$

Table 13.8 Correlation
Coefficient, r

n	$\alpha = 0.05$	$\alpha = 0.01$
4	0.950	0.990
5	0.878	0.959
6	0.811	0.917
7	0.754	0.875
8	0.707	0.834
9	0.666	0.798
10	0.632	0.765
11	0.602	0.735
12	0.576	0.708
13	0.553	0.684
14	0.532	0.661
15	0.514	0.641
16	0.497	0.623
17	0.482	0.606
18	0.468	0.590
19	0.456	0.575
20	0.444	0.561
22	0.423	0.537
27	0.381	0.487
32	0.349	0.449
37	0.325	0.418
42	0.304	0.393
47	0.288	0.372
52	0.273	0.354
62	0.250	0.325
72	0.232	0.302
82	0.217	0.283
92	0.205	0.267
102	0.195	0.254

The derivation of this table is beyond the scope of this text. It shows the critical values of the Pearson correlation coefficient.

Since the maximum possible value for r is 1.00, a correlation coefficient of 0.922 is a strong, positive correlation. This result implies that, generally, the more assembly line workers absent, the more defective parts produced. ●

In Example 1, had we found r to be a value greater than 1 or less than -1, it would have indicated that we had made an error. Also, from the scatter diagram, we should realize that r should be a positive value and not negative.

In Example 1, there appears to be a cause–effect relationship. That is, the more assembly line workers who are absent, the more defective parts are produced. *However, a correlation does not necessarily indicate a cause–effect relationship.* For example, there is a positive correlation between police officers' salaries and the cost of medical insurance over the past 10 years (both have increased), but that does not mean that the increase in police officers' salaries caused the increase in the cost of medical insurance.

Suppose in Example 1 that r had been 0.53. Would this value have indicated a correlation? What is the minimum value of r needed to assume that a correlation exists between the variables? To answer this question, we introduce the term *level of significance.* The *level of significance*, denoted α (alpha), is used to identify the cutoff between results attributed to chance and results attributed to an actual relationship between the two variables. Table 13.8 gives *critical values** (or cutoff values) that are sometimes used for determining whether two variables are related. The table indicates two different levels of significance: $\alpha = 0.05$ and $\alpha = 0.01$. A level of significance of 5%, written $\alpha = 0.05$, means that there is a 5% chance that, when you say the variables are related, they actually are *not* related. Similarly, a level of significance of 1%, or $\alpha = 0.01$, means that there is a 1% chance that, when you say the variables are related, they actually are *not* related. More complete critical value tables are available in statistics books.

To explain the use of the table, we use *absolute value,* symbolized $|\ |$. The absolute value of a nonzero number is the positive value of the number, and the absolute value of 0 is 0. Therefore,

$$|3| = 3, \qquad |-3| = 3, \qquad |5| = 5, \qquad |-5| = 5, \qquad \text{and} \qquad |0| = 0$$

If the absolute value of r, written $|r|$, is *greater than* the value given in the table under the specified α and appropriate sample size n, we assume that a correlation does exist between the variables. If $|r|$ is less than the table value, we assume that no correlation exists.

Returning to Example 1, if we want to determine whether there is a correlation at a 5% level of significance, we find the critical value (or cutoff value) that corresponds to $n = 6$ (there are 6 pieces of bivariate data) and $\alpha = 0.05$. The value to the right of $n = 6$ and under the $\alpha = 0.05$ column is the critical value 0.811. From the formula, we had obtained $r = 0.922$. Since $|0.922| > 0.811$, or $0.922 > 0.811$, we assume that a correlation between the variables exists.

Note in Table 13.8 that the larger the sample size, the smaller is the value of r needed for a significant correlation.

**EXAMPLE ② ** *Amount of Drug Remaining in the Bloodstream*

To test the length of time that an infection-fighting drug stays in a person's bloodstream, a doctor gives 300 milligrams of the drug to 10 patients, labeled 1–10 in the table on page 903. Once each hour, for 10 hours, one of the 10 patients is selected

*This table of values may be used only under certain conditions. If you take a statistics course, you will learn more about which critical values to use to determine whether a linear correlation exists.

at random and that person's blood is tested to determine the amount of the drug remaining in the bloodstream. The results are as follows.

Patient	1	2	3	4	5	6	7	8	9	10
Time (hr)	1	2	3	4	5	6	7	8	9	10
Drug remaining (mg)	250	230	200	210	140	120	210	100	90	85

Determine at a level of significance of 5% whether a correlation exists between the time elapsed and the amount of drug remaining.

SOLUTION Let time be represented by x and the amount of drug remaining by y. We first draw a scatter diagram (Fig. 13.42).

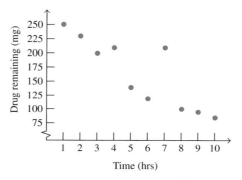

Figure 13.42

The scatter diagram suggests that, if a correlation exists, it will be negative. We now construct a table of values and calculate r.

x	y	x^2	y^2	xy
1	250	1	62,500	250
2	230	4	52,900	460
3	200	9	40,000	600
4	210	16	44,100	840
5	140	25	19,600	700
6	120	36	14,400	720
7	210	49	44,100	1470
8	100	64	10,000	800
9	90	81	8100	810
10	85	100	7225	850
55	1635	385	302,925	7500

$$r = \frac{n(\Sigma xy) - (\Sigma x)(\Sigma y)}{\sqrt{n(\Sigma x^2) - (\Sigma x)^2} \sqrt{n(\Sigma y^2) - (\Sigma y)^2}}$$

$$= \frac{10(7500) - (55)(1635)}{\sqrt{10(385) - (55)^2} \sqrt{10(302,925) - (1635)^2}}$$

$$= \frac{-14,925}{\sqrt{825}\sqrt{356,025}} \approx \frac{-14,925}{17,138.28} \approx -0.871$$

From Table 13.8, for $n = 10$ and $\alpha = 0.05$, we get 0.632. Since $|-0.871| = 0.871$ and $0.871 > 0.632$, a correlation exists. The correlation is negative, which indicates that the longer the time period, the smaller is the amount of drug remaining.   ●

Linear Regression

Let's now turn to regression. *Linear regression* is the process of determining the linear relationship between two variables. Recall from Section 6.6 that the slope–intercept form of a straight line is $y = mx + b$, where m is the slope and b is the y-intercept.

Using the set of bivariate data, we will determine the equation of *the line of best fit*. The line of best fit is also called *the regression line*, or *the least squares line*. The *line of best fit* is the line such that the sum of the squares of the vertical distances from the line to the data points (on the scatter diagram) is a minimum, as shown in Fig. 13.43. In Fig. 13.43, the line of best fit minimizes the sum of d_1 through d_8. To determine the equation of the line of best fit, $y = mx + b$,* we must find m and then b. The formulas for finding m and b are as follows.

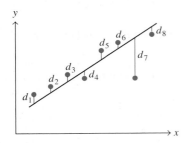

Figure 13.43

> **The equation of the line of best fit is**
> $$y = mx + b,$$
> where $\quad m = \dfrac{n(\Sigma xy) - (\Sigma x)(\Sigma y)}{n(\Sigma x^2) - (\Sigma x)^2} \quad$ and $\quad b = \dfrac{\Sigma y - m(\Sigma x)}{n}$

Note that the numerator of the fraction used to find m is identical to the numerator used to find r. Therefore, if you have previously found r, you do not need to repeat this calculation. Also, the denominator of the fraction used to find m is identical to the radicand of the first square root in the denominator of the fraction used to find r.

EXAMPLE ❸ *The Line of Best Fit*

a) Use the data in Example 1 on page 901 to find the equation of the line of best fit that relates the number of workers absent on an assembly line and the number of defective parts produced.

b) Graph the equation of the line of best fit on a scatter diagram that illustrates the set of bivariate points.

SOLUTION

a) In Example 1, we found $n(\Sigma xy) - (\Sigma x)(\Sigma y) = 520$ and $n(\Sigma x^2) - (\Sigma x)^2 = 161$. Thus,

$$m = \frac{n(\Sigma xy) - (\Sigma x)(\Sigma y)}{n(\Sigma x^2) - (\Sigma x)^2} = \frac{520}{161} \approx 3.23$$

---

*Some statistics books use $y = ax + b$, $y = b_0 + b_1 x$, or something similar for the equation of the line of best fit. In any case, the letter next to the variable x represents the slope of the line of best fit and the other letter represents the y-intercept of the graph.

Now we find the y-intercept, b. In Example 1, we found $n = 6$, $\Sigma x = 17$, and $\Sigma y = 106$.

$$b = \frac{\Sigma y - m(\Sigma x)}{n}$$

$$\approx \frac{106 - 3.23(17)}{6} \approx \frac{51.09}{6} \approx 8.52$$

Therefore, the equation of the line of best fit is

$$y = mx + b$$
$$y = 3.23x + 8.52$$

where x represents the number of workers absent and y represents the predicted number of defective parts produced.

b) To graph $y = 3.23x + 8.52$, we need to plot at least two points. We will plot three points and then draw the graph.

	$y = 3.23x + 8.52$	x	y
$x = 2$	$y = 3.23(2) + 8.52 = 14.98$	2	14.98
$x = 4$	$y = 3.23(4) + 8.52 = 21.44$	4	21.44
$x = 6$	$y = 3.23(6) + 8.52 = 27.90$	6	27.90

These three calculations indicate that if 2 assembly line workers are absent on the assembly line, the predicted number of defective parts produced is about 15. If 4 assembly line workers are absent, the predicted number of defective parts produced is about 21, and if 6 assembly line workers are absent, the predicted number of defective parts produced is about 28. Plot the three points (the three black points in Figure 13.44) and then draw a straight line through the three points. The scatter diagram and graph of the equation of the line of best fit are plotted in Fig. 13.44.

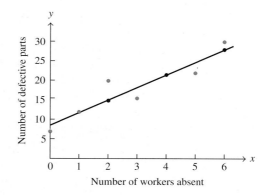

Figure 13.44

In Example 3, the line of best fit intersects the y-axis at 8.52, the value we determined for the y-intercept, b, in part (a).

EXAMPLE ❹ *Line of Best Fit for Example 2*

a) Determine the equation of the line of best fit between the time elapsed and the amount of drug remaining in a person's bloodstream in Example 2 on pages 902–904.

b) If the average person is given 300 mg of the drug, how much will remain in the person's bloodstream after 5 hr?

SOLUTION

a) From the scatter diagram on page 903, we see that the slope of the line of best fit, m, will be negative. In Example 2, we found that $n(\Sigma xy) - (\Sigma x)(\Sigma y) = -14{,}925$ and that $n(\Sigma x^2) - (\Sigma x)^2 = 825$. Thus,

$$m = \frac{n(\Sigma xy) - (\Sigma x)(\Sigma y)}{n(\Sigma x^2) - (\Sigma x)^2}$$

$$= \frac{-14{,}925}{825}$$

$$\approx -18.09$$

From Example 2, $n = 10$, $\Sigma x = 55$, and $\Sigma y = 1635$.

$$b = \frac{\Sigma y - m\Sigma x}{n}$$

$$= \frac{1635 - (-18.09)(55)}{10}$$

$$\approx 263.00$$

Thus, the equation of the line of best fit is

$$y = mx + b$$

$$y = -18.09x + 263.00$$

where x is the elapsed time and y is the amount of drug remaining.

b) We evaluate $y = -18.09x + 263.00$ at $x = 5$.

$$y = -18.09x + 263.00$$

$$y = -18.09(5) + 263.00 = 172.55$$

Thus, after 5 hr, about 173 mg of the drug remains in the average person's bloodstream.

TECHNOLOGY TIP We can use EXCEL and both the TI-83 Plus and the TI-84 Plus graphing calculators to determine the correlation coefficient, r, and the equation of the line of best fit. Below we use the data from Example 1 on page 901, where x represents the number of workers absent and y represents the number of defective parts for 6 selected days.

EXCEL

Begin by reading the Technology Tip on page 866. The instructions for determining the correlation coefficient and equation of the line of best fit are similar to the instructions given on page 866. In column A, rows 1 through 6, enter the 6 values representing the number of workers absent. In column B, rows 1 through 6, enter the 6 values that represent the number of defective parts. In general, the items listed on the horizontal axis in the scatter diagram (the independent variable if there is one) are placed in column A and the items listed on the vertical axis are placed in column B. Then select the following:

Insert > Function . . . > Statistical

Then to determine the value of the correlation coefficient, select **CORREL** and click OK . Excel will then generate a gray box and ask you for information about your data. In the box to the right of **Array1**, type in A1:A6, and in the box to the right of **Array2**, type in B1:B6. Then at the bottom of the box you will see *Formula results =* *.921927852*, which is the correlation coefficient. If you then wish to find the equation of the line of best fit, press CANCEL on the bottom of the gray box. Then select

Insert > Function . . . > Statistical > SLOPE > OK

Excel will then generate a gray box. In the box to the right of **Known_y's**, type in B1:B6. In the box to the right of **Known_x's**, type in A1:A6. At that point, at the bottom of the box you will see *Formula results = 3.229813665*, which is the slope of the equation of the line of best fit. To find the y-intercept, press cancel to remove the gray box. Then select

Insert > Function . . . > Statistical > INTERCEPT > OK

Excel will then generate a gray box. In the box to the right of **Known_y's**, type in B1:B6. In the box to the right of **Known_x's**, type in A1:A6. At that point, at the bottom of the box you will see *Formula results = 8.51552795*, which is the y-intercept of the equation of the line of best fit.

TI-83 PLUS AND TI-84 PLUS GRAPHING CALCULATORS
To determine the correlation coefficient and the equation of the line of best fit on a graphing calculator, press STAT . Then select Edit. If you have any data in **L1** or **L2**, delete the data by going to **L1** and pressing CLEAR and then ENTER . Follow a similar procedure to clear column **L2**. Now enter the 6 pieces of data representing the number of workers absent in column **L1** and enter the 6 pieces of data representing the number of defective parts in **L2**. Then press STAT and highlight **CALC**. At this point, **1: 1−Var Stats** should be highlighted. Scroll down to highlight **4: LinReg (ax+b)**. Then press the Enter key twice. You will get $r =$ *.921927852*, which represents the correlation coefficient. On the screen, you will also see values for a and b. Note that a represents the slope and b represents the y-intercept of the equation of the line of best fit. Thus, the slope is 3.229813665 and the y-intercept is 8.51552795.

SECTION 13.8 EXERCISES

CONCEPT/WRITING EXERCISES

1. What does the correlation coefficient measure?

2. What is the purpose of linear regression?

3. What value of r represents the maximum positive correlation?

4. What value of r represents the maximum negative correlation?

5. What value of r represents no correlation between the variables?

6. a) What does a negative correlation between two variables indicate?

   b) Give an example of two variables that have a negative correlation.

7. a) What does a positive correlation between two variables indicate?

b) Give an example of two variables that have a positive correlation.

8. What does the line of best fit represent?

9. What does the level of significance signify?

10. What is a scatter diagram?

In Exercises 11–14, indicate if you believe that a correlation exists between the quantities on the horizontal and vertical axis. If so, indicate if you believe that the correlation is a strong positive correlation, a strong negative correlation, a weak positive correlation, a weak negative correlation, or no correlation. Explain your answer.

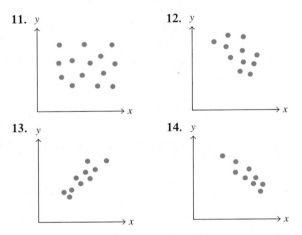

11.   **12.**

13.   **14.**

PRACTICE THE SKILLS

In Exercises 15–22, assume that a sample of bivariate data yields the correlation coefficient, r, indicated. Use Table 13.8 on page 902 for the specified sample size and level of significance to determine whether a linear correlation exists.

15. $r = 0.82$ when $n = 13$ at $\alpha = 0.01$

16. $r = 0.51$ when $n = 22$ at $\alpha = 0.01$

17. $r = -0.73$ when $n = 8$ at $\alpha = 0.05$

18. $r = -0.49$ when $n = 11$ at $\alpha = 0.05$

19. $r = -0.23$ when $n = 102$ at $\alpha = 0.01$

20. $r = -0.49$ when $n = 18$ at $\alpha = 0.01$

21. $r = 0.75$ when $n = 6$ at $\alpha = 0.01$

22. $r = 0.96$ when $n = 5$ at $\alpha = 0.01$

In Exercises 23–30, (a) draw a scatter diagram; (b) determine the value of r, rounded to the nearest thousandth; (c) determine whether a correlation exists at $\alpha = 0.05$; and (d) determine whether a correlation exists at $\alpha = 0.01$.

23.

x	y
4	7
5	9
6	11
7	11
10	15

24.

x	y
6	13
8	11
11	9
14	10
17	7

25.

x	y
23	29
35	37
31	26
43	20
49	39

26.

x	y
90	3
80	4
60	6
60	5
40	5
20	7

27.

x	y
5.3	10.3
4.7	9.6
8.4	12.5
12.7	16.2
4.9	9.8

28.

x	y
12	15
16	19
13	45
24	30
100	60
50	28

29.

x	y
100	2
80	3
60	5
60	6
40	6
20	8

30.

x	y
90	90
70	70
65	65
60	60
50	50
40	40
15	15

In Exercises 31–38, determine the equation of the line of best fit from the data in the exercise indicated. Round both the slope and the y-intercept to the nearest hundredth.

31. Exercise 23   **32.** Exercise 24

33. Exercise 25   **34.** Exercise 26

35. Exercise 27   **36.** Exercise 28

37. Exercise 29   **38.** Exercise 30

PROBLEM SOLVING

In Exercises 39–49, round both the slope and y-intercept to the nearest hundredth.

39. *Fitness* Six students provided the following data about the number of sit-ups completed and the number of push-ups completed during a fitness test in their physical education class.

Sit-ups	50	53	60	35	43	62
Push-ups	40	42	45	25	34	45

a) Determine the correlation coefficient between the number of sit-ups completed and the number of push-ups completed.

b) Determine whether a correlation exists at $\alpha = 0.05$.

c) Determine the equation of the line of best fit for the number of sit-ups completed and the number of push-ups completed.

40. *Amount of Fat in Margarine* The January 2006 issue of *Consumer Reports* provided the following information regarding the number of calories and the number of grams of fat per tablespoon of margarine for the top-rated margarines.

Calories	80	70	60	40	70	50
Fat (grams)	9	8	7	4.5	8	5

a) Determine the correlation coefficient between the number of calories and the number of grams of fat.

b) Determine whether a correlation exists at $\alpha = 0.05$.

c) Determine the equation of the line of best fit for the number of calories and the number of grams of fat.

41. *Time Spent Studying* Six students provided the following data about the lengths of time they studied for a psychology exam and the grades they received on the exam.

Time studied (minutes)	20	40	50	60	80	100
Grade received (percent)	40	45	70	76	92	95

a) Determine the correlation coefficient between the length of time studied and the grade received.

b) Determine whether a correlation exists at $\alpha = 0.01$.

c) Find the equation of the line of best fit for the length of time studied and the grade received.

▲ See Exercise 41

42. *Hiking* The following table shows the number of hiking permits issued for a specific trail at Yellowstone National Park for selected years and the corresponding number of mountain lions sighted by the hikers on that trail.

Hiking permits	765	926	1145	842	1485	1702
Mountain lions	119	127	150	119	153	156

a) Determine the correlation coefficient between the number of hiking permits issued and the number of mountain lions sighted by hikers.

b) Determine whether a correlation exists at $\alpha = 0.05$.

c) Determine the equation of the line of best fit for the number of hiking permits issued and the number of mountain lions sighted by hikers.

d) Use the equation in part (c) to estimate the number of mountain lions sighted by hikers if 1500 hiking permits were issued.

43. *Sports Drinks* The following table shows the energy provided (in kilocalories) and the amount of carbohydrates (in grams) in a 100 ml bottle of sports drinks for six different brands.

Carbohydrates (grams)	6.5	7	6	2	6.4	6
Energy (kilocalories)	27	30	25	10	28	24

a) Determine the correlation coefficient between amount of carbohydrates and the energy provided.

b) Determine whether a correlation exists at $\alpha = 0.05$.

c) Determine the equation of the line of best fit for the amounts of carbohydrates and the energy provided.

d) Use the equation in part (c) to estimate the amount of energy provided in a sports drink with 5 grams of carbohydrates.

44. *Selling Popcorn at the Movies* The number of movie tickets sold and the number of units of popcorn sold at AMC Cinema for 8 days is shown below.

Ticket sales	89	110	125	92	100	95	108	97
Units of popcorn	22	28	30	26	22	21	28	25

a) Determine the correlation coefficient between ticket sales and units of popcorn sold.

b) Determine whether a correlation exists at $\alpha = 0.05$.

c) Determine the equation of the line of best fit for tickets sold and units of popcorn sold.

d) Use the equation in part (c) to estimate the units of popcorn sold if 115 tickets are sold.

45. *Fuel Efficiency of Cars* The following table shows the weights, in hundreds of pounds, for six selected cars. Also shown is the corresponding fuel efficiency, in miles per gallon (mpg), for the car in city driving.

Weight (hundreds of pounds)	27	31	35	32	30	30
Fuel efficiency (mpg)	23	22	20	21	24	22

a) Determine the correlation coefficient between the weight of a car and the fuel efficiency.

b) Determine whether a correlation exists at $\alpha = 0.01$.

c) Determine the equation of the line of best fit for the weight of a car and the fuel efficiency of a car.

d) Use the equation in part (c) to estimate the fuel efficiency of a car that weighs 33 hundred pounds.

46. *City Muggings* In a certain section of a city, muggings have been a problem. The number of police officers patrolling that section of the city has varied. The following chart shows the number of police officers and the number of muggings for 8 successive days.

Police officers	20	12	18	15	22	10	20	12
Muggings	8	10	12	9	6	15	7	18

a) Determine the correlation coefficient for number of police officers and number of muggings.

b) Determine whether a correlation exists at $\alpha = 0.05$.

c) Find the equation of the line of best fit for number of police officers and number of muggings.

d) Use the equation in part (c) to estimate the average number of muggings when 14 police officers are patrolling that section of the city.

47. *Chlorine in a Swimming Pool* A gallon of chlorine is put into a swimming pool. Each hour later for the following 6 hr the percent of chlorine that remains in the pool is measured. The following information is obtained.

Time	1	2	3	4	5	6
Chlorine remaining (percent)	80.0	76.2	68.7	50.1	30.2	20.8

a) Determine the correlation coefficient for time and percent of chlorine remaining.

b) Determine whether a correlation exists at $\alpha = 0.01$.

c) Determine the equation of the line of best fit for time and amount of chlorine remaining.

d) Use the equation in part (c) to estimate the average amount of chlorine remaining after 4.5 hr.

48. *Social Security Numbers* a) Match the first 9 digits of your phone number (including area code) with the 9 digits in your social security number. To do so, match the first digit in your phone number with the first digit in your social security number to get one ordered pair. Match the second digits to get a second ordered pair. Continue this process until you get a total of nine ordered pairs.

b) Do you believe that this set of bivariate data has a positive correlation, a negative correlation, or no correlation? Explain your answer.

c) Construct a scatter diagram for the nine ordered pairs.

d) Calculate the correlation coefficient, r.

e) Is there a correlation at $\alpha = 0.05$? Explain.

f) Calculate the equation of the line of best fit.

g) Use the equation in part (f) to estimate the digit in a social security number that corresponds with a 7 in a telephone number.

49. *Hitting the Brakes* **a)** Examine the art below. Do you believe that there is a positive correlation, a negative correlation, or no correlation between speed of a car and stopping distance when the brakes are applied? Explain.

b) Do you believe that there is a stronger correlation between speed of a car and stopping distance on wet or dry roads? Explain.

c) Use the figure to construct two scatter diagrams, one for dry pavement and the other for wet pavement. Place the speed of the car on the horizontal axis.

d) Compute the correlation coefficient for speed of the car and stopping distance for dry pavement.

e) Repeat part (d) for wet pavement.

f) Were your answers to parts (a) and (b) correct? Explain.

g) Determine the equation of the line of best fit for dry pavement.

h) Repeat part (g) for wet pavement.

i) Use the equations in parts (g) and (h) to estimate the stopping distance of a car going 77 mph on both dry and wet pavements.

CHALLENGE PROBLEMS/GROUP ACTIVITIES

50. *Interchanging Variables* **a)** Assume that a set of bivariate data yields a specific correlation coefficient. If the x and y values are interchanged and the correlation coefficient is recalculated, will the correlation coefficient change? Explain.

b) Make up a table of five pieces of bivariate data and determine r using the data. Then switch the values of the x's and y's and recompute the correlation coefficient. Has the value of r changed?

51. *Height vs. Length* **a)** Do you believe that a correlation exists between a person's height and the length of a person's arm? Explain.

b) Select 10 people from your class and measure (in inches) their heights and the lengths of their arms.

c) Plot the 10 ordered pairs on a scatter diagram.

d) Calculate the correlation coefficient, r.

e) Determine the equation of the line of best fit.

f) Estimate the length of the arm of a person who is 58 in. tall.

52. *Calculating a Correlation Coefficient* **a)** Have your group select a category of bivariate data that it thinks has a strong positive correlation. Designate the independent variable and the dependent variable. Explain why your group believes that the bivariate data have a strong positive correlation.

b) Collect at least 10 pieces of bivariate data that can be used to determine the correlation coefficient. Explain how your group chose these data.

c) Plot a scatter diagram.

d) Calculate the correlation coefficient.

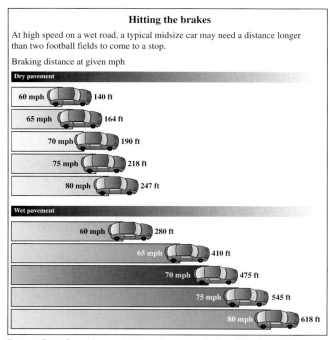

Hitting the brakes

At high speed on a wet road, a typical midsize car may need a distance longer than two football fields to come to a stop.

Braking distance at given mph

Dry pavement

60 mph — 140 ft
65 mph — 164 ft
70 mph — 190 ft
75 mph — 218 ft
80 mph — 247 ft

Wet pavement

60 mph — 280 ft
65 mph — 410 ft
70 mph — 475 ft
75 mph — 545 ft
80 mph — 618 ft

Source: Data from *Car and Driver*, American Automobile Association

e) Does there appear to be a strong positive correlation? Explain your answer.

f) Calculate the equation of the line of best fit.

g) Explain how the equation in part (f) may be used.

53. *CPI* Use the following table. CPI represents consumer price index.

Year	2000	2001	2002	2003	2004	2005
CPI	172.2	177.1	179.9	184.0	188.9	195.3

a) Calculate r.

b) If 2000 is subtracted from each year, the table obtained becomes:

Year	0	1	2	3	4	5
CPI	172.2	177.1	179.9	184.0	188.9	195.3

If r is calculated from these values, how will it compare with the r determined in part (a)? Explain.

c) Calculate r from the values in part (b) and compare the results with the value of r found in part (a). Are they the same? If not, explain why.

54. a) There are equivalent formulas that can be used to find the correlation coefficient and the equation of the line of best fit. A formula used in some statistics books to find the correlation coefficient is

$$r = \frac{SS(xy)}{\sqrt{SS(x)SS(y)}}$$

where

$$SS(x) = \Sigma x^2 - \frac{(\Sigma x)^2}{n}$$

$$SS(y) = \Sigma y^2 - \frac{(\Sigma y)^2}{n}$$

$$SS(xy) = \Sigma xy - \frac{(\Sigma x)(\Sigma y)}{n}$$

Use this formula to find the correlation coefficient of the set of bivariate data given in Example 1 on page 901.

b) Compare your answer with the answer obtained in Example 1.

INTERNET/RESEARCH ACTIVITIES

55. a) Obtain a set of bivariate data from a newspaper or magazine.

b) Plot the information on a scatter diagram.

c) Indicate whether you believe that the data show a positive correlation, a negative correlation, or no correlation. Explain your answer.

d) Calculate r and determine whether your answer to part (c) was correct.

e) Determine the equation of the line of best fit for the bivariate data.

56. Find a scatter diagram in a newspaper or magazine and write a paper on what the diagram indicates. Indicate whether you believe that the bivariate data show a positive correlation, a negative correlation, or no correlation and explain why.

CHAPTER ⑬ SUMMARY

RULES FOR DATA GROUPED BY CLASSES

1. The classes should be the same width.
2. The classes should not overlap.
3. Each piece of data should belong to only one class.

MEASURES OF CENTRAL TENDENCY

The **mean** is the sum of the data divided by the number of pieces of data: $\bar{x} = \dfrac{\Sigma x}{n}$.

The **median** is the value in the middle of a set of ranked data.

The **mode** is the piece of data that occurs most frequently (if there is one).

The **midrange** is the value halfway between the lowest and highest values: midrange $= \dfrac{L + H}{2}$.

STATISTICAL GRAPHS

Circle graph

Histogram

Frequency polygon

Stem-and-leaf display

MEASURES OF DISPERSION

The **range** is the difference between the highest value and lowest value in a set of data.

The **standard deviation**, s, is a measure of the spread of a set of data about the mean: $s = \sqrt{\dfrac{\Sigma(x - \bar{x})^2}{n - 1}}$.

z-SCORES

$$z = \frac{x - \mu}{\sigma}$$

CHEBYSHEV'S THEOREM

The *minimum percent* of data between plus and minus K standard deviations from the mean ($K > 1$) in any distribution can be determined by the formula

$$\text{Minimum percent} = 1 - \frac{1}{K^2}, \quad K > 1$$

LINEAR CORRELATION AND REGRESSION

Linear correlation coefficient, r, is

$$r = \frac{n(\Sigma xy) - (\Sigma x)(\Sigma y)}{\sqrt{n(\Sigma x^2) - (\Sigma x)^2}\sqrt{n(\Sigma y^2) - (\Sigma y)^2}}$$

EQUATION OF THE LINE OF THE BEST FIT

$y = mx + b$, where

$$m = \frac{n(\Sigma xy) - (\Sigma x)(\Sigma y)}{n(\Sigma x^2) - (\Sigma x)^2}$$

$$b = \frac{\Sigma y - m(\Sigma x)}{n}$$

CHAPTER ⑬ REVIEW EXERCISES

13.1

1. a) What is a population?

   b) What is a sample?

2. What is a random sample?

13.2

In Exercises 3 and 4, tell what possible misuses or misinterpretations may exist in the statements.

3. The Stay Healthy Candy Bar indicates on its label that it has no cholesterol. Therefore, it is safe to eat as many of these candy bars as you want.

4. More copies of *Time* magazine are sold than are copies of *Money* magazine. Therefore, *Time* is a more profitable magazine than *Money*.

5. *Tax Preparers* In 2000, 58% of taxpayers used a tax preparer to prepare their taxes. In 2004, 61% of taxpayers used a tax preparer to prepare their taxes. Draw a graph that appears to show a

   a) small increase in the use of tax preparers from 2000 to 2004.

   b) large increase in the use of tax preparers from 2000 to 2004.

13.3, 13.4

6. Consider the following set of data.

35	37	38	41	43
36	37	38	41	43
36	37	39	41	43
36	37	39	41	44
37	37	39	42	45

   a) Construct a frequency distribution letting each class have a width of 1.

   b) Construct a histogram.

   c) Construct a frequency polygon.

7. *Average Monthly High Temperature* Consider the following average monthly high temperature in July for 40 selected U.S. cities.

71	79	58	73	80	75	84	77
82	72	80	70	75	66	73	72
80	66	74	68	81	84	75	67
91	76	82	79	63	69	68	79
71	76	80	83	73	87	82	71

   a) Construct a frequency distribution. Let the first class be 58–62.

b) Construct a histogram of the frequency distribution.

c) Construct a frequency polygon of the frequency distribution.

d) Construct a stem-and-leaf display.

13.5, 13.6

In Exercises 8–13, for the following test scores 65, 76, 79, 83, 84, 93, determine the

8. mean.

9. median.

10. mode.

11. midrange.

12. range.

13. standard deviation.

In Exercises 14–19, for the set of data 4, 5, 12, 14, 19, 7, 12, 23, 7, 17, 15, 21, determine the

14. mean.

15. median.

16. mode.

17. midrange.

18. range.

19. standard deviation.

13.7

Police Response Time In Exercises 20–24, assume that police response time to emergency calls is normally distributed with a mean of 9 minutes and a standard deviation of 2 minutes. Determine the percent of emergency calls with a police response time

20. between 7 and 11 minutes.

21. between 5 and 13 minutes.

22. less than 12.2 minutes.

23. more than 12.2 minutes.

24. more than 7.8 minutes.

Pizza Delivery In Exercises 25–28, assume that the amount of time to prepare and deliver a pizza from Pepe's Pizza is normally distributed with a mean of 20 min and standard deviation of 5 min. Determine the percent of pizzas that were prepared and delivered

25. between 20 and 25 min.

26. in less than 18 min.

27. between 22 and 28 min.

28. If Pepe's Pizza advertises that the pizza is free if it takes more than 30 min to deliver, what percent of the pizza will be free?

13.8

29. *Advertising Rates* The following table shows the cost, in millions of dollars, for a 30-second television advertisement during the Super Bowl. The column labeled Year refers to the number of years since 1997. Thus, 0 would correspond to 1997 and 8 would correspond to 2005.

Year	0	1	2	3	4	5	6	7	8
Cost ($ millions)	1.2	1.3	1.6	2.0	2.0	2.0	2.3	2.3	2.4

a) Construct a scatter diagram with year on the horizontal axis.

b) Use the scatter diagram in part (a) to determine whether you believe that a correlation exists between the year and the cost of a Super Bowl advertisement. If so, is it a positive or negative correlation? Explain.

c) Calculate the correlation coefficient between the year and the cost of an advertisement.

d) Determine whether a correlation exists at $\alpha = 0.05$.

e) Determine the equation of the line of best fit between the year and the cost of an advertisement. Round both the slope and y-intercept to the nearest hundredth.

f) Assuming that this trend continues, use the equation of the line of best fit to estimate the cost of a 30-second commercial in 2010.

30. *Daily Sales* Ace Hardware recorded the number of a particular item sold per week for 6 weeks and the corresponding weekly price, in dollars, of the item as shown in the table below.

Price ($)	0.75	1.00	1.25	1.50	1.75	2.00
Number sold	200	160	140	120	110	95

a) Construct a scatter diagram with price on the horizontal axis.

b) Use the scatter diagram in part (a) to determine whether you believe that a correlation exists between the price of the item and number sold. If so, it is a positive or a negative correlation? Explain.

c) Determine the correlation coefficient between the price and the number sold.

d) Determine whether a correlation exists at $\alpha = 0.05$. Explain how you arrived at your answer.

e) Determine the equation of the line of best fit for the price and the number sold.

f) Use the equation in part (e) to estimate the number sold if the price is $1.60.

13.5–13.7

Men's Weight *In Exercises 31–38, use the following data obtained from a study of the weights of adult men.*

Mean	192 lb	First quartile	178 lb
Median	185 lb	Third quartile	232 lb
Mode	180 lb	86th percentile	239 lb
Standard deviation	23 lb		

31. What is the most common weight?

32. What weight did half of those surveyed exceed?

33. About what percent of those surveyed weighed more than 232 lb?

34. About what percent of those surveyed weighed less than 178 lb?

35. About what percent of those surveyed weighed more than 239 lb?

36. If 100 men were surveyed, what is the total weight of all men?

37. What weight represents two standard deviations above the mean?

38. What weight represents 1.8 standard deviations below the mean?

13.2–13.7

Presidential Children *The following list shows the names of the 42 U.S. presidents and the number of children in their families.*

Washington	0	Cleveland	5
J. Adams	5	B. Harrison	3
Jefferson	6	McKinley	2
Madison	0	T. Roosevelt	6
Monroe	2	Taft	3
J. Q. Adams	4	Wilson	3
Jackson	0	Harding	0
Van Buren	4	Coolidge	2
W. H. Harrison	10	Hoover	2
Tyler	14	F. D. Roosevelt	6
Polk	0	Truman	1
Taylor	6	Eisenhower	2
Fillmore	2	Kennedy	3
Pierce	3	L. B. Johnson	2
Buchanan	0	Nixon	2
Lincoln	4	Ford	4
A. Johnson	5	Carter	4
Grant	4	Reagan	4
Hayes	8	G. Bush	6
Garfield	7	Clinton	1
Arthur	3	G. W. Bush	2

In Exercises 39–50, use the data to determine the following.

39. Mean **40.** Mode

41. Median **42.** Midrange

43. Range

44. Standard deviation (round the mean to the nearest tenth)

45. Construct a frequency distribution; let the first class be 0–1.

46. Construct a histogram.

47. Construct a frequency polygon.

48. Does this distribution appear to be normal? Explain.

49. On the basis of this sample, do you think the number of children per family in the United States is a normal distribution? Explain.

50. Do you believe that this sample is representative of the population? Explain.

CHAPTER 13 TEST

In Exercises 1–6, for the set of data 27, 43, 43, 45, 52, determine the

1. mean. **2.** median.

3. mode. **4.** midrange.

5. range. **6.** standard deviation.

In Exercises 7–9, use the set of data

26	28	35	46	49	56
26	30	36	46	49	58
26	32	40	47	50	58
26	32	44	47	52	62
27	35	46	47	54	66

to construct the following.

7. a frequency distribution; let the first class be 25–30

8. a histogram of the frequency distribution

9. a frequency polygon of the frequency distribution

Statistics on Salaries *In Exercises 10–16, use the following data on weekly salaries at Donovan's Construction Company.*

Mean	$740	First quartile	$690
Median	$710	Third quartile	$745
Mode	$735	79th percentile	$752
Standard deviation	$40		

10. What is the most common salary?

11. What salary did half the employees exceed?

12. About what percent of employees' salaries exceeded $690?

13. About what percent of employees' salaries was less than $752?

14. If the company has 100 employees, what is the total weekly salary of all employees?

15. What salary represents one standard deviation above the mean?

16. What salary represents 1.5 standard deviations below the mean?

Anthropology *In Exercises 17–20, assume that anthropologists have determined that the akidolestes, a small primitive mammal believed to have lived with the dinosaurs, has a head circumference that was normally distributed with a mean of 42 cm and a standard deviation of 5 cm.*

17. What percent of head circumferences were between 36 and 53 cm?

18. What percent of head circumferences were greater than 35.75 cm?

19. What percent of head circumferences were greater than 48.25 cm?

20. What percent of head circumferences were less than 50 cm?

21. **Average Earnings** The following chart shows the average hourly earnings, to the nearest 10 cents, for U.S. production workers for 2001–2005, where the column labeled Year refers to the numbers of years since 2001.

Average Earnings for U.S. Production Workers

Year	Average Hourly Earnings
0	$14.5
1	$15.0
2	$15.4
3	$15.7
4	$16.1

Source: Bureau of Labor Statistics

a) Construct a scatter diagram placing the year on the horizontal axis.

b) Use the scatter diagram in part (a) to determine whether you believe that a correlation exists between the year and the average hourly earnings for a U.S. production worker. Explain.

c) Determine the correlation coefficient between the year and the average hourly earnings for a U.S. production worker.

d) Determine whether a correlation exists at $\alpha = 0.05$.

e) Determine the equation of the line of best fit between the year and the average hourly earnings for a U.S. production worker. Round both the slope and y-intercept to the nearest hundredth.

f) Use the equation in part (e) to predict the average hourly earnings for a U.S. production worker in 2030, or 29 years after 2001.

G R O U P   P R O J E C T S

1. Do you think that men or women, aged 17–20, watch more hours of TV weekly, or do you think that they watch the same number of hours?

   a) Write a procedure to use to determine the answer to that question. In your procedure, use a sample of 30 men and 30 women. State how you will obtain an unbiased sample.

   b) Collect 30 pieces of data from men aged 17–20 and 30 pieces of data from women aged 17–20. Round answers to the nearest 0.5 hr. Follow the procedure developed in part (a) to obtain your unbiased sample.

   c) Compute the mean for your two groups of data to the nearest tenth.

   d) Using the means obtained in part (c), answer the question asked at the beginning of the problem.

   e) Is it possible that your conclusion in part (d) is wrong? Explain.

   f) Compute the standard deviation for each group to the nearest tenth. How do the standard deviations compare?

   g) Do you believe that the distribution of data from either or both groups resembles a normal distribution? Explain.

   h) Add the two groups of data to get one group of 60 pieces of data. If these 60 pieces of data are added and divided by 60, will you obtain the same mean as when you add the two means from part (c) and divide the sum by 2? Explain.

   i) Compute the mean of the 60 pieces of data by using both methods mentioned in part (h). Are they the same? If so, why? If not, why not?

   j) Do you believe that this group of 60 pieces of data represents a normal distribution? Explain.

2. a) Have your group select a category of bivariate data that it thinks has a strong negative correlation. Indicate the variable that you will designate as the independent variable and the variable that you will designate as the dependent variable. Explain why your group believes that the bivariate data have a strong negative correlation.

   b) Collect at least 10 pieces of bivariate data that can be used to determine the correlation coefficient. Explain how your group chose these data.

   c) Plot a scatter diagram.

   d) Calculate the correlation coefficient.

   e) Is there a negative correlation at $\alpha = 0.05$? Explain your answer.

   f) Calculate the equation of the line of best fit.

   g) Explain how the equation in part (f) may be used.

A P P E N D I X Ⓐ Using Excel®

Microsoft Excel is a program that can be used to perform a multitude of tasks, including making spreadsheets and graphs. In this appendix, we will present a brief introduction to Excel. Many publications are available that offer detailed and complete explanations on using Excel. We will give instructions for a PC. The screens and instructions for a Mac are a little different.

Figure A.1 shows an Excel screen. Depending on the version of Excel you are using, the Excel screen on your computer may be a little different.

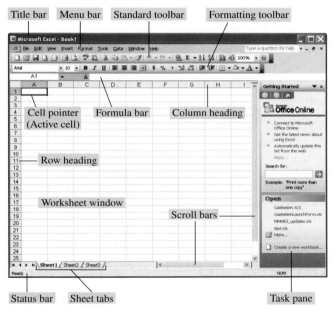

Figure A.1

In Excel, columns are referred to with letters and rows are referred to with numbers. The highlighted, or active cell, in Fig. A.1 is A1. When entering information in Excel, you can enter **labels**, used to identify information, **values** (or numbers), or **formulas** (calculations written in a special notation). When you enter a formula in a cell, Excel displays the result of the formula in the active cell, not the formula itself, after you press the Enter key. Formulas always begin with an equal ($=$) sign. After you enter a label, a value, or a formula in a cell, you press the Enter key to enter the information. Do not be concerned if, when listing labels, the labels overflow into a second cell. After you finish inserting all the labels, you can extend the column width by placing the mouse pointer on the line between the two columns at the top of the column and then double clicking the mouse button. The column widths will then automatically adjust in size.

Consider the Excel spreadsheet in Fig. A.2 on page AA-2. Labels, shaded in orange, are given across row 1 and down column A. Values, shaded in green, are given in cells B2 through D2 and B3 through D3. Calculations from formulas, shaded in yellow, are given in cells E2 and E3.

In Fig. A.2, we are using Excel to calculate simple interest on a loan, using the simple interest formula, as will be explained shortly. Under column A, we list the dates on which the loans were made.

	A	B	C	D	E
1	Date	Principal	Rate	Time	Interest
2	May 22, 2006	$ 2,000.00	0.06	1	$ 120.00
3	June 5, 2007	$ 5,000.00	0.05	3	$ 750.00

Sheet1 / Sheet2 / Sheet3 /

Ready

Figure A.2

To get the dollar signs in column B, highlight column B by placing the mouse pointer on the B at the top of column B and then click on the $ in the formatting toolbar. Repeat the process to get the dollar signs in column E. After you insert the labels and values, we use the formula

$$\text{Interest} = \text{principal} \times \text{rate} \times \text{time}$$

to determine the simple interest in column E. To use an Excel formula to calculate the interest for May 22, 2006, move the cursor to cell E2 and then click the mouse to activate that cell. Type in the formula =B2*C2*D2. After you press the Enter key, the answer, $120, is displayed. To obtain the answer for cell E3, use =B3*C3*D3. Notice that * is used to indicate multiplication and that there are no blank spaces in the formula.

Now consider the spreadsheet in Fig. A.3, which shows a budget.

	A	B	C	D
1		Budgeted	Actual	Difference
2	Income Items			
3	Sales income	$ 35,600.00	$ 39,200.00	$ 3,600.00
4	CD interest	$ 1,620.00	$ 1,490.00	$ (130.00)
5	Other income	$ 5,080.00	$ 6,580.00	$ 1,500.00
6	Total Income	$ 42,300.00	$ 47,270.00	
7				
8	Expense Items			
9	Rent	$ 10,230.00	$ 10,150.00	$ (80.00)
10	Food	$ 8,573.00	$ 8,450.00	$ (123.00)
11	Clothing	$ 2,510.00	$ 2,370.00	$ (140.00)
12	Medical	$ 1,080.00	$ 960.00	$ (120.00)
13	Entertainment	$ 1,280.00	$ 1,280.00	$ –
14	Insurance	$ 1,200.00	$ 1,420.00	$ 220.00
15	Other	$ 6,110.00	$ 7,190.00	$ 1,080.00
16	Total Expenses	$ 30,983.00	$ 31,820.00	
17				
18	Net Income	$ 11,317.00	$ 15,450.00	
19				

Sheet1 / Sheet2 / Sheet3 /

Ready

Figure A.3

To obtain the spreadsheet in Fig. A.3, do the following. First input the labels in cells B1, C1, and D1 and also under column A. Then input the values in cells B3 through B5, B9 through B15, C3 through C5, and C9 through C15. Next we can determine the difference between the actual amounts and budgeted amounts, column D, by subtracting the values in column B from the values in column C. Begin by activating cell D3. Then type =C3-B3 and press the Enter key. At this point, the difference, $39,200 − $35,600, or $3600, fills in cell D3. If we wanted to determine the amount to go in cell D4, we could type in =C4-B4 and continue this process for all amounts in column D. Excel, however, has a number of procedures that can be used to copy formulas from one cell to another cell that needs a similar formula. Copying can save time when building a spreadsheet with multiple columns or rows that need similar formulas. When copying formulas, Excel automatically rewrites the cell reference so that the formula refers to the appropriate cells. You can see the formula for a particular cell at any time by activating that cell and looking in the formula bar near the top of the screen. You can copy formulas using the **Copy** and **Paste** commands in the Edit menu. To copy a formula from one cell to another, click on the cell containing the formula you wish to copy, click on the Edit menu, and then click on Copy. Click on the cell where you want the copied formula to go. Then click on the Edit menu and click Paste. This method will copy the formula to the new cell, and the cell reference used in the formula will automatically change to the appropriate cells for the new calculation.

A quick way to copy a formula to one or more adjacent cells is with the *fill handle*. To copy this way, position the mouse pointer on the selection's *fill handle* (a tiny square in the bottom right-hand corner of the cell selected). The mouse pointer turns into a black cross. Press and hold the mouse button while you drag the cross down the column, or to the right across the row, until you reach the desired cell. A gray or black border stretches over the cells you pass, highlighting the desired cells. When you release the mouse button, the formula is copied to all the cells that were highlighted.

You can complete cells D4 and D5 using the fill handle. Then, in cell D9, we enter the formula =C9-B9. We then use the fill handle to complete cells D10 through D15.

To obtain the sum of the budgeted income, cell B6, we can use the auto sum button on the standard toolbar or we can enter a formula. To determine the sum of the values in cells B3, B4, and B5, we can enter the formula =SUM(B3:B5) in cell B6. After you press enter, the sum $42,300 is displayed. Then you can obtain the sum of cells C3 through C5, which will go in cell C6, by using =SUM(C3:C5) or by using the fill handle as explained earlier. We obtain the sum of the total budgeted expenses, B16, and total actual expenses, C16, in a similar manner. For example, in cell B16, we use the formula =SUM(B9:B15) to obtain the sum of columns B9 through B15.

Finally, to obtain the budgeted net income, cell B18, we subtract the total budgeted expenses from the total budgeted income. Thus, in cell B18 we use the formula =B6-B16. Similarly, in cell C18 we use =C6-C16.

The preceding explanation should give you a basic idea of how Excel works. Note that when you change a value in a cell in the spreadsheet, the corresponding formulas that use that value automatically recalculate the answer and display the resulting answer.

TIMELY TIP

In Microsoft Excel formulas, use

* for multiplication
/ for division
^ for exponents

Suppose that cell B3 of a spreadsheet has a value of 5. If in cell B4 you had the formula =B3^2, you would get an answer of 25 in cell B4 after pressing the Enter key. Suppose that you wanted to find the square root of the number 16, which is in cell D7 of a spreadsheet. In cell D8, you could use the formula =D7^(1/2) or =D7^0.5. After the Enter key is pressed, the answer 4 is displayed in cell D8.

If you find you left something out and wish to add another row or column to your spreadsheet, place the cursor where you want to add the new row or column. Then go to the Insert menu and select either Row or Column. If you want to delete either a row or column, highlight that row or column and then go to the Edit menu and click on Delete.

If you want to find the sum of the numbers in consecutive cells and another number in a non-consecutive cell, you can use a comma in the formula. For example, =SUM(C5:C10, C:13) adds the numbers in cells C5 through C10 and the number in cell C13.

If items such as dates are automatically converted to a format different than what you want, use the Format menu and select Cells. Here you will see many formats that can be adjusted. To change the format of dates, for example, select the Format menu, then select Cells, select Numbers, and then select Dates.

The only way to get to understand Excel is to work and experiment with it. When doing so, you may want to go to the Insert menu and select Function. Here you can select from many different types of functions in many different areas of mathematics and business.

A P P E N D I X Ⓑ Graph Theory

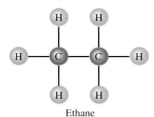
In the eighteenth-century Prussian town of Königsberg (now the city of Kaliningrad, Russia near the Baltic Sea) seven bridges crossed the Prigel River (Fig. B.1a). Individuals in the area tried to determine whether it was possible to walk a path that would cross each of the seven bridges exactly once. They found that they ended up either not crossing one of the bridges, or crossing one of the bridges more than once. The problem was brought to the attention of the Swiss mathematician Leonhard Euler (pronounced "oiler," 1707–1783). His study of this problem, now known as the Königsberg bridge problem, laid the groundwork for a modern branch of mathematics called *graph theory*, a topic in a more general area called *topology*. To solve the problem, Euler drew figures called *graphs* or *networks* like that shown in red in Fig. B.1(b). Each dot represented a plot of land and each line a bridge or path. Can you find a path that crosses each bridge exactly once?

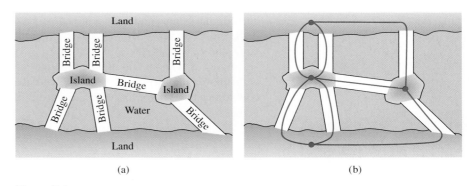

(a)   (b)

Figure B.1

Before we determine whether there is a path that will cross each bridge exactly once, let's consider Example 1.

EXAMPLE ❶

In Fig. B.2 start at any point and try to trace each figure without retracing a line and without removing your pencil from the paper. If you succeed, indicate your starting point and ending point.

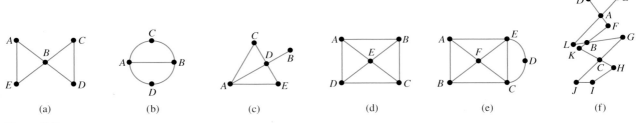

(a)   (b)   (c)   (d)   (e)   (f)

Figure B.2

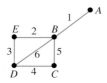

Odd vertices: *A* and *C*
Even vertex: *B*

(a)

Odd vertices: *A* and *D*
Even vertices: *B*, *C*, and *E*

(b)

Figure B.3

SOLUTION

a) The figure can be traced if you start at any point. You will end at the point at which you started.

b) The figure can be traced, but only if you start at point *A* or point *B*. If you start at point *A*, you will end at point *B*, and vice versa.

c) The figure can be traced, but only if you start at point *A* or point *B*. If you start at point *A*, you will end at point *B*, and vice versa.

d) The figure cannot be traced without retracing a line.

e) The figure can be traced, but only if you start at point *A* or point *B*. If you start at point *A*, you will end at point *B*, and vice versa.

f) The figure can be traced if you start at any point. You will end at the point at which you started.

In order for you to be able to answer the Königsberg bridge problem and understand why we were able to trace all but one of the figures in Example 1 without retracing a line, we must introduce some new terms and concepts.

A *vertex* is any designated point. An *edge* (or an *arc*) is any line, either straight or curved, that begins and ends at a vertex. Figure B.3(a) has three designated vertices, *A*, *B*, and *C*, and two edges, 1 and 2. Figure B.3(b) has five designated vertices, *A*, *B*, *C*, *D*, and *E*, and six edges.

A vertex with an odd number of edges attached is called an *odd vertex*. A vertex with an even number of edges attached is called an *even vertex*. Figure B.3(a) has two odd vertices and one even vertex. Figure B.3(b) has two odd vertices and three even vertices.

A *network* is any continuous (not broken) system of edges and vertices.

A network is said to be **traversable** if it can be traced without removing the pencil from the paper and without tracing an edge more than once.

After completing Example 1, do you have an intuitive feeling as to when a figure is traversable? Think about odd and even vertices. Leonhard Euler discovered an important scientific principle concealed in the Königsberg bridge problem. He presented his simple and ingenious solution of that problem to the Russian Academy at St. Petersburg in 1735. Euler developed the following rules of traversability in solving the problem.

RULES OF TRAVERSABILITY

1. A network with no odd (all even) vertices is traversable; you may start from any vertex, and you will end where you began.

2. A network with exactly two odd vertices is traversable; you must start at either of the odd vertices and you will finish at the other.

3. A network with more than two odd vertices is not traversable.

The network in the Königsberg bridge problem (Fig. B.1b) has four odd vertices, so it cannot be traversed. Therefore crossing each bridge only once is impossible. Note that it is impossible for a network to contain an odd number of odd vertices. (If you don't believe this statement, try to construct such a network.)

Now go back to Example 1 and determine which figures are traversable, using these rules. Note that Figs. B.2(a) and B.2(f) are traversable from any point because they contain only even vertices. Figures B.2(b), (c), and (e) have exactly two odd vertices and can be traversed but only by starting at one of the odd vertices, either point *A* or point *B*. Figure B.2(d) contains more than two odd vertices and therefore cannot be traversed.

EXAMPLE ❷

The floor plan of a six-gallery art museum is shown in Fig. B.4(a). The openings represent doors, and the letters represent galleries.

a) Determine the galleries that contain an odd number of doors; an even number of doors.

b) Each gallery can be represented as an odd or even vertex. Use this information to determine whether it is possible to walk through each gallery by using each door only once.

c) Determine a path to walk through each gallery by using each door only once.

SOLUTION

a) Galleries *B* and *D* contain three doors each. Galleries *A* and *F* contain two doors each. Galleries *C* and *E* have four doors.

b) There are only two odd vertices, *B* and *D*, so the figure is traversable, and you can walk through the museum by using each door only once.

c) You must start in either Gallery *B* or *D* (see Fig. B.4b). If you start in *B*, you will end in *D*, and vice versa. When you leave Gallery *B*, you can leave by any of the three doors.   ●

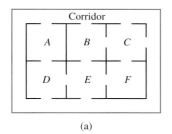

Corridor

(a)

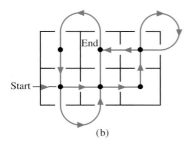

(b)

Figure B.4

The floor plan in Example 2 can be reduced to a map, where the rooms are the vertices and the doors are the paths. Construct a map of that floor plan now.

APPENDIX Ⓑ EXERCISES

CONCEPT/WRITING EXERCISES

1. What is a vertex?

2. What is an edge (or an arc)?

3. Explain how to determine whether a vertex is odd or even.

4. In your own words, explain the rules for determining whether a graph is traversable.

PRACTICE THE SKILLS

In Exercises 5–8, determine the number of vertices and the number of edges.

5.

6.

7.

8.

In Exercises 9 and 10, explain why these two figures represent the same graph.

9.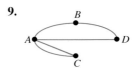

10.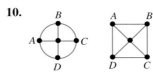

In Exercises 11 and 12, list the vertices that are odd and the vertices that are even.

11.

12.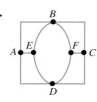

PROBLEM SOLVING

In Exercises 13–20, determine whether the network is traversable. If it is, state the points from which you may start and end.

13.

14.

15.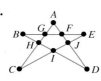

16.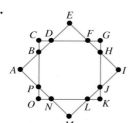

17.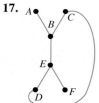

18.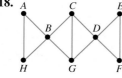

19.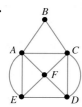

20.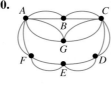

In Exercises 21–28, the floor plan of a building is shown.
  a) *Determine the number of rooms that contain an odd number of doors; an even number of doors.*
  b) *Use the rules of traversability to determine whether it is possible to walk through the building using each door only once.*
  c) *If the answer to part (b) is yes, indicate where you can start and where you will end and describe one such path (for example, A to D to B to . . . etc.).*

21.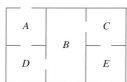

22.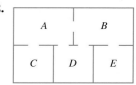

23.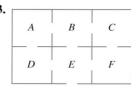

24.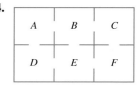

25.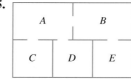

26.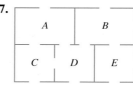

27.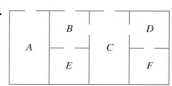

28.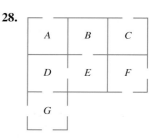

In Exercises 29 and 30, the floor plan for a suite of rooms is shown. Add an exit door in one of the rooms so that a security guard can enter through the door marked Enter, *pass through each door only once locking it behind him, and then exit by the door you added. Explain why there is only one possible room in which the door may be placed.*

29.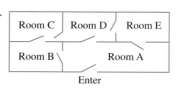

30.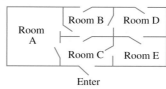

In Exercises 31 and 32, is it possible to cross each bridge exactly once? If it is possible, indicate where the person can start and where the person will finish. Explain your answer.

31.

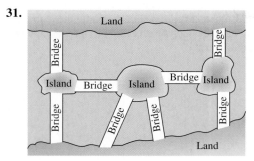

32.

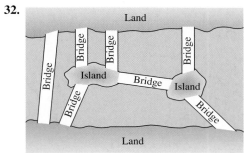

33. Draw a graph that contains four vertices and is traversable from exactly two vertices.

34. Draw a graph that contains five vertices that is traversable from exactly two vertices.

35. In the figure, lines connecting two states indicate that the two states share a common border. Which of these states share a common border with (a) Tennessee? (b) Missouri?

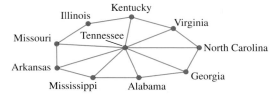

36. In the figure, a line connecting two countries indicates that they share a common border. Which of these countries share a common border with (a) Brazil? (b) Bolivia?

37. The remaining games in a soccer league are illustrated in the graph.

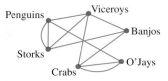

a) How many games do the Viceroys have remaining?

b) How many games do the Penguins have remaining?

c) How many games still need to be played?

38. Dawn, Jessica, Pam, Bill, Ed, and Scott go to a dance. Dawn dances with Bill and Scott. Jessica dances with all the boys and Pam dances only with Scott. Draw a graph that displays this information.

39. France has common borders with Belgium, Germany, Switzerland, Italy, and Spain. Belgium has common borders with the Netherlands, France, and Germany. Germany has common borders with Belgium, Poland, the Czech Republic, Austria, Switzerland, and France. Switzerland has common borders with France, Italy, Austria, and Germany. Draw a graph that displays this information.

40. Can you draw a graph that contains an odd number of odd vertices? If you answer yes, draw such a graph.

CHALLENGE PROBLEMS/GROUP ACTIVITIES

41. Gretchen's Delivery service, located in town C, makes deliveries every day to each town shown on the map. The map also shows the highways connecting the towns and the distances between towns. The delivery service's expenses are lowest when the driver's route is the shortest.

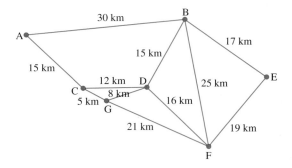

a) Is the map traversable? Explain.

b) The least number of miles that can be driven, starting at C and returning to C, that covers every city is 110 miles. Determine a path that covers all the cities and whose distance is 110 miles.

42. Networks (a) and (b) illustrate a relationship between the number of edges, regions, and vertices. Network (a) has three vertices (*A*, *B*, and *C*), four edges (1, 2, 3, and 4), and three regions (*x*, *y*, and *z*). Network (b) has five vertices (*A*, *B*, *C*, *D*, and *E*), seven edges (1, 2, 3, 4, 5, 6, 7), and four regions (*w*, *x*, *y*, and *z*). Using these networks and others that you can make up yourself, develop a formula expressing the number of edges in terms of the number of vertices and the number of regions. This formula is known as *Euler's formula for networks*.

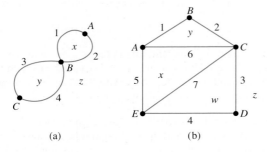

(a)   (b)

INTERNET/RESEARCH ACTIVITY

43. In 1856 William Rowan Hamilton (1805–1865) introduced a problem similar to the Königsberg bridge problem. Hamilton turned his problem into a game that was marketed in 1856. Write a short paper explaining the game. (References include encyclopedias, history of mathematics books, and the Internet.)

A N S W E R S

CHAPTER 1

SECTION 1.1, PAGE 5

1. **a)** 1, 2, 3, 4, 5, . . .
   b) Counting numbers

3. Inductive reasoning is the process of reasoning to a general conclusion through observation of specific cases.

5. A counterexample is a specific case that satisfies the conditions of the conjecture but shows the conjecture is false.

7. Inductive reasoning

9. Inductive reasoning, a general conclusion is obtained from observation of specific cases.

11. $5 \times 7 = 35$

13. 1 5 10 10 5 1

15.   17. ⬡

19. 25, 30, 35   21. $-1, 1, -1$

23. $\dfrac{1}{16}, \dfrac{1}{64}, \dfrac{1}{256}$ 25. 36, 49, 64

27. 34, 55, 89   29. Y

31. **a)** 36, 49, 64
    b) square 6, 7, 8, 9 and 10
    c) No, 72 is between 8^2 and 9^2, so it is not a square number.

33. Blue: 1, 5, 7, 10, 12   Purple: 2, 4, 6, 9, 11   Yellow: 3, 8

35. **a)** $\approx$ \$6 billion
    b) We are using specific cases to make a prediction.

37.

39. **a)** You should obtain the original number.
    b) You should obtain the original number.
    c) The result is the original number.
    d) $n, 8n, 8n + 16, \dfrac{8n + 16}{8} = n + 2, n + 2 - 2 = n$

41. **a)** 5
    b) You should obtain the number 5.
    c) The result is always the number 5.
    d) $n, n + 1, \dfrac{n + (n + 1) + 9}{2} = \dfrac{2n + 10}{2} = n + 5,$
    $n + 5 - n = 5$

43. $3 + 5 = 8$, which is not an odd number.

45. $(3 + 2)/2 = 5/2$, which is not an even number.

47. $1 - 2 = -1$, which is not a counting number.

49. **a)** The sum of the measures of the interior angles should be 180°.
    b) Yes, the sum of the measures of the interior angles should be 180°.
    c) The sum of the measures of the interior angles of a triangle is 180°.

51. 129, the numbers in positions are found as follows:
    $a \quad b$
    $c \quad a + b + c$

53. (c)

SECTION 1.2, PAGE 14

Answers in this section will vary depending on how you round your numbers. All answers are approximate.

1. 2210   3. 1,200,000,000   5. 8000   7. 900

9. 200   11. 1,200,000,000   13. \$240   15. \$32.80

17. 180 miles   19. 13,200 lb   21. \$3.90   23. 16

25. \$37   27. \$120   29. \$41   31. $\approx$ 20 mi

33. **a)** 100
    b) 50
    c) 125

35. **a)** 5 million
    b) 98 million
    c) 65 million
    d) 280 million

37. **a)** 85%
    b) 15%
    c) 59,500,000 acres
    d) No, since we are not given the area of each state.

39. 25   41. $\approx$ 160 bananas   43. 150°   45. 10%

47. 9 square units   49. 150 feet

51.–59. Answers will vary.

61. There are 336 dimples on a regulation golf ball.

SECTION 1.3, PAGE 29

1. 76.5 mi   3. 19.36 ft   5. \$29,026

7. **a)** \$196,800
   b) \$26,600
   c) \$220,320

9. \$12.50   11. \$70   13. \$71,989.20

15. **a)** $\approx$ 122
    b) Answers will vary. A close approximation can be obtained by multiplying the U.S. sizes by 2.54.

17. a) 9.2 min
  b) 62 min
  c) 40 min
  d) 47 min

19. a) $1.5 trillion
  b) $22,000

21. $82.08

23. a) $74.40
  b) $264
  c) $64

25. a) 3,153,600 cm^3
  b) $\approx$ 1.4 days

27. a) $75
  b) $15
  c) Long term by $3

29. a) Divide the Total Emissions by the Emissions per Capita.
  b) $\approx$ 298.6 million
  c) $\approx$ 1307.6 million or 1.3076 billion

31. $990, less than initial investment

33. a) 48 rolls
  b) $198 if she purchases four 10 packs and two 4 packs

35. a) Water/milk: 3 cups; salt: $\frac{3}{8}$ tsp; Cream of Wheat: 9 tbsp (or $\frac{9}{16}$ cup)
  b) Water/milk: $2\frac{7}{8}$ cups; salt: $\frac{3}{8}$ tsp; Cream of Wheat: $\frac{5}{8}$ cup (or 10 tbsp)
  c) Water/milk: $2\frac{3}{4}$ cups; salt: $\frac{3}{8}$ tsp; Cream of Wheat: $\frac{9}{16}$ cup (or 9 tbsp)
  d) Differences exist in water/milk because the amount for 4 servings is not twice that for 2 servings. Differences also exist in Cream of Wheat because $\frac{1}{2}$ cup is not twice 3 tbsp.

37. 144 square inches

39. The area is 4 times as large.

41. 66 ft   **43.** at -1 **45.** $60,000

47. a) 30
  b) 140

49.

51.

8	6	16
18	10	2
4	14	12

53. The sum of the four corners is 4 times the number in the center.

55. Multiply the center number by 9.

57. 6 ways

59.

	7	
3	1	4
5	8	6
	2	

Other answers are possible, but 1 and 8 must appear in the center.

61.

1	2	3	4	5
2	3	4	5	1
3	4	5	1	2
4	5	1	2	3
5	1	2	3	4

Other answers are possible.

63. Mary is the skier.   **65.** 714 square units   **67.** $120

REVIEW EXERCISES, PAGE 37

1. 31, 36, 41   **2.** 25, 36, 49   **3.** $-48, 96, -192$
4. 25, 32, 40   **5.** 10, 4, -3 **6.** $\frac{3}{8}, \frac{3}{16}, \frac{3}{32}$

7.

8.

9. (c)

10. a) The final number is twice the original number.
  b) The final number is twice the original number.
  c) The final number is twice the original number.
  d) $n, 10n, 10n + 5, \dfrac{10n + 5}{5} = 2n + 1,$
    $2n + 1 - 1 = 2n$

11. This process will always result in an answer of 3.

12. $1^2 + 2^2 = 5$

Answers to Exercises 13–25 will vary depending on how you round your numbers. All answers are approximate.

13. 420,000,000   **14.** 2000   **15.** 200

16. Answers will vary.   **17.** $300   **18.** $36

19. 3 mph   **20.** $14.00   **21.** 2 mi   **22.** 0.15 million

23. 0.8 million   **24.** 13 square units

25. Length $\approx$ 22 ft; height $\approx$ 8 ft

26. $7.50   **27.** $1.16

28. Berkman's is cheaper by $20.00.

29. $32,996

30. a) 288 lb
  b) 12,500 ft^2

31. $311   **32.** 7.05 mg

33. $882   **34.** 6 hr 45 min   **35.** July 26, 11:00 A.M.

36. a) 6.45 cm^2
  b) 16.39 cm^3
  c) 1 cm $\approx$ 0.39 in.

37. 201

38.

21	7	8	18
10	16	15	13
14	12	11	17
9	19	20	6

39.

23	25	15
13	21	29
27	17	19

40. 59 min 59 sec   **41.** 6

42. $25 Room
  $ 3 Men
  $ 2 Clerk
  $30

43. 140 lb

44. Yes; 3 quarters and 4 dimes, or 1 half dollar, 1 quarter and 4 dimes, or 1 quarter and 9 dimes. Other answers are possible.

45. 216 cm^3

46. Place six coins in each pan with one coin off to the side. If it balances, the heavier coin is the one on the side. If the pan does not balance, take the six coins on the heavier side and split them into two groups of three. Select the three heavier coins and weigh two coins. If the pan balances, it is the third coin. If the pan does not balance, you can identify the heavier coin.

47. 125,250 **48.** 16 blue **49.** 90

50. The fifth figure will be an octagon with sides of equal length. Inside the octagon will be a seven sided figure with each side of equal length. The figure will have one antenna.

51. 61

52. Some possible answers are shown. Others are possible.

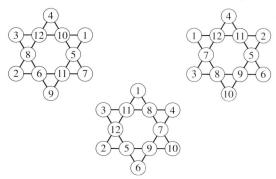

53. a) 2 **b)** 6 **c)** 24 **d)** 120
 e) $n(n-1)(n-2)\ldots 1$, (or $n!$), where $n =$ the number of people in line

CHAPTER TEST, PAGE 41

1. 19, 23, 27

2. $\frac{1}{16}, \frac{1}{32}, \frac{1}{64}$

3. a) The result is the original number plus 1.
 b) The result is the original number plus 1.
 c) The result will always be the original number plus 1.
 d) $n, 5n, 5n + 10, \dfrac{5n + 10}{5} = n + 2, n + 2 - 1 = n + 1$

The answers for Exercises 4–6 are approximate.

4. 12,000 **5.** 2,100,000 **6.** 9 square units

7. a) ≈ 23.03
 b) He is in the at risk range.

8. 36 min **9.** 32 cans **10.** $7\frac{1}{2}$ min

11. $\approx$ 39.5 in. by 29.6 in. (The actual dimensions are 100.5 cm by 76.5 cm.)

12. $49.00

13.

40	15	20
5	25	45
30	35	10

14. Less time if she had driven at 45 mph for the entire trip

15. $2 \cdot 6 \cdot 8 \cdot 9 \cdot 13$; 11 does not divide 11,232.

16. 243 jelly beans

17. a) $11.97
 b) $11.81
 c) Save 16 cents by using the 25% off coupon.

18. 24

CHAPTER 2

SECTION 2.1, PAGE 50

1. A set is a collection of objects.

3. Description, roster form, and set-builder notation; the set of counting numbers less than 7, $\{1, 2, 3, 4, 5, 6\}$, and $\{x \mid x \in N \text{ and } x < 7\}$

5. A set is finite if it either contains no elements or the number of elements in the set is a natural number.

7. Two sets are equivalent if they contain the same number of elements.

9. The empty set is a set that contains no elements.

11. A universal set is a set that contains all the elements for any specific discussion.

13. Not well defined

15. Well defined **17.** Well defined

19. Infinite **21.** Infinite **23.** Infinite

25. {Maine, Maryland, Massachusetts, Michigan, Minnesota, Mississippi, Missouri, Montana}

27. $\{11, 12, 13, 14, \ldots, 177\}$

29. $B = \{2, 4, 6, 8, \ldots\}$

31. $\{\ \}$ or $\varnothing$

33. $E = \{14, 15, 16, 17, \ldots, 84\}$

35. {Switzerland, Denmark, Sweden, United Kingdom, Germany, New Zealand}

37. {Switzerland, Denmark, Sweden, United Kingdom, Germany}

39. $\{2004, 2005\}$

41. $\{1998, 1999, 2000\}$

43. $B = \{x \mid x \in N \text{ and } 4 < x < 13\}$ or $B = \{x \mid x \in N \text{ and } 5 \le x \le 12\}$

45. $C = \{x \mid x \in N \text{ and } x \text{ is a multiple of } 3\}$

47. $E = \{x \mid x \in N \text{ and } x \text{ is odd}\}$

49. $C = \{x \mid x \text{ is February}\}$

51. Set A is the set of natural numbers less than or equal to 7.

53. Set V is the set of vowels in the English alphabet.

55. Set T is the set of species of trees.

57. Set S is the set of seasons.

59. {Johnson & Johnson, Google, Home Depot}

61. {United Airlines}

63. {1996, 1997, 1998, 1999}

65. {1998, 1999, 2000, 2001, 2002, 2003, 2004}

67. False; $\{e\}$ is a set, and not an element of the set.

69. False; h is not an element of the set.

71. False; 3 is an element of the set.

73. True **75.** 4 **77.** 0

79. Both **81.** Neither

83. Equivalent

85. a) Set A is the set of natural numbers greater than 2. Set B is the set of all numbers greater than 2.
b) Set A contains only natural numbers. Set B contains other types of numbers, including fractions and decimal numbers.
c) $A = \{3, 4, 5, 6, \dots\}$
d) No; because there are an infinite number of elements between any two elements in set B, we cannot write set B in roster form.

87. Cardinal **89.** Ordinal

91. Answers will vary.

93. Answers will vary.

SECTION 2.2 PAGE 58

1. Set A is a subset of set B, symbolized $A \subseteq B$, if and only if all the elements of set A are also elements of set B.

3. If $A \subseteq B$, then every element of set A is an element of set B. If $A \subset B$, then every element of set A is an element of set B and set $A \neq$ set B.

5. The number of proper subsets is determined by the formula $2^n - 1$, where n is the number of elements in the set.

7. False; Spanish is an element of the set, not a subset.

9. True **11.** True

13. False; the set $\{\varnothing\}$ contains the element $\varnothing$.

15. True

17. False; the set $\{0\}$ contains the element 0.

19. False; {swimming} is a set not an element.

21. True **23.** False; no set is a proper subset of itself.

25. $B \subseteq A, B \subset A$ **27.** $A \subseteq B, A \subset B$ **29.** $B \subseteq A, B \subset A$

31. $A = B, A \subseteq B, B \subseteq A$ **33.** { }

35. { }, {pen}, {pencil}, {pen, pencil}

37. a) { }, $\{a\}$, $\{b\}$, $\{c\}$, $\{d\}$, $\{a, b\}$, $\{a, c\}$, $\{a, d\}$, $\{b, c\}$, $\{b, d\}$, $\{c, d\}$, $\{a, b, c\}$, $\{a, b, d\}$, $\{a, c, d\}$, $\{b, c, d\}$, $\{a, b, c, d\}$
b) $\{a, b, c, d\}$

39. False **41.** True **43.** True **45.** True **47.** True

49. True **51.** 2^4 or 16 **53.** 2^6 or 64 **55.** $E = F$

57. a) Yes **b)** No **c)** Yes **59.** 1 **61.** Yes

SECTION 2.3, PAGE 68

1.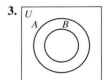

3.

5.

7. Determine the elements that are in the universal set that are not in set A.

9. Select the elements common to both set A and set B.

11. a) *Or* is generally interpreted to mean *union*.
b) *And* is generally interpreted to mean *intersection*.

13. The difference of two sets A and B is the set of elements that belong to set A but not to set B.

15.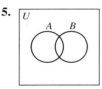

17.

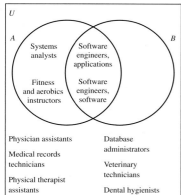

19. The set of animals in U.S. zoos that are not in the San Diego Zoo

21. The set of insurance companies in the United States that do not offer life insurance

23. The set of insurance companies in the United States that offer life insurance or car insurance

25. The set of insurance companies in the United States that offer life insurance and do not offer car insurance

27. The set of furniture stores that sell mattresses and outdoor furniture

29. The set of furniture stores that do not sell outdoor furniture and sell leather furniture

31. The set of furniture stores that sell mattresses or outdoor furniture or leather furniture

33. $\{b, c, t, w, a, h\}$ **35.** $\{a, h\}$

37. $\{c, w, b, t, a, h, f, r, d, g\}$ **39.** $\{p, m, z\}$

41. $\{L, \Delta, @, \$, *\}$

43. $\{L, \Delta, @, *, \$, R, \Box, \alpha, \infty, \Sigma, Z\}$

45. $\{R, \Box, \alpha, *, \$, \infty, Z, \Sigma\}$ **47.** $\{R, \Box, \alpha\}$

49. $\{1, 2, 3, 4, 5, 6, 8\}$ **51.** $\{1, 5, 7, 8\}$ **53.** $\{7\}$

55. $\{\ \}$ **57.** $\{7\}$ **59.** $\{a, e, h, i, j, k\}$

61. $\{a, f, i\}$ **63.** $\{b, c, d, e, g, h, j, k\}$

65. $\{a, c, d, e, f, g, h, i, j, k\}$

67. $\{a, b, c, d, e, f, g, h, i, j, k\}$, or U

69. $\{2, 6, 9\}$ **71.** $\{1, 4\}$ **73.** $\{1, 3, 4, 5, 7, 8, 10\}$

75. $\{4, 9\}$ **77.** $\{(a, 1), (a, 2), (b, 1), (b, 2), (c, 1), (c, 2)\}$

79. No. The ordered pairs are not the same. For example, $(a, 1) \neq (1, a)$.

81. 6   **83.** $\{\ \}$ **85.** $\{2, 4, 6, 8\}$, or B **87.** $\{7, 9\}$

89. $\{1, 3, 5, 6, 7, 8, 9\}$ **91.** $\{6, 8\}$

93. $\{1, 2, 3, 4, 5, 6, 7, 8, 9\}$, or U

95. $\{1, 2, 3, 4, 5\}$, or C

97. A set and its complement will always be disjoint. For example, if $U = \{1, 2, 3\}$ and $A = \{1, 2\}$, then $A' = \{3\}$, and $A \cap A' = \{\ \}$.

99. 49

101. **a)** $8 = 4 + 6 - 2$ **b)** and **c)** Answers will vary.

103. $\{1, 2, 3, 4, \dots\}$, or A **105.** $\{4, 8, 12, 16, \dots\}$, or B

107. $\{2, 4, 6, 8, \dots\}$, or C **109.** $\{2, 6, 10, 14, 18, \dots\}$

111. $\{2, 6, 10, 14, 18, \dots\}$ **113.** U **115.** A

117. U **119.** U **121.** $B \subseteq A$

123. A and B are disjoint sets.   **125.** $A \subseteq B$

SECTION 2.4, PAGE 77

1. 8   **3.** II, IV, VI   **5.** 5

7. a) Yes

b) No, one specific case cannot be used as proof.

c) No

9.

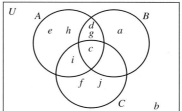

11.

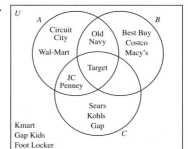

13.

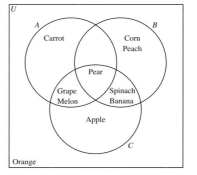

15.

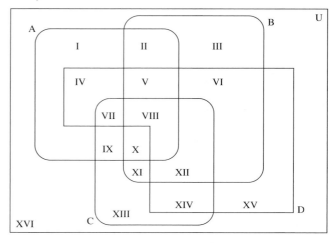

17. V   **19.** I   **21.** III   **23.** II   **25.** VIII   **27.** III
29. VI   **31.** III   **33.** III   **35.** V   **37.** II   **39.** VII
41. I   **43.** VIII   **45.** VI   **47.** $\{1, 3, 4, 5, 7, 9\}$
49. $\{2, 3, 4, 5, 6, 8, 12, 14\}$ **51.** $\{3, 4, 5\}$
53. $\{1, 2, 3, 7, 9, 10, 11, 12, 13, 14\}$
55. $\{1, 2, 3, 4, 5, 6, 7, 8, 9, 12, 14\}$
57. $\{2, 11, 12, 13, 14\}$
59. $\{2, 6, 8, 10, 11, 12, 13, 14\}$
61. Yes   **63.** No   **65.** No   **67.** Yes   **69.** No
71. Yes   **73.** Yes   **75.** Yes   **77.** No
79. $(A \cup B)'$ **81.** $(A \cup B) \cap C'$
83. a) Both equal $\{6, 7\}$.   **b)** Answers will vary.
    c) Both are represented by the regions IV, V, VI.

85.

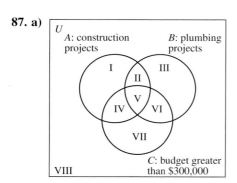

87. a)

```
U
A: construction        B: plumbing
projects               projects
        I        III
           II
        V
     IV    VI
        VII
                  C: budget greater
VIII              than $300,000
```

b) V; $A \cap B \cap C$
c) VI; $A' \cap B \cap C$
d) I; $A \cap B' \cap C'$

89. a)

```
A                                      B      U
      I          II          III
         IV       V        VI
            VII  VIII
         IX   X
            XI     XII
                XIV      XV
            XIII                    D
XVI   C
```

b)

Region	Set	Region	Set
I	$A \cap B' \cap C' \cap D'$	IX	$A \cap B' \cap C \cap D'$
II	$A \cap B \cap C' \cap D'$	X	$A \cap B \cap C \cap D'$
III	$A' \cap B \cap C' \cap D'$	XI	$A' \cap B \cap C \cap D'$
IV	$A \cap B' \cap C' \cap D$	XII	$A' \cap B \cap C \cap D$
V	$A \cap B \cap C' \cap D$	XIII	$A' \cap B' \cap C \cap D'$
VI	$A' \cap B \cap C' \cap D$	XIV	$A' \cap B' \cap C \cap D$
VII	$A \cap B' \cap C \cap D$	XV	$A' \cap B' \cap C' \cap D$
VIII	$A \cap B \cap C \cap D$	XVI	$A' \cap B' \cap C' \cap D'$

SECTION 2.5, PAGE 86

1.
```
U
Clubs          Intramural
               sports
      14   18   9
109
```
a) 14
b) 9
c) 109

3.
```
U
Family room    Deck
      17   30   12
24
```
a) 17
b) 12
c) 59

5.
```
U  Professional
   sports team   Symphony
     3    6    2
        2  5  4
          4
7            Children's museum
```
a) 3
b) 6
c) 22
d) 11
e) 12

7.
```
U
Mysteries  Science fiction
     22   11   17
        9  2  3
          15
6                Romances
```
a) 22
b) 11
c) 64
d) 50
e) 23

9.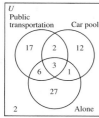

a) 17
b) 27
c) 2
d) 31
e) 2

11.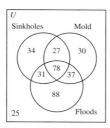

a) 67
b) 237
c) 37
d) 25

13. In a Venn diagram, regions II, IV, and V contain a total of 37 cars driven by women. This total is greater than the 35 cars driven by women, as given in the exercise.

15.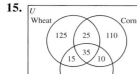

a) 410
b) 35
c) 90
d) 50

SECTION 2.6, PAGE 93

1. An infinite set is a set that can be placed in a one-to-one correspondence with a proper subset of itself.

3. $\{5, 6, 7, 8, 9, \ldots, n + 4, \ldots\}$
$\downarrow \downarrow \downarrow \downarrow \downarrow \qquad \downarrow$
$\{6, 7, 8, 9, 10, \ldots, n + 5, \ldots\}$

5. $\{3, 5, 7, 9, 11, \ldots, 2n + 1, \ldots\}$
$\downarrow \downarrow \downarrow \downarrow \downarrow \qquad \downarrow$
$\{5, 7, 9, 11, 13, \ldots, 2n + 3, \ldots\}$

7. $\{3, 7, 11, 15, 19, \ldots, 4n - 1, \ldots\}$
$\downarrow \downarrow \downarrow \downarrow \downarrow \qquad \downarrow$
$\{7, 11, 15, 19, 23, \ldots, 4n + 3, \ldots\}$

9. $\{6, 11, 16, 21, 26, \ldots, 5n + 1, \ldots\}$
$\downarrow \downarrow \downarrow \downarrow \downarrow \qquad \downarrow$
$\{11, 16, 21, 26, 31, \ldots, 5n + 6, \ldots\}$

11. $\left\{\dfrac{1}{2}, \dfrac{1}{4}, \dfrac{1}{6}, \dfrac{1}{8}, \dfrac{1}{10}, \ldots, \dfrac{1}{2n}, \ldots\right\}$
$\downarrow \downarrow \downarrow \downarrow \downarrow \qquad \downarrow$
$\left\{\dfrac{1}{4}, \dfrac{1}{6}, \dfrac{1}{8}, \dfrac{1}{10}, \dfrac{1}{12}, \ldots, \dfrac{1}{2n + 2}, \ldots\right\}$

13. $\{1, 2, 3, 4, 5, \ldots, n, \ldots\}$
$\downarrow \downarrow \downarrow \downarrow \downarrow \qquad \downarrow$
$\{3, 6, 9, 12, 15, \ldots, 3n, \ldots\}$

15. $\{1, 2, 3, 4, 5, \ldots, n, \ldots\}$
$\downarrow \downarrow \downarrow \downarrow \downarrow \qquad \downarrow$
$\{4, 6, 8, 10, 12, \ldots, 2n + 2, \ldots\}$

17. $\{1, 2, 3, 4, 5, \ldots, n, \ldots\}$
$\downarrow \downarrow \downarrow \downarrow \downarrow \qquad \downarrow$
$\{2, 5, 8, 11, 14, \ldots, 3n - 1, \ldots\}$

19. $\{1, 2, 3, 4, 5, \ldots, n, \ldots\}$
$\downarrow \downarrow \downarrow \downarrow \downarrow \qquad \downarrow$
$\{5, 9, 13, 17, 21, \ldots, 4n + 1, \ldots\}$

21. $\{1, 2, 3, 4, 5, \ldots, n, \ldots\}$
$\downarrow \downarrow \downarrow \downarrow \downarrow \qquad \downarrow$
$\left\{\dfrac{1}{3}, \dfrac{1}{4}, \dfrac{1}{5}, \dfrac{1}{6}, \dfrac{1}{7}, \ldots, \dfrac{1}{n + 2}, \ldots\right\}$

23. $\{1, 2, 3, 4, 5, \ldots, n, \ldots\}$
$\downarrow \downarrow \downarrow \downarrow \downarrow \qquad \downarrow$
$\{1, 4, 9, 16, 25, \ldots, n^2, \ldots\}$

25. $\{1, 2, 3, 4, 5, \ldots, n, \ldots\}$
$\downarrow \downarrow \downarrow \downarrow \downarrow \qquad \downarrow$
$\{3, 9, 27, 81, 243, \ldots, 3^n, \ldots\}$

27. $=$ **29.** $=$ **31.** $=$

REVIEW EXERCISES, PAGE 94

1. True

2. False; the word *best* makes the statement not well defined.

3. True

4. False; no set is a proper subset of itself.

5. False; the elements $6, 12, 18, 24, \ldots$ are members of both sets.

6. True

7. False; both sets do not contain exactly the same elements.

8. True   **9.** True   **10.** True   **11.** True   **12.** True

13. True   **14.** True   **15.** $A = \{7, 9, 11, 13, 15\}$

16. $\{\text{Colorado, Nebraska, Missouri, Oklahoma}\}$

17. $C = \{1, 2, 3, 4, \ldots, 161\}$

18. $D = \{9, 10, 11, 12, \ldots, 96\}$

19. $A = \{x \mid x \in N \text{ and } 52 < x < 100\}$

20. $B = \{x \mid x \in N \text{ and } x > 42\}$

21. $C = \{x \mid x \in N \text{ and } x < 5\}$

22. $D = \{x \mid x \in N \text{ and } 27 \le x \le 51\}$

23. A is the set of capital letters in the English alphabet from E through M, inclusive.

24. B is the set of U.S. coins with a value of less than a dollar.

25. C is the set of the last three lowercase letters in the English alphabet.

26. D is the set of numbers greater than or equal to 3 and less than 9.

27. $\{5, 7\}$ **28.** $\{1, 2, 3, 4, 5, 6, 7, 8\}$ **29.** $\{9, 10\}$

30. $\{1, 2, 4, 6, 7, 8, 10\}$ **31.** $\{1, 3\}$ **32.** $\{1, 7\}$

33. $\{(1, 1), (1, 7), (1, 10), (3, 1), (3, 7), (3, 10), (5, 1), (5, 7),$
$(5, 10), (7, 1), (7, 7), (7, 10)\}$

34. $\{(5, 1), (5, 3), (5, 5), (5, 7), (7, 1), (7, 3), (7, 5), (7, 7), (9, 1),$
$(9, 3), (9, 5), (9, 7), (10, 1), (10, 3), (10, 5), (10, 7)\}$

35. 16   **36.** 15

37.

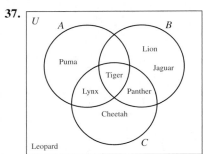

38. $\{a, c, d, f, g, i, k, l\}$ **39.** $\{i, k\}$

40. $\{a, b, c, d, f, g, h, i, k, l\}$ **41.** $\{f\}$ **42.** $\{a, f, i\}$

43. $\{a, b, d, f, h, i, l\}$ **44.** True   **45.** True   **46.** II

47. III   **48.** I   **49.** IV   **50.** IV   **51.** II   **52.** $450

53.

```
U Chocolate    Peanut Butter
  Chip
   60    30    10
      40  70  80
         20
  5            Sugar
```

a) 315
b) 10
c) 30
d) 110

54.

```
U
  CSI: NY    CSI: Miami
   38    41    99
      37  59  28
         161
           CSI: Crime
  47         Scene
             Investigation
```

a) 38
b) 298
c) 28
d) 236
e) 106

55. $\{2, 4, 6, 8, 10, \ldots, \quad 2n, \ldots\}$
$\downarrow \downarrow \downarrow \downarrow \downarrow \qquad \downarrow$
$\{4, 6, 8, 10, 12, \ldots, 2n + 2, \ldots\}$

56. $\{3, 5, 7, 9, 11, \ldots, 2n + 1, \ldots\}$
$\downarrow \downarrow \downarrow \downarrow \downarrow \qquad \downarrow$
$\{5, 7, 9, 11, 13, \ldots, 2n + 3, \ldots\}$

57. $\{1, 2, 3, 4, 5, \ldots, \quad n, \ldots\}$
$\downarrow \downarrow \downarrow \downarrow \downarrow \qquad \downarrow$
$\{5, 8, 11, 14, 17, \ldots, 3n + 2, \ldots\}$

58. $\{1, 2, 3, 4, 5, \ldots, \quad n, \ldots\}$
$\downarrow \downarrow \downarrow \downarrow \downarrow \qquad \downarrow$
$\{4, 9, 14, 19, 24, \ldots, 5n - 1, \ldots\}$

CHAPTER TEST, PAGE 97

1. True

2. False; the sets do not contain exactly the same elements.

3. True

4. False; the second set has no subset that contains the element 7.

5. False; the empty set is a subset of every set.

6. False; the set has 2^4, or 16 subsets.   **7.** True

8. False; for any set A, $A \cup A' = U$, not $\{\ \}$.   **9.** True

10. $A = \{1, 2, 3, 4, 5, 6, 7, 8\}$

11. Set A is the set of natural numbers less than 9.

12. $\{7, 9\}$ **13.** $\{3, 5, 7, 9, 13\}$

14. $\{3, 5, 7, 9\}$, or A **15.** 2   **16.** $\{3, 5\}$

17. $\{(3, 3), (3, 11), (3, 15), (5, 3), (5, 11), (5, 15), (7, 3),$
$(7, 11), (7, 15), (9, 3), (9, 11), (9, 15)\}$

18.

```
U
  A              B
   5    7 9    13
      3     11
         15
              C
```

19. Equal

20.

```
U
  Cotton candy   Peanuts
   5    17    16
      19  35  22
         31
  10           Popcorn
```

a) 52   b) 10   c) 93   d) 17   e) 38   f) 31

21. $\{7, 8, 9, 10, 11, \ldots, n + 6, \ldots\}$
$\downarrow \downarrow \downarrow \downarrow \downarrow \qquad \downarrow$
$\{8, 9, 10, 11, 12, \ldots, n + 7, \ldots\}$

22. $\{1, 2, 3, 4, 5, \ldots, \quad n, \ldots\}$
$\downarrow \downarrow \downarrow \downarrow \downarrow \qquad \downarrow$
$\{1, 3, 5, 7, 9, \ldots, 2n - 1, \ldots\}$

CHAPTER 3

SECTION 3.1, PAGE 109

1. a) A sentence that can be judged either true or false is called a statement.
 b) A simple statement is a statement that conveys only one idea.
 c) Compound statements are statements consisting of two or more simple statements.

3. *All, none,* and *some* are quantifiers.

5. a) Some are.   **b)** All are.
 c) Some are not.   **d)** None are.

7. a) No, the *exclusive or* is used when one or the other of the events can take place, but not both.
 b) Yes, the *inclusive or* is used when one or the other, or both events can take place.
 c) *Inclusive or*

9. Compound; disjunction, $\vee$

11. Compound; biconditional, $\leftrightarrow$

13. Compound; conjunction, $\wedge$

15. Simple statement

17. Compound; negation, $\sim$

19. Compound; conjunction, $\wedge$

21. Compound; negation, $\sim$

23. Some butterflies are not insects.

25. Some aldermen are running for mayor.

27. All turtles have claws.

29. Some bicycles have three wheels.

31. All pine trees produce pinecones.

33. No pedestrians are in the crosswalk.

35. $\sim p$ **37.** $\sim q \vee \sim p$ **39.** $\sim p \rightarrow \sim q$

41. $\sim p \wedge q$ **43.** $\sim q \leftrightarrow p$ **45.** $\sim(p \vee q)$

47. Ken Jennings did not win more than $3 million.

49. Ken Jennings won 74 games of *Jeopardy!* and Ken Jennings won more than $3 million.

51. If Ken Jennings did not win 74 games of *Jeopardy!* then Ken Jennings won more than $3 million.

53. Ken Jennings did not win 74 games of *Jeopardy!* or Ken Jennings did not win more than $3 million.

55. It is false that Ken Jennings won 74 games of *Jeopardy!* and Ken Jennings won more than $3 million.

57. $(p \wedge \sim q) \wedge r$ **59.** $(p \wedge q) \vee r$ **61.** $p \rightarrow (q \vee \sim r)$

63. $(r \leftrightarrow q) \wedge p$ **65.** $q \rightarrow (p \leftrightarrow r)$

67. The water is 70° or the sun is shining, and we do not go swimming.

69. The water is not 70°, and the sun is shining or we go swimming.

71. If we do not go swimming, then the sun is shining and the water is 70°.

73. If the sun is shining then we go swimming, and the water is 70°.

75. The sun is shining if and only if the water is 70°, and we go swimming.

77. Not permissible, you cannot have both soup and salad. The *or* used on menus is the *exclusive or.*

79. Not permissible, you cannot have both potatoes and pasta. The *or* used on menus is the *exclusive or.*

81. a) $w \wedge \sim p$ **b)** Conjunction

83. a) $\sim(b \rightarrow \sim p)$ **b)** Negation

85. a) $(f \vee v) \rightarrow h$ **b)** Conditional

87. a) $c \leftrightarrow (\sim f \vee p)$ **b)** Biconditional

89. a) $(c \leftrightarrow w) \vee s$ **b)** Disjunction

91. a) Answers will vary.
 b) Answers will vary.

SECTION 3.2, PAGE 122

1. a) 4   **b)**

p	q
T	T
T	F
F	T
F	F

3. a)

p	q	$p \wedge q$
T	T	T
T	F	F
F	T	F
F	F	F

 b) Only when both p and q are true

 c)

p	q	$p \vee q$
T	T	T
T	F	T
F	T	T
F	F	F

 d) Only when both p and q are false

5. F   **7.** T   **9.** F   **11.** T
 F   F   T   F
       T   T   T
       T   T   T

13. T   **15.** T   **17.** F   **19.** T
 F   F   F   T
 T   T   T   T
 T   T   F   T
 F   T   F   F
 F   F   F   F
 T   T   T   T
 T   F   T   F

A-10 ANSWERS

21. $p \wedge q$
T
F
F
F

23. $p \wedge {\sim}q$
F
T
F
F

25. ${\sim}(p \wedge q)$
F
T
T
T

27. $p \vee (q \vee r)$
T
T
T
T
T
T
T
F

29. $p \wedge (q \vee {\sim}q)$
T
T
F
F

31. a) False   b) True
33. a) True   b) True
35. a) True   b) False
37. a) False   b) True
39. a) True   b) True
41. a) True   b) True
43. True   45. True   47. False   49. False
51. False   53. True   55. True   57. False

59. $p \wedge {\sim}q$
F
T
F
F
True in case 2

61. $p \vee {\sim}q$
T
T
F
T
True in cases 1, 2, and 4, when p is true, or when p and q are both false.

63. $(r \vee q) \wedge p$
T
T
T
F
F
F
F
F
True in cases 1, 2, and 3

65. $q \vee (p \wedge {\sim}r)$
T
T
F
T
T
T
F
F
True in cases 1, 2, 4, 5, and 6. True except when p, q, r have truth values TFT, FFT, or FFF.

67. a) Mr. Duncan and Mrs. Tuttle qualify.
b) Mrs. Rusinek does not qualify, since their combined income is less than $46,000.

69. a) Wing Park qualifies; the other four do not.
b) Gina Vela is returning on April 2. Kara Sharo is returning on a Monday. Christos Supernaw is not staying over on a Saturday. Alex Chang is returning on a Monday.

71. T
T
T
T
F
T
F
T

73. Yes

SECTION 3.3, PAGE 133

1. a)

p	q	$p \to q$
T	T	T
T	F	F
F	T	T
F	F	T

b) The conditional is false only when the antecedent is true and the consequent is false.

c)

p	q	$p \leftrightarrow q$
T	T	T
T	F	F
F	T	F
F	F	T

d) The biconditional is true only when both p and q are true or when p and q are both false.

3. a) Substitute the truth values for the simple statements. Then evaluate the compound statement, using the assigned truth values.
b) True

5. A self-contradiction is a compound statement that is always false.

7. T
T
T
F

9. T
F
F
F

11. F
T
T
F

13. T
T
F
T

15. F
T
T
T

17. T
T
T
T
T
F
F
F

19. T
T
T
F
F
F
F
T

21. F
F
T
F
T
T
F
T

23. T
T
T
T
T
F
F
F

25. T
T
T
F
T
T
F
T

27. $p \to (q \wedge r)$
T
F
F
F
T
T
T
T

29. $(p \leftrightarrow q) \vee r$
T
T
T
F
T
F
T
T

31. $(\sim p \rightarrow q) \vee r$
T
T
T
T
T
T
T
F

33. Neither   **35.** Self-contradiction   **37.** Tautology

39. Not an implication   **41.** Implication   **43.** Implication

45. True   **47.** False   **49.** False   **51.** True

53. True   **55.** True   **57.** True   **59.** False

61. True   **63.** True   **65.** True   **67.** False

69. False   **71.** True   **73.** True   **75.** True

77. No, the statement only states what will occur if your sister gets straight A's. If your sister does not get straight A's, your parents may still get her a computer.

79. F
F
T
T
T
F
F
F

81. It is a tautology. The statement may be expressed as $(p \rightarrow q) \vee (\sim p \rightarrow q)$, where *p:* It is a head and *q:* I win. This statement is a tautology.

83.
Tiger	Boots	Sam	Sue
Blue	Yellow	Red	Green
Nine Lives	Whiskas	Friskies	Meow Mix

SECTION 3.4, PAGE 146

1. a) Statements that have exactly the same truth values

b) Construct truth tables for each statement. If both have the same truth values in the answer columns of the truth tables, the statements are equivalent.

3. $\sim (p \wedge q) \Leftrightarrow \sim p \vee \sim q$
$\sim (p \vee q) \Leftrightarrow \sim p \wedge \sim q$

5. a and c, b and d   **7.** $p \wedge \sim q$ **9.** Not equivalent

11. Not equivalent   **13.** Equivalent   **15.** Equivalent

17. Equivalent   **19.** Equivalent   **21.** Equivalent

23. Equivalent   **25.** Not equivalent

27. Not equivalent   **29.** Equivalent

31. The Rocky Mountains are not in the East or the Appalachian Mountains are not in the West.

33. It is false that the watch was a Swatch or the watch was a Swiss Army watch.

35. It is false that the hotel has a weight room and the conference center has an auditorium.

37. If Ashley Tabai takes the new job, then it is false that she will move and she will not buy a new house in town.

39. Ena Salter does not select a new textbook or she will have to write a new syllabus.

41. If Bob the Tomato didn't visit the nursing home then he did not visit the Cub Scout meeting.

43. The plumbers do not meet in Kansas City or the Rainmakers will provide the entertainment.

45. If Chase is hiding, then the pitcher is broken.

47. We go to Cincinnati and we will not go to the zoo.

49. It is false that if I am cold then the heater is working.

51. Borders has a sale and we will not buy $100 worth of books.

53. It is false that if John Deere will hire new workers then the city of Dubuque will not retrain the workers.

55. *Converse:* If we can finish the quilt in 1 week, then we work every night.
Inverse: If we do not work every night, then we cannot finish the quilt in 1 week.
Contrapositive: If we cannot finish the quilt in 1 week, then we do not work every night.

57. *Converse:* If I buy silver jewelry, then I go to Mexico.
Inverse: If I do not go to Mexico, then I do not buy silver jewelry.
Contrapositive: If I do not buy silver jewelry, then I do not go to Mexico.

59. *Converse:* If I scream, then that annoying paper clip shows up on my computer screen.
Inverse: If that annoying paper clip does not show up on my computer screen, then I will not scream.
Contrapositive: If I do not scream, then that annoying paper clip does not show up on my screen.

61. If a natural number is divisible by 10, then the natural number is divisible by 5. True.

63. If a natural number is not divisible by 6, then the natural number is not divisible by 3. False.

65. If two lines are not parallel, then the two lines intersect in at least one point. True.

67. b) and **c)** are equivalent.

69. a) and **c)** are equivalent.

71. b) and **c)** are equivalent.

73. b) and **c)** are equivalent.

75. None are equivalent.

77. None are equivalent.

79. a) and **c)** are equivalent.

81. a) and **b)** are equivalent.

83. True. If $p \rightarrow q$ is false, it must be of the form $\text{T} \rightarrow \text{F}$. Therefore, the converse must be of the form $\text{F} \rightarrow \text{T}$, which is true.

85. False. A conditional statement and its contrapositive always have the same truth values.

87. Answers will vary.

89. Answers will vary.

SECTION 3.5, PAGE 159

1. a) The conclusion necessarily follows from the given set of premises.
   b) The conclusion does not necessarily follow from the given set of premises.

3. Yes, if the conclusion does not necessarily follow from the premises, the argument is invalid, even if the conclusion is a true statement.

5. Yes, if the conclusion does not follow from the set of premises.

7. a) $p \rightarrow q$
$$\frac{p}{\therefore q}$$
   b) Answers will vary.

9. a) $p \rightarrow q$
$$\frac{\sim q}{\therefore \sim p}$$
   b) Answers will vary.

11. a) $p \rightarrow q$
$$\frac{q}{\therefore p}$$
   b) Answers will vary.

13. Invalid   **15.** Valid   **17.** Valid   **19.** Invalid

21. Valid   **23.** Valid   **25.** Valid   **27.** Invalid

29. Invalid   **31.** Valid

33. a) $p \rightarrow q$
$$\frac{\sim p}{\therefore \sim q}$$
   b) Invalid

35. a) $p \rightarrow q$
$$\frac{p}{\therefore q}$$
   b) Valid

37. a) $p \rightarrow q$
$$\frac{\sim q}{\therefore \sim p}$$
   b) Valid

39. a) $p \rightarrow q$
$$\frac{q}{\therefore p}$$
   b) Invalid

41. a) $p \vee q$
$$\frac{\sim p}{\therefore q}$$
   b) Valid

43. a) $p \rightarrow q$
$$\frac{q \rightarrow r}{\therefore p \rightarrow r}$$
   b) Valid

45. a) $p \wedge q$
$$\frac{q \rightarrow r}{\therefore r \rightarrow p}$$
   b) Valid

47. a) $s \wedge g$
$$\frac{g \rightarrow c}{\therefore s \rightarrow c}$$
   b) Valid

49. a) $h \rightarrow b$
$$\frac{\sim p \rightarrow \sim b}{\therefore h \rightarrow p}$$
   b) Valid

51. a) $p \rightarrow q$
$$\frac{\sim q}{\therefore \sim p}$$
   b) Valid

53. a) $p \vee q$
$$\frac{\sim p}{\therefore q}$$
   b) Valid

55. a) $t \wedge g$
$$\frac{\sim t \vee \sim g}{\therefore \sim t}$$
   b) Valid

57. a) $c \wedge \sim h$
$$\frac{h \rightarrow c}{\therefore h}$$
   b) Invalid

59. a) $f \rightarrow d$
$$\frac{d \rightarrow \sim s}{\therefore f \rightarrow s}$$
   b) Invalid

61. Therefore, your face will break out.

63. Therefore, I am stressed out.

65. Therefore, you did not close the deal.

67. Therefore, if you do not pay off your credit card bills, then the bank makes money.

69. No. The conditional statement will always be true, and therefore it will be a tautology, and a valid argument.

SECTION 3.6, PAGE 167

1. a) It is a valid argument.
   b) It is an invalid argument.

3. a)

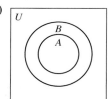

   b)

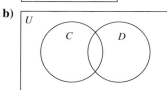

   c)

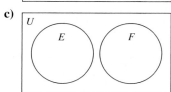

5. Yes, if the conclusion necessarily follows from the premises, the argument is valid.

7. Valid   **9.** Valid   **11.** Invalid

13. Valid   **15.** Invalid   **17.** Invalid

19. Invalid   **21.** Valid   **23.** Invalid   **25.** Invalid

27. Valid   **29.** Invalid

SECTION 3.7, PAGE 174

1. a) Answers will vary.
   b) ∧ (and)

3. It is a series circuit; therefore, both switches must be closed for current to flow and the lightbulb to go on. When the p switch is closed, the $\overline{p}$ switch is open and no current will flow through the circuit. When the $\overline{p}$ switch is closed, the p switch is open and no current will flow through the circuit.

5. a) $p \wedge q$
   b) The lightbulb will be on when both p and q are closed.

7. a) $(p \vee q) \wedge \sim q$
   b) The lightbulb will be on when p is closed and q is open.

9. a) $(p \wedge q) \wedge [(p \wedge \sim q) \vee r]$
   b) The lightbulb will be on when p, q, and r are all closed.

11. a) $p \vee q \vee (r \wedge \sim p)$
   b) The lightbulb will be on in all cases except when p, q, and r are all open.

13.
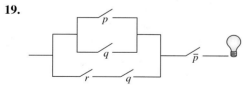

15.
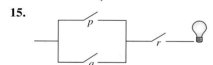

17.
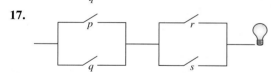

19.
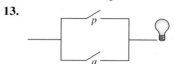

21. $p \vee q$; $\sim p \wedge \sim q$; not equivalent

23. $[(p \wedge q) \vee r] \wedge p$; $(q \vee r) \wedge p$; equivalent

25. $(p \vee \sim p) \wedge q \wedge r$; $p \wedge q \wedge r$; not equivalent

27. a) **b)**
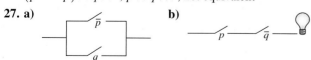

REVIEW EXERCISES, PAGE 176

1. Some gift cards are exchangeable.

2. Some bears are not mammals.

3. No women are presidents.

4. All pine trees are green.

5. The coffee is Maxwell House or the coffee is hot.

6. The coffee is not hot and the coffee is strong.

7. If the coffee is hot, then the coffee is strong and the coffee is not Maxwell House.

8. The coffee is Maxwell House if and only if the coffee is not strong.

9. The coffee is not Maxwell House, if and only if the coffee is strong and the coffee is not hot.

10. The coffee is Maxwell House or the coffee is not hot, and the coffee is not strong.

11. $r \wedge q$ **12.** $p \rightarrow r$ **13.** $(r \rightarrow q) \vee \sim p$
14. $(q \leftrightarrow p) \wedge \sim r$ **15.** $(r \wedge q) \vee \sim p$ **16.** $\sim (r \wedge q)$

17. F **18.** T **19.** T **20.** T **21.** F **22.** F

17	18	19	20	21	22
F	F	T	F	T	T
T	F	T	T	F	T
F	F	T	T	F	T
		T	F	T	T
		F	F	T	T
		F	F	T	T
		T	F	T	T

23. False **24.** True **25.** False **26.** True **27.** True
28. True **29.** False **30.** False **31.** Not equivalent
32. Equivalent **33.** Equivalent **34.** Not equivalent

35. It is false that if Bobby Darin sang *Mack the Knife* then Elvis wrote *Memphis*.

36. If Lynn Swann did not play for the Steelers, then Jack Tatum played for the Raiders.

37. Altec Lansing does not produce only speakers and Harman Kardon does not produce only stereo receivers.

38. It is false that Travis Tritt won an Academy Award or Randy Jackson does commercials for Milk Bone Dog Biscuits.

39. The temperature is above 32° or we will go ice fishing at O'Leary's Lake.

40. a) If you soften your opinion, then you hear a new voice today.
   b) If you do not hear a new voice today, then you do not soften your opinion.
   c) If you do not soften your opinion, then you do not hear a new voice today.

41. a) If we will learn the table's value, then we take the table to *Antiques Roadshow*.
   b) If we do not take the table to *Antiques Roadshow*, then we will not learn the table's value.
   c) If we will not learn the table's value, then we do not take the table to *Antiques Roadshow*.

42. a) If Maureen Gerald is helping at the school, then she is not in attendance.

b) If Maureen Gerald is in attendance, then she is not helping at the school.

c) If Maureen Gerald is not helping at the school, then she is in attendance.

43. a) If we will not buy a desk at Miller's Furniture, then the desk is made by Winner's Only and the desk is in the Rose catalog.

b) If the desk is not made by Winner's Only or the desk is not in the Rose catalog, then we will buy a desk at Miller's Furniture.

c) If we will buy a desk at Miller's Furniture, then the desk is not made by Winner's Only or the desk is not in the Rose catalog.

44. a) If I let you attend the prom, then you will get straight A's on your report card.

b) If you do not get straight A's on your report card, then I will not let you attend the prom.

c) If I will not let you attend the prom, then you did not get straight A's on your report card.

45. a), b), and **c)** are equivalent.   **46.** None are equivalent.

47. a) and **c)** are equivalent.   **48.** None are equivalent.

49. Invalid **50.** Valid **51.** Valid **52.** Invalid

53. Invalid **54.** Invalid **55.** Invalid **56.** Invalid

57. a) $p \wedge [(q \wedge r) \vee \sim p]$

b) The lightbulb will be on when p, q, and r are all closed.

58.

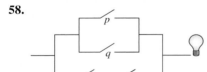

59. Equivalent

CHAPTER TEST, PAGE 179

1. $(p \wedge r) \vee \sim q$ **2.** $(r \rightarrow q) \vee \sim p$ **3.** $\sim (r \leftrightarrow \sim q)$

4. Ann is not the secretary and Elaine is the president, if and only if Dick is not the vice president.

5. If Ann is the secretary or Dick is not the vice president, then Elaine is the president.

6. F **7.** T
   T   T
   F   T
   F   T
   F   F
   F   T
   F   T
   F   F

8. True **9.** True **10.** True **11.** True **12.** Equivalent

13. a) and **b)** are equivalent.

14. a) and **b)** are equivalent.

15. $s \rightarrow f$ **16.** Invalid
$\dfrac{f \rightarrow p}{\therefore\ s \rightarrow p}$
Valid

17. Some highways are not roads.

18. Nick did not play football or Max did not play baseball.

19. *Converse:* If today is Saturday, then the garbage truck comes.
Inverse: If the garbage truck does not come, then today is not Saturday.
Contrapositive: If today is not Saturday, then the garbage truck does not come.

20.

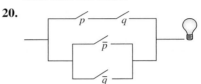

CHAPTER 4

SECTION 4.1, PAGE 188

1. A number is a quantity, and it answers the question "How many?" A numeral is a symbol used to represent the number.

3. A system of numeration consists of a set of numerals and a scheme or rule for combining the numerals to represent numbers.

5. The Hindu–Arabic numeration system

7. In a multiplicative system, there are numerals for each number less than the base and for powers of the base. Each numeral less than the base is multiplied by a numeral for the power of the base, and these products are added to obtain the number.

9. 345   **11.** 2423   **13.** 334,214   **15.** ∩∩∩∩∩||

17. ⌞⌞∩∩∩∩||||| **19.** ◁⟍⟍⟍⟍⟍⟍⌞⌞⌞99999999∩∩∩||||||

21. 8   **23.** 43   **25.** 1236   **27.** 2946   **29.** 12,666

31. 9464   **33.** XXVII   **35.** CCCXLI   **37.** MMV

39. $\overline{\text{IVDCCXCIII}}$ **41.** $\overline{\text{IXCMXCIX}}$ **43.** $\overline{\text{XXDCXLIV}}$

45. 74   **47.** 4081   **49.** 8550   **51.** 4003

53. 五
十
三
   55. 三
百
七
十
八
   57. 四
千
二
百
六
十
   59. 七
千
零
五
十
六

61. 26 **63.** 279 **65.** 2883
67. $\nu\theta$ **69.** $\psi\kappa f$ **71.** $^\iota\varepsilon\varepsilon$
73. 1021, MXXI, 一, $^\iota\alpha\kappa\alpha$

千
零
二十
一

75. 527, $\text{99999} \cap \cap \text{IIIIII}$,
DXXVII, $\phi\kappa\zeta$

77. $\overline{\text{CMXCIX}}\text{CMXCIX}$

79. Advantage: You can write some numerals more compactly.
Disadvantage: There are more numerals to memorize.

81. Advantage: You can write some numerals more compactly.
Disadvantage: There are more numerals to memorize.

83. MM

SECTION 4.2, PAGE 196

1. Positional value system

3. The 4 in 40 represents four tens. The 4 in 400 represents 4 hundreds.

5. a) 10 **b)** 0, 1, 2, 3, 4, 5, 6, 7, 8, 9

7. Write the sum of the products of each digit times its corresponding positional value.

9. a) There may be confusion because numerals could be interpreted in different ways. For example, ▌ could be interpreted to be either 1 or 60.
b) ▌▌ ◄▌▌▌ for both numerals.

11. 1, 20, 18×20, $18 \times (20)^2$, $18 \times (20)^3$

13. $(2 \times 10) + (3 \times 1)$

15. $(3 \times 100) + (5 \times 10) + (9 \times 1)$

17. $(8 \times 100) + (9 \times 10) + (7 \times 1)$

19. $(4 \times 1000) + (3 \times 100) + (8 \times 10) + (7 \times 1)$

21. $(1 \times 10{,}000) + (6 \times 1000) + (4 \times 100) + (0 \times 10) + (2 \times 1)$

23. $(3 \times 100{,}000) + (4 \times 10{,}000) + (6 \times 1000) + (8 \times 100) + (6 \times 10) + (1 \times 1)$

25. 14 **27.** 784 **29.** 4868 **31.** ◄◄◄▌▌▌▌▌

33. ◄▌▌▌▌ ◄◄◄◄◄▌ **35.** ▌ ▌ ◄◄▌▌▌▌▌ **37.** 57

39. 4682 **41.** 4000 **43.** ☰ **45.** ☰ **47.**

49. 1944, ◄◄◄▌▌ ◄◄▌▌▌▌

51. $\left(\triangle \times \square^2\right) + \left(\square \times \square\right) + \left(\diamond \times 1\right)$

53. a) No largest numeral
b)

55. ▌▌ ◄◄◄◄◄▌▌▌▌ **57.**

59. a) Answers will vary. **b)** Answers will vary.
c) Answers will vary.

SECTION 4.3, PAGE 202

1. a) Answers will vary. **b)** Answers will vary.

3. a) There is no digit 4 in base 4.
b) There is no digit 3 in base 2.
c) There is no digit L in base 12.
d) There is no digit G in base 16.

5. 1 **7.** 13 **9.** 184 **11.** 441 **13.** 1395 **15.** 53

17. 4012 **19.** 1549 **21.** 50,809 **23.** 110_2 **25.** 110212_3

27. 311_4 **29.** 402_5 **31.** 2112_8 **33.** 1861_9 **35.** 5264_{12}

37. $1ED_{16}$ **39.** $24EF_{16}$ **41.** 2202102_3 **43.** 31014_5

45. 5600_7 **47.** 1567_{11} **49.** $8DE_{15}$ **51.** 23 **53.** 78

55. ⊖⌾ $_5$ **57.** ⌾⌾⌾ $_5$ **59.** 14 **61.** 36 **63.** ●● $_4$

65. ●●● $_4$

67. a) Answers will vary. **b)** 10213_5 **c)** 1373_8

69. Answers will vary. **71.** $b = 6$

73. a) 876 **b)** ●●●● $_4$

SECTION 4.4, PAGE 212

1. a) 1, b, b^2, b^3, b^4 **b)** 1, 2, 2^2, 2^3, 2^4

3. No, cannot have a 3 in base 3.

5. Answers will vary. **7.** 111_3 **9.** 2130_5

11. $9B5_{12}$ **13.** 2200_3 **15.** 24001_7 **17.** 101000_2

19. 11_3 **21.** 831_9 **23.** 110_2 **25.** 11_2 **27.** 3616_7

29. 1011_3 **31.** 121_3 **33.** 4103_8 **35.** 21020_6

37. 77676_{12} **39.** 100011_2 **41.** 6031_7 **43.** 101_2

45. $223_6 \, R1_6$ **47.** 123_4 **49.** $103_4 \, R1_4$ **51.** $41_5 \, R1_5$

53. $45_7 \, R2_7$ **55.** ⊖⊖ $_5$ **57.** ⌾⊖ $_5$ **59.** ●● $_4$

61. ●●● $_4$ **63.** ●●● $_4$ **65.** ●●● $_4$

67. 2302_5, 327 **69.** $3EAC_{16}$ **71.** $114R3_4$

73. a) 21252_8 **b)** 306 and 29 **c)** 8874 **d)** 8874

    e) Yes

75. ⬤ = 0, ⬤ = 1, ⬤ = 2, ⬤ = 3,

SECTION 4.5, PAGE 217

1. Duplation and mediation, lattice multiplication, and Napier's rods

3. a) Answers will vary. **b)** 3718

5. 1539 **7.** 1431 **9.** 8260 **11.** 8649

13. 955 **15.** 3752 **17.** 900 **19.** 204,728

21. 147 **23.** 315 **25.** 625 **27.** 60,678

29. a) 46×253 **b)** 11,638

31. a) 4×382 **b)** 1528

33. 99∩∩∩∩∩∩∩∩IIIIII **35.** 1211_3

37. a) 1776 **b)** Answers will vary.

REVIEW EXERCISES, PAGE 219

1. 2121 **2.** 1214 **3.** 1311 **4.** 2114 **5.** 2314

6. 2312 **7.** *bbba* **8.** *cbbaaaaa*

9. *ccbbbbbbbbbaaa* **10.** *ddaaaaaaaaa*

11. *dddddddccccccccbbbbba* **12.** *ddcccbaaaa*

13. 32 **14.** 85 **15.** 749 **16.** 4068 **17.** 5648

18. 6905 **19.** *cxg* **20.** *ayexg* **21.** *hyfxb*

22. *czixd* **23.** *fzd* **24.** *bza* **25.** 93 **26.** 203

27. 568 **28.** 46,883 **29.** 64,481 **30.** 60,529

31. la **32.** tpd **33.** vrc **34.** BArg **35.** ODvog

36. QFvrf **37.** 𝄢99999999∩∩∩∩∩∩IIIIII

38. MDCCLXXVI **39.** 千七百七十六 **40.** 'αψof

41. <<<𝄐| <<<IIIIII **42.** •••• **43.** 222,035

44. 8254 **45.** 685 **46.** 1991 **47.** 1277 **48.** 2690 **49.** 39

50. 5 **51.** 28 **52.** 1244 **53.** 1552 **54.** 186

55. 111001111_2 **56.** 122011_3 **57.** 13033_4

58. 717_8 **59.** 327_{12} **60.** $1CF_{16}$ **61.** 140_7 **62.** 101111_2

63. 166_{12} **64.** $70F_{16}$ **65.** 12102_5 **66.** 12423_8

67. 3411_7 **68.** 100_2 **69.** $9A6_{12}$ **70.** 3324_5 **71.** 450_8

72. $CC1_{16}$ **73.** 110111_2 **74.** 21102_3 **75.** 1314_5

76. 13632_8 **77.** 5656_{12} **78.** $1D76_{16}$ **79.** 21_3R1_3

80. 130_4 **81.** 23_5R1_5 **82.** 433_6 **83.** $411_6 R1_6$

84. $664_8 R 2_8$ **85.** 3408 **86.** 3408 **87.** 3408

CHAPTER TEST, PAGE 220

1. A number is a quantity and answers the question "How many?" A numeral is a symbol used to represent a number.

2. 2484 **3.** 1275 **4.** 8090 **5.** 969 **6.** 122,142

7. 2745 **8.** 𝄢𝄢9∩∩IIIII **9.** 'β υ o f

10. ⦙⦙ **11.** <<IIIIII <<<IIIIII

12. MMMDCCVI

13. In an additive system, the number represented by a particular set of numerals is the sum of the values of the numerals.

14. In a multiplicative system, there are numerals for each numeral less than the base and for powers of the base. Each numeral less than the base is multiplied by a numeral for the power of the base, and these products are added to obtain the number.

15. In a ciphered system, the number represented by a particular set of numerals is the sum of the values of the numerals. There are numerals for each number up to and including the base and multiples of the base.

16. In a place-value system, each numeral is multiplied by a power of the base. The position of the numeral indicates the power of the base by which it is multiplied.

17. 11 **18.** 103 **19.** 45 **20.** 559 **21.** 100100_2

22. 135_8 **23.** 1444_{12} **24.** $B7A_{16}$ **25.** 11000_2

26. 142_6 **27.** 2003_6 **28.** 220_5 **29.** 980 **30.** 8428

CHAPTER 5

SECTION 5.1, PAGE 232

1. Number theory is the study of numbers and their properties.

3. a) *a* divides *b* means that *b* divided by *a* has a remainder of zero.

    b) *a* is divisible by *b* means that *a* divided by *b* has a remainder of zero.

5. A composite number is a natural number that is divisible by a number other than itself and 1.

7. a) The LCM of a set of natural numbers is the smallest natural number that is divisible by each number in the set.

    b) Answers will vary. **c)** 80

9. Mersenne primes are prime numbers of the form $2^n - 1$, where *n* is a prime number.

11. Goldbach's conjecture states that every even number greater than or equal to 4 can be represented as the sum of two (not necessarily distinct) prime numbers.

13. The prime numbers between 1 and 100 are 2, 3, 5, 7, 11, 13, 17, 19, 23, 29, 31, 37, 41, 43, 47, 53, 59, 61, 67, 71, 73, 79, 83, 89, and 97.

15. True   **17.** False; 26 is a multiple of 13.

19. False; 56 is divisible by 8.   **21.** True

23. False; if a number is divisible by 3, then the sum of the digits of the number is divisible by 3.

25. True   **27.** 11,115 is divisible by 3, 5, and 9.

29. 474,138 is divisible by 2, 3, 6, and 9.

31. 1,882,320 is divisible by 2, 3, 4, 5, 6, 8, and 10.

33. 60 (other answers are possible)

35. $48 = 2^4 \cdot 3$ **37.** $168 = 2^3 \cdot 3 \cdot 7$

39. $332 = 2^2 \cdot 83$ **41.** $513 = 3^3 \cdot 19$

43. $1336 = 2^3 \cdot 167$ **45.** $2001 = 3 \cdot 23 \cdot 29$

47. a) 3   **b)** 42   **49. a)** 5   **b)** 140   **51. a)** 20   **b)** 1800

53. a) 4   **b)** 5088   **55. a)** 8   **b)** 384

57. 17, 19, and 29, 31

59. a) Yes   **b)** No   **c)** Yes   **d)** Yes

61. 5, 17, and 257 are all prime.

63. $2 \times 60, 3 \times 40, 4 \times 30, 5 \times 24, 6 \times 20, 8 \times 15,$ $10 \times 12, 12 \times 10, 15 \times 8, 20 \times 6, 24 \times 5, 30 \times 4,$ $40 \times 3, 60 \times 2$

65. 210 days   **67.** 35 cars   **69.** 30 trees   **71.** 30 days

73. A number is divisible by 15 if both 3 and 5 divide the number.

75. 5   **77.** 35   **79.** 30   **81.** No   **83.** No

85. a) 12   **b)** 1, 2, 3, 4, 5, 6, 10, 12, 15, 20, 30, 60

87. For any three consecutive natural numbers, one of the numbers is divisible by 2 and another number is divisible by 3. Therefore, the product of the three numbers would be divisible by 6.

89. Yes

91. $8 = 2 + 3 + 3, 9 = 3 + 3 + 3, 10 = 2 + 3 + 5,$ $11 = 2 + 2 + 7, 12 = 2 + 5 + 5, 13 = 3 + 3 + 7,$ $14 = 2 + 5 + 7, 15 = 3 + 5 + 7, 16 = 2 + 7 + 7,$ $17 = 5 + 5 + 7, 18 = 2 + 5 + 11, 19 = 3 + 5 + 11,$ $20 = 2 + 7 + 11$

93. The answer most people select is Denmark, Kangaroo, and Orange.

SECTION 5.2, PAGE 242

1. Begin at zero. Represent the first addend with an arrow. Draw the arrow to the right if the addend is positive, to the left if negative. From the tip of the first arrow, represent the second addend with a second arrow. The sum of the two integers is at the tip of the second arrow.

3. To rewrite a subtraction problem as an addition problem, rewrite the minus sign as a plus sign and change the second number to its opposite.

5. The product of two numbers with like signs is positive. The product of two numbers with unlike signs is negative.

7. 3   **9.** -4 **11.** -5 **13.** 2   **15.** -21 **17.** -6

19. -9 **21.** -2 **23.** -6 **25.** -2 **27.** -30 **29.** 64

31. 96   **33.** -60 **35.** -720 **37.** 7   **39.** -1

41. -7 **43.** -15 **45.** -48

In Exercises 47–55, false answers can be modified in a variety of ways. We give one possible answer.

47. True

49. False; the difference of two negative integers may be a positive integer, a negative integer, or zero.

51. True   **53.** True

55. False; the sum of a positive integer and a negative integer may be a positive integer, a negative integer, or zero.

57. 6   **59.** 20   **61.** -12 **63.** -5 **65.** -6

67. $-9, -6, -3, 0, 3, 6$ **69.** $-6, -5, -4, -3, -2, -1$

71. 11,109   **73.** 14,777 ft   **75.** 9 yards; no

77. a) 9 hours   **b)** 2 hours   **79.** -1

81. $0 + 1 - 2 + 3 + 4 - 5 + 6 - 7 - 8 + 9 = 1$

SECTION 5.3, PAGE 255

1. The set of rational numbers is the set of numbers of the form $\frac{p}{q}$, where p and q are integers and $q \neq 0$.

3. a) Divide both the numerator and the denominator by their greatest common factor.
   b) $\frac{4}{5}$

5. For positive mixed numbers, multiply the denominator of the fraction by the integer preceding it. Add this product to the numerator. This sum is the numerator of the improper fraction; the denominator is the same as the denominator in the mixed number. For negative mixed numbers, temporarily ignore the negative sign, perform the conversion described above, and then add the negative sign.

7. a) The reciprocal of a number is 1 divided by the number.
   b) $-\frac{1}{2}$

9. a) To add or subtract two fractions with a common denominator, perform the indicated operation on the numerators. Keep the common denominator. Reduce the new fraction to lowest terms, if possible.
   b) $\frac{7}{12}$ **c)** $\frac{1}{2}$

11. Answers will vary.   **13.** $\frac{1}{2}$ **15.** $\frac{4}{9}$ **17.** $\frac{19}{25}$ **19.** $\frac{7}{11}$

21. $\frac{1}{11}$ **23.** $\frac{29}{8}$ **25.** $-\frac{31}{16}$ **27.** $-\frac{79}{16}$ **29.** $\frac{9}{8}$ **31.** $\frac{15}{8}$

33. $2\frac{3}{5}$ **35.** $-12\frac{1}{6}$ **37.** $-58\frac{8}{15}$ **39.** 0.7 **41.** $0.\overline{2}$
43. 0.375 **45.** $2.1\overline{6}$ **47.** $5.\overline{6}$ **49.** $\frac{75}{100} = \frac{3}{4}$
51. $\frac{45}{1000} = \frac{9}{200}$ **53.** $\frac{2}{10} = \frac{1}{5}$ **55.** $\frac{131}{10,000}$ **57.** $\frac{1}{10,000}$ **59.** $\frac{1}{9}$
61. $\frac{2}{1}$ **63.** $\frac{15}{11}$ **65.** $\frac{37}{18}$ **67.** $\frac{574}{165}$ **69.** $\frac{2}{5}$ **71.** $\frac{2}{5}$ **73.** $\frac{49}{64}$
75. $\frac{36}{35}$ **77.** $\frac{20}{21}$ **79.** $\frac{11}{12}$ **81.** $\frac{9}{22}$ **83.** $\frac{23}{54}$ **85.** $\frac{17}{144}$
87. $-\frac{109}{600}$ **89.** $\frac{19}{24}$ **91.** $-\frac{1}{24}$ **93.** $\frac{19}{24}$ **95.** 1 **97.** $\frac{11}{10}$
99. $\frac{23}{42}$ **101.** $1\frac{1}{4}$ in.   **103.** $120\frac{3}{4}$ in.   **105.** $9\frac{15}{16}$ in.
107. $\frac{1}{10}$ **109.** $58\frac{7}{8}$ in.
111. a) $1\frac{49}{60}, 2\frac{48}{60}, 9\frac{6}{60}, 6\frac{3}{60}, 2\frac{9}{60}, \frac{22}{60}$
  b) $22\frac{17}{60}$; 22 hours 17 minutes
113. $26\frac{5}{32}$ in.   **115. a)** $29\frac{3}{16}$ in.   **b)** 33 in.   **c)** $32\frac{3}{4}$ in.

In Exercises 117–121, an infinite number of answers are possible. We give one answer.

117. 0.105 **119.** -2.1755 **121.** 4.8725
123. $\frac{1}{2}$ **125.** $\frac{11}{200}$ **127.** $\frac{11}{200}$
129. a) $1\frac{3}{8}$ cup water (or milk) and $\frac{3}{4}$ cup oatmeal
  b) $1\frac{1}{2}$ cup water (or milk) and $\frac{3}{4}$ cup oatmeal
131. a) $\frac{1}{8}$ **b)** $\frac{1}{16}$ **c)** 5   **d)** 6

SECTION 5.4, PAGE 266

1. A rational number can be written as a ratio of two integers. Real numbers that cannot be written as a ratio of two integers are irrational numbers.
3. A perfect square is any number that is the square of a natural number.
5. a) To add or subtract two or more square roots with the same radicand, add or subtract their coefficients and then multiply the sum or difference by the common radical.
  b) $5\sqrt{5}$
7. a) Multiply both the numerator and denominator by a radical that will result in the radicand in the denominator becoming a perfect square.
  b) $\dfrac{2\sqrt{3}}{3}$
9. Rational   **11.** Rational   **13.** Irrational
15. Rational   **17.** Irrational   **19.** 4   **21.** 10
23. -13 **25.** -9 **27.** -10
29. Rational number, integer, natural number
31. Rational number, integer, natural number
33. Rational number   **35.** Rational number
37. Rational number
39. $2\sqrt{3}$ **41.** $4\sqrt{3}$ **43.** $3\sqrt{7}$ **45.** $2\sqrt{21}$ **47.** $9\sqrt{2}$
49. $5\sqrt{5}$ **51.** $\sqrt{2}$ **53.** $-13\sqrt{3}$ **55.** $4\sqrt{3}$ **57.** $23\sqrt{2}$
59. 9   **61.** $2\sqrt{15}$ **63.** $10\sqrt{2}$ **65.** 2   **67.** 3

69. $\dfrac{\sqrt{5}}{5}$ **71.** $\dfrac{\sqrt{21}}{7}$ **73.** $\dfrac{2\sqrt{15}}{3}$ **75.** $\dfrac{\sqrt{15}}{3}$ **77.** $\dfrac{\sqrt{15}}{3}$

79. $\sqrt{5}$ is between 2 and 3 since 5 is between 4 and 9. $\sqrt{5}$ is between 2 and 2.5 since 5 is closer to 4 than to 9. $\sqrt{5} \approx 2.24$.
81. $\sqrt{107}$ is between 10 and 11 since 107 is between 100 and 121. $\sqrt{107}$ is between 10 and 10.5 since 107 is closer to 100 than to 121. $\sqrt{107} \approx 10.34$.
83. $\sqrt{170}$ is between 13 and 14 since 170 is between 169 and 196. $\sqrt{170}$ is between 13 and 13.5 since 170 is closer to 169 than to 196. $\sqrt{170} \approx 13.04$.

In Exercises 85–89, false answers can be modified in a variety of ways. We give one possible answer.

85. False. $\sqrt{c}$ may be a rational number or an irrational number for a composite number c. (For example, $\sqrt{25}$ is a rational number; $\sqrt{8}$ is an irrational number.)
87. True
89. False. The product of a rational number and an irrational number may be a rational number or an irrational number.
91. $3\sqrt{2} + 5\sqrt{2} = 8\sqrt{2}$ **93.** $\sqrt{2} \cdot \sqrt{3} = \sqrt{6}$
95. $\sqrt{2} \neq 1.414$ since $\sqrt{2}$ is irrational and 1.414 is rational.
97. No. π is irrational; therefore, it cannot equal $\frac{22}{7}$ or 3.14, both of which are rational.
99. $\sqrt{4 \cdot 9} = \sqrt{4} \cdot \sqrt{9}$, $\sqrt{36} = 2 \cdot 3$, $6 = 6$
101. a) 10 mph   **b)** 20 mph   **c)** 40 mph   **d)** 80 mph
103. a) Rational. $\sqrt{0.04} = 0.2$, which is a rational number.
  b) Irrational. $\sqrt{0.7} = 0.8366600265 \ldots$. Since the decimal number is not a terminating or a repeating decimal number, this number is an irrational number.
105. a) $(44 \div \sqrt{4}) \div \sqrt{4} = 11$ **b)** $(44 \div 4) + \sqrt{4} = 13$
  c) $4 + 4 + 4 + \sqrt{4} = 14$
  d) $\sqrt{4}(4 + 4) + \sqrt{4} = 18$
  Other answers are possible.

SECTION 5.5, PAGE 273

1. The real numbers are the union of the rational numbers and the irrational numbers.
3. If whenever the operation is performed on two elements of a set the result is also an element of the set, then the set is closed under that operation.
5. $a \cdot b = b \cdot a$, the order in which two numbers are multiplied is immaterial. One example is $4(5) = 5(4)$.
7. $(a + b) + c = a + (b + c)$, when adding three numbers, you may place parentheses around any two adjacent numbers. One example is $(1 + 2) + 3 = 1 + (2 + 3)$.
9. No   **11.** Yes   **13.** Yes   **15.** Yes   **17.** Yes
19. No   **21.** No   **23.** No   **25.** Yes   **27.** Yes

29. Commutative property of addition. The only difference between the expressions on both sides of the equal sign is the order of 5 and x.

31. $(-3) + (-4) = (-4) + (-3) = -7$

33. No. $4 - 3 \neq 3 - 4$.

35. $[(-2) + (-3)] + (-4) = (-2) + [(-3) + (-4)] = -9$

37. No. $(16 \div 8) \div 2 \neq 16 \div (8 \div 2)$.

39. No. $(81 \div 9) \div 3 \neq 81 \div (9 \div 3)$.

41. Distributive property

43. Associative property of multiplication

45. Associative property of addition

47. Commutative property of multiplication

49. Distributive property

51. Commutative property of multiplication

53. Distributive property

55. Commutative property of multiplication

57. $4z + 4$ **59.** $-\frac{3}{4}x + 9$ **61.** $3x + 4$

63. $2x - 1$ **65.** 2   **67.** $5\sqrt{2} + 5\sqrt{3}$

69. a) Distributive property
b) Associative property of addition

71. a) Distributive property
b) Associative property of addition
c) Commutative property of addition
d) Associative property of addition

73. a) Distributive property
b) Commutative property of addition
c) Associative property of addition
d) Commutative property of addition

75. Yes   **77.** No   **79.** Yes   **81.** No   **83.** Yes

85. Yes   **87.** Yes   **89.** Answers will vary.

91. No. $0 \div a = 0$ (when $a \neq 0$), but $a \div 0$ is undefined.

SECTION 5.6, PAGE 284

1. The 2 is the base and the 3 is the exponent or power.

3. a) To multiply two exponential expressions with the same base, add the exponents and use this sum as the exponent on the common base.
b) $2^3 \cdot 2^4 = 2^{3+4} = 2^7 = 128$

5. a) Any nonzero expression raised to the power of 0 equals 1.
b) $7^0 = 1$

7. a) Any base with an exponent raised to another exponent is equal to the base raised to the product of the exponents.
b) $(3^2)^4 = 3^{2 \cdot 4} = 3^8 = 6561$

9. a) -1^{500} means $-(1)^{500}$ or $-1 \cdot 1^{500}$. Since 1 raised to any power equals 1, $-1^{500} = -1 \cdot 1^{500} = -1 \cdot 1 = -1$.
b) $(-1)^{500}$ means (-1) multiplied by itself 500 times. Since 500 is even, $(-1)^{500} = 1$.

c) -1^{501} means $-(1)^{501}$ or $-1 \cdot 1^{501}$. Since 1 raised to any power equals 1, $-1^{501} = -1 \cdot 1^{501} = -1 \cdot 1 = -1$.
d) $(-1)^{501}$ means (-1) multiplied by itself 501 times. Since 501 is odd, $(-1)^{501} = -1$.

11. a) If the exponent is positive, move the decimal point in the number to the right the same number of places as the exponent, adding zeros where necessary. If the exponent is negative, move the decimal point in the number to the left the same number of places as the exponent, adding zeros where necessary.
b) 0.0000291   **c)** 7,020,000

13. a) 9   **b)** 8   **15. a)** 25   **b)** -25

17. a) -16 **b)** 16   **19. a)** -64 **b)** -64

21. a) $\frac{1}{64}$ **b)** $\frac{9}{16}$ **23. a)** 1000   **b)** 1

25. a) 243   **b)** -243 **27. a)** 25   **b)** 25

29. a) 1   **b)** -1 **31. a)** 1   **b)** 6

33. a) $\frac{1}{27}$ **b)** $\frac{1}{49}$ **35. a)** $-\frac{1}{81}$ **b)** $\frac{1}{81}$

37. a) 64   **b)** 64   **39. a)** 4   **b)** $\frac{1}{16}$

41. 1.75×10^5 **43.** 2.3×10^{-4} **45.** 5.6×10^{-1}

47. 1.9×10^4 **49.** 1.86×10^{-4} **51.** 4.23×10^{-6}

53. 7.11×10^2 **55.** 1.53×10^{-1} **57.** 170

59. 0.0001097   **61.** 0.0000862   **63.** 0.312

65. 9,000,000   **67.** 231   **69.** 35,000   **71.** 10,000

73. 750,000   **75.** 0.0153   **77.** 250   **79.** 0.0021

81. 20   **83.** 1.0×10^{11} **85.** 4.5×10^{-7}

87. 7.0×10^1 **89.** 2.0×10^{-7} **91.** 3.0×10^8

93. 3.6×10^{-3}; 1.7; 9.8×10^2; 1.03×10^4

95. 8.3×10^{-5}; 0.00079; 4.1×10^3; 40,000

97. 0.046   **99.** 0.168

101. 2.708×10^{51} sec   **103.** $6779

105. 11.95 hours   **107.** 2.9×10^8 cells

109. 8.64×10^9 ft^3

111. a) $720,000,000   **b)** $300,000,000   **c)** $120,000,000
d) $60,000,000

113. 1000   **115.** 333,333 times

117. a) About 5.87×10^{12} (5.87 trillion) mi
b) About 500 sec or 8 min 20 sec

SECTION 5.7, PAGE 294

1. A sequence is a list of numbers that are related to each other by a given rule. One example is 1, 3, 5, 7, 9, ...

3. a) An arithmetic sequence is one in which each term differs from the preceding term by a constant amount. One example is 4, 7, 10, 13, 16, ...
b) A geometric sequence is one in which the ratio of any two successive terms is a constant amount. One example is 3, 6, 12, 24, ...

5. a) a_n is the nth term or the general term.
b) a_1 is the first term.
c) d is the common difference.
d) s_n is the sum of the first n terms.

7. 5, 6, 7, 8, 9   **9.** 12, 10, 8, 6, 4

11. 5, 3, 1, -1, -3 **13.** $\frac{3}{4}$, 1, $\frac{5}{4}$, $\frac{3}{2}$, $\frac{7}{4}$ **15.** 8   **17.** 13

19. $-\frac{91}{5}$ **21.** -8 **23.** $a_n = n$ **25.** $a_n = 2n$

27. $a_n = \frac{3}{4}n - \frac{1}{2}$ **29.** $a_n = \frac{3}{2}n - \frac{9}{2}$ **31.** $s_{50} = 1275$

33. $s_{50} = 2500$ **35.** $s_8 = -52$ **37.** $s_{24} = 60$

39. 1, 5, 25, 125, 625   **41.** 2, -4, 8, -16, 32

43. -3, 3, -3, 3, -3 **45.** 81, -27, 9, -3, 1

47. 160   **49.** $\frac{3}{4}$ **51.** -3645 **53.** $a_{10} = -39{,}366$

55. $a_n = 2^{n-1}$ **57.** $a_n = (-1)(-1)^{n-1}$

59. $a_n = 2 \cdot \left(\frac{1}{2}\right)^{n-1}$ **61.** $a_n = 9 \cdot \left(\frac{1}{3}\right)^{n-1}$

63. 186   **65.** -4095 **67.** $-620{,}011$

69. $-10{,}923$ **71.** 5050   **73.** 10,100

75. a) 63 in.   **b)** 954 in.

77. a) \$44,800   **b)** \$319,200   **79.** 496 pinecones

81. 52.4288 g   **83.** $\approx$\$70,088   **85.** \$486,000

87. 161.4375   **89.** 267   **91.** 191.3568 ft

SECTION 5.8, PAGE 302

1. The first and second terms are 1. Each term thereafter is the sum of the previous two terms.

3. a) The golden number is $\dfrac{\sqrt{5}+1}{2}$.
b) When a line segment AB is divided at a point C, such that the ratio of the whole, AB, to the larger part, AC, is equal to the ratio of the larger part, AC, to the smaller part, CB, then each of the two ratios AB/AC and AC/CB is known as the golden ratio.
c) The proportion made by using the two golden ratios, $AB/AC = AC/CB$, is known as the golden proportion.
d) A golden rectangle is one where the ratio of the length to the width is equal to the golden number.

5. Answers will vary.

7. a) 1.618   **b)** 0.618   **c)** 1

9. $\frac{1}{1} = 1$, $\frac{2}{1} = 2$, $\frac{3}{2} = 1.5$, $\frac{5}{3} \approx 1.667$, $\frac{8}{5} = 1.6$, $\frac{13}{8} = 1.625$, $\frac{21}{13} \approx 1.615$, $\frac{34}{21} \approx 1.619$, $\frac{55}{34} \approx 1.6176$, $\frac{89}{55} \approx 1.6182$. The consecutive ratios alternate, increasing and decreasing about the golden ratio.

11. Answers will vary.   **13.** Answers will vary.

15. Answers will vary.   **17.** Answers will vary.

19. Answers will vary.   **21.** Answers will vary.

23. No   **25.** Yes; 3, 5   **27.** Yes; 105, 170

29. Yes; -1, -1 **31.** Answers will vary.

33. Answers will vary.

35. a) 1, 3, 4, 7, 11, 18, 29, 47
b) $8 + 21 = 29$, $13 + 34 = 47$
c) It is the Fibonacci sequence.

37. Answers will vary.

39. Answers will vary.

REVIEW EXERCISES, PAGE 306

1. 2, 3, 4, 5, 6, 10   **2.** 2, 3, 4, 6, 9   **3.** $2^2 \cdot 3^3 \cdot 5$

4. $3^2 \cdot 7 \cdot 11$ **5.** $2^3 \cdot 3 \cdot 5 \cdot 7$ **6.** $2 \cdot 3^2 \cdot 7^2$

7. $2^2 \cdot 3 \cdot 11^2$ **8.** 15; 210   **9.** 9; 756   **10.** 5; 2250

11. 30; 900   **12.** 4; 480   **13.** 36; 432   **14.** 45 days

15. -3 **16.** 3   **17.** -6 **18.** -4 **19.** -9 **20.** 3

21. 0   **22.** 4   **23.** -15 **24.** 24   **25.** -56 **26.** 5

27. -2 **28.** 6   **29.** 4   **30.** 3   **31.** 0.3   **32.** 0.44

33. 0.375   **34.** 3.25   **35.** $0.\overline{857142}$ **36.** $0.58\overline{3}$

37. 0.375   **38.** 0.6875   **39.** $0.\overline{714285}$ **40.** $\frac{9}{40}$

41. $\frac{14}{10} = \frac{7}{5}$ **42.** $\frac{2}{3}$ **43.** $\frac{51}{99}$ **44.** $\frac{83}{1000}$ **45.** $\frac{73}{10{,}000}$ **46.** $\frac{211}{90}$

47. $\frac{7}{4}$ **48.** $\frac{25}{6}$ **49.** $-\frac{13}{4}$ **50.** $-\frac{283}{8}$ **51.** $2\frac{1}{5}$ **52.** $9\frac{3}{8}$

53. $-1\frac{5}{7}$ **54.** $-27\frac{1}{5}$ **55.** $\frac{13}{12}$ **56.** $\frac{1}{4}$ **57.** $\frac{17}{12}$ **58.** $\frac{1}{4}$

59. $\frac{35}{54}$ **60.** $\frac{53}{28}$ **61.** $\frac{1}{6}$ **62.** $\frac{13}{40}$ **63.** $\frac{8}{15}$ **64.** $2\frac{7}{32}$ tsp

65. $3\sqrt{5}$ **66.** $10\sqrt{2}$ **67.** $8\sqrt{5}$ **68.** $-3\sqrt{2}$

69. $8\sqrt{2}$ **70.** $-20\sqrt{3}$ **71.** $5\sqrt{7}$ **72.** $3\sqrt{2}$

73. $4\sqrt{3}$ **74.** 10   **75.** $2\sqrt{7}$ **76.** $\dfrac{4\sqrt{3}}{3}$ **77.** $\dfrac{\sqrt{35}}{5}$

78. $6 + 3\sqrt{7}$ **79.** $4\sqrt{3} + 3\sqrt{2}$ **80.** $3\sqrt{2} + 3\sqrt{5}$

81. Commutative property of addition
82. Commutative property of multiplication
83. Associative property of addition
84. Distributive property
85. Associative property of addition
86. Commutative property of addition
87. Associative property of multiplication
88. Commutative property of multiplication
89. Distributive property
90. Commutative property of multiplication

91. No   **92.** Yes   **93.** No   **94.** Yes   **95.** No   **96.** No

97. 25   **98.** $\frac{1}{25}$ **99.** 81   **100.** 125   **101.** 1   **102.** $\frac{1}{64}$

103. 64   **104.** 81   **105.** 8.2×10^9 **106.** 1.58×10^{-5}

107. 2.309×10^{-2} **108.** 4.95×10^6 **109.** 280,000

110. 0.000139   **111.** 0.000175   **112.** 10,000,000

113. 6.0×10^{-5} **114.** 3.75×10^{12} **115.** 2.1×10^1

116. 3.0×10^0 **117.** 1,100,000,000,000   **118.** 0.7

119. 120   **120.** 5   **121.** $\approx$388 times   **122.** $\approx$\$5555.56

123. Arithmetic; 17, 21 **124.** Geometric; 8, 16
125. Arithmetic; $-15, -18$ **126.** Geometric; $\frac{1}{32}, \frac{1}{64}$
127. Arithmetic; 16, 19 **128.** Geometric; $\frac{1}{2}, -\frac{1}{2}$
129. 27 **130.** 10 **131.** 25 **132.** 48 **133.** $\frac{1}{4}$
134. -48 **135.** 3825 **136.** -25 **137.** 632
138. 57.5 **139.** 682 **140.** 45 **141.** 33 **142.** -21
143. Arithmetic; $a_n = 3n$
144. Arithmetic; $a_n = 3n - 2$
145. Arithmetic; $a_n = -\frac{3}{2}n + \frac{11}{2}$
146. Geometric; $a_n = 3(2)^{n-1}$
147. Geometric; $a_n = 2(-1)^{n-1}$
148. Geometric; $a_n = 5\left(\frac{1}{3}\right)^{n-1}$ **149.** No
150. Yes; $-8, -13$ **151.** No **152.** No

CHAPTER TEST, PAGE 309

1. 5 **2.** $2 \cdot 3^2 \cdot 23$ **3.** 8 **4.** -20
5. -175 **6.** $\frac{37}{8}$ **7.** $19\frac{5}{9}$ **8.** 0.625 **9.** $\frac{129}{20}$
10. $\frac{121}{240}$ **11.** $\frac{1}{8}$ **12.** $9\sqrt{3}$ **13.** $\frac{\sqrt{14}}{7}$
14. Yes; the product of any two integers is an integer.
15. Associative property of addition
16. Distributive property **17.** 64 **18.** 1024 **19.** $\frac{1}{81}$
20. 8.0×10^{11} **21.** $a_n = -4n + 2$ **22.** -187
23. 486 **24.** -510 **25.** $a_n = 3(2)^{n-1}$
26. 1, 1, 2, 3, 5, 8, 13, 21, 34, 55

CHAPTER 6

SECTION 6.1, PAGE 315

1. Letters of the alphabet used to represent numbers are called variables.
3. The solution to an equation is the number or numbers that replace the variable to make the equation a true statement.
5. a) The 4 is the base and the 5 is the exponent.
  b) Answers will vary.
7. a) 12 **b)** 27 **9.** 25 **11.** -4 **13.** 686 **15.** -3
17. 12 **19.** -20 **21.** $-\frac{10}{9}$ **23.** 7 **25.** 9 **27.** 39
29. No **31.** No **33.** No **35.** Yes **37.** Yes
39. $62.93 **41.** 96.8 million **43.** 88.72 min **45.** 1.71 in.
47. The two expressions are not equal.

SECTION 6.2, PAGE 327

1. The parts that are added or subtracted in an algebraic expression are called terms. In $3x - 2y$, the $3x$ and $-2y$ are terms.

3. The numerical part of a term is called its numerical coefficient. For the term $3x$, 3 is the numerical coefficient.
5. To simplify an expression means to combine like terms by using the commutative, associative, and distributive properties.
7. If $a = b$, then $a \cdot c = b \cdot c$ for all real numbers a, b, and c, where $c \neq 0$. If $\frac{x}{3} = 2$, then $3\left(\frac{x}{3}\right) = 3(2)$.
9. If $a = b$, then $a/c = b/c$ for all real numbers a, b, and c, where $c \neq 0$. If $4x = 8$, then $\frac{4x}{4} = \frac{8}{4}$.
11. A ratio is a quotient of two quantities. An example is $\frac{7}{9}$.
13. Yes. They have the same variable and the same exponent on the variable.
15. $10x$ **17.** $2x + 12$ **19.** $3x + 11y$ **21.** $-8x + 2$
23. $-5x + 3$ **25.** $13.3x - 8.3$ **27.** $-\frac{2}{15}x - 4$
29. $10x - 9y + 3$ **31.** $8s - 17$ **33.** $1.4x - 2.8$
35. $-\frac{5}{12}x + \frac{4}{5}$ **37.** $4.52x - 13.5$ **39.** 17 **41.** -1 **43.** $\frac{24}{7}$
45. $\frac{2}{3}$ **47.** 4 **49.** 3 **51.** 17 **53.** -8 **55.** No solution
57. All real numbers **59.** 3 **61.** -3 **63.** 5
65. $209.25 **67.** 4 gallons
69. $\approx$ 15,868,800 households
71. a) 1.6 kph **b)** 56.25 mph **73.** 0.375 cc
75. a) Answers will vary. **b)** -1
77. a) An equation that has no solution.
  b) You will obtain a false statement.
79. a) $2:5$ **b)** $m : m + n$

SECTION 6.3, PAGE 337

1. A formula is an equation that typically has a real-life application.
3. Subscripts are numbers (or letters) placed below and to the right of variables. They are used to help clarify a formula.
5. An exponential equation is of the form $y = a^x$, $a > 0$, $a \neq 1$.
7. 56 **9.** 56 **11.** 10 **13.** 251.2 **15.** 37.1
17. 2 **19.** 3000 **21.** 12 **23.** 25 **25.** 6
27. 200 **29.** 7.2 **31.** 14 **33.** 3240
35. 66.67 **37.** 39 **39.** 7609.81
41. $y = \frac{4x - 14}{9}$ or $y = \frac{4}{9}x - \frac{14}{9}$
43. $y = \frac{-8x + 21}{7}$ or $y = -\frac{8}{7}x + 3$
45. $y = \frac{2x + 6}{3}$ or $y = \frac{2}{3}x + 2$

47. $y = \dfrac{2x - z + 15}{3}$ or $y = \dfrac{2}{3}x - \dfrac{1}{3}z + 5$

49. $y = \dfrac{9x + 4z - 7}{8}$ or $y = \dfrac{9}{8}x + \dfrac{1}{2}z - \dfrac{7}{8}$

51. $r = \dfrac{d}{t}$ **53.** $a = p - b - c$

55. $B = \dfrac{3V}{h}$ **57.** $r = \dfrac{C}{2\pi}$

59. $b = y - mx$ **61.** $w = \dfrac{P - 2l}{2}$

63. $c = 3A - a - b$ **65.** $T = \dfrac{PV}{K}$

67. $C = \frac{5}{9}(F - 32)$ **69.** $h = \dfrac{S - 2\pi r^2}{2\pi r}$

71. a) \$112.50   **b)** \$4612.50   **73.** ≈ 4.19 in.^{3}
75. 486,000 bacteria   **77.** $\approx \$4.49 \times 10^{14}$
79. ≈ 1051.47 in.^{3}

SECTION 6.4, PAGE 343

1. A mathematical expression is a collection of variables, numbers, parentheses, and operation symbols. An equation is two algebraic expressions joined by an equal sign.
3. 4 more than x **5.** 2 times x, decreased by 3
7. $8 + x$ **9.** $3 + 2z$ **11.** $6w + 9$ **13.** $4x + 6$
15. $\dfrac{18 - s}{4}$ **17.** $3(x + 7)$ **19.** $x + 5 = 11; 6$
21. $x - 4 = 20; 24$ **23.** $4x - 10 = 42; 13$
25. $4x + 12 = 32; 5$ **27.** $x + 6 = 2x - 3; 9$
29. $x + 10 = 2(x + 3); 4$
31. $150 + 0.42x = 207.54; 137$ miles
33. $x + 0.05x = 42; \$40$ per half hour
35. $0.08x = 250; 3125$ copies
37. $x + 3x = 1000; \$250$ for business, \$750 for liberal arts
39. $2w + 2(w + 3) = 54;$ width: 12 ft, length: 15 ft
41. $x + 6x + 2515 = 21,730;$ Utah: 2745 mustangs; Nevada: 18,985 mustangs
43. $x + 14x + 11 = 341;$ December: 22 tornados; May: 319 tornados
45. $3w + 2(2w) = 140;$ width: 20 ft, length: 40 ft
47. $70x = 760; \approx 11$ months
49. $\dfrac{r}{2} + 0.07r = 257; \$450.88$
51. Deduct \$720 from Mr. McAdams's income and \$2920 from Mrs. McAdams's income.

53. $x + (x + 1) + (x + 2) = 3(x + 2) - 3$
$$3x + 3 = 3x + 6 - 3$$
$$3x + 3 = 3x + 3$$
55. $-40°$

SECTION 6.5, PAGE 352

1. Direct variation: As one variable increases, so does the other, and as one variable decreases, so does the other.
3. Joint variation: One quantity varies directly as the product of two or more other quantities.
5. Direct   **7.** Inverse   **9.** Direct   **11.** Inverse
13. Inverse   **15.** Inverse   **17.** Direct   **19.** Direct
21. Answers will vary.   **23. a)** $y = kx$ **b)** 120
25. a) $m = \dfrac{k}{n^2}$ **b)** 0.25   **27. a)** $A = \dfrac{kB}{C}$ **b)** 2.5
29. a) $F = kDE$ **b)** 210   **31. a)** $t = \dfrac{kd^2}{f}$ **b)** 200
33. a) $Z = kWY$ **b)** 100   **35. a)** $H = kL$ **b)** 3
37. a) $A = kB^2$ **b)** 720   **39. a)** $F = \dfrac{kq_1q_2}{d^2}$ **b)** 1200
41. a) $t = kv$ **b)** \$2700   **43. a)** $l = \dfrac{k}{d^2}$ **b)** 80 dB
45. a) $R = \dfrac{kA}{P}$ **b)** 4800 tapes
47. a) $v = \dfrac{k\sqrt{t}}{l}$ **b)** 4 vibrations per second
49. a) $N = \dfrac{kp_1p_2}{d}$ **b)** $\approx 121,528$ calls
51. a) Inversely   **b)** Stays 0.3   **53.** \$132.27

SECTION 6.6, PAGE 360

1. $a < b$ means that a is less than b, $a \le b$ means that a is less than or equal to b, $a > b$ means that a is greater than b, $a \ge b$ means that a is greater than or equal to b.
3. When both sides of an inequality are multiplied or divided by a negative number, the direction of the inequality symbol must be reversed.
5. Yes, the inequality symbol points to the -3 in both cases.
7. a) An inequality of the form $a < x < b$ is called a compound inequality.
   b) $-5 < x < 3$
9.
11.
13.
15.
17.

19.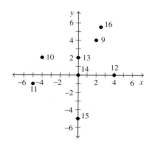
(number line: 0, 4)

21. No solution
(number line: 0)

23. (number line: −1, 3)

25. (number line: 10, 13)

27. (number line: −1 0 1 2 3 4 5 6)

29. (number line: −11 −10 −9 −8 −7 −6 −5 −4)

31. (number line: −1 0 1 2 3 4 5 6)

33. (number line: −9 −8 −7 −6 −5 −4 −3 −2)

35. (number line: −11 −10 −9 −8 −7 −6)

37. (number line: −2 −1 0 1 2 3 4 5)

39. (number line: −6 −5 −4 −3 −2 −1 0 1)

41. (number line: −5 −4 −3 −2 −1 0 1 2)

43. (number line: −1 0 1 2 3 4 5 6)

45. (number line: −3 −2 −1 0 1 2 3 4)

47. a) 2009–2015 **b)** 2005–2008
  c) 2006–2015 **d)** 2005–2006

49. 19 videos **51.** 350 hours

53. 6 hours **55.** $0.5 < t < 1.5$

57. $94 \le x \le 100$, assuming 100 is the highest grade possible

59. $6.875 \le x \le 11$

61. The student's answer is $x \le -12$, whereas the correct answer is $x \ge -12$. Yes, -12 is in both solution sets.

SECTION 6.7, PAGE 372

1. A graph is an illustration of all the points whose coordinates satisfy an equation.

3. To find the y-intercept, set $x = 0$ and solve the equation for y.

5. a) Answers will vary. **b)** $-\frac{1}{3}$

7. a) First **b)** Third

For Exercises 9–15, see the following figure.

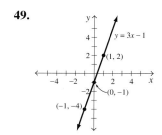

For Exercises 17–23, see the following figure.

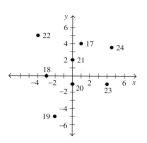

25. $(0, 2)$ **27.** $(-2, 0)$ **29.** $(-5, -3)$ **31.** $(2, -3)$
33. $(2, 2)$ **35.** $(5, 2), (1, 4)$ **37.** $(8, 2), \left(0, -\frac{10}{3}\right)$
39. $(-3, -2)$ **41.** $(8, 0), (0, 3)$

43.

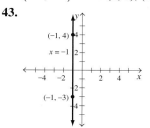

Slope: undefined

45.

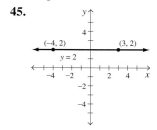

Slope is 0.

47.

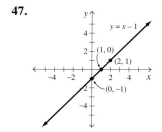

49.

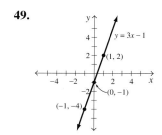

51.

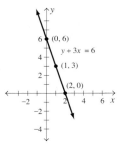

53.

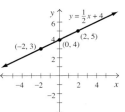

55.

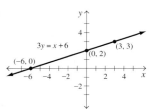

57.

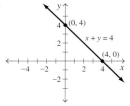

59.

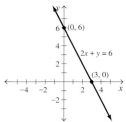

61.

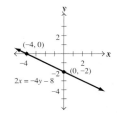

63.

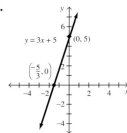

65.

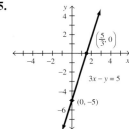

67. 2   **69.** $-\frac{5}{4}$ **71.** 0   **73.** Undefined   **75.** $-\frac{8}{11}$

77.

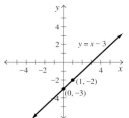

79.

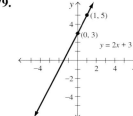

81.

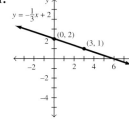

83.

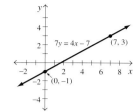

85.

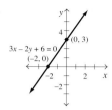

87. $y = -2x + 4$ **89.** $y = 3x + 2$

91. a) $D(3, -2)$ **b)** $A = 20$ square units

93. $(7, 2)$ or $(-1, 2)$ **95.** -3 **97.** 3

99. a)

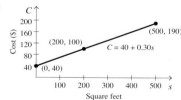

b) $130   **c)** 100 square feet

101. a)

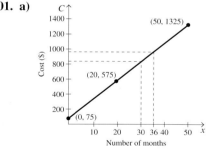

b) $825   **c)** 36 months

103. a) 2   **b)** $y = 2x + 9$ **c)** 15 defects   **d)** 4 workers

105. a) ≈ -0.05 **b)** $y = -0.05x + 2.60$
   c) $\approx \$2.50$ billion   **d)** 4 years after 2000, or in 2004

107. a) Solve the equations for y to put them in slope–intercept
   form. Then compare the slopes and y-intercepts. If the
   slopes are equal but the y-intercepts are different, then
   the lines are parallel.
   b) The lines are parallel.

SECTION 6.8, PAGE 378

1. (1) Mentally substitute the equal sign for the inequality
   sign and plot points as if you were graphing the equation.
   (2) If the inequality is $<$ or $>$, draw a dashed line through
   the points. If the inequality is $\leq$ or $\geq$, draw a solid line
   through the points. (3) Select a test point not on the line
   and substitute the x- and y-coordinates into the inequality.
   If the substitution results in a true statement, shade in the
   area on the same side of the line as the test point. If the test
   point results in a false statement, shade in the area on the
   opposite side of the line as the test point.

3. A half plane is the set of all the points in a plane on one
   side of a line.

5. a) No   **b)** Yes   **c)** Yes   **d)** No

7.

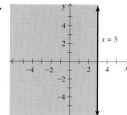

9.

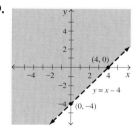

11.

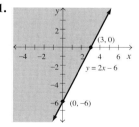

13.

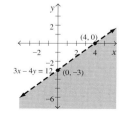

15.

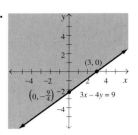

17.

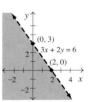

19.

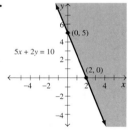

21.

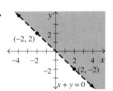

23.

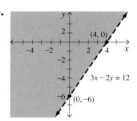

25.

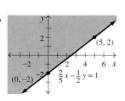

27.

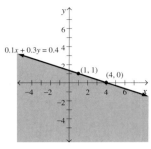

29. a) $x + y \le 300$

b)

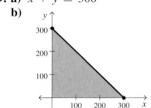

31. a) No, you cannot have a negative number of shirts.

b)

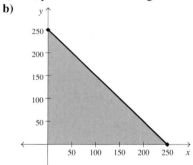

c) Answers will vary.

SECTION 6.9, PAGE 388

1. A binomial is an expression that contains two terms in which each exponent that appears on the variable is a whole number. $2x + 3$, $x - 7$, $x^2 - 9$

3. Answers will vary.   **5.** $ax^2 + bx + c = 0$, $a \ne 0$

7. $(x + 5)(x + 3)$ **9.** $(x - 2)(x + 1)$

11. $(x + 6)(x - 4)$ **13.** $(x + 1)(x - 3)$

15. $(x - 7)(x - 3)$ **17.** $(x - 7)(x + 7)$

19. $(x + 7)(x - 4)$ **21.** $(x + 9)(x - 7)$

23. $(2x + 3)(x - 2)$ **25.** $(5x + 1)(x + 3)$

27. $(5x + 2)(x + 2)$ **29.** $(4x + 3)(x + 2)$

31. $(4x - 3)(x - 2)$ **33.** $(4x + 1)(2x - 3)$

35. $3, -6$ **37.** $-\frac{4}{3}, \frac{1}{2}$ **39.** $-5, -2$ **41.** $6, 1$ **43.** $5, -3$

45. $3, 1$ **47.** $9, -9$ **49.** $-9, 4$ **51.** $\frac{2}{3}, -4$ **53.** $-\frac{1}{5}, -2$

55. $\frac{1}{3}, 1$ **57.** $\frac{1}{3}, \frac{3}{2}$ **59.** $3, -5$ **61.** $6, -3$ **63.** $9, -1$

65. No real solution   **67.** $2 \pm \sqrt{2}$

69. $\dfrac{4 \pm \sqrt{13}}{3}$ **71.** $\dfrac{3 \pm 2\sqrt{6}}{3}$ **73.** $-1, -\dfrac{5}{2}$ **75.** $\dfrac{7}{3}, 1$

77. No real solution

79. Width $= 12$ m, length $= 22$ m

81. a) The zero-factor property cannot be used.
    b) $\approx 8.37, \approx 2.63$

83. $x^2 - 2x - 3 = 0$

SECTION 6.10, PAGE 401

1. A function is a special type of relation in which each value of the independent variable corresponds to a unique value of the dependent variable.

3. The domain of a function is the set of values that can be used for the independent variable.

5. If a vertical line touches more than one point on the graph, then for each value of x there is not a unique value for y and the graph does not represent a function.

7. $x = -\dfrac{b}{2a}$

9. Not a function

11. Function, domain: $\mathbb{R}$; range: $\mathbb{R}$

13. Not a function

15. Function, domain: $\mathbb{R}$; range: $y \geq -4$

17. Not a function

19. Function, domain: $0 \leq x < 12$; range: $y = 1, 2, 3$

21. Not a function

23. Function, domain: $\mathbb{R}$; range: $y > 0$

25. Not a function

27. Yes   **29.** No   **31.** Yes   **33.** 8   **35.** 1

37. -6 **39.** 5   **41.** -23 **43.** 45   **45.** -17

47.

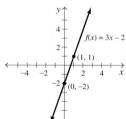

49.

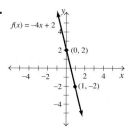

51.

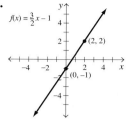

53. a) Upward   **b)** $x = 0$ **c)** $(0, -9)$ **d)** $(0, -9)$
    e) $(3, 0), (-3, 0)$
    f)

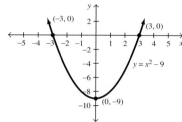

    g) Domain: $\mathbb{R}$; range: $y \geq -9$

55. a) Downward   **b)** $x = 0$ **c)** $(0, 4)$ **d)** $(0, 4)$
    e) $(-2, 0), (2, 0)$
    f)

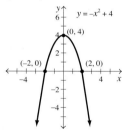

    g) Domain: $\mathbb{R}$; range: $y \leq 4$

57. a) Downward   **b)** $x = 0$ **c)** $(0, -8)$ **d)** $(0, -8)$
    e) No x-intercepts
    f)

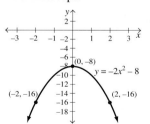

    g) Domain: $\mathbb{R}$; range: $y \leq -8$

59. a) Upward   **b)** $x = 0$ **c)** $(0, -3)$ **d)** $(0, -3)$
   e) $(-1.22, 0), (1.22, 0)$
   f)

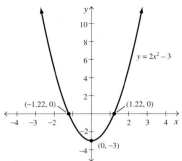

   g) Domain: $\mathbb{R}$; range: $y \geq -3$

61. a) Upward   **b)** $x = -1$ **c)** $(-1, 5)$ **d)** $(0, 6)$
   e) No x-intercepts
   f)

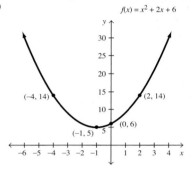

   g) Domain: $\mathbb{R}$; range: $y \geq 5$

63. a) Upward   **b)** $x = -\frac{5}{2}$ **c)** $(-2.5, -0.25)$ **d)** $(0, 6)$
   e) $(-3, 0), (-2, 0)$
   f)

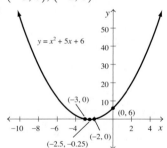

   g) Domain: $\mathbb{R}$; range: $y \geq -0.25$

65. a) Downward   **b)** $x = 2$ **c)** $(2, -2)$ **d)** $(0, -6)$
   e) No x-intercepts

f)

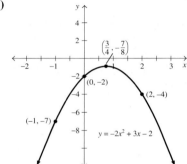

   g) Domain: $\mathbb{R}$; range: $y \leq -2$

67. a) Downward   **b)** $x = \frac{3}{4}$ **c)** $(\frac{3}{4}, -\frac{7}{8})$ **d)** $(0, -2)$
   e) No x-intercepts
   f)

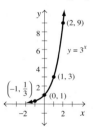

   g) Domain: $\mathbb{R}$; range: $y \leq -\frac{7}{8}$

69. Domain: $\mathbb{R}$; range: $y > 0$

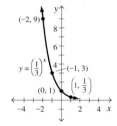

71. Domain: $\mathbb{R}$; range: $y > 0$

73. Domain: $\mathbb{R}$; range: $y > 1$

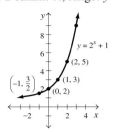

75. Domain: $\mathbb{R}$; range: $y > 1$

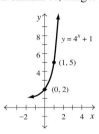

77. Domain: $\mathbb{R}$; range: $y > 0$

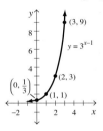

79. Domain: $\mathbb{R}$; range: $y > 0$

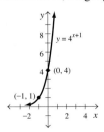

81. \$41,000   **83. a)** $\approx 13\%$ **b)** 1970   **c)** $x \approx 36$; $\approx 5\%$

85. a) 5200 people   **b)** $\approx 14{,}852$ people

87. a) Yes   **b)** $\approx \$59$

89. a) 23.2 cm   **b)** 55.2 cm   **c)** 69.5 cm

91. a) 170 beats per minute
   b) ≈ 162 beats per minute
   c) ≈ 145 beats per minute
   d) 136 beats per minute
   e) 120 years of age

REVIEW EXERCISES, PAGE 407

1. 19   **2.** -8 **3.** 17   **4.** $\frac{1}{4}$ **5.** -13 **6.** 13

7. $4x + 5$ **8.** $15x - 10$ **9.** $7x - 3$ **10.** -10

11. -3 **12.** -13 **13.** -31 **14.** $\frac{128}{5}$ **15.** $\frac{1}{2}$ cup

16. 250 min, or 4 hr 10 min   **17.** 48   **18.** ≈ 173.1

19. 101.5   **20.** 25

21. $y = 2x - 6$

22. $y = \dfrac{-2x + 15}{7}$ or $y = -\dfrac{2}{7}x + \dfrac{15}{7}$

23. $y = \dfrac{2x + 22}{3}$ or $y = \dfrac{2}{3}x + \dfrac{22}{3}$

24. $y = \dfrac{-3x + 5z - 4}{4}$ or $y = -\dfrac{3}{4}x + \dfrac{5}{4}z - 1$

25. $w = \dfrac{A}{l}$ **26.** $w = \dfrac{P - 2l}{2}$

27. $l = \dfrac{L - 2wh}{2h}$ or $l = \dfrac{L}{2h} - w$

28. $d = \dfrac{a_n - a_1}{n - 1}$

29. $7 - 4x$ **30.** $2y + 7$ **31.** $10 + 3r$ **32.** $\dfrac{9}{q} - 15$

33. $3 + 7x = 17$; $x = 2$ **34.** $3x + 8 = x - 6$; $x = -7$

35. $5(x - 4) = 45$; $x = 13$

36. $10x + 14 = 8(x + 12)$; $x = 41$

37. $x + 2x = 15{,}000$; bonds: \$5000, mutual funds: \$10,000

38. $9.50x + 15{,}000 = 95{,}000$; ≈ 8421 chairs

39. $x + 6x + 2 = 79$; 11 species of threatened mammals, 68 species of endangered mammals

40. $x + (x + 12{,}000) = 68{,}000$; \$28,000 for B and \$40,000 for A

41. 64   **42.** 2   **43.** 20   **44.** ≈ 426.7

45. a) 150 lb   **b)** 5 bags   **46.** 4 in.

47. \$119.88   **48.** 1.75 in.

49.

50.

51.

52.

53.

54.

55.

56.

For Exercises 57–60, see the following figure.

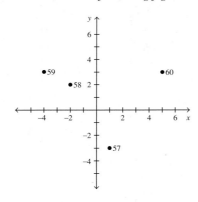

61. $D(-3, -1)$; area = 20 square units

62. $D(4, 1)$; area = 21 square units

63.

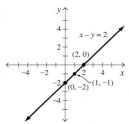

64.

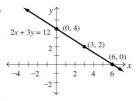

65.

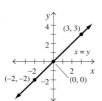

66.

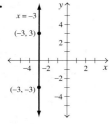

67.

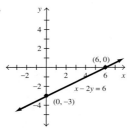

68.

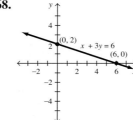

69.

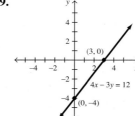

70.

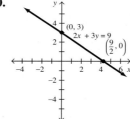

71. $\frac{2}{5}$ **72.** $-\frac{3}{2}$ **73.** $\frac{7}{3}$ **74.** Undefined

75.

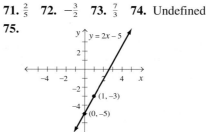

76.

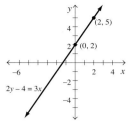

77.

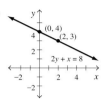

78.

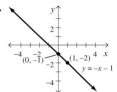

79. $y = 2x + 4$ **80.** $y = -x + 1$

81. a)

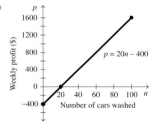

b) $600   **c)** 70 cars

82. a)

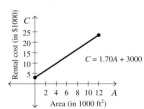

b) $\approx$ $6400   **c)** $\approx 4120 \text{ ft}^2$

83.

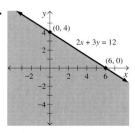

84.

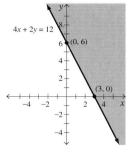

85.

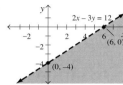

86.

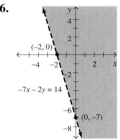

87. $(x + 2)(x + 9)$ **88.** $(x + 6)(x - 5)$

89. $(x - 6)(x - 4)$ **90.** $(x - 5)(x - 4)$

91. $(3x - 1)(2x + 3)$ **92.** $(2x - 1)(x + 7)$

93. $-1, -3$ **94.** $-6, 3$ **95.** $\frac{2}{3}, 5$

96. $-2, -\frac{1}{3}$ **97.** $2 \pm \sqrt{5}$ **98.** $-2, 8$

99. No real solution   **100.** $-1, \frac{3}{2}$

101. Function, domain: $x = -2, -1, 2, 3$;
range: $y = -1, 0, 2$

102. Not a function   **103.** Not a function

104. Function, domain: $\mathbb{R}$; range: $\mathbb{R}$

105. 5   **106.** 15   **107.** 39   **108.** -21

109. a) Downward   **b)** $x = -2$ **c)** $(-2, 25)$ **d)** $(0, 21)$
e) $(-7, 0), (3, 0)$
f)

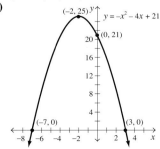

g) Domain: $\mathbb{R}$; range: $y \leq 25$

110. a) Upward   **b)** $x = -2$ **c)** $(-2, -2)$ **d)** $(0, 6)$
e) $(-3, 0), (-1, 0)$
f)

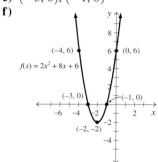

g) Domain: $\mathbb{R}$; range: $y \geq -2$

111. Domain: $\mathbb{R}$; range: $y > 0$

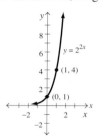

112. Domain: $\mathbb{R}$; range: $y > 0$

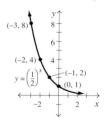

113. 22.8 mpg
114. a) 4208   **b)** 4250
115. $\approx 68.7\%$

CHAPTER TEST, PAGE 411

1. 9   **2.** $\frac{19}{5}$ **3.** 18   **4.** $3x + 5 = 17; 4$
5. $350 + 0.06x = 710;$ \$6000   **6.** 77
7. $y = \dfrac{-3x + 11}{5}$ or $y = -\dfrac{3}{5}x + \dfrac{11}{5}$
8. $3\frac{1}{3}$ **9.** 6.75 ft
10.

11. 2

12.

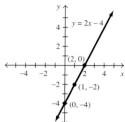

13.

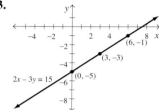

14.

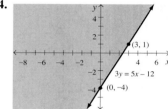

15. $-1, -4$ **16.** $\frac{4}{3}, -2$
17. It is a function.   **18.** 17
19. a) Upward   **b)** $x = 1$ **c)** $(1, 3)$ **d)** $(0, 4)$
e) No x-intercepts
f)

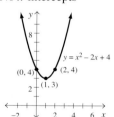

g) Domain: $\mathbb{R}$; range: $y \geq 3$

CHAPTER 7

SECTION 7.1, PAGE 419

1. Two or more linear equations form a system of linear equations.

3. An inconsistent system of equations is one that has no solution.

5. A dependent system of equations is one that has an infinite number of solutions.

7. The graphs of the equations will be parallel lines.

9. The graphs of the equations will be the same line.

11. $(3, 5)$

13.

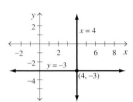

15.

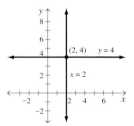

17.

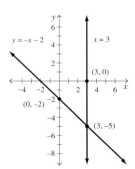

19.

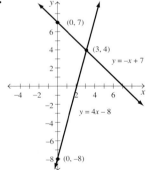

21.

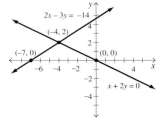

23.

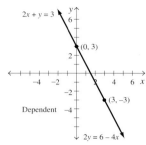

25.

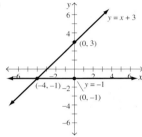

27.

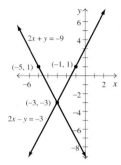

29.

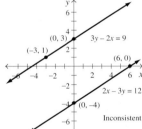

31.

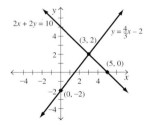

33. a) One unique solution; the lines intersect at one and only one point.

   b) No solution; the lines do not intersect.

   c) Infinitely many solutions; the lines coincide.

35. An infinite number of solutions

37. One solution   **39.** No solution

41. An infinite number of solutions

43. No solution   **45.** One solution

47. Not perpendicular   **49.** Perpendicular

51. a) Cost to repair: $C = 375x + 250$
      Cost to replace: $C = 225x + 700$

b)

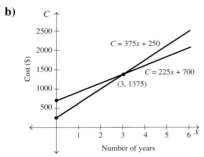

c) 3 years

53. a) $C = 15x + 400$
$R = 25x$

b)

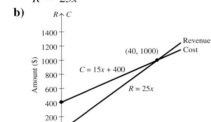

c) 40 backpacks   **d)** $P = 10x - 400$
e) Loss of \$100   **f)** 140 backpacks

55. a) $C = 230x + 8400, R = 300x$

b)

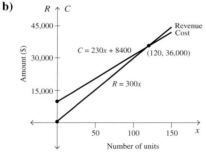

c) 120 units   **d)** $P = 70x - 8400$
e) Loss of \$1400   **f)** 138 units

57. a) Job 1: $s = 0.15x + 500$
Job 2: $s = 650$

b)

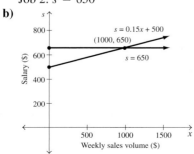

c) \$1000

59. a) One   **b)** Three   **c)** Six   **d)** Ten
e) To determine the number of points of intersection for n lines, add $n - 1$ to the number of points of intersection for $n - 1$ lines. For example, for 5 lines there were 10 points of intersection. Therefore, for 6 lines ($n = 6$) there are $10 + (6 - 1) = 15$ points of intersection.

SECTION 7.2, PAGE 431

1. Answers will vary.

3. The system is dependent if the same value is obtained on both sides of the equal sign.

5. x, in the first equation

7. $(-2, 6)$ **9.** $(1, -1)$

11. No solution; inconsistent system   **13.** $\left(-2, \frac{8}{3}\right)$

15. An infinite number of solutions; dependent system

17. $(-3, -6)$ **19.** $\left(\frac{11}{5}, -\frac{13}{5}\right)$ **21.** $\left(-\frac{1}{5}, -\frac{8}{5}\right)$

23. No solution; inconsistent system

25. $(3, 0)$ **27.** $(7, 5)$ **29.** $(-2, 0)$

31. $(-4, 5)$ **33.** $(3, 5)$ **35.** $(1, -2)$

37. No solution; inconsistent system   **39.** $(2, 1)$

41. $s = 0.15p + 12{,}000$
$s = 0.05p + 27{,}000$
\$150,000 annual profit

43. $m + l = 50$
$10.95m + 14.95l = 663.50$
21 medium, 29 large

45. $x + y = 10$
$0.25x + 0.50y = 0.40(10)$
4ℓ of 25%, 6ℓ of 50%

47. $y = 0.02x + 18$
$y = 0.015x + 24$
1200 copies

49. $x + y = 20$
$3x + y = 30$
Mix 5 lb of nuts with 15 lb of pretzels.

51. $x + y = 4600$
$27x + 14y = 104{,}700$
3100 amphitheatre tickets and 1500 lawn tickets

53. ≈ 11.2 years after 2000 or in 2011

55. $\left(\frac{1}{2}, \frac{1}{3}\right)$ **57.–61.** Answers will vary.

SECTION 7.3, PAGE 441

1. A matrix is a rectangular array of elements.

3. A square matrix contains the same number of rows and columns.

5. 4

7. a) Answers will vary.   **b)** $\begin{bmatrix} 7 & 9 & -7 \\ 2 & 16 & 9 \end{bmatrix}$

9. a) The number of columns of the first matrix must be the same as the number of rows of the second matrix.
b) 2×3

11. a) $I = \begin{bmatrix} 1 & 0 \\ 0 & 1 \end{bmatrix}$ **b)** $I = \begin{bmatrix} 1 & 0 & 0 \\ 0 & 1 & 0 \\ 0 & 0 & 1 \end{bmatrix}$

13. $\begin{bmatrix} -3 & 9 \\ 9 & 9 \end{bmatrix}$ **15.** $\begin{bmatrix} -1 & 4 \\ -5 & 4 \\ 7 & 6 \end{bmatrix}$

17. $\begin{bmatrix} 6 & -7 \\ -12 & 4 \end{bmatrix}$ **19.** $\begin{bmatrix} 1 & 9 \\ 18 & 17 \\ -2 & 2 \end{bmatrix}$

21. $\begin{bmatrix} 6 & 4 \\ 10 & 0 \end{bmatrix}$ **23.** $\begin{bmatrix} -2 & 16 \\ 26 & 0 \end{bmatrix}$

25. $\begin{bmatrix} 16 & 2 \\ 12 & 0 \end{bmatrix}$ **27.** $\begin{bmatrix} 26 & 18 \\ 48 & 24 \end{bmatrix}$

29. $\begin{bmatrix} 15 \\ 22 \end{bmatrix}$ **31.** $\begin{bmatrix} 4 & 7 & 6 \\ -2 & 3 & 1 \\ 5 & 1 & 2 \end{bmatrix}$

33. $A + B = \begin{bmatrix} 9 & 1 & 8 \\ 6 & -1 & 4 \end{bmatrix}$; cannot be multiplied

35. Cannot be added; $A \times B = \begin{bmatrix} 26 & 38 \\ 24 & 24 \end{bmatrix}$

37. Cannot be added; $\begin{bmatrix} 1 \\ -1 \end{bmatrix}$

39. $A + B = B + A = \begin{bmatrix} 7 & 10 \\ 4 & 4 \end{bmatrix}$

41. $A + B = B + A = \begin{bmatrix} 8 & 0 \\ 6 & -8 \end{bmatrix}$

43. $(A + B) + C = A + (B + C) = \begin{bmatrix} 7 & 10 \\ 6 & 13 \end{bmatrix}$

45. $(A + B) + C = A + (B + C) = \begin{bmatrix} 5 & 5 \\ 7 & -37 \end{bmatrix}$

47. No   **49.** No   **51.** Yes

53. $(A \times B) \times C = A \times (B \times C) = \begin{bmatrix} 41 & 13 \\ 56 & 16 \end{bmatrix}$

55. $(A \times B) \times C = A \times (B \times C) = \begin{bmatrix} 16 & -10 \\ -24 & 2 \end{bmatrix}$

57. $(A \times B) \times C = A \times (B \times C) = \begin{bmatrix} 17 & 0 \\ -7 & 0 \end{bmatrix}$

59.
	Tomatoes	Onions	Carrots	
	88	58	70	Chase's Farm
	78	54	71	Gro-More Farms

61. Total cost
53	Java's Coffee Shop
55	Spot Coffee Shop

63.
Large	Small	
38	50	Sugar
56	72	Flour
17	26	Milk
10	14	Eggs

65. [36.04   47.52]
67. Answers will vary.
69. Yes   **71.** False

73. a) $28.70   **b)** $60.10   **c)** $\begin{bmatrix} 28.7 & 24.6 \\ 41.3 & 35.7 \\ 69.3 & 60.1 \end{bmatrix}$

75. Yes. Answers will vary. One example is

$A = \begin{bmatrix} 2 & 7 & 6 \\ -3 & 0 & 8 \end{bmatrix}$, $B = \begin{bmatrix} 1 & 2 \\ 3 & 4 \\ 5 & 6 \end{bmatrix}$.

SECTION 7.4, PAGE 452

1. a) An augmented matrix is a matrix formed with the coefficients of the variables and the constants. The coefficients of the variables are separated from the constants by a vertical bar.
b) $\begin{bmatrix} 1 & 3 & | & 7 \\ 2 & -1 & | & 4 \end{bmatrix}$

3. If you obtain an augmented matrix in which a 0 appears across an entire row, the system of equations is dependent.

5. Change the -2 to a 1 by multiplying the numbers in the second row by $-\frac{1}{2}$.

7. $(1, 2)$ **9.** $(3, 2)$

11. An infinite number of solutions; dependent system
13. $\left(\frac{7}{2}, -1\right)$ **15.** $(1, 1)$
17. No solution; inconsistent system
19. $(3, 4)$
21. Fitted caps: 18, stretch-fit caps: 14
23. Truck driver: $7\frac{1}{9}$ hours; laborer: $9\frac{1}{9}$ hours
25. Premium paper: 150 reams, paper for color printers: 50 reams

SECTION 7.5, PAGE 456

1. The solution set of a system of linear inequalities is the set of points that satisfy all inequalities in the system.

3. Yes. A point of intersection satisfies both inequalities and is, therefore, a solution.

5.

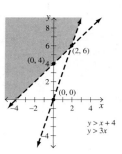

$$y > x + 4$$
$$y > 3x$$

7.

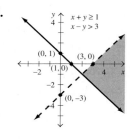

$$x + y \geq 1$$
$$x - y > 3$$

19.

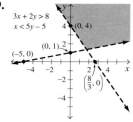

$$3x + 2y > 8$$
$$x < 5y - 5$$

21. a) $20x + 30y \leq 600, x \geq 2y, x \geq 10, y \geq 5$

b)

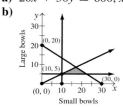

Large bowls

Small bowls

c) One example is 15 small bowls, 7 large bowls

23. $x \leq 0, y \geq 0$

25. Yes. One example is $x \geq 0, y \geq 0, x \leq 0, y \leq 0$ which has solution $(0, 0)$.

27. Answers will vary.

9.

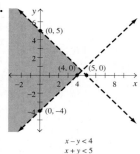

$$x - y < 4$$
$$x + y < 5$$

SECTION 7.6, PAGE 461

1. Constraints are restrictions that are represented as linear inequalities.

3. Vertices

5. Answers will vary.

7. Maximum is 30 at $(5, 0)$, minimum is 0 at $(0, 0)$.

9. Maximum is 190 at $(50, 30)$, minimum is 70 at $(20, 10)$.

11.

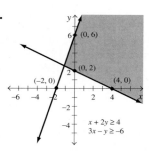

$$x + 2y \geq 4$$
$$3x - y \geq -6$$

11. a)

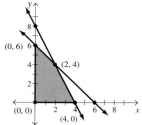

b) Maximum is 30 at $(0, 6)$, minimum is 0 at $(0, 0)$.

13.

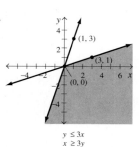

$$y \leq 3x$$
$$x \geq 3y$$

13. a)

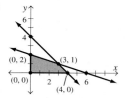

b) Maximum is 28 at $(4, 0)$, minimum is 0 at $(0, 0)$.

15.

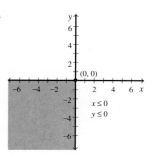

$$x \leq 0$$
$$y \leq 0$$

17.

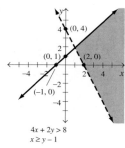

$$4x + 2y > 8$$
$$x \geq y - 1$$

15. a)

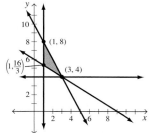

b) Maximum is 15.4 at $(1, 8)$, minimum is 11 at $\left(1, \frac{16}{3}\right)$.

17. a) $x + y \leq 24, x \geq 2y, y \geq 4, x \geq 0, y \geq 0$

b) $P = 40x + 55y$

c)

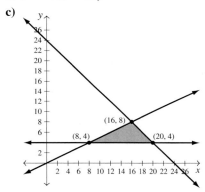

d) $(8, 4), (16, 8), (20, 4)$

e) 16 Kodak cameras and 8 Canon cameras

f) \$1080

19. a) $3x + 4y \geq 60, 10x + 5y \geq 100, x \geq 0, y \geq 0$

b) $C = 28x + 33y$

c)

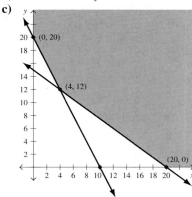

d) $(0, 20), (4, 12), (20, 0)$

e) 4 hours for Machine I and 12 hours for Machine II

f) \$508

21. Three car seats and seven strollers, \$320

REVIEW EXERCISES, PAGE 464

1.

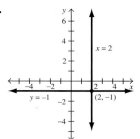

2.

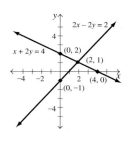

3.

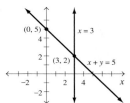

4.

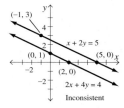

5. An infinite number of solutions   **6.** No solution

7. One solution   **8.** One solution   **9.** $(3, 1)$

10. $(-1, -5)$ **11.** $(-2, -8)$

12. No solution; inconsistent   **13.** $(4, -2)$ **14.** $(-7, 16)$

15. $(4, -2)$ **16.** An infinite number of solutions; dependent

17. $(2, -1)$ **18.** $(2, 0)$

19. $\begin{bmatrix} -1 & -8 \\ 8 & 7 \end{bmatrix}$ **20.** $\begin{bmatrix} 3 & 2 \\ -4 & 1 \end{bmatrix}$

21. $\begin{bmatrix} 2 & -6 \\ 4 & 8 \end{bmatrix}$ **22.** $\begin{bmatrix} 8 & 9 \\ -14 & -1 \end{bmatrix}$

23. $\begin{bmatrix} -20 & -14 \\ 20 & 2 \end{bmatrix}$ **24.** $\begin{bmatrix} -12 & -14 \\ 12 & -6 \end{bmatrix}$

25. $(2, 2)$ **26.** $(-2, 2)$ **27.** $(3, -3)$

28. $(1, 0)$ **29.** $\left(\frac{12}{11}, \frac{7}{11}\right)$ **30.** $(1, 2)$

31. \$350,000 at 4%, \$250,000 at 6%

32. Mix $83\frac{1}{3}\ell$ of 80% acid solution with $16\frac{2}{3}\ell$ of 50% acid solution.

33. \$245 per ton for topsoil, \$183 per ton for mulch

34. a) 32.5 months   **b)** Model 6070B

35. a) 3 hr   **b)** All-Day parking lot

36.

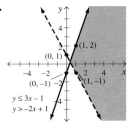

37.

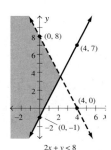

38.

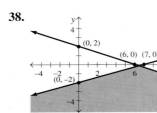

$$x + 3y \leq 6$$
$$2x - 7y \geq 14$$

39.

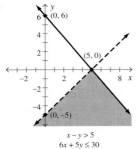

$$x - y > 5$$
$$6x + 5y \leq 30$$

40. a)

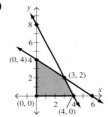

b) Maximum is 21 at (3, 2), minimum is 0 at (0, 0).

CHAPTER TEST, PAGE 466

1. If the lines do not intersect (are parallel), the system of equations is inconsistent. The system of equations is consistent if the lines intersect. If both equations represent the same line, the system of equations is dependent.

2.

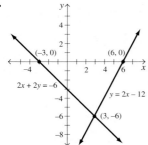

3. One solution   **4.** (2, −3)   **5.** (−2, −13)
6. (−2, −6)   **7.** (−1, 3)   **8.** (2, 0)
9. (−2, 2)   **10.** $\begin{bmatrix} 1 & -8 \\ 6 & 5 \end{bmatrix}$

11. $\begin{bmatrix} 4 & 1 \\ -9 & -1 \end{bmatrix}$ **12.** $\begin{bmatrix} -27 & -16 \\ 14 & 3 \end{bmatrix}$

13.

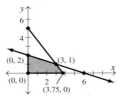

$$y < -2x + 2$$
$$y > 3x + 2$$

14. Daily fee: $35, mileage charge: $0.18
15. a) 40 checks   **b)** Citrus Bank
16. a)

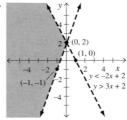

b) Maximum is 22.5 at (3.75, 0), minimum is 0 at (0, 0).

CHAPTER 8

SECTION 8.1, PAGE 474

1. The metric system
3. It is the standard of measurement accepted worldwide. There is only one basic unit of measurement for each quantity. It is based on the number 10, which makes many calculations easier than the U.S. customary system.
5. a) Answers will vary.   **b)** 0.002 146 km   **c)** 60 800 dm
7. Answers will vary.
9. a) 10,000 times   **b)** 10 000 cm   **c)** 0.0001 hm
11. Yard   **13.** 5   **15.** 22   **17.** (b)   **19.** (c)   **21.** (f)
23. a) 100   **b)** 0.001   **c)** 1000   **d)** 0.01   **e)** 10   **f)** 0.1
25. cg; $\frac{1}{100}$ g   **27.** dg; $\frac{1}{10}$ g   **29.** hg; 100 g
31. 3 000 000 g   **33.** 5000   **35.** 0.0085   **37.** 0.024 26
39. 0.024 35   **41.** 13 400   **43.** 325 hg   **45.** 895 000 mℓ
47. 1.40 g   **49.** 4.0302 daℓ   **51.** 590 cm, 2.3 dam, 0.47 km
53. 1.4 kg, 1600 g, 16 300 dg
55. 203 000 mm, 2.6 km, 52.6 hm
57. Jim, 1 m > 1 yd
59. The pump that removes 1 daℓ per minute
61. a) 346 cm   **b)** 3460 mm
63. a) 6.417 km/ℓ   **b)** 6417 m/ℓ
65. a) 2160 mℓ   **b)** 2.16 ℓ   **c)** $1.13 per liter

67. a) 108 m **b)** 0.108 km **c)** 108 000 mm

69. a) 11 120 km **b)** 11 120 000 m **71.** 1000

73. 1×10^{24} = 1 000 000 000 000 000 000 000 000

75. ≈ 30 eggs **77.** ≈ 4.1 cups **79.** 7 dam

81. 6 mg **83.** 2 daℓ **85.** gram **87.** liter **89.** meter

91. kilometer **93.** degrees celsius

SECTION 8.2, PAGE 485

1. Volume **3.** Area **5.** Volume **7.** Volume

9. Area **11.** Length **13.–17.** Answers will vary.

19. A cubic decimeter **21.** A cubic centimeter

23. Area **25.** Centimeters **27.** Centimeters or millimeters

29. Centimeters **31.** Kilometers **33.** Centimeters

35. Kilometers **37.** (c) **39.** (c) **41.** (b) **43.** (c)

45.–49. Answers will vary. **51.** Centimeter, kilometer

53. Meter **55.** Centimeter **57.** Square centimeters

59. Square centimeters or square meters

61. Square meters or hectares **63.** Square centimeters

65. Square meters **67.** (a) **69.** (b) **71.** (a)

73. (c) **75.–79.** Answers will vary.

81. Liters **83.** Kiloliters

85. Cubic meters or cubic centimeters

87. Liters **89.** Cubic meters **91.** (c) **93.** (c)

95. (c) **97.** (a) **99. b)** 152 561 cm^3

101. ≈ 0.20 m^3

103. Longer side ≈ 4 cm, shorter side ≈ 2.2 cm,
area ≈ 8.8 cm^2

105. ≈ 326.85 m^2 **107. a)** 3869 m^2 **b)** 369 m^2

109. a) 3151.2 m^2 **b)** 0.315 12 ha

111. $304 **113. a)** 56 000 cm^3 **b)** 56 000 mℓ **c)** 56 ℓ

115. 100 times larger **117.** 1000 times larger

119. 100 **121.** 100 **123.** 0.000 001

125. 1 000 000 **127.** 218 **129.** 76 **131.** 60 kℓ

133. Answers will vary. **135.** 6700

137. a) 4,014,489,600 sq in. **b)** Answers will vary.

139. a) Answers will vary. The average use is 5150.7 ℓ/day.
b) Answers will vary. The average use is 493.2 ℓ/day.

SECTION 8.3, PAGE 495

1. Kilogram **3.** 2

5. Answers will vary. One possible answer is 32°C.

7. Answers will vary. **9.** Kilograms

11. Grams **13.** Grams **15.** Kilograms

17. Kilograms or metric tonnes **19.** (b)

21. (b) **23.** (b) **25.–27.** Answers will vary.

29. (c) **31.** (b) **33.** (c) **35.** (c) **37.** (c) **39.** 77°F

41. ≈ 33.3°C **43.** ≈ −17.8°C **45.** 98.6°F

47. ≈ −10.6°C **49.** 32°F **51.** ≈ −28.9°C

53. ≈ 73.9 by the formula **55.** 71.6°F

57. 95.18°F **59.** 64.04°F–74.30°F **61.** $20.25

63. 444 g **65. a)** 2304 m^3 **b)** 2304 kℓ **c)** 2304 t

67. Yes: 78°F is about 25.6°C.

69. 0.0042 **71.** 17 400 000 g

73. a) 1200 g **b)** 1200 cm^3

75. a) 5.625 ft^3 **b)** ≈ 351.6 lb **c)** ≈ 42.4 gal

77. a) −79.8°F **b)** 36.5°F **c)** 510 000 000°C

SECTION 8.4, PAGE 505

1. Dimensional analysis is a procedure used to convert from one unit of measurement to a different unit of measurement.

3. $\dfrac{60 \text{ seconds}}{1 \text{ minute}}$ or $\dfrac{1 \text{ minute}}{60 \text{ seconds}}$

5. $\dfrac{1 \text{ lb}}{0.45 \text{ kg}}$ **7.** $\dfrac{3.8 \text{ ℓ}}{1 \text{ gal}}$ **9.** 157.48 cm **11.** 1.26 m

13. 266.67 lb **15.** 62.4 km **17.** 1687.5 acres

19. 33.19 pints **21.** 1.46 mi^2 **23.** 54 kg **25.** 28 grams

27. 0.45 kilogram **29.** 2.54 centimeters, 1.6 kilometers

31. 0.9 meter **33.** ≈ 561.11 yd **35.** ≈ 1146.67 ft

37. 37.5 mph **39.** 43.2 m^2 **41.** 50 mph **43.** 0.21 oz

45. 360 m^3 **47.** $0.495 per pound **49.** ≈ 9078.95 gal

51. 6 qt **53. a)** −8460 cm **b)** −84.6 m

55. a) 10.89 ft^2 **b)** 35.937 ft^3 **57.** 25.2 mg

59. 6840 mg, or 6.84 g

61. a) 25 mg **b)** 900 mg

63. a) 289.2 m **b)** 76 500 t **c)** 44.8 kph

65. a) 0.9 € per pound **b)** $1.17 per pound

67. 1.0 cc, or b)

69. a) 4000 cc **b)** ≈ 244.09 in.^{3} **71.** A kilogram

73. A liter **75.** A decimeter **77.** wonton **79.** 1 kilohurtz

81. 1 megaphone **83.** 2 kilomockingbird **85.** 1 decoration

REVIEW EXERCISES, PAGE 509

1. $\frac{1}{100}$ of base unit **2.** 1000 × base unit

3. $\frac{1}{1000}$ of base unit **4.** 100 × base unit

5. 10 × base unit **6.** $\frac{1}{10}$ of base unit **7.** 0.040 g

8. 320 cℓ **9.** 0.016 mm **10.** 1 kg **11.** 4620 ℓ

12. 19 260 dg **13.** 3000 mℓ, 14 630 cℓ, 2.67 kℓ

14. 0.047 km, 47 000 cm, 4700 m **15.** Centimeters

16. Grams **17.** Degrees Celsius

18. Millimeters or centimeters **19.** Square meters

20. Milliliters or cubic centimeters   21. Millimeters

22. Kilograms or tonnes   23. Kilometers

24. Meters or centimeters

25. a) Answers will vary. b) Answers will vary.

26. a) Answers will vary. b) Answers will vary.

27. (c) 28. (b) 29. (c) 30. (a) 31. (a) 32. (b)

33. 3.6 t 34. 4 300 000 g 35. 75.2°F 36. 20°C

37. ≈ -21.1°C 38. 102.2°F

39. $l = 4$ cm, $w = 1.6$ cm, $A = 6.4$ cm^2

40. $r = 1.5$ cm, $A \approx 7.07$ cm^2

41. a) 80 m^3 b) 80 000 kg

42. a) 899.79 cm^2 b) 0.089 979 m^2

43. a) 96 000 cm^3 b) 0.096 m^3
    c) 96 000 mℓ d) 0.096 kℓ

44. 10,000 times larger 45. ≈ 9.84 in. 46. ≈ 233.33 lb

47. 74.7 m 48. ≈ 111.11 yd 49. 72 kph 50. ≈ 63.16 qt

51. 76 ℓ 52. ≈ 78.95 yd^3 53. ≈ 12.77 in.^{2} 54. 3.8 ℓ

55. 11.4 m^3 56. 99.2 km 57. 0.9 ft 58. 82.55 mm

59. a) 1050 kg b) ≈ 2333.33 lb 60. 32.4 m^2

61. a) 190 kℓ b) 190 000 kg

62. a) 104 kph b) 104 000 meters per hour

63. a) 252 ℓ b) 252 kg

64. $1.58 per pound

CHAPTER TEST, PAGE 512

1. 0.497 daℓ 2. 2 730 000 cm 3. 100 times greater

4. 2.4 km 5. (b) 6. (a) 7. (c) 8. (c) 9. (b)

10. 10,000 times greater 11. 1,000,000,000 times greater

12. 6300 g 13. ≈ 28.13 mi 14. ≈ -26.11°C

15. 68°F 16. a) 300 000 g b) ≈ 666.67 lb

17. a) 3200 m^3 b) 3 200 000 ℓ (or 3200 kℓ)
    c) 3 200 000 kg

18. $245

CHAPTER 9

SECTION 9.1, PAGE 523

1. a) Undefined terms, definitions, postulates (axioms), and
      theorems
   b) First, Euclid introduced undefined terms. Second, he
      introduced certain definitions. Third, he stated primitive
      propositions called postulates about the undefined
      terms and definitions. Fourth, he proved, using deduc-
      tive reasoning, other propositions called theorems.

3. Two lines that do not lie in the same plane and do not intersect are called skew lines.

5. Two angles in the same plane are adjacent angles when
   they have a common vertex and a common side but no
   common interior points.

7. Two angles, the sum of whose measure is 180°, are
   called supplementary angles.

9. An angle whose measure is greater than 90° but less than
   180° is an obtuse angle.

11. An angle whose measure is less than 90° is an acute angle.

13. Ray, $\overrightarrow{BA}$ 15. Half line, $\overset{\circ}{B}A$ 17. Ray, $\overrightarrow{AB}$

19. Half open line segment, $\overset{\circ}{A}B$ 21. $\overrightarrow{BG}$ 23. $\overrightarrow{BD}$

25. $\{B, F\}$ 27. $\{C\}$ 29. $\angle CFG$ 31. $\overleftrightarrow{BC}$ 33. $\{B\}$

35. $\overrightarrow{BC}$ 37. $\angle ABE$ 39. $\overline{BF}$ 41. $\overleftrightarrow{AC}$ 43. $\overrightarrow{BE}$

45. Obtuse 47. Straight 49. Right

51. None of these angles 53. 64° 55. $57\frac{1}{4}$° 57. 25.3°

59. 91° 61. 159.5° 63. $136\frac{2}{7}$° 65. (b) 67. (f)

69. (a) 71. $m\angle 1 = 49°$, $m\angle 2 = 41°$ 73. 134° and 46°

75. Angles 3, 4, and 7 each measure 125°; angles 1, 2, 5, and
    6 each measure 55°.

77. Angles 2, 4, and 5 each measure 120°; angles 1, 3, 6, and
    7 each measure 60°.

79. $m\angle 1 = 64°$, $m\angle 2 = 26°$

81. $m\angle 1 = 33°$, $m\angle 2 = 57°$

83. $m\angle 1 = 134°$, $m\angle 2 = 46°$

85. $m\angle 1 = 29°$, $m\angle 2 = 151°$

87. a) An infinite number b) An infinite number

89. An infinite number

*For Exercises 91–97, each answer given is one of many
possible answers.*

91. Plane ABG and plane JCD 93. $\overleftrightarrow{BG}$ and $\overleftrightarrow{DG}$

95. Plane $AGB \cap$ plane $ABC \cap$ plane $BCD = \{B\}$

97. $\overleftrightarrow{BC} \cap$ plane $ABG = \{B\}$

99. Always true. If any two lines are parallel to a third line,
    then they must be parallel to each other.

101. Sometimes true. Vertical angles are only complementary
     when each is equal to 45°.

103. Sometimes true. Alternate interior angles are only com-
     plementary when each is equal to 45°.

105. Answers will vary.

107. No. Line l and line n may be parallel or skew.

109. 360°

SECTION 9.2, PAGE 533

1. A polygon is a closed figure in a plane determined by
   three or more straight line segments.

3. The different types of triangles are acute, obtuse, right,
   isosceles, equilateral, and scalene. Descriptions will vary.

5. If the corresponding sides of two similar figures are the same length, the figures are congruent figures.

7. a) Triangle b) Regular

9. a) Octagon b) Regular

11. a) Rhombus b) Not regular

13. a) Octagon b) Not regular

15. a) Isosceles b) Acute

17. a) Isosceles b) Right

19. a) Scalene b) Acute

21. a) Scalene b) Right

23. Rectangle 25. Square 27. Rhombus

29. 17° 31. 150°

33. $m\angle 1 = 90°, m\angle 2 = 50°, m\angle 3 = 130°, m\angle 4 = 50°,$
$m\angle 5 = 50°, m\angle 6 = 40°, m\angle 7 = 90°, m\angle 8 = 130°,$
$m\angle 9 = 140°, m\angle 10 = 40°, m\angle 11 = 140°, m\angle 12 = 40°$

35. 720° 37. 1080° 39. 3240°

41. a) 60° b) 120° 43. a) 108° b) 72°

45. a) 144° b) 36° 47. $x = 2, y = 1.6$

49. $x = 2\frac{2}{5}, y = 7\frac{1}{2}$ 51. $x = 20, y = 21\frac{1}{4}$

53. 3 55. $3\frac{1}{3}$ 57. 28 59. 30 61. 28° 63. 9

65. 10 67. 70° 69. 55° 71. 35° 73. 70 ft

75. a) ≈ 113.14 mi b) ≈ 75.43 mi

77. $D'E' = 4, E'F' = 5, D'F' = 3$

79. a) $m\angle HMF = m\angle TMB, m\angle HFM = m\angle TBM,$
$m\angle MHF = m\angle MTB$
    b) 44 ft

SECTION 9.3, PAGE 545

Throughout this section, we used the $\boxed{\pi}$ key on a scientific calculator to determine answers in calculations involving π. If you use 3.14 for π, your answers may vary slightly.

1. a) Answers will vary.
   b) Answers will vary.
   c)

The area of this rectangle is 12 square units. The perimeter of this rectangle is 16 units.

3. a) To determine the number of square feet, multiply the number of square yards by 9.
   b) To determine the number of square yards, divide the number of square feet by 9.

5. 17.5 in.² 7. 17.5 cm² 9. a) 210 ft² b) 62 ft

11. a) 6000 cm² b) 654 cm

13. a) 288 in.² b) 74 in.

15. a) 50.27 m² b) 25.13 m

17. a) 132.73 ft² b) 40.84 ft

19. a) 17 yd b) 40 yd c) 60 yd²

21. a) 12 km b) 30 km c) 30 km²

23. ≈ 21.46 m² 25. 8 in.² 27. 90 yd²

29. ≈ 65.73 in.² 31. ≈ 307.88 cm² 33. 23 yd²

35. 132.3 ft² 37. 234,000 cm² 39. 0.8625 m²

41. a) $5973 b) $7623 43. $2890

45. $2908.80 47. $234.21 49. a) 288 ft b) 4700 tiles

51. 21 ft 53. ≈ 312 ft

55. a) $A = s^2$ b) $A = 4s^2$ c) Four times larger

57. 24 cm² 59. Answers will vary.

SECTION 9.4, PAGE 561

Throughout this section, we used the $\boxed{\pi}$ key on a scientific calculator to determine answers in calculations involving π. If you use 3.14 for π, your answers may vary slightly.

1. a) Volume is a measure of the capacity of a figure.
   b) Surface area is the sum of the areas of the surfaces of a three-dimensional figure.

3. A polyhedron is a closed surface formed by the union of polygonal regions. A regular polyhedron is one whose faces are all regular polygons of the same size and shape.

5. Answers will vary. 7. a) 8 m³ b) 28 m²

9. a) 125 ft³ b) 150 ft²

11. a) 150.80 in.³ b) 175.93 in.²

13. a) 131.95 cm³ b) 163.22 cm²

15. a) 381.70 cm³ b) 254.47 cm²

17. 384 in.³ 19. 524.33 cm³ 21. 324 mm³ 23. 392 ft³

25. 284.46 cm³ 27. 24 ft³ 29. 243 ft³ 31. ≈ 5.67 yd³

33. 3,700,000 cm³ 35. 7.5 m³

37. Tubs ≈ 141.37 in.³; boxes $= 125$ in.³

39. 40,840 mm² 41. ≈ 2.50 qt

43. a) 120,000 cm³ b) 120,000 mℓ c) 120 ℓ

45. ≈ 283.04 in.³

47. a) ≈ 323.98 in.³ b) ≈ 0.19 ft³

49. ≈ 14.14 in.³ 51. Ten edges

53. Six vertices 55. Fourteen edges

57. a) $\approx 5.11 \times 10^8$ km² b) $\approx 3.79 \times 10^7$ km²
    c) ≈ 13 times larger d) $\approx 1.09 \times 10^{12}$ km³
    e) $\approx 2.20 \times 10^{10}$ km³ f) ≈ 50 times larger

59. a)–e) Answers will vary.
    f) If we double the length of each edge of a cube, the new volume will be eight times the original volume.

61. a) Answers will vary.

b) $V_1 = a^3$; $V_2 = a^2b$; $V_3 = a^2b$; $V_4 = ab^2$;
$V_5 = a^2b$; $V_6 = ab^2$; $V_7 = b^3$

c) ab^2

SECTION 9.5, PAGE 579

1. The act of moving a geometric figure from some starting position to some ending position without altering its shape or size is called rigid motion. The four main rigid motions studied in this section are reflections, translations, rotations, and glide reflections.

3. A reflection is a rigid motion that moves a figure to a new position that is a mirror image of the figure in the starting position.

5. A rotation is a rigid motion performed by rotating a figure in the plane about a specific point.

7. A translation is a rigid motion that moves a figure by sliding it along a straight line segment in the plane.

9. A glide reflection is a rigid motion formed by performing a translation (or glide) followed by a reflection.

11. A geometric figure is said to have reflective symmetry if the positions of a figure before and after a reflection are identical (except for vertex labels).

13. A tessellation is a pattern consisting of the repeated use of the same geometric figures to entirely cover a plane, leaving no gaps.

This figure contains the answers for Exercises 15 and 16.

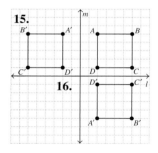

This figure contains the answers for Exercises 17 and 18.

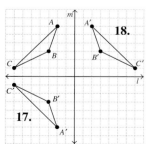

This figure contains the answers for Exercises 19 and 20.

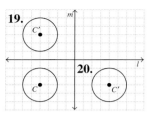

This figure contains the answers for Exercises 21 and 22.

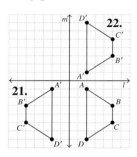

This figure contains the answers to Exercises 23 and 24.

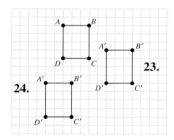

This figure contains the answers to Exercises 25 and 26.

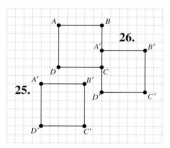

This figure contains the answers to Exercises 27 and 28.

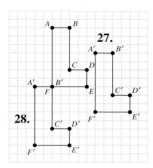

This figure contains the answers to Exercises 35 and 36.

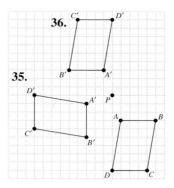

29.

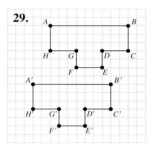

This figure contains the answers to Exercises 37 and 38.

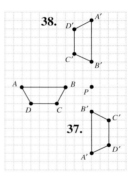

This figure contains the answers to Exercises 31 and 32.

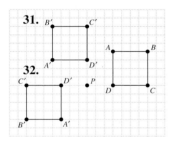

This figure contains the answers to Exercises 39 and 40.

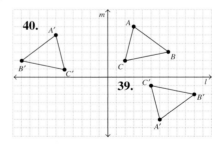

This figure contains the answers to Exercises 33 and 34.

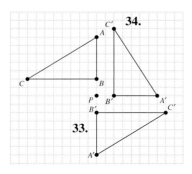

This figure contains the answers to Exercises 41 and 42.

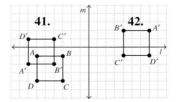

This figure contains the answers to Exercises 43 and 44.

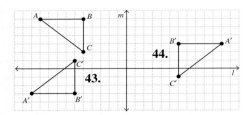

This figure contains the answers to Exercises 45 and 46.

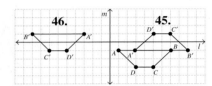

47. a)

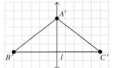

  b) Yes
  c) Yes

49. a)

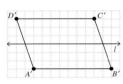

  b) No
  c) No

51. a)

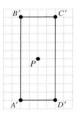

  b) No
  c) No
  d)

  e) Yes
  f) Yes

53. a)–c)

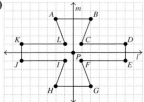

d) No. Any 90° rotation will result in the figure being in a different position than the starting position.

55. a) and **b)**

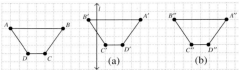

  c) No.
  d) The order in which the translation and the reflection are performed is important. The figure obtained in part (a) is the glide reflection.

57. Answers will vary.

59. a) Answers will vary.
  b) A regular pentagon cannot be used as a tessellating shape.

61. Although answers will vary depending on the font, the following capital letters have reflective symmetry about a vertical line drawn through the center of the letter: A, H, I, M, O, T, U, V, W, X, Y.

SECTION 9.6, PAGE 590

1. Topology is sometimes referred to as "rubber sheet geometry" because it deals with bending and stretching of geometric figures.

3. Take a strip of paper, give one end a half twist, and tape the ends together.

5. Four

7. A Jordan curve is a topological object that can be thought of as a circle twisted out of shape.

9. The number of holes that go through the object determines the genus of an object.

11.–19. Answers will vary.   **21.** Outside   **23.** Inside

25. Outside   **27.** Outside   **29.** 1   **31.** 5

33. Larger than 5   **35.** 5   **37.** 0   **39.** Larger than 5

41. a)–d) Answers will vary.   **43.** One   **45.** Two

47. a) No, it has an inside and an outside.   **b)** Two
  c) Two   **d)** Two strips, one inside the other

49.–51. Answers will vary.

SECTION 9.7, PAGE 600

1.–5. Answers will vary.

7. a) *Euclidean:* Given a line and a point not on the line, one and only one line can be drawn parallel to the given line through the given point.
  b) *Elliptical:* Given a line and a point not on the line, no line can be drawn through the given point parallel to the given line.
  c) *Hyperbolic:* Given a line and a point not on the line, two or more lines can be drawn through the given point parallel to the given line.

9. A plane

11. A pseudosphere

13. Spherical: elliptical geometry; flat: Euclidean geometry; saddle-shaped: hyperbolic geometry

15.

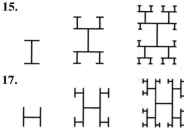

17.

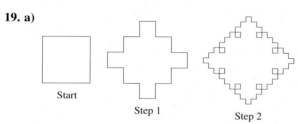

19. a)

Start   Step 1   Step 2

b) Infinite
c) Finite

REVIEW EXERCISES, PAGE 603

In the Review Exercises and Chapter Test questions, we used the $\boxed{\pi}$ *key on a scientific calculator to determine answers in calculations involving* π. *If you use 3.14 for* π, *your answers may vary slightly.*

1. $\{B\}$ **2.** $\overline{AD}$ **3.** $\triangle BFC$ **4.** $\overleftrightarrow{BH}$ **5.** $\{F\}$

6. $\{\ \}$ **7.** 66.3°   **8.** 55.3°   **9.** 10.2 in.   **10.** 2 in.

11. 58°   **12.** 92°

13. $m\angle 1 = 50°, m\angle 2 = 120°, m\angle 3 = 120°, m\angle 4 = 70°,$
$m\angle 5 = 110°, m\angle 6 = 70°$

14. 540°   **15. a)** 80 cm² **b)** 36 cm

16. a) 13 in.² **b)** 19.4 in.

17. a) 84 in.² **b)** 42 in.

18. a) 6 km² **b)** 12 km

19. a) 530.93 cm² **b)** 81.68 cm

20. 41.20 in.²   **21.** 35.43 cm²   **22.** $1176

23. a) 120 cm³ **b)** 164 cm²

24. a) 2035.75 in.³ **b)** 904.78 in.²

25. a) 603.19 mm³ **b)** 435.20 mm²

26. a) 268.08 ft³ **b)** 201.06 ft²

27. 432 m³   **28.** 28 ft³   **29.** 75.40 cm³   **30.** 791.68 cm³

31. a) $\approx$ 67.88 ft³ **b)** 4610.7 lb; yes **c)** $\approx$ 510.3 gal

This figure contains the answers for Exercises 32 and 33.

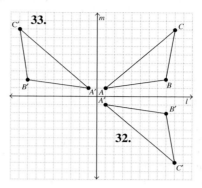

This figure contains the answers for Exercises 34 and 35.

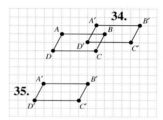

This figure contains the answers for Exercises 36–38.

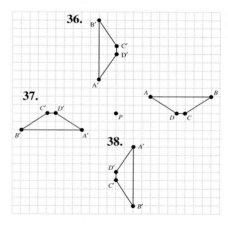

This figure contains the answers for Exercises 39 and 40.

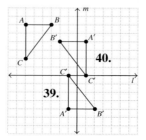

41. Yes **42.** No **43.** No **44.** Yes

45. a)–d) Answers will vary. **46.** Answers will vary.

47. Outside

48. Euclidean: Given a line and a point not on the line, one and only one line can be drawn parallel to the given line through the given point. Elliptical: Given a line and a point not on the line, no line can be drawn through the given point parallel to the given line. Hyperbolic: Given a line and a point not on the line, two or more lines can be drawn through the given point parallel to the given line.

49.

50.

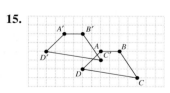

CHAPTER TEST, PAGE 607

1. $\overleftrightarrow{EF}$ **2.** $\triangle BCD$ **3.** $\{D\}$ **4.** $\overleftrightarrow{AC}$ **5.** 77.6°

6. 128.3° **7.** 64° **8.** 1440° **9.** ≈ 2.69 cm

10. a) 12 in. **b)** 30 in. **c)** 30 in.^{2}

11. a) 1436.76 cm^3 **b)** 615.75 cm^2

12. 59.43 m^3 **13.** 112 ft^3

14.

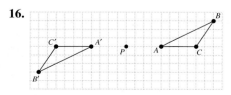

15.

16.

17.

18. a) No **b)** Yes

19. A surface with one side and one edge

20. a)–b) Answers will vary.

21. Euclidean: Given a line and a point not on the line, one and only one line can be drawn parallel to the given line through the given point. Elliptical: Given a line and a point not on the line, no line can be drawn through the given point parallel to the given line. Hyperbolic: Given a line and a point not on the line, two or more lines can be drawn through the given point parallel to the given line.

CHAPTER 10

SECTION 10.1, PAGE 617

1. A binary operation is an operation, or rule, that can be performed on two and only two elements of a set. The result is a single element.

3. a) When we add two numbers, the sum is one number: 4 + 5 = 9.
   b) When we subtract two numbers, the difference is one number: 5 − 4 = 1.
   c) When we multiply two numbers, the product is one number: 5 × 4 = 20.
   d) When we divide two numbers, the quotient is one number: 20 ÷ 5 = 4.

5. A mathematical system is a commutative group if all five of the following conditions hold.
   1. The set of elements is closed under the given operation.
   2. An identity element exists for the set.
   3. Every element in the set has an inverse.
   4. The set of elements is associative under the given operation.
   5. The set of elements is commutative under the given operation.

7. An identity element is an element in a set such that when a binary operation is performed on it and any given element in the set, the result is the given element. For the set of integers, the additive identity element is 0 and the multiplicative identity element is 1. Examples: 5 + 0 = 5, 5 × 1 = 5.

9. When a binary operation is performed on two elements in a set and the result is the identity element for the binary operation, each element is said to be the *inverse* of the other. For the set of rational numbers, the additive inverse of 2 is −2 since 2 + (−2) = 0 and the multiplicative inverse of 2 is $\frac{1}{2}$ since $2 \times \frac{1}{2} = 1$.

11. Yes; for a group the commutative property need not apply.

13. (d); the commutative property need not apply.

15. $a + b = b + a$ for any elements a and b; $3 + 4 = 4 + 3$

17. $(a \cdot b) \cdot c = a \cdot (b \cdot c)$ for any elements a, b, and c;
$(2 \cdot 3) \cdot 4 = 2 \cdot (3 \cdot 4)$

19. $4 \div 2 \neq 2 \div 4$

21. $(6 - 4) - 1 \neq 6 - (4 - 1)$
$\qquad 2 - 1 \neq 6 - 3$
$\qquad\qquad 1 \neq 3$

23. Yes; it satisfies the five properties needed.

25. No; there is no identity element.

27. No; the system is not closed.

29. No; there is no identity element.

31. No; not all elements have inverses.

33. Yes; it satisfies the four properties needed.

35. No; the system is not closed. For example, $\frac{1}{0}$ is undefined.

37. No; it does not have an identity element and does not satisfy the associative property.

39. Yes

41. No; the system is not closed. For example, $\sqrt{2} + (-\sqrt{2}) = 0$, which is rational. There is also no identity element.

43. Answers will vary.

SECTION 10.2, PAGE 625

1. Numbers are obtained by starting at the first addend (on a clock face) and then moving clockwise the number of hours equal to the second addend.

3. a) Add $2 + 11$ to get 1, then add $1 + 5$.   **b)** 6

5. a) Add 12 to 2 to get $14 - 6$.   **b)** 8
c) Since 12 is the identity element, you can add 12 to any number without changing its value.

7. Yes, 12

9. Yes; 1:11, 2:10, 3:9, 4:8, 5:7, 6:6, 7:5, 8:4, 9:3, 10:2, 11:1, and 12:12

11. Yes, $6 + 9 = 9 + 6$ since both equal 3

13. a) 7   **b)** 5. The additive inverse of 2 is 5 since $2 + 5 = 7$.

15. No; the elements are not symmetric about the main diagonal.

17. Yes; C is the identity element since the row next to C is identical to the top row, and the column under C is identical to the left-hand column.

19. a) The inverse of A is B since $A \otimes B = B \otimes A = C$.
b) The inverse of B is A since $B \otimes A = A \otimes B = C$.
c) The inverse of C is C since $C \otimes C = C$.

21. 7   **23.** 4   **25.** 4   **27.** 8   **29.** 6   **31.** 6

33. 5   **35.** 11   **37.** 3   **39.** 1   **41.** 12   **43.** 12

45.

+	1	2	3	4	5	6
1	2	3	4	5	6	1
2	3	4	5	6	1	2
3	4	5	6	1	2	3
4	5	6	1	2	3	4
5	6	1	2	3	4	5
6	1	2	3	4	5	6

47. 3   **49.** 3   **51.** 2   **53.** 4

55.

+	1	2	3	4	5	6	7
1	2	3	4	5	6	7	1
2	3	4	5	6	7	1	2
3	4	5	6	7	1	2	3
4	5	6	7	1	2	3	4
5	6	7	1	2	3	4	5
6	7	1	2	3	4	5	6
7	1	2	3	4	5	6	7

57. 4   **59.** 6   **61.** 4   **63.** 7

65. Yes; it satisfies the five required properties.

67. a) $\{0, 2, 4, 6\}$ **b)** £   **c)** Yes
d) Yes; 0   **e)** Yes; 0–0, 2–6, 4–4, 6–2
f) $(2 \pounds 4) \pounds 6 = 2 \pounds (4 \pounds 6)$
g) Yes; $2 \pounds 6 = 6 \pounds 2$ **h)** Yes

69. a) $\{ *, 5, L\}$
b)
c) Yes
d) Yes, L
e) Yes, $*$–5, 5–$*$, L–L
f) $\left(* \,\text{🐎}\, 5 \right) \text{🐎}\, 5 = * \,\text{🐎}\, \left(5 \,\text{🐎}\, 5 \right)$
g) Yes, $L \,\text{🐎}\, * = * \,\text{🐎}\, L$
h) Yes

71. a) $\{f, r, o, m\}$ **b)**   **c)** Closed
d) m **e)** f **f)** f **g)** m **h)** r

73. Not closed

75. No inverse for $\odot$ or for $*$, not associative

77. No identity element, no inverses, not associative, not commutative

79. a)

+	E	O
E	E	O
O	O	E

b) Yes, it is a commutative group; it satisfies the five properties.

81. Answers will vary.

83. a) Is closed; identity element is 6; inverses: $1-5, 2-2,$
$3-3, 4-4, 5-1, 6-6$; is associative; for example,
$(2 \infty 5) \infty 3 = 2 \infty (5 \infty 3)$
$$3 \infty 3 = 2 \infty 2$$
$$6 = 6$$
b) $3 \infty 1 \neq 1 \infty 3$
$$2 \neq 4$$

85. a)

*	R	S	T	U	V	I
R	V	T	U	S	I	R
S	U	I	V	R	T	S
T	S	R	I	V	U	T
U	T	V	R	I	S	U
V	I	U	S	T	R	V
I	R	S	T	U	V	I

b) Yes. It is closed; identity element is I; inverses $R-V$,
$S-S, T-T, U-U, V-R, I-I$; and the associative
property will hold.
c) No, it is not commutative. For example, $R * S \neq S * R$

87.

+	0	1	2	3	4
0	0	1	2	3	4
1	1	2	3	4	0
2	2	3	4	0	1
3	3	4	0	1	2
4	4	0	1	2	3

89. Add the number in the top row and the number in the left-
hand column and divide the sum by 4. The remainder is
placed in the table.

SECTION 10.3, PAGE 638

1. A modulo m system consists of m elements, 0 through
$m - 1$, and a binary operation.

3. 3;

0	1	2
0	1	2
3	4	5
6	7	8
.	.	.
.	.	.

5. 16 classes   **7.** (b), (c) or (d)   **9.** Sunday   **11.** Friday
13. Saturday   **15.** Friday   **17.** February   **19.** May
21. September   **23.** July   **25.** 1   **27.** 2   **29.** 3
31. 2   **33.** 1   **35.** 2   **37.** 0   **39.** 0   **41.** 5   **43.** 2
45. 6   **47.** 9   **49.** 5   **51.** 5   **53.** 3   **55.** 5   **57.** 5
59. { }   **61.** 1 and 6   **63.** 5   **65.** 0
67. a) 2020, 2024, 2028, 2032, 2036   **b)** 3004
c) 2552, 2556, 2560, 2564, 2568, 2572
69. a) Resting (for the second of two days)
b) Resting (for the second of two days)
c) Morning and afternoon lessons
d) No

71. a) 5   **b)** No   **c)** 54 weeks from this week
73. a) Evening   **b)** Day   **c)** Day
75. a)

+	0	1	2
0	0	1	2
1	1	2	0
2	2	0	1

b) Yes   **c)** Yes, 0   **d)** Yes; 0-0, 1-2, 2-1
e) $(1 + 2) + 2 = 1 + (2 + 2)$
f) Yes; $2 + 1 = 1 + 2$ **g)** Yes   **h)** Yes

77. a)

×	0	1	2	3
0	0	0	0	0
1	0	1	2	3
2	0	2	0	2
3	0	3	2	1

b) Yes   **c)** Yes, 1
d) No; no inverse for 0 or for 2, inverse of 1 is 1, inverse
of 3 is 3
e) $(1 \times 2) \times 3 = 1 \times (2 \times 3)$
f) Yes, $2 \times 3 = 3 \times 2$ **g)** No

79. 7   **81.** 1, 2, 3   **83.** 0   **85.** 2
87. a) Tuesday   **b)** Wednesday   **89.** 0

REVIEW EXERCISES, PAGE 641

1. A mathematical system consists of a set of elements and at
least one binary operation.

2. A binary operation is an operation that can be performed
on two and only two elements of a set. The result is a
single element.

3. No; for example, $2 - 5 = -3$, and -3 is not a whole
number.

4. Yes; the difference of any two real numbers is a real
number.

5. 3   **6.** 5   **7.** 9   **8.** 8   **9.** 9   **10.** 11

11. Closure, identity element, inverses, and associative
property

12. A commutative group   **13.** Yes

14. No; no inverse for any integer except 1 and -1

15. No; no identity element   **16.** No; no inverse for 0

17. No identity element; no inverses

18. Not every element has an inverse; not associative. For
example, $(P \, ? \, P) \, ? \, 4 \neq P \, ? \, (P \, ? \, 4)$.

19. Not associative. For example, $(! \, \square \, p) \, \square \, ? \neq \, ! \, \square \, (p \, \square \, ?)$

20. a) $\{\text{☺}, \text{●}, \text{♀}, \text{♂}\}$ **b)** △   **c)** Yes   **d)** Yes; ☺
e) Yes; ☺$-$☺, ●$-$♂, ♀$-$♀, ♂$-$●
f) $(\text{●} \, △ \, \text{♀}) \, △ \, \text{♂} = \text{●} \, △ \, (\text{♀} \, △ \, \text{♂})$
g) Yes; ●$△$♂ $=$ ♂$△$●   **h)** Yes

21. 0   **22.** 5   **23.** 1   **24.** 3   **25.** 11   **26.** 2   **27.** 4
28. 12   **29.** 9   **30.** 11   **31.** 1   **32.** 1   **33.** 6   **34.** 1
35. 0, 2, 4, 6   **36.** 4   **37.** 5   **38.** 9   **39.** 7   **40.** 8
41.

+	0	1	2	3	4	5
0	0	1	2	3	4	5
1	1	2	3	4	5	0
2	2	3	4	5	0	1
3	3	4	5	0	1	2
4	4	5	0	1	2	3
5	5	0	1	2	3	4

Yes, it is a commutative group.

42.

×	0	1	2	3
0	0	0	0	0
1	0	1	2	3
2	0	2	0	2
3	0	3	2	1

No; no inverse for 0 or 2

43. a) Yes   **b)** Yes

CHAPTER TEST, PAGE 643

1. A set of elements and a binary operation
2. Closure, identity element, inverses, associative property, commutative property
3. Yes
4.

+	1	2	3	4	5
1	2	3	4	5	1
2	3	4	5	1	2
3	4	5	1	2	3
4	5	1	2	3	4
5	1	2	3	4	5

5. Yes, it is a commutative group.
6. 3   **7.** 2
8. a) □   **b)** Yes   **c)** Yes, T **d)** S **e)** S
9. No, not closed.
10. Yes, it is a commutative group.
11. Yes, it is a commutative group.
12. 2   **13.** 0   **14.** 6   **15.** 2   **16.** 5
17. 2   **18.** { }   **19.** 7
20. a)

×	0	1	2	3	4
0	0	0	0	0	0
1	0	1	2	3	4
2	0	2	4	1	3
3	0	3	1	4	2
4	0	4	3	2	1

b) No; no inverse for 0

CHAPTER 11

SECTION 11.1, PAGE 653

1. A percent is a ratio of some number to 100.
3. Divide the numerator by the denominator, multiply the quotient by 100, and add a percent sign.

5. Percent change $= \dfrac{\left(\begin{array}{c}\text{amount in}\\\text{latest period}\end{array}\right) - \left(\begin{array}{c}\text{amount in}\\\text{previous period}\end{array}\right)}{\text{amount in the previous period}} \times 100$

7. 75.0%   **9.** 55.0%   **11.** 0.8%   **13.** 378.0%
15. 0.05   **17.** 0.0515   **19.** 0.0025   **21.** 0.002
23. 0.01   **25.** 25%   **27.** 4.7 grams   **29.** $208,341.12
31. $651,066.00   **33.** $1550   **35.** $2100   **37.** 41.3%
39. 10.0%   **41.** 0.9% decrease
43. a) 98.8% increase   **b)** 224.9% increase
   c) 145.9% increase   **d)** 58.5% increase
45. a) 78.3% increase   **b)** 27.4% decrease
   c) 28.5% increase   **d)** 66.2% increase
47. $6.75   **49.** 25%   **51.** 300
53. a) $2.61   **b)** $46.11   **c)** $6.92   **d)** $53.03
55. 12 students   **57.** $39,055   **59.** 5.3% decrease
61. 12.5% increase   **63.** 18.6% decrease   **65.** $3750
67. He will have a loss of $10.   **69.** $21.95

SECTION 11.2, PAGE 665

1. Interest is the money the borrower pays for the use of the lender's money.
3. Security or collateral is anything of value pledged by the borrower that the lender may sell or keep if the borrower does not repay the loan.
5. i is the *interest*, p is the *principal*, r is the interest *rate* expressed as a percent, and t is the *time*.
7. The United States rule states that if a partial payment is made on a loan, interest is computed on the principal from the first day of the loan until the date of the partial payment.
9. $15   **11.** $24.06   **13.** $15.85   **15.** $80.06
17. $113.20   **19.** 5%   **21.** $600   **23.** 2 years   **25.** $6630
27. a) $131.25   **b)** $3631.25
29. a) $182.50   **b)** $3467.50   **c)** $\approx 7.9\%$
31. $23,793.75   **33.** 284 days   **35.** 272 days   **37.** 264 days
39. June 13   **41.** March 24   **43.** $2017.03   **45.** $1459.33
47. $5278.99   **49.** $850.64   **51.** $6086.82   **53.** $2646.24
55. a) November 3, 2007   **b)** $978.06   **c)** $21.94
   d) $\approx 4.44\%$
57. a) $\approx 409.0\%$ **b)** $\approx 204.5\%$ **c)** $\approx 102.3\%$
59. a) 6.663%   **b)** $\approx 7.139\%$ **c)** $6663   **d)** $6996.15

SECTION 11.3, PAGE 675

1. An investment is the use of money or capital for income or profit.

3. A variable investment is one in which neither the principal nor the interest is guaranteed.

5. a) The effective annual yield is the simple interest rate that gives the same amount of interest as a compound rate over the same period of time.
   b) Another name for effective annual yield is annual percentage yield.

In the remainder of this exercise set, your answers may vary in the last digit, depending on the calculator used.

7. $A = \$1216.65$; $i = \$216.65$

9. $A = \$2253.98$; $i = \$253.98$

11. $A = \$8252.64$; $i = \$1252.64$

13. $A = \$8666.26$; $i = \$666.26$

15. $30,695.66   **17.** $85,282.13   **19.** $54,142.84

21. $1653.36   **23.** $2341.82

25. a) $4195.14   **b)** $4214.36

27. $3106.62   **29.** $7609.45

31. $\approx 3.53\%$ **33.** Yes, the APY should be 2.43%.

35. He will earn more interest in the account that pays the 5% simple interest

37. a) $555,000   **b)** $58,907.61   **c)** $98.51

39. $212,687.10   **41.** $12,015.94

43. a) $1040.60, $40.60   **b)** $1082.43, $82.43
   c) $1169.86, $169.86   **d)** No

45. $1.53

47. a) 24 years   **b)** 12 years   **c)** 9 years   **d)** 6 years
   e) 3.27%

49. The simple interest is $20,000. The compound interest is $22,138.58. The compound interest is greater by $2,138.58.

SECTION 11.4, PAGE 688

1. An open-end installment loan is one with which you can make different payments each month. A fixed installment loan is one in which you pay a fixed amount each month for a set number of months.

3. The APR is the true rate of interest charged on a loan.

5. The total installment price is the sum of all the monthly payments and the down payment, if any.

7. The unpaid balance method and the average daily balance method

9. a) $1719.55   **b)** $170.33

11. a) $1834.57   **b)** $223.85

13. a) $628.40   **b)** 9.0%

15. a) $1752   **b)** 9%

17. a) 6%   **b)** $726.00   **c)** $7858.00

19. a) $2818.20   **b)** $689.39   **c)** $347.90   **d)** $8614.17

21. a) $26   **b)** $46.01, which rounds up to $47

23. a) $21.14, which rounds up to $22
   b) $34.39, which rounds up to $35

25. a) $19.76   **b)** $743.41

27. a) $1.56   **b)** $133.11

29. a) $512.00   **b)** $6.66   **c)** $638.43

31. a) $121.78   **b)** $1.52   **c)** $133.07
   d) The interest charged using the average daily balance method is $0.04 less than the interest charged using the unpaid balance method.

33. a) $11.96   **b)** $886.96

35. a) $25   **b)** $35.60   **c)** 8.5%   **d)** 6.5%

37. $14,077.97

39. a) $6872.25   **b)** $610.37   **c)** $2637.42   **d)** $2501.05

41. $201.48

SECTION 11.5, PAGE 702

1. A mortgage is a long-term loan in which the property is pledged as security for payment of the difference between the down payment and the sale price.

3. The major difference is that the interest rate for a conventional loan is fixed for the duration of the loan, whereas the interest rate for a variable-rate loan may change every period, as specified in the loan agreement.

5. A buyer's adjusted monthly income is found by subtracting any fixed monthly payments with more than 10 months remaining from the gross monthly income.

7. An amortization schedule lists payment dates and payment numbers. For each payment, it lists the amount that goes to pay the interest and the principal. It also gives the balance remaining on the loan after each payment.

9. Equity is the difference between the appraised value of your home and the loan balance.

11. a) $70,000   **b)** $2438.80

13. a) $262,500   **b)** $9579.50

15. a) $39,000   **b)** $156,000   **c)** $3120

17. a) $802.20   **b)** $1411.50   **c)** No

19. a) $187,736.40   **b)** $112,736.40   **c)** $38.68

21. a) $17,025   **b)** $2894.25   **c)** $1212.40   **d)** $930.98
   e) $1057.65   **f)** Yes   **g)** $127.02

23. Bank B

25. a) $664,704   **b)** $927,360   **c)** $1,231,488

27. a) 805

b)

Payment Number	Interest	Principal	Balance of Loan
1	$750.00	$55.00	$99,945.00
2	$749.59	$55.41	$99,889.59
3	$749.17	$55.83	$99,833.76

c) 9.38%

d)

Payment Number	Interest	Principal	Balance of Loan
4	$780.37	$24.63	$99,809.13
5	$780.17	$24.83	$99,784.30
6	$779.98	$25.02	$99,759.28

e) 9.46%

29. a) The variable-rate loan   **b)** $2160

SECTION 11.6, PAGE 714

1. An annuity is an account into which, or out of which, a sequence of scheduled payments is made.

3. a) An annuity into which equal payments are made at regular intervals, with interest compounded at the end of each interval and with a fixed interest rate for each compounding period, is called an ordinary annuity.
b) A sinking fund is a type of annuity in which the goal is to save a specific amount of money in a specified amount of time.

5. An immediate annuity is an annuity that is established with a lump sum of money for the purpose of providing the investor with regular, usually monthly, payments for the rest of the investor's life.

7. With a 401k plan, the money invested is not subject to taxes; however, when money is withdrawn, it is subject to income taxes. With a Roth 401k plan, the investor has already paid taxes on the money invested, and money withdrawn is not subject to income taxes.

9. $199,316.54   **11.** $299,929.32   **13.** $493.00

15. $175.48   **17.** $37,078.18   **19.** $56,559.36

21. $331.46   **23.** $5160.71

25. a) $23,003.87   **b)** $826,980.88   **c)** $349,496.41
d) $12,000   **e)** $36,000   **f)** Alberto

REVIEW EXERCISES, PAGE 717

1. 75.0%   **2.** 83.3%   **3.** 62.5%   **4.** 4.1%

5. 0.98% ≈ 1.0%   **6.** 314.1%   **7.** 0.09   **8.** 0.141

9. 1.23   **10.** 0.0025   **11.** 0.008$\overline{3}$ **12.** 0.0000045

13. ≈ 17.6%   **14.** ≈ 11.0%   **15.** 18.75%   **16.** 80

17. 91.8   **18.** $6.42   **19.** 40 people   **20.** 26.7%

21. $10   **22.** 5%   **23.** $450   **24.** 0.5 year

25. $6214.25   **26. a)** $162   **b)** $3162

27. a) $1380   **b)** $4620   **c)** ≈ 14.9%

28. a) $7\frac{1}{2}\%$ **b)** $830   **c)** at least $941.18

29. a) $6691.13; $1691.13   **b)** $6719.58; $1719.58
c) $6734.28; $1734.28   **d)** $6744.25; $1744.25
e) $6749.13; $1749.13

30. $5076.35   **31.** 5.76%   **32.** $13,415.00

33. a) 6.0%   **b)** 253.16   **c)** $4150.34

34. a) 6.5%   **b)** $64.32   **c)** $1962.51

35. a) 4.5%   **b)** $32.06   **c)** $1420.43

36. a) $6.31   **b)** $847.61   **c)** $508.99   **d)** $6.62
e) $847.92

37. a) $2.60   **b)** $546.92   **c)** $382.68   **d)** $5.36
e) $549.68

38. a) $14,400   **b)** $57,600   **c)** $8415.60   **d)** 5.5%

39. a) $10.44   **b)** 8.5%

40. a) $33,925   **b)** $1345.49
c) $855.93   **d)** $1172.60   **e)** Yes

41. a) $13,485   **b)** $756.51   **c)** $24.20   **d)** $285,828.60
e) $195,928.60

42. a) $550.46   **b)** 8%   **c)** 7.75%

43. $48,378.57   **44.** $955.34

CHAPTER TEST, PAGE 720

1. a) $40   **b)** 3 years   **2.** $819.38   **3.** $6519.38

4. $2523.20   **5.** $123.20

6. a) $7961.99, $461.99   **b)** $3036.68, $536.68

7. $1997.50   **8.** $181.46   **9.** 8.5%

10. a) 4.5%   **b)** $64.02   **c)** $2836.28

11. a) $12.30   **b)** $1146.57   **c)** $765.67   **d)** $10.72
e) $1144.99

12. $21,675   **13.** $2456.50   **14.** $1848.93   **15.** $1123.85

16. $1428.02   **17.** Yes   **18. a)** $428,717.50   **b)** $284,217.50

19. $231,020.45   **20.** $277.28

CHAPTER 12

SECTION 12.1, PAGE 729

1. An experiment is a controlled operation that yields a set of results.

3. Empirical probability is the relative frequency of occurrence of an event. It is determined by actual observation of an experiment.

$$P(E) = \frac{\text{number of times event } E \text{ has occurred}}{\text{number of times experiment was performed}}$$

5. Answers will vary.

7. No, it means that if a coin was flipped many times, about $\frac{1}{2}$ of the tosses would land heads up.

9. a) Roll a die many times and then find the relative frequency of 5's to the total number of rolls.   **b)** Answers will vary.   **c)** Answers will vary.

11.–13. Answers will vary.

15. a) $\frac{7}{15}$ **b)** $\frac{1}{3}$ **c)** $\frac{1}{5}$ **17. a)** $\frac{3}{7}$ **b)** $\frac{8}{21}$ **c)** $\frac{1}{21}$

19. a) $\frac{4737}{129,098}$, or ≈ 0.0367 **b)** $\frac{21,922}{129,098}$, or ≈ 0.1698

   c) $\frac{11,418}{129,098}$, or ≈ 0.0884

21. a) $\frac{29}{186}$ **b)** $\frac{1}{2}$ **c)** $\frac{2}{31}$

23. a) $\frac{11}{40}$ **b)** $\frac{9}{40}$ **c)** $\frac{1}{4}$ **d)** $\frac{7}{40}$ **e)** $\frac{3}{40}$

25. a) $\frac{6}{20} = \frac{3}{10}$ **b)** $\frac{14}{20} = \frac{7}{10}$ **c)** $\frac{14}{20} = \frac{7}{10}$

   d) $\frac{2}{20} = \frac{1}{10}$

27. a) 0   **b)** $\frac{50}{250} = 0.2$ **c)** 1

29. a) $\frac{224}{929} \approx 0.2411$ **b)** $\frac{705}{929} \approx 0.7589$

31. Answers will vary.

SECTION 12.2, PAGE 737

1. If each outcome of an experiment has the same chance of occurring as any other outcome, they are said to be equally likely outcomes.

3. $P(A) + P(\text{not } A) = 1$

5. 0.3   **7.** $\frac{7}{12}$

9. Answers will vary.   **11.** 0 and 1

13. a) $\frac{1}{5}$ **b)** $\frac{1}{4}$

15. $\frac{1}{40}$ **17.** $\frac{1}{13}$ **19.** $\frac{12}{13}$ **21.** $\frac{1}{2}$ **23.** 1   **25.** $\frac{4}{13}$

27. a) $\frac{1}{2}$ **b)** $\frac{1}{4}$ **c)** $\frac{1}{4}$ **d)** 0

29. a) $\frac{1}{3}$ **b)** $\frac{1}{6}$ **c)** $\frac{1}{3}$ **d)** $\frac{1}{6}$ **31.** $\frac{1}{5}$ **33.** $\frac{9}{10}$ **35.** $\frac{1}{12}$

37. $\frac{1}{6}$ **39.** $\frac{1}{2}$ **41.** $\frac{2}{3}$ **43.** $\frac{11}{17}$ **45.** $\frac{12}{17}$ **47.** $\frac{2}{9}$

49. $\frac{5}{9}$ **51.** 0   **53.** $\frac{3}{51}$ **55.** $\frac{27}{51}$ **57.** $\frac{1}{26}$ **59.** $\frac{5}{26}$

61. $\frac{17}{26}$ **63.** $\frac{83}{130}$ **65.** $\frac{11}{26}$ **67.** $\frac{6}{19}$ **69.** $\frac{15}{38}$ **71.** $\frac{5}{19}$

73. $\frac{13}{36}$ **75.** $\frac{1}{3}$ **77.** $\frac{23}{36}$ **79. a)** 0   **b)** 1

81. a) $\frac{1}{4}$ **b)** $\frac{1}{4}$ **c)** $\frac{1}{4}$ **83.** 29 dots

SECTION 12.3, PAGE 745

1. a) Answers will vary.   **b)** Answers will vary.

3. Odds against

5. 7:2   **7. a)** $\frac{1}{2}$ **b)** $\frac{1}{2}$

9. a) $\frac{8}{15}$ **b)** $\frac{7}{15}$ **c)** 7:8   **d)** 8:7

11. 6:1, 1:6   **13.** 5:1   **15.** 4:2 or 2:1   **17.** 12:1, 1:12

19. 10:3, 3:10   **21.** 1:1   **23.** 5:3   **25. a)** 8:7   **b)** 7:8

27. 8:7   **29.** 7:8   **31.** 8:7   **33. a)** $\frac{3}{10}$ **b)** 7:3

35. 1:18   **37. a)** $\frac{7}{11}$ **b)** $\frac{4}{11}$ **39.** $\frac{11}{15}$ **41.** $\frac{1}{5}$ **43.** 1:4

45. 74:1   **47.** 0.34   **49.** 33:17   **51.** 43:57   **53.** 1:9

55. 7:1   **57. a)** $\frac{1}{33}$ **b)** 32:1

59. Horse 2, $\frac{2}{9}$; Horse 3, $\frac{1}{3}$; Horse 4, $\frac{1}{16}$; Horse 5, $\frac{5}{12}$; Horse 6, $\frac{1}{2}$

61. $\approx 97:3$

SECTION 12.4, PAGE 755

1. The expected value is the expected gain or loss of an experiment over the long run.

3. The fair price is the amount that should be charged for the game to be fair and result in an expectation of 0.

5. To obtain the fair price, add the cost to the expected value.

7. $0.50. Since you would lose $1.00 on average for each game you played, the price of the game should be $1.00 less than the actual cost. Then the expectation would be $0, and the game would be fair. The results could also be obtained from the fair price formula, fair price = expectation + cost to play.

9. $-$1.20   **11.** 10,080 people   **13.** 70 points

15. 1.44 million viewers   **17.** $3840   **19.** $1.60 off

21. a) $\approx -\$0.17$ **b)** $\approx \$0.17$

23. a) Yes, because you have a positive expectation of $\frac{1}{5}$
   b) Yes, because you have a positive expectation of $\frac{1}{2}$

25. a) -1.20 **b)** $0.80 **27. a)** $-2.00 **b)** $1.00

29. $3.00 **31.** $-1.25 **33.** $800 **35.** $400

37. a) $5.50 **b)** $7.50 **39. a)** $2.25 **b)** $4.25

41. a) $2.50 **b)** $12.50 **43. a)** $-6.00 **b)** $4.00

45. 0.75 base **47.** 2.9 points **49.** 56 employees

51. $7200 **53.** 3.5 **55.** ≈ 141.51 service calls

57. a) $\dfrac{9}{16}, \dfrac{1}{4}, \dfrac{1}{8}, \dfrac{1}{16}$ **b)** $11.81 **c)** $11.81

59. An amount greater than $1200

61. $-$0.053 or $-5.3¢$

63. a) $458.33 **b)** $308.33

SECTION 12.5, PAGE 766

1. If a first experiment can be performed in M distinct ways and a second experiment can be performed in N distinct ways, then the two experiments in that specific order can be performed in $M \cdot N$ distinct ways.

3. 14

5. The first selection is made. Then the second selection is made without the first selection being returned to the group of items being selected.

7. a) 2500 **b)** 2450

9. a) 343 **b)** 210

11. a) 4

b)

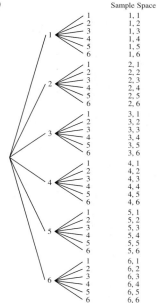

Sample Space

$\qquad$ H $\qquad$ HH
$\qquad$ T $\qquad$ HT
$\qquad$ H $\qquad$ TH
$\qquad$ T $\qquad$ TT

c) $\dfrac{1}{4}$ **d)** $\dfrac{1}{2}$ **e)** $\dfrac{1}{4}$

13. a) 9

b)

Sample Space

S — S   SS
S — Q   SQ
S — A   SA
Q — S   QS
Q — Q   QQ
Q — A   QA
A — S   AS
A — Q   AQ
A — A   AA

c) $\dfrac{1}{9}$ **d)** $\dfrac{1}{9}$ **e)** $\dfrac{5}{9}$

15. a) 12

b)

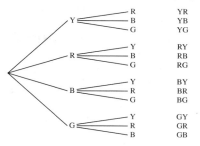

Sample Space

Y — R   YR
Y — B   YB
Y — G   YG
R — Y   RY
R — B   RB
R — G   RG
B — Y   BY
B — R   BR
B — G   BG
G — Y   GY
G — R   GR
G — B   GB

c) $\dfrac{1}{2}$ **d)** 1 **e)** $\dfrac{1}{2}$

17. a) 9

b)

Sample Space

S — A   SA
S — W   SW
S — O   SO
J — A   JA
J — W   JW
J — O   JO
C — A   CA
C — W   CW
C — O   CO

c) $\dfrac{1}{3}$ **d)** $\dfrac{1}{9}$ **e)** $\dfrac{2}{3}$

19. a) 36

b)

Sample Space

1 — 1   1, 1
1 — 2   1, 2
1 — 3   1, 3
1 — 4   1, 4
1 — 5   1, 5
1 — 6   1, 6
2 — 1   2, 1
2 — 2   2, 2
2 — 3   2, 3
2 — 4   2, 4
2 — 5   2, 5
2 — 6   2, 6
3 — 1   3, 1
3 — 2   3, 2
3 — 3   3, 3
3 — 4   3, 4
3 — 5   3, 5
3 — 6   3, 6
4 — 1   4, 1
4 — 2   4, 2
4 — 3   4, 3
4 — 4   4, 4
4 — 5   4, 5
4 — 6   4, 6
5 — 1   5, 1
5 — 2   5, 2
5 — 3   5, 3
5 — 4   5, 4
5 — 5   5, 5
5 — 6   5, 6
6 — 1   6, 1
6 — 2   6, 2
6 — 3   6, 3
6 — 4   6, 4
6 — 5   6, 5
6 — 6   6, 6

c) $\dfrac{1}{6}$ **d)** $\dfrac{1}{6}$ **e)** $\dfrac{1}{36}$ **f)** No

21. a) 6

b)

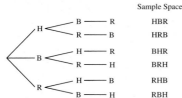

Sample Space

HBR
HRB
BHR
BRH
RHB
RBH

c) $\frac{1}{3}$ **d)** $\frac{1}{6}$ **e)** $\frac{1}{6}$

23. a) 18

b)

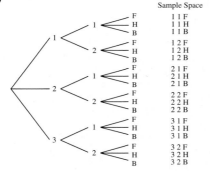

Sample Space

1 1 F
1 1 H
1 1 B
1 2 F
1 2 H
1 2 B
2 1 F
2 1 H
2 1 B
2 2 F
2 2 H
2 2 B
3 1 F
3 1 H
3 1 B
3 2 F
3 2 H
3 2 B

c) $\frac{1}{3}$ **d)** $\frac{1}{9}$ **e)** $\frac{2}{3}$

25. a) 27

b)

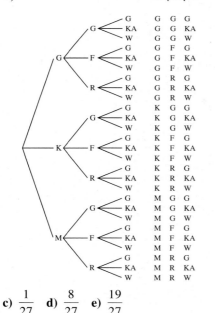

Sample Space

G G G
G G KA
G G W
G F G
G F KA
G F W
G R G
G R KA
G R W
K G G
K G KA
K G W
K F G
K F KA
K F W
K R G
K R KA
K R W
M G G
M G KA
M G W
M F G
M F KA
M F W
M R G
M R KA
M R W

c) $\frac{1}{27}$ **d)** $\frac{8}{27}$ **e)** $\frac{19}{27}$

27. a) 24

b)

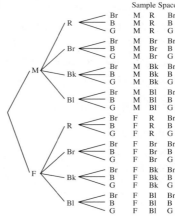

Sample Space

Br M R Br
B M R B
G M R G
Br M Br Br
B M Br B
G M Br G
Br M Bk Br
B M Bk B
G M Bk G
Br M Bl Br
B M Bl B
G M Bl G
Br F R Br
B F R B
G F R G
Br F Br Br
B F Br B
G F Br G
Br F Bk Br
B F Bk B
G F Bk G
Br F Bl Br
B F Bl B
G F Bl G

c) $\frac{1}{24}$ **d)** $\frac{1}{8}$

29. a) $\frac{1}{3}$ **b)** $\frac{2}{3}$ **c)** No, the probability of selecting a red chip is not the same as the probability of selecting a white chip.
d) Answers will vary.

31. 3; 1 red, 1 blue, and 1 brown

SECTION 12.6, PAGE 778

1. a) At least one event, A *or* B, must occur.
b) Both events, A *and* B, must occur.

3. a) Events that cannot happen simultaneously are mutually exclusive events.
b) $P(A \text{ or } B) = P(A) + P(B)$

5. We assume that event A has already occurred.

7. a) No, both can like classical music.
b) No, the daughter may be more or less likely to like classical music because the mother likes it.

9. Events A and B cannot occur at the same time. Therefore, $P(A \text{ and } B) = 0$.

11. 0.7 **13.** 0.4 **15.** 0.75 **17.** $\frac{1}{3}$ **19.** $\frac{1}{2}$ **21.** $\frac{2}{13}$

23. $\frac{8}{13}$ **25.** $\frac{17}{26}$ **27. a)** $\frac{1}{16}$ **b)** $\frac{1}{19}$ **29. a)** $\frac{1}{16}$ **b)** $\frac{5}{76}$

31. a) $\frac{3}{80}$ **b)** $\frac{3}{76}$ **33. a)** $\frac{9}{25}$ **b)** $\frac{33}{95}$ **35.** $\frac{11}{20}$ **37.** $\frac{2}{5}$

39. $\frac{1}{4}$ **41.** $\frac{1}{8}$ **43.** $\frac{9}{64}$ **45.** $\frac{1}{8}$ **47.** $\frac{3}{8}$ **49.** $\frac{4}{7}$ **51.** $\frac{9}{49}$

53. $\frac{1}{35}$ **55.** $\frac{1}{35}$ **57.** $\frac{1}{8}$ **59.** $\frac{1}{8}$ **61. a)** $\frac{1}{32}$ **b)** $\frac{1}{2}$

63. a) $\frac{4}{49}$ **b)** $\frac{2}{21}$ **65. a)** $\frac{24}{49}$ **b)** $\frac{11}{21}$ **67.** $\frac{93}{245}$

69. $\dfrac{152}{245}$ **71.** $\dfrac{1771}{9880}$ **73.** $\dfrac{7}{988}$ **75.** 0.7 **77.** $\dfrac{343}{1000}$

79. $\dfrac{1}{4}$ **81.** $\dfrac{27}{1024}$ **83.** $\dfrac{243}{1024}$ **85.** $\dfrac{5}{22}$ **87.** $\dfrac{1050}{1331}$

89. $\dfrac{1}{24}$ **91.** $\dfrac{5}{12}$ **93.** 0.36 **95.** 0.36

97. a) No **b)** 0.001 **c)** 0.00004 **d)** 0.00096
e) 0.000999 **f)** 0.998001

99. $\dfrac{9}{250}$ **101.** $\dfrac{2169}{62,500}$ **103.** $\dfrac{14}{45}$

105. Favors dealer. The probability of at least one diamond is
≈ 0.44, which is less than 0.5.

107. $\dfrac{1}{9}$ **109.** $\dfrac{1}{2}$

SECTION 12.7, PAGE 787

1. The probability of E_2 given that E_1 has occurred

3. $\dfrac{1}{3}$ **5.** $\dfrac{1}{3}$ **7.** $\dfrac{2}{3}$ **9.** $\dfrac{2}{3}$ **11.** $\dfrac{3}{4}$ **13.** $\dfrac{2}{3}$ **15.** $\dfrac{2}{3}$ **17.** $\dfrac{1}{5}$

19. $\dfrac{1}{3}$ **21.** $\dfrac{3}{5}$ **23.** $\dfrac{1}{7}$ **25.** $\dfrac{1}{16}$ **27.** $\dfrac{1}{7}$ **29.** $\dfrac{5}{36}$ **31.** $\dfrac{1}{6}$

33. $\dfrac{2}{3}$ **35.** $\dfrac{1}{3}$ **37.** $\dfrac{1}{3}$ **39.** $\dfrac{1}{2}$ **41.** 0.5941 **43.** 0.3605

45. 0.6251 **47.** $\dfrac{7}{13}$ **49.** $\dfrac{4}{15}$ **51.** $\dfrac{11}{15}$ **53.** $\dfrac{29}{59}$ **55.** $\dfrac{33}{50}$

57. $\dfrac{30}{61}$ **59.** $\dfrac{10}{11}$ **61.** $\dfrac{3}{19}$ **63.** $\dfrac{44}{47}$ **65.** $\dfrac{11}{27}$ **67.** $\dfrac{10}{29}$

69. $\dfrac{11}{29}$ **71.** $\dfrac{93}{200}$ **73.** $\dfrac{15}{52}$

75. a) 140 **b)** 120 **c)** $\dfrac{7}{10}$ **d)** $\dfrac{3}{5}$ **e)** $\dfrac{2}{3}$

f) $\dfrac{4}{7}$ **g)** Because A and B are not independent events

77. a) 0.3 **b)** 0.5 **c)** Yes; $P(A \mid B) = P(A) \cdot P(B)$

79. $\dfrac{2}{3}$ **81.** $\dfrac{1}{3}$ **83.** $\dfrac{1}{3}$

SECTION 12.8, PAGE 799

1. Answers will vary.

3. a) $n! = n(n-1)(n-2) \cdots (3)(2)(1)$

b) $\dfrac{n!}{n_1! n_2! \cdots n_r!}$

5. The number of permutations of n items taken r at a time.

7. $_nP_r = \dfrac{n!}{(n-r)!}$

9. 24 **11.** 42 **13.** 1 **15.** 1 **17.** 3024 **19.** 336
21. 10,000 **23. a)** 1,404,000 **b)** 1,757,600
25. a) $5^5 = 3125$ **b)** $\dfrac{1}{3125} = 0.00032$

27. 57,106,944 **29.** 336

31. a) 720 **b)** 120 **c)** 24 **d)** 600

33. 720 **35. a)** 479,001,600 **b)** 3,628,800 **c)** 14,400

37. 78,624,000 **39.** 131,040 **41.** 676,000 **43.** 104,000

45. a) 8,000,000 **b)** 6,400,000,000
c) 64,000,000,000,000

47. 3,603,600 **49.** 5040 **51.** 280 **53.** 362,880

55. 302,400 **57.** 630 **59.** 15,120

61. a) 40,320 **b)** 362,880

63. a) 3125 **b)** ≈ 128 **c)** 0.00032

65. 12,600 sec, or 3.5 hr **67.** No **69.** 600

71. a) 2520 **b)** SCROOGE

SECTION 12.9, PAGE 806

1. Answers will vary. **3.** $_nC_r = \dfrac{n!}{(n-r)!r!}$

5. Answers will vary. **7.** 6 **9. a)** 15 **b)** 360

11. a) 1 **b)** 1 **13. a)** 120 **b)** 720 **15.** $\dfrac{1}{6}$ **17.** $\dfrac{7}{2}$

19. 72 **21.** 28 **23.** 5 **25.** 56 **27.** 35 **29.** 495

31. 70 **33.** 28 **35.** 6160 **37.** 5880 **39.** 8820

41. 700 **43.** 1200 **45. a)** 45 **b)** 56

47. a) and **b)**

```
                   1
               1       1
            1     2       1
         1     3      3      1
      1     4      6      4      1
   1     5     10     10     5      1
```

49. a) 24 **b)** 24 **51.** 60,060

SECTION 12.10, PAGE 813

1. $\dfrac{_8C_4}{_{12}C_4}$ **3.** $\dfrac{_5C_3}{_{26}C_3}$ **5.** $\dfrac{_8C_5}{_{15}C_5}$ **7.** $\dfrac{_{28}C_8}{_{50}C_8}$ **9.** $\dfrac{5}{42}$ **11.** $\dfrac{4}{143}$

13. $\dfrac{1}{12}$ **15.** $\dfrac{2}{11}$ **17.** $\dfrac{1}{9,366,819}$ **19.** $\dfrac{3}{10}$ **21.** $\dfrac{7}{10}$

23. $\dfrac{1}{115}$ **25.** $\dfrac{27}{230}$ **27.** 0.0012 **29.** 0.3083 **31.** $\dfrac{2}{55}$

33. $\dfrac{4}{33}$ **35.** $\dfrac{1}{77}$ **37.** $\dfrac{5}{77}$ **39.** $\dfrac{15}{253}$

41. a) $\dfrac{1}{123,760}$ **b)** $\dfrac{1}{30,940}$

43. a) $\dfrac{33}{54{,}145}$ **b)** $\dfrac{1}{2{,}598{,}960}$

45. a) $\dfrac{1}{2{,}162{,}160}$ **b)** $\dfrac{1}{6435}$

47. 1; Since there are more hairs than people, two or more people must have the same number of hairs on their head.

SECTION 12.11, PAGE 822

1. A probability distribution shows the probability associated with each specific outcome of an experiment. In a probability distribution, every possible outcome must be listed and the sum of all the probabilities must be 1.

3. $P(x) = (_nC_x)p^x q^{n-x}$ **5.** 0.0512

7. 0.3456   **9.** 0.015625

11. a) $P(x) = (_nC_x)(0.14)^x(0.86)^{n-x}$
    b) $P(2) = (_{12}C_2)(0.14)^2(0.86)^{10}$

13. 0.24576   **15.** 0.25412   **17.** 0.06877   **19.** 0.4096

21. a) 0.00098   **b)** 0.08789   **c)** 0.10352

23. a) ≈ 0.1119 **b)** ≈ 0.2966 **25.** 0; it will be midnight.

REVIEW EXERCISES, PAGE 825

1. Answers will vary.   **2.** Answers will vary.

3. $\dfrac{1}{5}$ **4.** Answers will vary.   **5.** $\dfrac{2}{5}$ **6.** $\dfrac{1}{2}$ **7.** $\dfrac{7}{10}$

8. 1   **9.** $\dfrac{1}{10}$ **10.** $\dfrac{7}{25}$ **11.** $\dfrac{11}{50}$ **12.** $\dfrac{16}{25}$ **13.** $\dfrac{43}{50}$

14. a) 69:31   **b)** 31:69   **15.** 5:3   **16.** $\dfrac{3}{85}$ **17.** 7:3

18. a) $-\$1.20$ **b)** $-\$3.60$ **c)** \$0.80

19. a) $-\$0.23$ **b)** \$0.23   **c)** Lose \$23.08

20. 660 people

21. a)

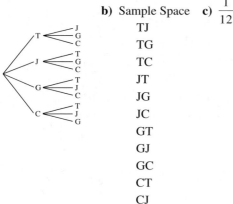

    b) Sample Space   **c)** $\dfrac{1}{12}$

       TJ
       TG
       TC
       JT
       JG
       JC
       GT
       GJ
       GC
       CT
       CJ
       CG

22. a)

H1
H2
H3
H4
T1
T2
T3
T4

    b) Sample Space   **c)** $\dfrac{1}{4}$ **d)** $\dfrac{3}{4}$

23. $\dfrac{1}{4}$ **24.** $\dfrac{9}{64}$ **25.** $\dfrac{5}{16}$ **26.** $\dfrac{7}{8}$ **27.** 1   **28.** $\dfrac{3}{16}$

29. $\dfrac{1}{22}$ **30.** $\dfrac{14}{55}$ **31.** $\dfrac{41}{55}$ **32.** $\dfrac{1}{22}$ **33.** $\dfrac{1}{4}$

34. Against, 3:1; in favor, 1:3   **35.** \$13.75

36. $\dfrac{1}{8}$ **37.** $\dfrac{5}{8}$ **38.** In favor, 3:5; against, 5:3   **39.** \$3.75

40. $\dfrac{7}{8}$ **41.** $\dfrac{15}{17}$ **42.** $\dfrac{17}{19}$ **43.** $\dfrac{2}{15}$ **44.** $\dfrac{1}{2}$ **45.** $\dfrac{23}{40}$ **46.** $\dfrac{3}{17}$

47. $\dfrac{3}{4}$ **48.** $\dfrac{12}{17}$ **49. a)** 24   **b)** \$4500   **50.** 30   **51.** 720

52. 504   **53.** 20   **54. a)** 3003   **b)** 3,628,800

55. a) $\dfrac{1}{3{,}819{,}816}$ **b)** $\dfrac{1}{175{,}711{,}536}$ **56.** 35,640   **57.** 560

58. $\dfrac{1}{221}$ **59.** $\dfrac{1}{12}$ **60.** $\dfrac{1}{18}$ **61.** $\dfrac{1}{24}$ **62.** $\dfrac{11}{12}$ **63.** $\dfrac{5}{182}$

64. $\dfrac{45}{364}$ **65.** $\dfrac{2}{13}$ **66.** $\dfrac{11}{13}$

67. a) $P(x) = (_nC_x)(0.6)^x(0.4)^{n-x}$
    b) $P(75) = (_{100}C_{75})(0.6)^{75}(0.4)^{25}$

68. 0.0512   **69. a)** 0.01024   **b)** 0.98976

CHAPTER TEST, PAGE 829

1. $\dfrac{11}{20}$ **2.** $\dfrac{2}{9}$ **3.** $\dfrac{5}{9}$ **4.** $\dfrac{7}{9}$ **5.** $\dfrac{1}{3}$ **6.** $\dfrac{1}{6}$ **7.** $\dfrac{1}{6}$

8. $\dfrac{5}{18}$ **9.** $\dfrac{5}{12}$ **10.** $\dfrac{8}{13}$ **11.** 18

12.

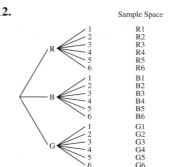

Sample Space

R1
R2
R3
R4
R5
R6
B1
B2
B3
B4
B5
B6
G1
G2
G3
G4
G5
G6

13. $\dfrac{1}{18}$ **14.** $\dfrac{4}{9}$ **15.** $\dfrac{5}{6}$ **16.** 1,581,840

17. a) 5:4   **b)** 5:4   **18.** $\dfrac{2}{9}$ **19.** $0

20. a) $\dfrac{107}{228}$ **b)** $\dfrac{115}{228}$ **c)** $\dfrac{68}{115}$ **d)** $\dfrac{60}{107}$

21. 120   **22.** $\dfrac{3}{38}$ **23.** $\dfrac{35}{38}$ **24.** $\dfrac{175}{396}$ **25.** 0.1323

CHAPTER 13

SECTION 13.1, PAGE 837

1. Answers will vary.

3.–5. Answers will vary.

7. a) A population is all items or people of interest.
b) A sample is a subset of the population.

9. a) A systematic sample is a sample obtained by selecting every nth item on a list or production line.
b) Use a random number table to select the first item and then select every nth item after that.

11. a) A cluster sample is a random selection of groups of units.
b) Divide a geographical area into sections. Randomly select sections or clusters. Either each member of the selected cluster is included in the sample or a random sample of the members of each selected cluster is used.

13. An unbiased sample is one that is a small replica of the entire population with regard to income, education, gender, race, religion, political affiliation, age, and so forth.

15. Stratified sample   **17.** Cluster sample

19. Systematic sample   **21.** Convenience sample

23. Random sample   **25. a)–c)** Answers will vary.

27. President; four out of 42 U.S. presidents have been assassinated (Lincoln, Garfield, McKinley, Kennedy).

SECTION 13.2, PAGE 841

1. Answers will vary.

3. Not all people who request a brochure will purchase a travel package.

5. Although the cookies are fat free, they still contain calories. Eating many of them may still cause you to gain weight.

7. The fact that Morgan's is the largest department store does not imply that it is inexpensive.

9. People with asthma may move to Arizona because of its climate. Therefore, more people with asthma may live in Arizona.

11. The quality of a steak does not necessarily depend on the price of the steak.

13. There may be deep sections in the pond, so it may not be safe to go wading.

15. Half the students in a population are expected to be below average.

17. a)

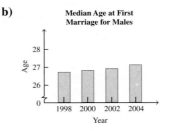

b)

19. a)

b)

21. a)

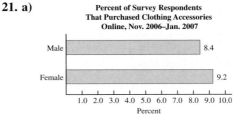

b) Answers will vary.

23. A decimal point

SECTION 13.3, PAGE 847

1. A frequency distribution is a listing of observed values and the corresponding frequency of occurrence of each value.

3. a) 7 **b)** 16–22 **c)** 16 **d)** 22

5. The modal class is the class with the greatest frequency.

7. a) 20 **b)** 7 **c)** 19 **d)** 16–22 **e)** 51–57

9.

Number of Visits	Number of Students
0	3
1	8
2	3
3	5
4	2
5	7
6	2
7	3
8	4
9	1
10	2

11.

IQ	Number of Students
78–86	2
87–95	15
96–104	18
105–113	7
114–122	6
123–131	1
132–140	1

13.

IQ	Number of Students
80–90	8
91–101	22
102–112	11
113–123	7
124–134	1
135–145	1

15.

Placement Test Scores	Number of Students
472–492	9
493–513	9
514–534	5
535–555	2
556–576	3
577–597	2

17.

Placement Test Scores	Number of Students
472–487	4
488–503	9
504–519	7
520–535	3
536–551	2
552–567	2
568–583	2
584–599	1

19.

Circulation (ten thousands)	Number of Magazines
157–306	34
307–456	9
457–606	2
607–756	1
757–906	1
907–1056	1

21.

Circulation (ten thousands)	Number of Magazines
157–256	29
257–356	8
357–456	6
457–556	2
557–656	0
657–756	1
757–856	1
857–956	0
957–1056	1

23.

Population (millions)	Number of Cities
6.0–6.9	2
7.0–7.9	5
8.0–8.9	6
9.0–9.9	2
10.0–10.9	3
11.0–11.9	2

25.

Population (millions)	Number of Cities
5.5–6.5	2
6.6–7.6	4
7.7–8.7	6
8.8–9.8	3
9.9–10.9	3
11.0–12.0	2

27.

Percent	Number of States
5.6–7.5	2
7.6–9.5	8
9.6–11.5	16
11.6–13.5	10
13.6–15.5	6
15.6–17.5	8

29.

Percent	Number of States
5.6–7.0	1
7.1–8.5	4
8.6–10.0	13
10.1–11.5	8
11.6–13.0	9
13.1–14.5	3
14.6–16.0	7
16.1–17.5	5

31. February, since it has the fewest number of days

32. a) Did You Know (page 845) There are 6 F's.
   b) Answers will vary.

SECTION 13.4, PAGE 855

1. Answers will vary.

3. Answers will vary.

5. a) Answers will vary.
   b)

Number of Textbooks Required

7. a) Answers will vary.
b)

Observed Values	Frequency
45	3
46	0
47	1
48	0
49	1
50	1
51	2

9. Tuition: $23,241.44; room: $4867.49; board: $3578.09; fees: $548.00

11.

Meals Eaten at a Fast Food Restaurant

Snack 11.8% Breakfast 7.7% Dinner 31.7% Lunch 48.8%

13. a) and **b)**

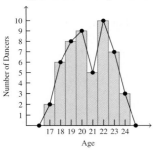

Age of Dancers Attending an Audition

15. a) and **b)**

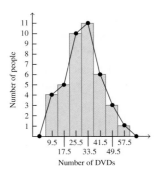

DVDs Owned

17. a) 28   **b)** 4   **c)** 2   **d)** 75
e)

Number of Televisions	Number of Homes
0	2
1	4
2	8
3	6
4	4
5	3
6	1

19. a) 7   **b)** 16   **c)** 36
d)

Number of Messages	Number of People	Number of Messages	Number of People
3	2	7	3
4	3	8	8
5	7	9	6
6	4	10	3

e)

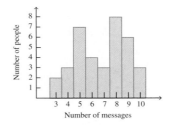

Number of Text Messages Sent

21.

23. 1 | 2 represents 12

0	4	6	7	8			
1	2	2	3	5	6	7	8	9
2	1	2	3	5	7		
3	3	4					
4	0						

25. a)

Salaries (1000s of dollars)	Number of Social Workers
27	1
28	7
29	4
30	3
31	2
32	3
33	3
34	2

b) and c)

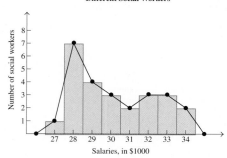

Starting Salaries for 25 Different Social Workers

d) 2|8 represents 28

```
2 | 7  8  8  8  8  8  8  8  9  9  9  9
3 | 0  0  0  1  1  2  2  2  3  3  3  4  4
```

27. a)

Number of Performances	Number of Shows
1508–2548	33
2549–3589	7
3590–4630	4
4631–5671	1
5672–6712	3
6713–7753	1
7754–8794	1

b) and c)

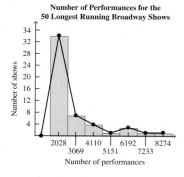

Number of Performances for the 50 Longest Running Broadway Shows

29. a)–e) Answers will vary.

SECTION 13.5, PAGE 867

1. a) The mean is the balancing point of a set of data. It is the sum of the data divided by the number of pieces of data.

b) The median is the value in the middle of a set of ranked data. To find the median, rank the data and select the value in the middle.

3. The median might be used when there are some values that differ greatly from the rest of the values in the set, for example, salaries.

5. The midrange might be used when the item being studied is constantly fluctuating, for example, daily temperature.

7. a) $\bar{x}$ **b)** μ **9.** Answers will vary.

11. 13, 12, 12, 16   **13.** 79.3, 82, none, 76

15. 8, 8, none, 8   **17.** 13.1, 11, 1, 18.5

19. 11.9, 12.5, 13, 11.5   **21.** 3.5, 3, 3, 4

23. a) 4.9, 5, 5, 6   **b)** 5.3, 5, 5, 6
   c) Only the mean   **d)** The mean and the midrange

25. A 79 mean average on 10 quizzes gives a total of 790 points. An 80 mean average on 10 quizzes requires a total of 800 points. Thus, Jim missed a B by 10 points, not 1 point.

27. a) 52.9 million   **b)** 43.8 million   **c)** None
   d) 61.8 million

29. a) 10.8 million   **b)** 10.1 million
   c) None   **d)** 11.5 million

31. 552

33. One example is 72, 73, 74, 76, 77, 78.

35. a) Yes   **b)** No   **c)** No   **d)** Yes

37. a) 29 or greater
   b) Yes, 99 or greater
   c) 20 or greater   **d)** 80 or greater

39. One example: 1, 2, 3, 3, 4, 5 changed to 1, 2, 3, 4, 4, 5.

41. No. By changing only one piece of the 6 pieces of data, you cannot alter both the median and the midrange.

43. The data must be ranked.

45. He is taller than approximately 35 percent of all kindergarten children.

47. a) $25   **b)** $22   **c)** $34

49. Second quartile, median

51. a) $530   **b)** $540   **c)** 25%
   d) 25%   **e)** 17%   **f)** $55,000

53. a)

Ruth	Mantle
0.290	0.300
0.359	0.365
0.301	0.304
0.272	0.275
0.315	0.321

b) Mantle's is greater in every case.

c) Ruth: 0.316; Mantle: 0.311; Ruth's is greater.

d) Answers will vary.

e) Ruth: 0.307; Mantle: 0.313; Mantle's is greater.

f) Answers will vary.   g) Answers will vary.

55. 90   57. a)–c) Answers will vary.

SECTION 13.6, PAGE 877

1. Range = highest value − lowest value

3. Answers will vary.

5. Zero   7. σ

9. Answers will vary.

11. They would be the same since the spread of data about each mean is the same.

13. a) The mean is the same for both classes.

b) The spread of the data about the mean is greater for the evening class since the standard deviation is greater for the evening class.

15. 11, $\sqrt{16.5} \approx 4.06$ 17. 6, $\sqrt{4.67} \approx 2.16$

19. 11, $\sqrt{15.2} \approx 3.90$ 21. 5, $\sqrt{3} \approx 1.73$

23. $32, $\sqrt{137.78} \approx \$11.74$

25. $150, $\sqrt{2600} \approx \$50.99$

27. a) $63, $\sqrt{631.6} \approx \$25.13$ b) Answers will vary.

c) Answers remain the same, range: $63, standard deviation ≈ $25.13.

29. a)–c) Answers will vary.

d) If each number in a distribution is multiplied by n, the mean and standard deviation of the new distribution will be n times that of the original distribution.

e) The mean of the second set is $4 \times 5 = 20$, and the standard deviation of the second set is $2 \times 5 = 10$.

31. a) The standard deviation increases. There is a greater spread from the mean as they get older.

b) ≈ 133 lb   c) ≈ 21 lb

d) Mean: ≈ 100 lb; normal range: ≈ 60 to 140 lb

e) Mean: ≈ 62 in.; normal range: ≈ 53 to 68 in.

f) 5%

33. a)

East		West	
Number of Oil Changes Made	Number of Days	Number of Oil Changes Made	Number of Days
15–20	2	15–20	0
21–26	2	21–26	0
27–32	5	27–32	6
33–38	4	33–38	9
39–44	7	39–44	4
45–50	1	45–50	6
51–56	1	51–56	0
57–62	2	57–62	0
63–68	1	63–68	0

b)

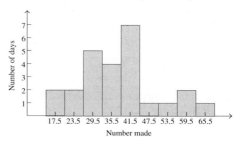

Number of Oil Changes Made Daily

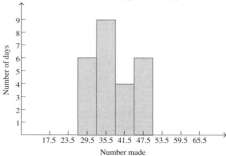

Number of Oil Changes Made Daily

c) They appear to have about the same mean since they are both centered around 38.

d) The distribution for East is more spread out. Therefore, East has a greater standard deviation.

e) East: 38, West: 38   f) East: ≈ 12.64, West: ≈ 5.98

35. 6, 6, 6, 6, 6

SECTION 13.7, PAGE 894

1. A rectangular distribution is one in which all the values have the same frequency.

3. A bimodal distribution is one in which two nonadjacent values occur more frequently than any other values in a set of data.

5. A distribution skewed to the left is one that has a "tail" on its left.

7. A z-score measures how far, in terms of standard deviations, a given score is from the mean.

9. a) Below the mean

b) Above the mean

11. a) B b) C c) A

13.–15. Answers will vary.

17. Normal   19. Skewed right

21. The mean is the greatest value. The median is lower than the mean. The mode is the lowest value.

23. Answers will vary.   25. They all have the same value.

27. 0.5000   29. 0.8185   31. 0.0901   33. 0.0375

35. 0.0429   37. 0.0526   39. 76.11%   41. 89.74%

43. 97.13%   **45.** 97.50%   **47.** 21.96%

49. a) Emily, Sarah, Carol   **b)** Jason, Juan
   c) Omar, Heather, Kim

51. 50%   **53.** 10.56%   **55.** 69.15%   **57.** 24.17%

59. 44.00%   **61.** 29.02%   **63.** 59.87%   **65.** 50.00%

67. 11.51%   **69.** ≈ 23 cars   **71.** 95.47%

73. 13,380 boxes   **75.** 69.15%   **77.** 0.62%

79. ≈ 83 children   **81.** 1.79%

83. The standard deviation is too large.

85. a) Katie: $z = 2.4$; Stella: $z = 1.7$
   b) Katie. Her z-score is higher than Stella's z-score, which
   means her sales are further above the mean than
   Stella's sales.

87. a)–f) Answers will vary.

89. -1.18 **91.** 2

SECTION 13.8, PAGE 907

 1. The correlation coefficient measures the strength of the relationship between the quantities.

 3. 1   **5.** 0

 7. a) A positive correlation indicates that as one quantity increases, the other increases.
   b) Answers will vary.

 9. The level of significance is used to identify the cutoff between results attributed to chance and results attributed to
   an actual relationship between the two variables.

11.–13. Answers will vary.

15. Yes   **17.** Yes

19. No   **21.** No

*The answers in the remainder of this section may differ
slightly from your answers, depending on how your answers are rounded and which calculator you used. The answers given here were obtained from a Texas Instruments
TI-36x solar calculator.*

23. a)

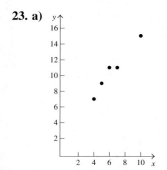

   b) 0.981   **c)** Yes   **d)** Yes

25. a)

   b) 0.228   **c)** No   **d)** No

27. a)

   b) 0.999   **c)** Yes   **d)** Yes

29. a)

   b) -0.968 **c)** Yes   **d)** Yes

31. $y = 1.26x + 2.51$

33. $y = 0.18x + 23.82$

35. $y = 0.81x + 5.84$

37. $y = -0.08x + 9.50$

39. a) 0.974   **b)** Yes   **c)** $y = 0.74x + 1.26$

41. a) 0.950   **b)** Yes   **c)** $y = 0.77x + 24.86$

43. a) 0.993   **b)** Yes   **c)** $y = 3.90x + 1.94$
   d) 21.4 kilocalories

45. a) -0.804 **b)** No   **c)** $y = -0.43x + 35.28$
   d) 21.1 mpg

47. a) -0.977 **b)** Yes   **c)** $y = -12.93x + 99.59$
   d) 41.4%

49. a) and **b)** Answers will vary.
c)

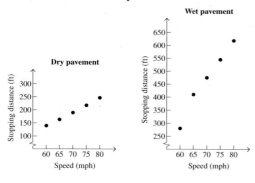

Dry pavement

Wet pavement

d) 0.999   **e)** 0.990   **f)** Answers will vary.
g) $y = 5.36x - 183.40$ **h)** $y = 16.22x - 669.80$
i) Dry, 229.3 ft; wet, 579.1 ft

51. a)–f) Answers will vary.

53. a) 0.993   **b)** Should be the same.

　c) 0.993, the values are the same.

REVIEW EXERCISES, PAGE 913

1. a) A population consists of all items or people of interest.
　b) A sample is a subset of the population.

2. A random sample is one where every item in the population has the same chance of being selected.

3. The candy bars may have lots of calories, or fat, or sodium. Therefore, it may not be healthy to eat them.

4. Sales may not necessarily be a good indicator of profit. Expenses must also be considered.

5. a)

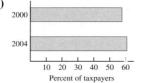

b)

6. a)

Class	Frequency
35	1
36	3
37	6
38	2
39	3
40	0
41	4
42	1
43	3
44	1
45	1

b) and **c)**

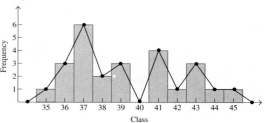

7. a)

High Temperature	Number of Cities
58–62	1
63–67	4
68–72	9
73–77	10
78–82	11
83–87	4
88–92	1

b) and **c)**

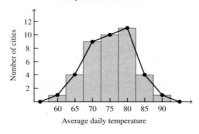

Average Monthly High Temperature
in July for Selected Cities

d) 5|8 represents 58

```
5 | 8
6 | 3 6 6 7 8 8 9
7 | 0 1 1 1 2 2 3 3 3 4 5 5 5 6 6 7 9 9 9
8 | 0 0 0 0 1 2 2 2 3 4 4 7
9 | 1
```

8. 80   **9.** 81   **10.** None   **11.** 79   **12.** 28
13. $\sqrt{87.2} \approx 9.34$ **14.** 13   **15.** 13
16. 7 and 12   **17.** 13.5   **18.** 19
19. $\sqrt{40} \approx 6.32$ **20.** 68.26%   **21.** 95.44%
22. 94.52%   **23.** 5.48%   **24.** 72.57%   **25.** 34.1%
26. 34.5%   **27.** 29.0%   **28.** 2.3%

29. a)

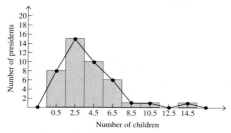

b) Yes; positive   **c)** 0.957   **d)** Yes
e) $y = 0.15x + 1.29$ **f)** \$3.2 million

30. a)

b) Yes; negative   **c)** -0.973 **d)** Yes
e) $y = -79.4x + 246.7$ **f)** ≈ 120 sold

31. 180 lb   **32.** 185 lb   **33.** 25%   **34.** 25%   **35.** 14%
36. 19,200 lb   **37.** 238 lb   **38.** 150.6 lb   **39.** ≈ 3.57
40. 2   **41.** 3   **42.** 7   **43.** 14   **44.** $\sqrt{8.105} \approx 2.85$

45.

Number of Children	Number of Presidents
0–1	8
2–3	15
4–5	10
6–7	6
8–9	1
10–11	1
12–13	0
14–15	1

46. and 47.

Number of Children of U.S. Presidents

48. No, it is skewed to the right.
49. Answers will vary.
50. Answers will vary.

CHAPTER TEST, PAGE 915

1. 42   **2.** 43   **3.** 43   **4.** 39.5   **5.** 25   **6.** $\sqrt{84} \approx 9.17$

7.

Class	Frequency
25–30	7
31–36	5
37–42	1
43–48	7
49–54	5
55–60	3
61–66	2

8.

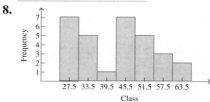

9.

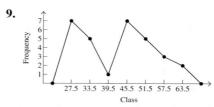

10. \$735   **11.** \$710   **12.** 75%   **13.** 79%
14. \$74,000   **15.** \$780   **16.** \$680   **17.** 87.10%
18. 89.44%   **19.** 10.56%   **20.** 94.52%
21. a)

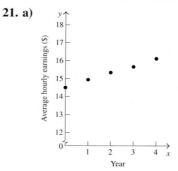

b) Yes   **c)** 0.996   **d)** Yes   **e)** $y = 0.39x + 14.56$
f) \$25.87

APPENDIX B

APPENDIX B, PAGE AB-3

1. A vertex is a designated point.
3. To determine whether a vertex is odd or even, count the
number of edges attached to the vertex. If the number of
edges is odd, the vertex is odd. If the number of edges is
even, the vertex is even.

5. 5 vertices, 7 edges   **7.** 7 vertices, 11 edges

9. Each graph has the same number of edges between corresponding vertices.

11. odd vertices: *C*, *D*; even vertices: *A*, *B*

13. Yes; start at *C* and end at *D*, or start at *D* and end at *C*.

15. Yes; start at any point and end where you started.

17. No.

19. Yes; start at *A* and end at *C*, or start at *C* and end at *A*.

21. a) 0 odd, 5 even   **b)** Yes
   c) Start in any room and end where you began. One path is *A* to *D* to *B* to *C* to *E* to *A*.

23. a) 2 odd, 4 even   **b)** Yes
   c) Start at *B* and end at *F*, or start at *F* and end at *B*. One path is *B* to *C* to *F* to *E* to *D* to *A* to *B* to *E* to *F*.

25. a) 4 odd, 1 even   **b)** Not possible

27. a) 3 odd, 2 even   **b)** Not possible

29. The door must be placed in room D. Room D is the only room with an odd number of doors.

31. Yes; there are two odd vertices. Begin at either the island on the left or on the right and end at the other island.

33.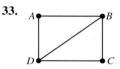

35. a) Kentucky, Virginia, North Carolina, Georgia, Alabama, Mississippi, Arkansas, Missouri
   b) Illinois, Arkansas, Tennessee

37. a) 4   **b)** 4   **c)** 11

39.

41. a) Yes, the graph has exactly 2 odd vertices.
   b) One possiblity is *C* to *A* to *B* to *E* to *F* to *D* to *G* to *C*.

C R E D I T S

Page 1, Couple working on budgets, Digital Vision; Page 2, DisneyWorld finger scanner, Apani Networks; Page 3, ATM eye scan, International Business Machines Corporation; Page 4, Astronaut on moon, NASA; Page 9, Jury, Corbis; Page 9, Buying stamps in post office, Beth Anderson; Page 10, Bushels of grapes in vineyard, PhotoDisc Red; Page 13, Counting birds, Art Wolfe/Stone/Getty Images; Page 14, Repeat detail of birds, Art Wolfe/Stone/Getty Images; Page 15, Picking strawberries, PhotoDisc Blue; Page 18, Bananas, Allen R. Angel; Page 18, Blueberries, PhotoDisc; Page 18, Statue of Liberty, Allen R. Angel; Page 19, Three men and palm tree, Corbis Royalty Free; Page 20, Buying CDs in office supply store, PhotoDisc Red; Page 22, George Polya at blackboard, Palo Alto Weekly; Page 23, Archimedes, The Bridgeman Art Library International; Page 25, Restaurant waitstaff with customers, PhotoDisc Red; Page 26, Vacation in the mountains, Allen R. Angel; Page 27, Spraying weed killer, Corbis; Page 30, Large fishing boat, Digital Vision; Page 33, African safari, PhotoDisc Red; Page 42, Van Gogh's *Sunflowers*, Christie's Images/Corbis; Page 44, Child playing with abacus, Stockbyte Platinum Getty RF; Page 45, Horses, Allen R. Angel; Page 45, Georg Cantor, The Granger Collection; Page 46, Planets in Earth's solar system, Bennett/Donahue/Schneider/Voit, *The Essential Cosmic Perspective, Fourth Edition*, Pearson Addison-Wesley, © 2007; Page 50, Astronauts on the moon, NASA; Page 51, Snow White and the Seven Dwarfs, Walt Disney/The Kobal Collection; Page 52, The Beatles, The Everett Collection; Page 53, J.K. Rowling, Corbis; Page 54, Fireman, PhotoDisc Red; Page 57, Pizza with toppings, Stockbyte Platinum Getty RF; Page 58, Exercise class at gym, Purestock Getty RF; Page 60, Koala and Mrs. Angel, Allen R. Angel; Page 60, Buying a soft drink, Image Source Getty RF; Page 69, San Diego Zoo, PhotoDisc Red; Page 68, Yosemite National Park, PhotoDisc; Page 71, Person with dog, Ingram Publishing Getty RF; Page 71, High school band, Beth Anderson; Page 72, Doctors examining x-rays, PhotoDisc Blue; Page 77, Walmart, Beth Anderson; Page 78, Athlete from summer Olympics, Digital Vision; Page 82, Using treadmill or Stairmaster, PhotoDisc; Page 85, Hawaii, Beth Anderson; Page 87, Movie theatre attendees, PhotoDisc Red; Page 87, Water slide at amusement park, Digital Vision; Page 88, Women at restaurant, Digital Vision; Page 89, Farmer and wheatfield, PhotoDisc; Page 89, Georg Cantor, The Granger Collection; Page 91, Leopold Kronecker, The Granger Collection; Page 95, Tiger, PhotoDisc; Page 97, Actors from *CSI:NY*, Getty Editorial; Page 98, Cotton candy snack, PhotoDisc Red; Page 100, Lawyer arguing case, Digital Vision; Page 101, Morton salt ad, Morton International, Inc.; Page 102, Brooklyn Bridge, Corbis RF; Page 103, Abbott and Costello, Bettmann/Corbis; Page 105, Billie Joe Armstrong/Green Day, AP Wideworld Photos; Page 106, George Boole, The Granger Collection; Page 108, Painting by Beth Anderson, Beth Anderson; Page 109, Martin St. Louis, Getty Images Sport; Page 110, Louis Armstrong playing trumpet, Time & Life Pictures/Getty Images; Page 110, Butterflies and flowers, Allen R. Angel; Page 111, Ken Jennings, Jeopardy champ, Getty Images News; Page 113, Idaho potatoes, Digital Vision; Page 116, Guitarists, PhotoDisc Red; Page 123, Girl with cookies and milk, Corbis Royalty Free; Page 123, Collie, PhotoDisc Blue; Page 123, John Madden, sports announcer, AP Wideworld Photos; Page 125, Airplane travel, Digital Vision; Page 126, Car for A student, Digital Vision; Page 133, Soccer, Corbis Royalty Free; Page 134, Nike shoes, Corbis; Page 136, Sunny beach, Dennis Runde; Page 137, Charles Dodgson, The Granger Collection; Page 137, Alice in Wonderland, The Granger Collection; Page 141, Augustus de Morgan, The Granger Collection; Page 144, Sitar, PhotoDisc; Page 146, Digital photographer, ThinkStock RF; Page 147, Timex watch, Beth Anderson; Page 148, *Jimmy Neutron*, Paramount Pictures/Courtesy: Everett Collection; Page 148, Sailboat, Beth Anderson; Page 149, Yellow lab, Christine Abbott; Page 149, People fishing, PhotoDisc Blue; Page 150, FedEx truck, Beth Anderson; Page 150, Person taking a picture, PhotoDisc Red; Page 151, John Mellencamp, Major League Baseball/Getty Images; Page 153, Alaska glacier, PhotoDisc Blue; Page 156, U.S. Constitution photo, Corbis RF; Page 158, Prices at gas station, Getty Images News; Page 160, Les Paul and guitar, Corbis; Page 160, Graduation, StockDisc; Page 161, Football quarterback about to throw, Stockbyte Platinum/Getty RF; Page 162, Meg Ryan in *In the Land of Women*, Warner Independent/Courtesy: Everett Collection; Page 165, Barcode scanner, PhotoDisc; Page 167, Gingerbread man, National Geographic/Getty Royalty Free; Page 168, Morel mushrooms, PhotoDisc; Page 168, Caterpillar, PhotoDisc Red; Page 169, Reading lamp, Digital Vision; Page 176, Ellen Johnson-Sirleaf, President of Liberia, Jason Szenes/epa/Corbis; Page 177, Bobby Darin and Sandra Dee, Hulton Archive/Getty Images; Page 180, Ontario Science Center logic game, Courtesy Ontario Science Center; Page 181, Kids using math manipulatives, Richard Hutchings/PhotoEdit Inc.; Page 182, Hines Ward and Super Bowl XL logo, Getty Images Sport; Page 182, Denise Schmandt-Besserat, Courtesy Denise Schmandt-Besserat; Page 183, Rhind papyrus, Public domain; Page 184, Clock with Roman numerals, Allen R. Angel; Page 186, Sign showing Hindu-Arabic numerals, Mark Gibson; Page 190, Great pyramid at Khufu, Giza Egypt, Digital Vision (PP); Page 190, Bob Barker game in *Price is Right*, CBS/Photofest; Page 192, Counting board, Taxi/Getty Images; Page 193, Globe, PhotoDisc; Page 194, Photo of Jan Fleck's *Numbers*, Allen R. Angel; Page 197, Boys with iPods, Christine Abbott; Page 198, Students in computer lab, Blend Images/Getty RF; Page 200, Arabic and Chinese numerals, PhotoAlto/Getty RF; Page 204, Middle school kids in computer lab, PhotoDisc; Page 204, Arithmetic teacher and students, Purestock/Getty RF; Page 213, Internet researcher, Stockbyte Platinum/Getty RF; Page 214, Pay check/time clock, PhotoDisc; Page 215, Gradeschool class—new old math, PhotoDisc; Page 216, John Napier, The Granger Collection; Page 223, Teenagers on cell phones. PhotoDisc Red (PP); Page 224, Box of chocolates, Beth Anderson; Page 227, Factoring machine 1914, Jeffrey Shallit; Page 228, Srinivasa Ramanujan, The Granger Collection; Page 230, Bank vault, Digital Vision; Page 233, Barbie dolls, Beth Anderson; Page 233, School band, Merrill Education; Page 235, Playing in snow, PhotoDisc; Page 238, Mount Everest, Corbis RF; Page 243, NYSE floor traders, PhotoDisc; Page 243, Reggie Bush, New Orleans Saints, Getty Editorial; Page 245, Preparing cake mix, Pixland/Corbis Royalty Free; Page 253, Waves of string vibration, Fundamental Photos; Page 257, Measuring boy's height, Corbis RF; Page 258, Farmer and silo, Digital Vision; Page 259, San Antonio, Texas, Allen R. Angel; Page 261, Superbowl champs playing, Getty Editorial; Page 262, Pythagoras of Samos, Corbis; Page 268, Car in motion, Allen R. Angel; Page 269, Elementary school students doing arithmetic, Digital Vision; Page 271, Daniel Tammet, Colin McPherson/Corbis; Page 275, English bulldog, PhotoDisc Red; Page 276, Breaking an egg into a bowl, PhotoDisc; Page 276, Galaxy, NASA headquarters; Page 280, Another galaxy, NASA Media Services; Page 281, Preda Mihailescu, Used with permission of Preda Mihailescu; Page 283, WWI poster, U.S. bonds, Library of Congress; Page 286, Jupiter, U.S. Geological Survey/U.S. Department of the Interior; Page 286, IBM BlueGene/L system computer, Kim Kulish/Corbis; Page 287, Niagara Falls, PhotoDisc; Page 288, U.S. mint/ uncut sheets of currency, Charles O'Rear/Corbis; Page 289, Scientists in lab with microscope, Digital Vision; Page 290, Carl Frederick Gauss, Public domain; Page 292, Sun and planets, PhotoDisc; Page 296, Squirrel, Digital Vision; Page 296, Cuckoo clock, PhotoDisc Red; Page 296, Samurai sword production, Bettmann/Corbis; Page 297, Black Jack game, PhotoDisc; Page 298, Beehive, Digital Vision; Page 298, Leonardo of Pisa, Fibonacci, Corbis;

Page 299, Sunflower center, Corbis RF; Page 300, Pyramids of Giza, PhotoDisc Blue; Page 300, Parthenon, Corbis RF; Page 300, Chambered nautilus, PhotoDisc; Page 301, Quilt, *Fibonacci's Garden*, Carol Bryer Fallert; Page 301, Seurat, *La Parade de Cirque*, 1887, Metropolitan Museum of Art; Page 306, Milwaukee Road Railroad Company, Milwaukee Road Historical Association; Page 307, Cooked turkey, PhotoDisc; Page 308, Sun and planets, PhotoDisc; Page 311, Cooking and recipe, Westend61/Getty RF; Page 312, Buying new tires, Digital Vision; Page 313, Google, Linda Stinchfield Hamilton; Page 314, Demuth painting *I Saw the Figure 5 in Gold*, Metropolitan Museum of Art; Page 316, Buying a refrigerator, Corbis RF; Page 317, Active senior citizens, PhotoDisc Blue; Page 319, François Viete, The Bridgeman Art Library International; Page 328, Topsoil to cover 480 ft., Amana Images/Getty RF; Page 329, Niagara Falls, Allen R. Angel; Page 330, Carpeting a room wall-to-wall, PunchStock RF; Page 330, Rectangular box of ice cream, Beth Anderson; Page 333, Fossil, GettyRF; Page 335, Albert Einstein Lucien Aigner/Corbis; Page 336, Sophie Germaine, Stock Montage; Page 338, Volume of ice cream in cone, PhotoDisc Red; Page 339, Sales rep's commission, PhotoDisc Red; Page 344, Renting a jet ski, Digital Vision; Page 345, Men building a deck, PhotoDisc; Page 345, Mustangs running wild, PhotoDisc Blue; Page 346, Hotel in San Diego, Allen R. Angel; Page 346, Nice home worth $170K, PhotoDisc Blue; Page 351, Henrietta Hots sales, Christine Abbott; Page 353, Children and balloons, Getty RF; Page 353, Light filtering through water, PhotoDisc Red; Page 354, Ice cube melting in water, Beth Anderson; Page 355, Flash picture, Digital Vision; Page 355, College bookstore revenue, PhotoDisc Red; Page 361, College student working as cashier, Blend Images/Getty RF; Page 362, Painting a house, PhotoDisc; Page 362, Mailing a package, Stockbyte Platinum/Getty RF; Page 363, Mike Myers and Shrek, Reuters New Media/Corbis; Page 364, René Descartes, International Business Machines Corporation; Page 366, Grid at archaeological dig, Richard T. Nowitz/Corbis; Page 368, Thomas Morgenstern, Olympic skier, str/Reuters/Corbis; Page 374, Woman hanging wallpaper, Blend Images/Getty RF; Page 374, Gas grills in a store, Getty Editorial; Page 379, Purchasing DVDs and CDs, PhotoDisc Red; Page 379, Rectangular inground swimming pool, Amana Images/Getty RF; Page 389, Rectangular flower garden, Stockdisc Premium/Getty RF; Page 390, Oranges in supermarket, MIXA/Getty RF; Page 392, Cost of operating taxi, Beth Anderson; Page 394, NWS prediction algorithm, Information and Publications; Page 401, Number of new Starbucks stores, Beth Anderson; Page 403, Distance a car travels, PhotoDisc Red; Page 408, Endangered U.S. panther, Digital Vision; Page 408, Reading an electric meter, Beth Anderson; Page 409, Car wash profits, Corbis RF; Page 413, T-shirt business, Beth Anderson; Page 414, Landscaping service cost, Paul A. Souders/Corbis; Page 418, Model car, Corbis Royalty Free; Page 421, Landscaping worker, Allen R. Angel; Page 422, Personal digital assistant (PDA), Stockdisc Premium/Getty RF; Page 423, Cell phone plans, Westend61/Getty RF; Page 423, University of Maryland women's basketball team, Getty Editorial; Page 433, Purchasing/installing a hardwood floor, PhotoDisc Blue; Page 434, College students at table or walking, Getty RF; Page 435, Yosemite sign, Allen R. Angel; Page 439, James Sylvester, Stock Montage; Page 439, William Rowan Hamilton, Photo Researchers; Page 439, Arthur Cayley, Stock Montage; Page 443, Tomatoes, onions, carrots at market, Blend Images/Getty RF; Page 444, Bakery display, Allen R. Angel; Page 445, Sofa factory, Billy E. Barnes/Photo Edit; Page 446, Buying chocolates in candy store, PhotoDisc Blue; Page 448, Race cars from the movie, *Cars*, The Everett Collection; Page 452, Lids, baseball hats store, Corbis Royalty Free; Page 452, Buying caramel corn and nuts, Beth Anderson; Page 453, Camcorders in a store, PhotoDisc Red; Page 456, Artist decorating or selling bowls, PhotoDisc Red; Page 457, Skateboards, Stockbyte Platinum/Getty RF; Page 458, D-Day schematic, Allen R. Angel; Page 459, George B. Dantzig, Professor Vladimir F. Demyanov, St. Petersburg State University, Russia; Page 460, Washer and dryer, Corbis Royalty Free; Page 463, Skaters at Central Park, Allen R. Angel; Page 463, Baby in car seat or stroller, PhotoDisc; Page 465, Chemistry class, Corbis Royalty Free; Page 466, Moving with a rental truck, PhotoDisc Red; Page 468, Kilometers speed limit sign, Corbis Royalty Free; Page 469, Liter graduated cylinder in chemistry lab or class, PhotoDisc; Page 469, *Mars Climate Orbiter*, NASA; Page 470, One and two liter soda bottles, Allen R. Angel; Page 471, 11,10%, Allen R. Angel; Page 471, Jackpot, Allen R. Angel; Page 471, Person with new laptop, Digital Vision; Page 472, Road sign in kilometers, Allen R. Angel; Page 473, Subway sign, Allen R. Angel; Page 475, 3000 KG sign, Allen R. Angel; Page 476, Picasso in frame, Allen R. Angel; Page 477, Wimbledon sign, Allen R. Angel; Page 478, U.S. cars on big cargo ship, Getty Images Photographer's Choice; Page 479, Ted Willams statue, Allen R. Angel; Page 480, Yellowstone water falls, Allen R. Angel; Page 481, Photo of WA quarter, U.S. Mint; Page 481, 1000ml graduated cylinder, Corbis Royalty Free; Page 482, Volume of swimming pool, Allen R. Angel; Page 485, Tennis, Allen R. Angel; Page 486, New River Gorge bridge, Allen R. Angel; Page 486, Riverwalk, San Antonio, Allen R. Angel; Page 487, U.S. flag, Artville RF; Page 487, Air in a soccer ball, Rubberball Productions/Getty RF; Page 488, Framing a painting, Allen R. Angel; Page 488, Painting a house, Corbis Royalty Free; Page 489, Glacier, Allen R. Angel; Page 490, Astronaut floating in space capsule, NASA; Page 491, Young child, Allen R. Angel; Page 492, Steve Thorburn, British grocer, Alan Glen Wright/First Voice; Page 495, Whale, Corbis Royalty Free; Page 495, Freezing rain, Allen R. Angel; Page 496, Seismograph pool, Allen R. Angel; Page 497, Popcorn and sabu dhana, Allen R. Angel; Page 498, International Falls, MN, Northwinds courtesy Lauren Beager; Page 498, Smart car, Allen R. Angel; Page 500, Mexican pesos or Mexican money exchange, Silver Burdett Ginn; Page 502, Sloping floor, tall man in elevator, Allen R. Angel; Page 502, Land for sale in hectares, Allen R. Angel; Page 502, Peppers, Allen R. Angel; Page 503, Key West Southernmost sign, Beth Anderson; Page 504, Bottle of Vicks Formula 44D, PhotoDisc; Page 505, Astronauts on the moon, NASA; Page 506, Speed limit in kph, Allen R. Angel; Page 506, Poison dart frog, Allen R. Angel; Page 507, St. Emilion sign, Allen R. Angel; Page 507, Lecheria #2 sign, Allen R. Angel; Page 508, Disney Magic Cruise Ship, Allen R. Angel; Page 508, Peppers at 2E/kg, Allen R. Angel; Page 508, Curry, Allen R. Angel; Page 510, Dolphin, Allen R. Angel; Page 511, Milk tank, Allen R. Angel; Page 512, Italian blue Priano8, Allen R. Angel; Page 512, 4 pers 300 kg sign, Allen R. Angel; Page 514, Baseball diamond, istockphoto.com; Page 515, Billiards game, Corbis RF; Page 516, Euclid, Edward R. Tufte, Graphics Press 1990; Page 527, Stop sign, Art Explosion clip art; Page 527, Yield sign, Art Explosion clip art; Page 527, Speed limit sign, Art Explosion clip art; Page 529, Mr. Tumnus, *The Chronicles of Narnia*, PhotoFest; Page 531, Soccer ball, PhotoDisc Blue; Page 538, Dwayne Wade, Miami Heat, NBAE/Getty Images; Page 541, Replacing sod, PhotoEdit; Page 542, Dorothy and the Scarecrow, *The Wizard of Oz*, The Kobal Collection; Page 544, Andrew J. Wiles, AP/Wideworld Photos; Page 549, Fenway Park, Allen R. Angel; Page 550, Choosing paint colors, PhotoDisc Red; Page 554, Sand volleyball, PhotoDisc; Page 556, *Les Desmoiselle D'Avignon*, Picasso, Museum of Modern Art, New York; Page 563, Model globe, PhotoDisc Blue; Page 563, Pyramid of Cheops, Corbis Royalty-Free; Page 563, Fish tank, PhotoDisc Red; Page 563, 1957 Corvette, Getty RM; Page 566, Child writing capital letters, Digital Vision; Page 577, Maurits Cornelius Escher, The M.C. Escher Company; Page 587, Klein bottle, Beth Anderson; Page 593, Map of New Mexico Counties, © Compare Infobase Pvt Ltd 2004–2005. Used with permission. www.mapsofworld.com/usa/states/new-mexico; Page 594, Galaxy, NASA; Page 595, Conformal Brain Map photo, Image courtesy of Dr. Monica K. Hurdal, Department of Mathematics, Florida State University; Page 598, Fractal image, RFPP; Page 598, Fractal image, Gregory Sams/Photo Researchers, Inc.; Page 598, Fractal triangle antenna, © Andy Ryan Photography, Inc. All Rights Reserved; Page 601, M.C. Escher, *Circle Limit III*, The M.C. Escher Company; Page 610, Brain MRI, Image Source/Getty RF; Page 611, Milky Way, Space Telescope Science Institute; Page 616, Diane Keaton and Woody Allen, *Annie Hall*, The Kobal Collection; Page 618, Slow cooker, Foodcollection/Getty RF; Page 620, Clock tower, St. Mark's Basillica, Allen R. Angel; Page 623, Rubik's cube, Silver Burdett Ginn; Page 631, Birthday celebration, PhotoDisc Red; Page 634, Enigma encrypting machine, Allen R. Angel; Page 635, Bus driver, PhotoDisc Red; Page 636, Protons and neutrons, Fermilab/Peter Arnold; Page 637, Amalie Emmy Noether, The Granger Collection; Page 639, Tennis pro, PhotoDisc; Page 639, Movie theater manager, Corbis RF; Page 640, Birthday party, Stockbyte/Getty RF; Page 643, Fire fighters, Corbis RF; Page 645, College graduates, Beth Anderson; Page 646, Woman in the rain, Blend Images/Getty Royalty Free; Page 648, Cherries, PhotoDisc; Page 651, Waitress, Rubberball Productions/Getty Royalty Free; Page 652, Chess game, Corbis Royalty Free; Page 653, Taj Mahal, Photosindia/Getty Royalty Free; Page 656, Charter fishing boat, Digital Vision; Page 656, Man on weight scale, Blend Images/Getty Royalty Free; Page 657, Auto mechanic, PhotoDisc; Page 658, Eye examination, PhotoDisc; Page 659, Pawnshop, Dana White/PhotoEdit; Page 665, Restaurant patrons, PhotoDisc; Page 666, Pawnbroker, Beth Anderson; Page 667, U.S. Treasury Building, MedioImages/Getty Royalty Free; Page 668, Albert Einstein, Library of Congress; Page 669, Benjamin Franklin, The Granger Collection; Page 670, Manhattan, Allen R. Angel; Page 673, Bunker Hill Community College, Beth Anderson; Page 675, Little League game, Courtesy of authors; Page 676, Waitress, PhotoDisc; Page 677, Kieler water tower, Allen R. Angel; Page 677, Larger tractor with cab, Dennis Runde; Page 677, People golfing, Allen R. Angel; Page 678, Woman trying on shoes, PhotoDisc Red; Page 679, Stoves at appliance store, PhotoDisc; Page 680, 12-ft boat, PhotoDisc; Page 681, 1965 Mustang, Corbis/Bettmann; Page 683, Credit cards, Beth Anderson; Page 686, Stereo system, Digital Vision; Page 688, 2006 PT Cruiser GT, AFP/Getty Editorial; Page 690, Paint store shoppers, Somos/Getty Royalty Free; Page 691, Kids watching TV, Digital Vision; Page 693, Young family with their home, Digital Vision; Page 693, Sears catalog page, Public domain; Page 694, Couple with new home, Photographer's Choice RF/Getty Royalty Free; Page 695, Cape-style house, PhotoDisc; Page 699, Cape-style house for sale, PhotoDisc; Page 702, Brooklyn brownstone, PhotoDisc Red; Page 702, Couple in front of house for sale, PhotoDisc; Page 703, Couple applying for mortgage, PhotoDisc; Page 704, House on lake, Digital Vision; Page 706, Active retirement-age couple, PhotoDisc Blue; Page 707, Coke bottle, Beth Anderson; Page 708, Bonds, Corbis Royalty Free; Page 710, Richard playing piano, Dennis Runde; Page 715, Grandchild and grandparents, Stockbyte Silver/Getty Royalty Free; Page 715, Campaign volunteer, Digital Vision; Page 717, Skateboarder, Duomo/Corbis; Page 718, Woman buying new clothes, PhotoDisc Red; Page 720, House for sale (bungalow), PhotoDisc; Page 720, John Deere combine harvesting corn, Digital Vision; Page 721, New touring bicycle, Corbis; Page 723, Lottery winning family, AFP/Getty Editorial; Page 724, Buying music CDs, Corbis Royalty Free; Page 724, Jacob Bernoulli, Corbis/Bettmann; Page 726, Husky with brown and blue eyes, Allen R. Angel; Page 728, Joe Mauer, Minnesota Twins, Getty Images Sport; Page 729, Benjamin Franklin Commemorative Coin, U.S. Mint; Page 729, Bird feeder, PhotoDisc; Page 730, Rabbit, PhotoDisc Red; Page 730, MapQuest web page, © 2007 Mapquest, Inc. All Rights Reserved; Page 733, Casino games, Corbis Royalty Free; Page 734, Northern cardinal, Allen R. Angel; Page 739, Young boy with a basketball, Image Source/Getty Royalty Free; Page 741, Chicago White Sox, 2005 World Series, Major League Baseball/Getty Images; Page 744, NBC game show *Deal or No Deal*, Chris Haston © NBC/Courtesy: Everett Collection; Page 747, NASCAR driver Tony Stewart, Getty Images Sport; Page 747, Bingo board, Allen R. Angel; Page 748, Horse race, Kevin R. Morris/Corbis; Page 749, Rolling die, fStop/Getty Royalty Free; Page 750, JetBlue plane, Beth Anderson; Page 751, Parking ticket, PhotoDisc; Page 752, Hot dog vendor, Digital Vision; Page 756, Candace Parker, University of Tennessee, Corbis; Page 756, Hollywood Bowl, Corbis; Page 757, Student taking a test, PhotoDisc Blue; Page 759, Construction site planning, Digital Vision; Page 761, Parents with three children, PhotoDisc Red; Page 763, Kids eating in restaurant, Stockbyte Platinum/Getty Royalty Free; Page 764, Beyoncé Knowles, Getty Images Entertainment; Page 767, Making paint choices, PhotoDisc Red; Page 769, Couple buying kitchen appliances, Stockbyte Platinum/Getty Royalty Free; Page 770, Pea plant, PhotoDisc; Page 771, Renting a movie, Stockdisc Premium/Getty Royalty Free; Page 774, Family with 9 girls, Corbis/Bettmann; Page 776, 24 kids on steps, PhotoDisc; Page 777, Slot machines, Allen R. Angel; Page 781, Golfers, PhotoDisc; Page 782, Slot machine, Allen R. Angel; Page 784, Basket of apples, PhotoDisc; Page 788, U.S. currency, Beth Anderson; Page 790, Katie Couric, *CBS Evening News*, CBS/Getty Images; Page 791, Display of televisions, Digital Vision; Page 792, Illustration of slot machine, © Tomo Narashima. Used with permission; Page 793, Man shopping for clothes, PhotoDisc Red; Page 794, The Three Stooges, Bettmann/Corbis; Page 794, Seven children, Corbis Royalty Free; Page 796, Ski club, Digital Vision; Page 797, Biking club, Corbis Royalty Free; Page 800, Nurses, Getty Royalty Free; Page 802, Monet's *Water Lily Pond*, Musee d'Orsay Paris/Lauros-Giradon, Paris/SuperStock; Page 803, Student meeting, Ingram Publishing/Getty Royalty Free; Page 805, Bridge hand, Beth Anderson; Page 805, Woman arranging flowers, PhotoDisc Red; Page 806, Hawaii, Getty RF; Page 807, Theatre district, New York City, Beth Anderson; Page 807, Jai alai game, Tom McCarthy/PhotoEdit; Page 808, Tray of hors d'oeuvres, PhotoDisc; Page 809, Woman with playing cards, PhotoDisc Red; Page 810, The Dead Man's Hand, Allen R. Angel; Page 811, Security guard, PhotoAlto/Getty Royalty Free; Page 812, Rare coin collection, PhotoDisc; Page 813, Yellow Lab puppies, Stockbyte/Getty RF; Page 813, Customers at bookstore, Getty Royalty Free; Page 814, Baseball game, Allen R. Angel; Page 816, Waiter and customer, Corbis Royalty Free; Page 820, Flashlights, Beth Anderson; Page 823, Dolphin, Allen R. Angel; Page 825, Person tasting cheese, Stockbyte Platinum/Getty Royalty Free; Page 826, Baseball game, Allen R. Angel; Page 828, Spelling bee, Photo Edit; Page 828, Sled dogs, Corbis Royalty Free; Page 829, Deep sea fishing, PhotoDisc Red; Page 830, Toll booth at Golden Gate bridge Beth Anderson; Page 832, Numbers presentation in a bar graph, Stockbyte/Getty Royalty Free; Page 833, Customer at pharmacy, PhotoDisc; Page 834, Neilsen survey family, Neilsen Media Research; Page 838, iPods on assembly line, PhotoEdit; Page 839, Chewing bubble gum, Westend61/Getty RF; Page 843, Man organizing data, Getty RF; Page 847, Seattle, Digital Vision; Page 848, Eating a hot dog, Digital Vision; Page 849, Mumbai, India, Digital Vision; Page 849, Student graph presentation, Image Source/Getty RF; Page 850, Circus clown, Image Source/Getty RF; Page 854, Bed and Breakfast, courtesy Janet and Rick Wolf; Page 857, Dancers at an audition, Digital Vision; Page 859, Jogging on treadmill, PhotoDisc Red; Page 859, Visiting a museum, Beth Anderson; Page 860, Putting gas in a car, Photographer's Choice RF/Getty RF; Page 862, San Jose, California, Getty; Page 862, Youngstown, Ohio, U.S. Department of Justice; Page 863, Lissy, 2 months old, Bruce Anderson; Page 868, Bookstore, Photographer's Choice RF/Getty RF; Page 868, Airport, Beth Anderson; Page 871, Water park, Allen R. Angel; Page 871, Babe Ruth, Bettmann/Corbis; Page 871, Mickey Mantle, Bettmann/Corbis; Page 872, Airplane engine, Stockbyte/Getty RF; Page 875, Sydney opera house, Corbis Royalty Free; Page 878, Fishermen with poles, Digital Vision; Page 881, Students taking exam, Digital Vision; Page 884, David. H Blackwell, Courtesy David Blackwell, University of California, Berkeley; Page 885, Motorola phones, Beth Anderson; Page 894, Woman with tire, Corbis Royalty Free; Page 896, Cup in vending machine, Allen R. Angel; Page 896, Box of Corn Flakes, Beth Anderson; Page 896, Children in daycare, Corbis Royalty Free; Page 897, Taking a test, PhotoDisc; Page 898, Buying a used car, PhotoDisc Red; Page 909, Fitness class, PhotoDisc; Page 909, Girl studying, PhotoDisc Red; Page 909, Gatorade bottle, Beth Anderson; Page 910, Hotel swimming pool, Allen R. Angel; Page 911, Woman measuring an arm, Stockbyte/PhotoDisc Blue; Page 914, Police car, Corbis Royalty Free.

I N D E X of Applications

INDEX

Note: Page numbers preceded by AA or AB indicate appendices.

Markov Chains

CHAPTER 9

INTRODUCTION

In this chapter we consider a mathematical model that combines probability and matrices to analyze a *stochastic process*, which consists of a sequence of trials that satisfy certain conditions. The sequence of trials is called a *Markov chain* after the Russian mathematician Andrei Markov (1856–1922), who is credited with supplying much of the foundation work in stochastic processes. Many of the early applications of Markov chains were in the physical sciences. More recent applications of Markov chains involve a wide variety of topics, including finance, market research, genetics, medicine, demographics, psychology, and political science.

In the first section we introduce the basic properties of Markov chains. In the remaining sections we discuss the long-term behavior of two different types of Markov chains.

Section 9-1   PROPERTIES OF MARKOV CHAINS

▓ Introduction
▓ Transition and State Matrices
▓ Powers of Transition Matrices
▓ Application

▓ Introduction

In this section we are going to be interested in physical *systems* and their possible *states*. To understand what this means, consider the following examples:

1. A stock listed on the New York Stock Exchange either increases, decreases, or does not change in price each day the exchange is open. The stock can be thought of as a physical system with three possible states: increase, decrease, or no change.

2. A commuter, relative to a rapid transit system, can be thought of as a physical system with two states, a user or a nonuser.

3. A voting precinct casts a simple majority vote during each congressional election for a Republican candidate, a Democratic candidate, or a third-party candidate. The precinct, relative to all congressional elections past, present, and future, constitutes a physical system that can be thought of as being in one (and only one) of three states after each election: Republican, Democratic, or other.

If a system evolves from one state to another in such a way that chance elements are involved in progressing from one state to the next, the progression of the system through a sequence of states is called a **stochastic process** (*stochos* is the Greek word for "guess"). We now consider a simple example of a stochastic process in detail, and out of it will arise further definitions and methodology.

A toothpaste company markets a product (brand A) that currently has 10% of the toothpaste market. The company hires a market research firm to estimate the percentage of the market it might acquire in the future if it launches an aggressive sales campaign. The research firm uses test marketing and extensive surveys to predict the effect of the campaign. They find that if a person is using brand A, the probability is .8 that this person will buy it again when he or she runs out of toothpaste. On the other hand, a person using another brand will switch to brand A with a probability of .6 when he or she runs out of toothpaste. Thus, each toothpaste consumer can be considered to be in one of two possible states:

$$A = \text{uses brand } A \qquad \text{and} \qquad A' = \text{uses another brand}$$

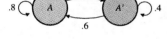

FIGURE 1 Transition diagram

The probabilities determined by the market research firm can be represented graphically in a **transition diagram** as shown in Figure 1.

We can also represent the information from the market research firm numerically in a **transition probability matrix:**

$$\begin{array}{cc} & \begin{array}{cc} \text{Next state} \\ A \quad A' \end{array} \\ \text{Current state} \begin{array}{c} A \\ A' \end{array} & \begin{bmatrix} .8 & .2 \\ .6 & .4 \end{bmatrix} = P \end{array}$$

Explore & Discuss 1

(A) Refer to the transition diagram in Figure 1. What is the probability that a person using brand A will switch to another brand when he or she runs out of toothpaste?

(B) Refer to transition probability matrix P. What is the probability that a person who is not using brand A will not switch to brand A when he or she runs out of toothpaste?

(C) In Figure 1, the sum of the probabilities on the arrows leaving each state is 1. Will this be true for any transition diagram? Explain your answer.

(D) In transition probability matrix P, the sum of the probabilities in each row is 1. Will this be true for any transition probability matrix? Explain your answer.

The toothpaste company's 10% share of the market at the beginning of the sales campaign can be represented as an **initial-state distribution matrix:**

$$\begin{matrix} & A & A' \\ S_0 = & [.1 & .9] \end{matrix}$$

If a person is chosen at random, the probability that this person uses brand A (state A) is .1, and the probability that this person does not use brand A (state A') is .9. Thus, S_0 also can be interpreted as an **initial-state probability matrix.**

What are the probabilities of a person being in state A or A' on the first purchase after the start of the sales campaign? Let us look at the probability tree given below.

Note: A_0 represents state A at the beginning of the campaign, A'_1 represents state A' on the first purchase after the campaign, and so on.

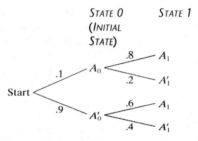

Proceeding as in Chapter 8, we can read the required probabilities directly from the tree:

$$P(A_1) = P(A_0 \cap A_1) + P(A'_0 \cap A_1)$$
$$= (.1)(.8) + (.9)(.6) = .62$$

$$P(A'_1) = P(A_0 \cap A'_1) + P(A'_0 \cap A'_1)$$
$$= (.1)(.2) + (.9)(.4) = .38$$

Note: $P(A_1) + P(A'_1) = 1$, as expected.

Thus, the **first-state matrix** is

$$\begin{matrix} & A & A' \\ S_1 = & [.62 & .38] \end{matrix}$$

This matrix gives us the probabilities of a randomly chosen person being in state A or A' on the first purchase after the start of the campaign. We see that brand A's market share has increased from 10% to 62%.

Now, if you were asked to find the probabilities of a person being in state A or state A' on the tenth purchase after the start of the campaign, you might start to draw additional branches on the probability tree, but you would soon become discouraged—and for good reason, because the number of branches doubles for each successive purchase. By the tenth purchase, there would be $2^{11} = 2,048$ branches! Fortunately, we can convert the summing of branch products to matrix multiplication. In particular, if we multiply the initial-state matrix S_0 by the transition matrix P, we obtain the first-state matrix S_1:

$$S_0 P = \begin{matrix} A & A' \\ [.1 & .9] \end{matrix} \begin{bmatrix} .8 & .2 \\ .6 & .4 \end{bmatrix} = [(.1)(.8) + (.9)(.6) \quad (.1)(.2) + (.9)(.4)] = \begin{matrix} A & A' \\ [.62 & .38] \end{matrix} = S_1$$

Initial
state Transition
matrix

Compare with the tree
computations above

First
state

As you might guess, we can get the second-state matrix S_2 (for the second purchase) by multiplying the first-state matrix by the transition matrix:

$$S_1 P = \begin{matrix} A & A' \\ [.62 & .38] \end{matrix} \begin{bmatrix} .8 & .2 \\ .6 & .4 \end{bmatrix} = \begin{matrix} A & A' \\ [.724 & .276] \end{matrix} = S_2$$

First   Second
state   state

The third-state matrix S_3 is computed in a similar manner:

$$S_2 P = \begin{matrix} A & A' \\ [.724 & .276] \end{matrix} \begin{bmatrix} .8 & .2 \\ .6 & .4 \end{bmatrix} = \begin{matrix} A & A' \\ [.7448 & .2552] \end{matrix} = S_3$$

Second   Third
state   state

Examining the values in the first three state matrices, we see that brand A's market share increases after each toothpaste purchase. Will the market share for brand A continue to increase until it approaches 100%, or will it level off at some value less than 100%? These questions are answered in the next section when we develop techniques for determining the long-run behavior of state matrices.

■ Transition and State Matrices

The sequence of trials (toothpaste purchases) with the constant transition matrix P described above is a special kind of stochastic process called a *Markov chain*. In general, a **Markov chain,** or **process,** is a sequence of experiments, trials, or observations such that the transition probability matrix from one state to the next is constant. A Markov process has no memory. The various matrices associated with a Markov chain are defined in the next box.

DEFINITION   **Markov Chains**

Given a Markov chain with n states, a **kth-state matrix** is a matrix of the form

$$S_k = [s_{k1} \quad s_{k2} \quad \cdots \quad s_{kn}]$$

Each entry s_{ki} is the proportion of the population that is in state i after the kth trial, or, equivalently, the probability of a randomly selected element of the population being in state i after the kth trial. The sum of all the entries in the kth state matrix S_k must be 1.

A **transition matrix** is a constant square matrix P of order n such that the entry in the ith row and jth column indicates the probability of the system moving from the ith state to the jth state on the next observation or trial. The sum of the entries in each row must be 1.

INSIGHT

1. Since the entries in a kth-state matrix or a transition matrix are probabilities, they must be real numbers between 0 and 1, inclusive.

2. Rearranging the various states and corresponding transition probabilities in a transition matrix will produce a different, but equivalent, transition matrix. For example, both of the following matrices are transition matrices for the toothpaste manufacturer discussed earlier:

$$P = \begin{matrix} & A & A' \\ A & \\ A' & \end{matrix} \begin{bmatrix} .8 & .2 \\ .6 & .4 \end{bmatrix} \qquad P' = \begin{matrix} & A' & A \\ A' & \\ A & \end{matrix} \begin{bmatrix} .4 & .6 \\ .2 & .8 \end{bmatrix}$$

Such rearrangements will affect the form of the matrices used in the solution of a problem but will not affect any of the information obtained from these matrices. In Section 9-3 we encounter situations where it will be helpful to select a transition matrix that has a special form. For now, you can choose any order for the states in a transition matrix.

As we indicated in the preceding discussion, matrix multiplication can be used to compute the various state matrices of a Markov chain:

If S_0 is the initial-state matrix and P is the transition matrix for a Markov chain, the subsequent state matrices are given by

$$S_1 = S_0 P \qquad \text{First-state matrix}$$
$$S_2 = S_1 P \qquad \text{Second-state matrix}$$
$$S_3 = S_2 P \qquad \text{Third-state matrix}$$
$$\vdots$$
$$S_k = S_{k-1} P \qquad \text{kth-state matrix}$$

EXAMPLE 1

Insurance An insurance company found that on the average, over a period of 10 years, 23% of the drivers in a particular community who were involved in an accident one year were also involved in an accident the following year. They also found that only 11% of the drivers who were not involved in an accident one year were involved in an accident the following year. Use these percentages as approximate empirical probabilities for the following:

(A) Draw a transition diagram.

(B) Find the transition matrix P.

(C) If 5% of the drivers in the community are involved in an accident this year, what is the probability that a driver chosen at random from the community will be involved in an accident next year? Year after next?

SOLUTION   (A)

```
        .77
  .23 ( A )  ──→  ( A' ) ) .89      A = accident
         ←──                        A' = no accident
        .11
```

Next year

(B)
```
              A     A'
This   A  [ .23   .77 ]  = P    Transition matrix
year   A' [ .11   .89 ]
```

(C) The initial-state matrix S_0 is

$$\begin{array}{cc} A & A' \end{array}$$
$$S_0 = [.05 \quad .95] \quad \text{Initial-state matrix}$$

Thus,

$$S_0 P = [.05 \quad .95] \begin{bmatrix} .23 & .77 \\ .11 & .89 \end{bmatrix} = [.116 \quad .884] = S_1$$

This year (initial state) \qquad Next year (first state)

$$S_1 P = [.116 \quad .884] \begin{bmatrix} .23 & .77 \\ .11 & .89 \end{bmatrix} = [.12392 \quad .87608] = S_2$$

Next year (first state) \qquad Year after next (second state)

The probability of a driver chosen at random from the community having an accident next year is .116 and having an accident year after next is .12392. That is, it is expected that 11.6% of the drivers in the community will have an accident next year and 12.392% the year after.

MATCHED PROBLEM 1

An insurance company classifies drivers as low-risk if they are accident-free for 1 year. Past records indicate that 98% of the drivers in the low-risk category (L) one year will remain in that category the next year, and 78% of the drivers who are not in the low-risk category (L') one year will be in the low-risk category the next year.

(A) Draw a transition diagram.

(B) Find the transition matrix P.

(C) If 90% of the drivers in the community are in the low-risk category this year, what is the probability that a driver chosen at random from the community will be in the low-risk category next year? Year after next?

Powers of Transition Matrices

Next we investigate the effective use of the powers of a transition matrix.

Explore & Discuss **2**

Given the transition matrix P and initial-state matrix S_0, where

$$P = \begin{array}{c} A \\ A' \end{array}\begin{bmatrix} .9 & .1 \\ .7 & .3 \end{bmatrix} \quad \text{and} \quad S_0 = \begin{array}{c} A \quad A' \end{array} [.5 \quad .5]$$

(A) Find S_2 and S_4.

(B) Find P^2 and P^4. (Recall that $P^2 = PP$ and $P^4 = P^2P^2$.)

(C) Find S_0P^2 and S_0P^4.

(D) Compare the results of parts (A) and (C). What interpretation of the entries in P^2 and P^4 does this suggest?

The state matrices for a Markov chain are defined **recursively;** that is, each state matrix is defined in terms of the preceding state matrix. For example, to find the fourth-state matrix S_4, it is necessary to compute the preceding three state matrices:

$$S_1 = S_0P \qquad S_2 = S_1P \qquad S_3 = S_2P \qquad S_4 = S_3P$$

Is there any way to compute a given state matrix directly without first computing all the preceding state matrices? If we substitute the equation for S_1 in the equation for S_2, substitute this new equation for S_2 in the equation for S_3, and so on, a definite pattern emerges:

$$S_1 = S_0P$$
$$S_2 = S_1P = (S_0P)P = S_0P^2$$
$$S_3 = S_2P = (S_0P^2)P = S_0P^3$$
$$S_4 = S_3P = (S_0P^3)P = S_0P^4$$
$$\vdots$$

In general, it can be shown that the kth-state matrix is given by $S_k = S_0P^k$. We summarize this important result in Theorem 1.

THEOREM 1   POWERS OF A TRANSITION MATRIX

If P is the transition matrix and S_0 is an initial-state matrix for a Markov chain, then the kth-state matrix is given by

$$S_k = S_0P^k$$

The entry in the ith row and jth column of P^k indicates the probability of the system moving from the ith state to the jth state in k observations or trials. The sum of the entries in each row of P^k is 1.

EXAMPLE 2

Using P^k to Compute S_k Find P^4 and use it to find S_4 for

$$P = \begin{array}{c} \\ A \\ A' \end{array} \begin{array}{cc} A & A' \\ \left[\begin{array}{cc} .1 & .9 \\ .6 & .4 \end{array} \right] \end{array} \quad \text{and} \quad S_0 = \begin{array}{cc} A & A' \\ [.2 & .8] \end{array}$$

SOLUTION

$$P^2 = PP = \left[\begin{array}{cc} .1 & .9 \\ .6 & .4 \end{array} \right]\left[\begin{array}{cc} .1 & .9 \\ .6 & .4 \end{array} \right] = \left[\begin{array}{cc} .55 & .45 \\ .3 & .7 \end{array} \right]$$

$$P^4 = P^2 P^2 = \left[\begin{array}{cc} .55 & .45 \\ .3 & .7 \end{array} \right]\left[\begin{array}{cc} .55 & .45 \\ .3 & .7 \end{array} \right] = \left[\begin{array}{cc} .4375 & .5625 \\ .375 & .625 \end{array} \right]$$

$$S_4 = S_0 P^4 = [.2 \quad .8]\left[\begin{array}{cc} .4375 & .5625 \\ .375 & .625 \end{array} \right] = [.3875 \quad .6125]$$

MATCHED PROBLEM 2

Find P^4 and use it to find S_4 for

$$P = \begin{array}{c} \\ A \\ A' \end{array} \begin{array}{cc} A & A' \\ \left[\begin{array}{cc} .8 & .2 \\ .3 & .7 \end{array} \right] \end{array} \quad \text{and} \quad S_0 = \begin{array}{cc} A & A' \\ [.8 & .2] \end{array}$$

If a graphing calculator or a computer is available for computing matrix products and powers of a matrix, finding state matrices for any number of trials becomes a routine calculation.

EXAMPLE 3

Using a Graphing Calculator and P^k to Compute S_k Use P^8 and a graphing calculator to find S_8 for P and S_0 as given in Example 2. Round values in S_8 to six decimal places.

SOLUTION

After storing the matrices P and S_0 in the graphing calculator's memory, use the equation

$$S_8 = S_0 P^8$$

to compute S_8. Figure 2 shows the result on a typical graphing calculator. Thus, we see that (to six decimal places)

$$S_8 = [.399219 \quad .600781]$$

```
P
        [[.1 .9]
         [.6 .4]]
S0
        [[.2 .8]]
S0*P^8
   [[.399219 .600781]]
```

FIGURE 2

MATCHED PROBLEM 3

Use P^8 and a graphing calculator to find S_8 for P and S_0 as given in Matched Problem 2. Round values in S_8 to six decimal places.

APPLICATION

The next example illustrates the use of Theorem 1 in an applied problem.

EXAMPLE 4

University Enrollment Part-time students admitted to an MBA program in a university are considered to be first-year students until they complete 15 credits successfully. Then they are classified as second-year students and may begin to take more advanced courses and to work on the thesis required for graduation. Past records indicate that at the end of each year 10% of the first-year students (F) drop out of the program (D) and 30% become second-year students (S). Also, 10% of the second-year students drop out of the program and 40% graduate (G) each year. Students that graduate or drop out never return to the program.

(A) Draw a transition diagram.

(B) Find the transition matrix P.

(C) What is the probability that a first-year student graduates within 4 years? Drops out within 4 years?

SOLUTION (A) If 10% of the first-year students drop out and 30% become second-year students, the remaining 60% must continue as first-year students for another year (see the diagram). Similarly, 50% of the second-year students must continue as second-year students for another year. Since students who drop out never return, all the students in state D in one year will continue in that state the next year. We indicate this by placing a 1 on the arrow from D back to D. State G is labeled in the same manner.

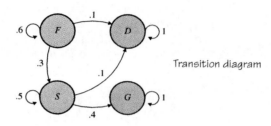

Transition diagram

(B) $P = \begin{array}{c} \\ F \\ D \\ S \\ G \end{array} \begin{array}{cccc} F & D & S & G \\ \begin{bmatrix} .6 & .1 & .3 & 0 \\ 0 & 1 & 0 & 0 \\ 0 & .1 & .5 & .4 \\ 0 & 0 & 0 & 1 \end{bmatrix} \end{array}$ Transition matrix

(C) The probability that a first-year student moves from state F to state G within 4 years is the entry in row 1 and column 4 of P^4 (Theorem 1). Hand computation of P^4 requires two multiplications:

$$P^2 = \begin{bmatrix} .6 & .1 & .3 & 0 \\ 0 & 1 & 0 & 0 \\ 0 & .1 & .5 & .4 \\ 0 & 0 & 0 & 1 \end{bmatrix} \begin{bmatrix} .6 & .1 & .3 & 0 \\ 0 & 1 & 0 & 0 \\ 0 & .1 & .5 & .4 \\ 0 & 0 & 0 & 1 \end{bmatrix} = \begin{bmatrix} .36 & .19 & .33 & .12 \\ 0 & 1 & 0 & 0 \\ 0 & .15 & .25 & .6 \\ 0 & 0 & 0 & 1 \end{bmatrix}$$

$$P^4 = P^2 P^2 = \begin{bmatrix} .36 & .19 & .33 & .12 \\ 0 & 1 & 0 & 0 \\ 0 & .15 & .25 & .6 \\ 0 & 0 & 0 & 1 \end{bmatrix} \begin{bmatrix} .36 & .19 & .33 & .12 \\ 0 & 1 & 0 & 0 \\ 0 & .15 & .25 & .6 \\ 0 & 0 & 0 & 1 \end{bmatrix}$$

$$= \begin{bmatrix} .1296 & .3079 & .2013 & .3612 \\ 0 & 1 & 0 & 0 \\ 0 & .1875 & .0625 & .75 \\ 0 & 0 & 0 & 1 \end{bmatrix}$$

Thus, the probability that a first-year student has graduated within 4 years is .3612. Similarly, the probability that a first-year student has dropped out within 4 years is .3079 (the entry in row 1 and column 2 of P^4). ■

MATCHED PROBLEM 4 Refer to Example 4. At the end of each year the faculty examines the progress each second-year student has made in writing the required thesis. Past records indicate that 30% of the second-year students (S) have their theses approved (A) and 10% of the students are dropped from the program for insufficient progress (D), never to return. The remaining students continue to work on their theses.

(A) Draw a transition diagram.

(B) Find the transition matrix P.

(C) What is the probability that a second-year student completes the thesis requirement within 4 years? Is dropped from the program for insufficient progress within 4 years?

Explore & Discuss 3

Refer to Example 4. States D and G are referred to as *absorbing states,* because a student who enters either one of these states never leaves it. Absorbing states are discussed in detail in Section 9-3.

(A) How can absorbing states be recognized from a transition diagram? Draw a transition diagram with two states, one that is absorbing and one that is not, to illustrate.

(B) How can absorbing states be recognized from a transition matrix? Write the transition matrix for the diagram you drew in part (A) to illustrate.

Answers to Matched Problems

1. (A)

L = Low-risk
L' = Not Low-risk

(B)

Next year

$$\begin{array}{cc} & L \quad L' \\ \text{This } L \\ \text{year } L' \end{array} \begin{bmatrix} .98 & .02 \\ .78 & .22 \end{bmatrix} = P$$

(C) Next year: .96; year after next: .972

2. $P^4 = \begin{bmatrix} .625 & .375 \\ .5625 & .4375 \end{bmatrix}$; $S_4 = [.6125 \quad .3875]$

3. $S_8 = [.600781 \quad .399219]$

4. (A)

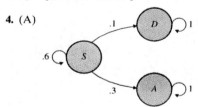

(B) $P = \begin{array}{c} S \\ A \\ D \end{array} \begin{bmatrix} .6 & .3 & .1 \\ 0 & 1 & 0 \\ 0 & 0 & 1 \end{bmatrix}$ with columns $S \; A \; D$

(C) .6528; .2176

Exercise 9-1

A Problems 1–8 refer to the following transition matrix:

$$P = \begin{array}{c} A \\ B \end{array} \begin{bmatrix} .8 & .2 \\ .4 & .6 \end{bmatrix}$$

with columns $A \; B$

In Problems 1–4, find S_1 for the indicated initial-state matrix S_0, and interpret with the aid of a tree diagram.

1. $S_0 = [1 \quad 0]$ **2.** $S_0 = [0 \quad 1]$

3. $S_0 = [.5 \quad .5]$ **4.** $S_0 = [.3 \quad .7]$

In Problems 5–8, find S_2 for the indicated initial-state matrix S_0, and explain what it represents.

5. $S_0 = [1 \quad 0]$ **6.** $S_0 = [0 \quad 1]$

7. $S_0 = [.5 \quad .5]$ **8.** $S_0 = [.3 \quad .7]$

In Problems 9–16, could the given matrix be the transition matrix of a Markov chain?

9. $\begin{bmatrix} .3 & .7 \\ 1 & 0 \end{bmatrix}$ **10.** $\begin{bmatrix} .9 & .1 \\ .4 & .8 \end{bmatrix}$

11. $\begin{bmatrix} .5 & .5 \\ .7 & -.3 \end{bmatrix}$

12. $\begin{bmatrix} 0 & 1 \\ 1 & 0 \end{bmatrix}$

13. $\begin{bmatrix} .1 & .3 & .6 \\ .2 & .4 & .4 \end{bmatrix}$

14. $\begin{bmatrix} .2 & .8 \\ .5 & .5 \\ .9 & .1 \end{bmatrix}$

15. $\begin{bmatrix} .5 & .1 & .4 \\ 0 & .5 & .5 \\ .2 & .1 & .7 \end{bmatrix}$

16. $\begin{bmatrix} .3 & .3 & .4 \\ .7 & .2 & .2 \\ .1 & .8 & .1 \end{bmatrix}$

In Problems 17–22, is there a unique way of filling in the missing probabilities in the transition diagram? If so, complete the transition diagram and write the corresponding transition matrix. If not, explain why.

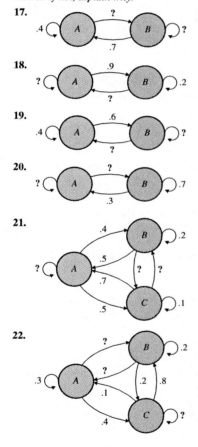

17.

18.

19.

20.

21.

22.

In Problems 23–28, are there unique values of a, b, and c that will make P a transition matrix? If so, complete the transition matrix and draw the corresponding transition diagram. If not, explain why.

$$\text{23. } P = \begin{array}{c} \\ A \\ B \\ C \end{array} \begin{array}{c} ABC \\ \begin{bmatrix} 0 & .5 & a \\ b & 0 & .4 \\ .2 & c & .1 \end{bmatrix} \end{array}$$

$$\text{24. } P = \begin{array}{c} \\ A \\ B \\ C \end{array} \begin{array}{c} ABC \\ \begin{bmatrix} a & 0 & .9 \\ .2 & .3 & b \\ .6 & c & 0 \end{bmatrix} \end{array}$$

$$\text{25. } P = \begin{array}{c} \\ A \\ B \\ C \end{array} \begin{array}{c} ABC \\ \begin{bmatrix} 0 & a & .3 \\ 0 & b & 0 \\ c & .8 & 0 \end{bmatrix} \end{array}$$

$$\text{26. } P = \begin{array}{c} \\ A \\ B \\ C \end{array} \begin{array}{c} ABC \\ \begin{bmatrix} 0 & 1 & a \\ 0 & 0 & b \\ c & .5 & 0 \end{bmatrix} \end{array}$$

$$\text{27. } P = \begin{array}{c} \\ A \\ B \\ C \end{array} \begin{array}{c} ABC \\ \begin{bmatrix} .2 & .1 & .7 \\ a & .4 & c \\ .5 & b & .4 \end{bmatrix} \end{array}$$

$$\text{28. } P = \begin{array}{c} \\ A \\ B \\ C \end{array} \begin{array}{c} ABC \\ \begin{bmatrix} a & .8 & .1 \\ .3 & b & .4 \\ .6 & .5 & c \end{bmatrix} \end{array}$$

B *In Problems 29–32, use the given information to draw the transition diagram and to find the transition matrix.*

29. A Markov process has two states, A and B. The probability of going from state A to state B in one trial is .7, and the probability of going from state B to state A in one trial is .9.

30. A Markov process has two states, A and B. The probability of going from state A to state A in one trial is .6, and the probability of going from state B to state B in one trial is .2.

31. A Markov chain has three states, A, B, and C. The probability of going from state A to state B in one trial is .1, the probability of going from state A to state C in one trial is .3, the probability of going from state B to state A in one trial is .2, the probability of going from state B to state C in one trial is .5, and the probability of going from state C to state C in one trial is 1.

32. A Markov chain has three states, A, B, and C. The probability of going from state A to state B in one trial is 1, the probability of going from state B to state A in one trial is .5, the probability of going from state B to state C in one trial is .5, and the probability of going from state C to state A in one trial is 1.

Problems 33–42 refer to the transition matrix P and the powers of P given below:

$$P = \begin{array}{c} \\ A \\ B \\ C \end{array} \begin{array}{c} ABC \\ \begin{bmatrix} .6 & .3 & .1 \\ .2 & .5 & .3 \\ .1 & .2 & .7 \end{bmatrix} \end{array} \qquad P^2 = \begin{array}{c} \\ A \\ B \\ C \end{array} \begin{array}{c} ABC \\ \begin{bmatrix} .43 & .35 & .22 \\ .25 & .37 & .38 \\ .17 & .27 & .56 \end{bmatrix} \end{array}$$

$$P^3 = \begin{array}{c} \\ A \\ B \\ C \end{array} \begin{array}{c} ABC \\ \begin{bmatrix} .35 & .348 & .302 \\ .262 & .336 & .402 \\ .212 & .298 & .49 \end{bmatrix} \end{array}$$

33. Find the probability of going from state A to state B in two trials.

34. Find the probability of going from state B to state C in two trials.

35. Find the probability of going from state C to state A in three trials.

36. Find the probability of going from state B to state B in three trials.

37. Find S_2 for $S_0 = \begin{bmatrix} 1 & 0 & 0 \end{bmatrix}$, and explain what it represents.

38. Find S_2 for $S_0 = \begin{bmatrix} 0 & 1 & 0 \end{bmatrix}$, and explain what it represents.

39. Find S_3 for $S_0 = \begin{bmatrix} 0 & 0 & 1 \end{bmatrix}$, and explain what it represents.

40. Find S_3 for $S_0 = \begin{bmatrix} 1 & 0 & 0 \end{bmatrix}$, and explain what it represents.

41. Using a graphing calculator to compute powers of P, find the smallest positive integer n such that the corresponding entries in P^n and P^{n+1} are equal to two decimal places.

42. Using a graphing calculator to compute powers of P, find the smallest positive integer n such that the corresponding entries in P^n and P^{n+1} are equal to three decimal places.

In Problems 43–46, given the transition matrix P and initial-state matrix S_0, find P^4 and use P^4 to find S_4.

43. $P = \begin{matrix} A \\ B \end{matrix} \begin{bmatrix} .1 & .9 \\ .6 & .4 \end{bmatrix}$ (with column headers A B); $S_0 = \begin{bmatrix} .8 & .2 \end{bmatrix}$

44. $P = \begin{matrix} A \\ B \end{matrix} \begin{bmatrix} .8 & .2 \\ .3 & .7 \end{bmatrix}$ (with column headers A B); $S_0 = \begin{bmatrix} .4 & .6 \end{bmatrix}$

45. $P = \begin{matrix} A \\ B \\ C \end{matrix} \begin{bmatrix} 0 & .4 & .6 \\ 0 & 0 & 1 \\ 1 & 0 & 0 \end{bmatrix}$ (with column headers A B C); $S_0 = \begin{bmatrix} .2 & .3 & .5 \end{bmatrix}$

46. $P = \begin{matrix} A \\ B \\ C \end{matrix} \begin{bmatrix} 0 & 1 & 0 \\ .8 & 0 & .2 \\ 1 & 0 & 0 \end{bmatrix}$ (with column headers A B C); $S_0 = \begin{bmatrix} .4 & .2 & .4 \end{bmatrix}$

47. A Markov process with two states has transition matrix P. If the initial-state matrix is $S_0 = \begin{bmatrix} 1 & 0 \end{bmatrix}$, discuss the relationship between the entries in the kth-state matrix and the entries in the kth power of P.

48. Repeat Problem 47 if the initial-state matrix is $S_0 = \begin{bmatrix} 0 & 1 \end{bmatrix}$.

49. Given the transition matrix

$$P = \begin{matrix} A \\ B \\ C \\ D \end{matrix} \begin{bmatrix} .2 & .2 & .3 & .3 \\ 0 & 1 & 0 & 0 \\ .2 & .2 & .1 & .5 \\ 0 & 0 & 0 & 1 \end{bmatrix}$$
(with column headers A B C D)

(A) Find P^4.

(B) Find the probability of going from state A to state D in four trials.

(C) Find the probability of going from state C to state B in four trials.

(D) Find the probability of going from state B to state A in four trials.

50. Repeat Problem 49 for the transition matrix

$$P = \begin{matrix} A \\ B \\ C \\ D \end{matrix} \begin{bmatrix} .5 & .3 & .1 & .1 \\ 0 & 1 & 0 & 0 \\ 0 & 0 & 1 & 0 \\ .1 & .2 & .3 & .4 \end{bmatrix}$$
(with column headers A B C D)

*A matrix is called a **probability matrix** if all its entries are real numbers between 0 and 1, inclusive, and the sum of the entries in each row is 1. Thus, transition matrices are square probability matrices and state matrices are probability matrices with one row.*

51. If

$$P = \begin{bmatrix} a & 1-a \\ 1-b & b \end{bmatrix}$$

is a probability matrix, show that P^2 is a probability matrix.

52. If

$$P = \begin{bmatrix} a & 1-a \\ 1-b & b \end{bmatrix} \quad \text{and} \quad S = \begin{bmatrix} c & 1-c \end{bmatrix}$$

are probability matrices, show that SP is a probability matrix.

Use a graphing calculator and the formula $S_k = S_0 P^k$ (Theorem 1) to compute the required state matrices in Problems 53–56.

53. The transition matrix for a Markov chain is

$$P = \begin{bmatrix} .4 & .6 \\ .2 & .8 \end{bmatrix}$$

(A) If $S_0 = \begin{bmatrix} 0 & 1 \end{bmatrix}$, find $S_2, S_4, S_8, \ldots$. Can you identify a state matrix S that the matrices S_k seem to be approaching?

(B) Repeat part (A) for $S_0 = \begin{bmatrix} 1 & 0 \end{bmatrix}$.

(C) Repeat part (A) for $S_0 = \begin{bmatrix} .5 & .5 \end{bmatrix}$.

(D) Find SP for any matrix S you identified in parts (A)–(C).

(E) Write a brief verbal description of the long-term behavior of the state matrices of this Markov chain based on your observations in parts (A)–(D).

54. Repeat Problem 53 for $P = \begin{bmatrix} .9 & .1 \\ .4 & .6 \end{bmatrix}$.

55. Refer to Problem 53. Find P^k for $k = 2, 4, 8, \ldots$. Can you identify a matrix Q that the matrices P^k are approaching? If so, how is Q related to the results you discovered in Problem 53?

56. Refer to Problem 54. Find P^k for $k = 2, 4, 8, \ldots$. Can you identify a matrix Q that the matrices P^k are approaching? If so, how is Q related to the results you discovered in Problem 54?

57. *Scheduling.* An outdoor restaurant in a summer resort closes only on days that it rains. From past records it is found that from May through September, when it rains one day, the probability of rain for the next day is .4; when it does not rain one day, the probability of rain the next day is .06.

(A) Draw a transition diagram.

(B) Write the transition matrix.

(C) If it rains on Thursday, what is the probability that the restaurant will be closed on Saturday? On Sunday?

58. *Scheduling.* Repeat Problem 57 if the probability of rain following a rainy day is .6 and the probability of rain following a nonrainy day is .1.

59. *Advertising.* A vigorous television advertising campaign is conducted during the football season to promote a well-known brand X shaving cream. For each of several weeks, a survey is made, and it is found that each week 80% of those using brand X continue to use it and 20% switch to another brand. It is also found that of those not using brand X, 20% switch to brand X while the other 80% continue using another brand.

(A) Draw a transition diagram.

(B) Write the transition matrix.

(C) If 20% of the people are using brand X at the start of the advertising campaign, what percentage will be using it 1 week later? 2 weeks later?

60. *Car rental.* A car rental agency has rental and return facilities at both Kennedy and LaGuardia airports, two of the principal airports in the New York City area. Assume that a car rented at either airport must be returned to one or the other airport. If a car is rented at LaGuardia, the probability that it will be returned there is .8; if a car is rented at Kennedy, the probability that it will be returned there is .7. Assume that the company rents all its 100 cars each day and that each car is rented (and returned) only once a day. If we start with 50 cars at each airport:

(A) What is the expected distribution the next day?

(B) What is the expected distribution 2 days later?

61. *Homeowner's insurance.* The market for homeowner's insurance in a particular city is dominated by two companies, National Property and United Family. Currently, National Property insures 50% of the homes in the city, United Family insures 30%, and the remainder are insured by a collection of smaller companies. United Family decides to offer rebates to increase its market share. This has the following effects on insurance purchases for the next several years: each year 25% of National Property's customers switch to United Family and 10% switch to other companies; 10% of United Family's customers switch to National Property and 5% switch to other companies; and 15% of the customers of other companies switch to National Property and 35% switch to United Family.

(A) Draw a transition diagram.

(B) Write the transition matrix.

(C) What percentage of the homes will be insured by National Property next year? The year after next?

(D) What percentage of the homes will be insured by United Family next year? The year after next?

62. *Service contracts.* A small community has two heating services that offer annual service contracts for home heating systems, Alpine Heating and Badger Furnaces. Currently, 25% of the homeowners have service contracts with Alpine, 30% have service contracts with Badger, and the remainder do not have service contracts. Both companies launch aggressive advertising campaigns to attract new customers, with the following effects on service contract purchases for the next several years: each year 35% of the homeowners with no current service contract decide to purchase a contract from Alpine and 40% decide to purchase one from Badger. In addition, 10% of the previous customers at each company decide to switch to the other company, and 5% decide they do not want a service contract.

(A) Draw a transition diagram.

(B) Write the transition matrix.

(C) What percentage of the homes will have service contracts with Alpine next year? The year after next?

(D) What percentage of the homes will have service contracts with Badger next year? The year after next?

63. *Employee training.* A nationwide chain of travel agencies maintains a training program for new travel agents. Initially, all new employees are classified as beginning agents requiring extensive supervision. Every 6 months the performance of each agent is reviewed. Past records indicate that after each semiannual review, 40% of the beginning agents are promoted to intermediate agents requiring only minimal supervision, 10% are terminated for unsatisfactory performance, and the remainder continue as beginning agents. Furthermore, 30% of the intermediate agents are promoted to qualified travel agents requiring no supervision, 10% are terminated for unsatisfactory performance, and the remainder continue as intermediate agents.

(A) Draw a transition diagram.

(B) Write the transition matrix.

(C) What is the probability that a beginning agent is promoted to qualified agent within 1 year? Within 2 years?

64. *Employee training.* All welders in a factory begin as apprentices. Every year the performance of each apprentice is reviewed. Past records indicate that after each review, 10% of the apprentices are promoted to professional welder, 20% are terminated for unsatisfactory performance, and the remainder continue as apprentices.

(A) Draw a transition diagram.

(B) Write the transition matrix.

(C) What is the probability that an apprentice is promoted to professional welder within 2 years? Within 4 years?

65. *Health insurance.* A midwestern university offers its employees three choices for health care: a clinic-based health maintenance organization (HMO), a preferred provider organization (PPO), and a traditional fee-for-service program (FFS). Each year the university designates an open enrollment period during which employees may change from one health plan to another. Prior to the last open enrollment period, 20% of the employees were enrolled in the HMO, 25% in the PPO, and the remainder in the FFS. During the open enrollment period, 15% of the employees in the HMO switched to the PPO and 5% switched to the FFS; 20% of the employees in the PPO switched to the HMO and 10% to the FFS; and 25% of the employees in the FFS switched to the HMO and 30% switched to the PPO.

(A) Write the transition matrix.

(B) What percentage of employees were enrolled in each plan after the last open enrollment period?

(C) If this trend continues, what percentage of employees will be enrolled in each program after the next open enrollment period?

66. *Dental insurance.* Refer to Problem 65. During the open enrollment period, employees at the university can switch between the two available dental care programs, the low-option plan (LOP) and the high-option plan (HOP). Prior to the last open enrollment period, 40% of the employees were enrolled in the LOP and 60% in the HOP. During the open enrollment program, 30% of the employees in the LOP switched to the HOP and 10% of the employees in the HOP switched to the LOP.

(A) Write the transition matrix.

(B) What percentage of employees were enrolled in each plan after the last open enrollment period?

(C) If this trend continues, what percentage of employees will be enrolled in each program after the next open enrollment period?

67. *Housing trends.* The 1990 census reported that 36.4% of the households in the District of Columbia were homeowners and the remainder were renters. During the next decade, 7.6% of the homeowners became renters and the rest continued to be homeowners. Similarly, 10.8% of the renters became homeowners and the rest continued to rent.

(A) Write the appropriate transition matrix.

(B) According to this transition matrix, what percentage of households were homeowners in 2000?

(C) If the transition matrix remains the same, what percentage of the households will be homeowners in 2010?

68. *Housing trends.* The 1990 census reported that 58.4% of the households in Alaska were homeowners and the remainder were renters. During the next decade, 2.1% of the homeowners became renters and the rest continued to be homeowners. Similarly, 23.4% of the renters became homeowners and the rest continued to rent.

(A) Write the appropriate transition matrix.

(B) According to this transition matrix, what percentage of households were homeowners in 2000?

(C) If the transition matrix remains the same, what percentage of the households will be homeowners in 2010?

Section 9-2 REGULAR MARKOV CHAINS

- Stationary Matrices
- Regular Markov Chains
- Applications
- Graphing Calculator Approximations

Given a Markov chain with transition matrix P and initial-state matrix S_0, the entries in the state matrix S_k are the probabilities of being in the corresponding states after k trials. What happens to these probabilities as the number of trials k increases? In this section we establish conditions on the transition matrix P that enable us to determine the long-run behavior of both the state matrices S_k and the powers of the transition matrix P^k.

■ Stationary Matrices

We begin by considering a concrete example—the toothpaste company discussed in the preceding section. Recall that the transition matrix was given by

$$P = \begin{matrix} A \\ A' \end{matrix} \begin{bmatrix} .8 & .2 \\ .6 & .4 \end{bmatrix} \quad \begin{matrix} A = \textit{uses brand A toothpaste} \\ A' = \textit{uses another brand} \end{matrix}$$

Initially, this company had a 10% share of the toothpaste market. If the probabilities in the transition matrix P remain valid over a long period of time, what will happen to the company's market share? Examining the first several state matrices will give us some insight into this situation (matrix multiplication details are omitted):

$$S_0 = [.1 \quad .9]$$
$$S_1 = S_0P = [.62 \quad .38]$$
$$S_2 = S_1P = [.724 \quad .276]$$
$$S_3 = S_2P = [.7448 \quad .2552]$$
$$S_4 = S_3P = [.74896 \quad .25104]$$
$$S_5 = S_4P = [.749792 \quad .250208]$$
$$S_6 = S_5P = [.7499584 \quad .2500416]$$

It appears that the state matrices are getting closer and closer to $S = [.75 \quad .25]$ as we proceed to higher states. Let us multiply the matrix S (the matrix the other state matrices appear to be approaching) by the transition matrix:

$$SP = [.75 \quad .25]\begin{bmatrix} .8 & .2 \\ .6 & .4 \end{bmatrix} = [.75 \quad .25] = S$$

No change occurs! The matrix $[.75 \quad .25]$ is called a **stationary matrix.** If we reach this state or are very close to it, the system is said to be at steady state; that is, later states either will not change or will not change very much. In terms of this example, this means that in the long run a person will purchase brand A with a probability of .75; that is, the company can expect to capture 75% of the market, assuming that the transition matrix does not change.

The general definition of a stationary matrix is given in the next box.

DEFINITION | **Stationary Matrix for a Markov Chain**

The state matrix $S = [s_1 \quad s_2 \quad \cdots \quad s_n]$ is a **stationary matrix** for a Markov chain with transition matrix P if

$$SP = S$$

where $s_i \geq 0, i = 1, \ldots, n$, and $s_1 + s_2 + \cdots + s_n = 1$.

Explore & Discuss **1**

(A) Suppose that the toothpaste company started with only 5% of the market instead of 10%. Write the initial-state matrix, find the next six state matrices, and discuss the behavior of these state matrices as you proceed to higher states.

(B) Repeat part (A) if the company started with 90% of the toothpaste market.

▓ Regular Markov Chains

Does every Markov chain have a unique stationary matrix? And if a Markov chain has a unique stationary matrix, will the successive state matrices always approach this stationary matrix? Unfortunately, the answer to both these questions is no (see Problems 31–34, Exercise 9-2). However, there is one important type of Markov chain for which both questions always can be answered in the affirmative. These are called *regular Markov chains*.

DEFINITION | **Regular Markov Chains**

A transition matrix P is **regular** if some power of P has only positive entries. A Markov chain is a **regular Markov chain** if its transition matrix is regular.

EXAMPLE 1 **Recognizing Regular Matrices** Which of the following matrices are regular?

(A) $P = \begin{bmatrix} .8 & .2 \\ .6 & .4 \end{bmatrix}$ (B) $P = \begin{bmatrix} 0 & 1 \\ 1 & 0 \end{bmatrix}$ (C) $P = \begin{bmatrix} .5 & .5 & 0 \\ 0 & .5 & .5 \\ 1 & 0 & 0 \end{bmatrix}$

SOLUTION (A) This is the transition matrix for the toothpaste company. Since all the entries in P are positive, we can immediately conclude that P is regular.

(B) P has two 0 entries, so we must examine higher powers of P:

$$P^2 = \begin{bmatrix} 1 & 0 \\ 0 & 1 \end{bmatrix} \quad P^3 = \begin{bmatrix} 0 & 1 \\ 1 & 0 \end{bmatrix} \quad P^4 = \begin{bmatrix} 1 & 0 \\ 0 & 1 \end{bmatrix} \quad P^5 = \begin{bmatrix} 0 & 1 \\ 1 & 0 \end{bmatrix}$$

Since the powers of P oscillate between P and I, the 2×2 identity, all powers of P will contain 0 entries. Hence, P is not regular.

(C) Again, we examine higher powers of P:

$$P^2 = \begin{bmatrix} .25 & .5 & .25 \\ .5 & .25 & .25 \\ .5 & .5 & 0 \end{bmatrix} \quad P^3 = \begin{bmatrix} .375 & .375 & .25 \\ .5 & .375 & .125 \\ .25 & .5 & .25 \end{bmatrix}$$

Since all the entries in P^3 are positive, P is regular.

MATCHED PROBLEM 1 Which of the following matrices are regular?

(A) $P = \begin{bmatrix} .3 & .7 \\ 1 & 0 \end{bmatrix}$ (B) $P = \begin{bmatrix} 1 & 0 \\ 1 & 0 \end{bmatrix}$

(C) $P = \begin{bmatrix} 0 & 1 & 0 \\ .5 & 0 & .5 \\ .5 & 0 & .5 \end{bmatrix}$

Explore & Discuss **2** Consider the toothpaste company (discussed at the beginning of this section) with regular transition matrix P and stationary matrix S, where

$$P = \begin{bmatrix} .8 & .2 \\ .6 & .4 \end{bmatrix} \quad \text{and} \quad S = [.75 \quad .25]$$

Compare P^2, P^4, and P^8. Discuss any apparent relationships between P^k and S.

The relationships among successive state matrices, powers of the transition matrix, and the stationary matrix for a regular Markov chain are given in Theorem 1. The proof of this theorem is left to more advanced courses.

THEOREM 1 **PROPERTIES OF REGULAR MARKOV CHAINS**

Let P be the transition matrix for a regular Markov chain.

(A) There is a unique stationary matrix S that can be found by solving the equation

$$SP = S$$

(B) Given any initial-state matrix S_0, the state matrices S_k approach the stationary matrix S.

(C) The matrices P^k approach a **limiting matrix** $\overline{P}$, where each row of $\overline{P}$ is equal to the stationary matrix S.

EXAMPLE 2   **Finding the Stationary Matrix** The transition matrix for a Markov chain is

$$P = \begin{bmatrix} .7 & .3 \\ .2 & .8 \end{bmatrix}$$

(A) Find the stationary matrix S.

(B) Discuss the long-run behavior of S_k and P^k.

SOLUTION   (A) Since P is regular, the stationary matrix S must exist. To find it, we must solve the equation $SP = S$. Let

$$S = [s_1 \quad s_2]$$

and write

$$[s_1 \quad s_2]\begin{bmatrix} .7 & .3 \\ .2 & .8 \end{bmatrix} = [s_1 \quad s_2]$$

After multiplying the left side, we obtain

$$[(.7s_1 + .2s_2) \quad (.3s_1 + .8s_2)] = [s_1 \quad s_2]$$

which is equivalent to the system

$$
\begin{array}{llll}
.7s_1 + .2s_2 = s_1 & \text{or} & -.3s_1 + .2s_2 = 0 & \\
.3s_1 + .8s_2 = s_2 & \text{or} & .3s_1 - .2s_2 = 0 & (1)
\end{array}
$$

System (1) is dependent and has an infinite number of solutions. However, we are looking for a solution that is also a state matrix. This gives us another equation that we can add to system (1) to obtain a system with a unique solution.

$$
\begin{aligned}
-.3s_1 + .2s_2 &= 0 \\
.3s_1 - .2s_2 &= 0 \\
s_1 + \quad s_2 &= 1
\end{aligned}
\qquad (2)
$$

System (2) can be solved using matrix methods or elimination to obtain

$$s_1 = .4 \quad \text{and} \quad s_2 = .6$$

Thus,

$$S = [.4 \quad .6]$$

is the stationary matrix.
Check:

$$SP = [.4 \quad .6]\begin{bmatrix} .7 & .3 \\ .2 & .8 \end{bmatrix} = [.4 \quad .6] = S$$

(B) Given any initial-state matrix S_0, Theorem 1 guarantees that the state matrices S_k will approach the stationary matrix S. Furthermore,

$$P^k = \begin{bmatrix} .7 & .3 \\ .2 & .8 \end{bmatrix}^k \qquad \text{approaches the limiting matrix} \qquad \overline{P} = \begin{bmatrix} .4 & .6 \\ .4 & .6 \end{bmatrix} \quad \blacksquare$$

MATCHED PROBLEM 2   The transition matrix for a Markov chain is

$$P = \begin{bmatrix} .6 & .4 \\ .1 & .9 \end{bmatrix}$$

Find the stationary matrix S and the limiting matrix $\overline{P}$.

APPLICATIONS

EXAMPLE 3 **Insurance** Refer to Example 1 in Section 9-1, where we found the following transition matrix for an insurance company:

$$P = \begin{matrix} & \begin{matrix} A & A' \end{matrix} \\ \begin{matrix} A \\ A' \end{matrix} & \begin{bmatrix} .23 & .77 \\ .11 & .89 \end{bmatrix} \end{matrix} \quad \begin{matrix} A = \text{accident} \\ A' = \text{no accident} \end{matrix}$$

If these probabilities remain valid over a long period of time, what percentage of drivers can the company expect to have an accident during any given year?

SOLUTION To determine what happens in the long run, we find the stationary matrix by solving the following system:

$$[s_1 \quad s_2]\begin{bmatrix} .23 & .77 \\ .11 & .89 \end{bmatrix} = [s_1 \quad s_2] \qquad \text{and} \qquad s_1 + s_2 = 1$$

which is equivalent to

$$\begin{aligned} .23s_1 + .11s_2 &= s_1 \\ .77s_1 + .89s_2 &= s_2 \\ s_1 + \quad s_2 &= 1 \end{aligned} \qquad \text{or} \qquad \begin{aligned} -.77s_1 + .11s_2 &= 0 \\ .77s_1 - .11s_2 &= 0 \\ s_1 + \quad s_2 &= 1 \end{aligned}$$

Solving this system, we obtain

$$s_1 = .125 \qquad \text{and} \qquad s_2 = .875$$

The stationary matrix is [.125 .875], which means, in the long run, assuming that the transition matrix does not change, that about 12.5% of the drivers in the community will have an accident during any given year.

MATCHED PROBLEM 3 Refer to Matched Problem 1 in Section 9-1, where we found the following transition matrix for an insurance company:

$$P = \begin{matrix} & \begin{matrix} L & L' \end{matrix} \\ \begin{matrix} L \\ L' \end{matrix} & \begin{bmatrix} .98 & .02 \\ .78 & .22 \end{bmatrix} \end{matrix} \quad \begin{matrix} L = \text{low-risk} \\ L' = \text{not low-risk} \end{matrix}$$

If these probabilities remain valid over a long period of time, what percentage of drivers can the company expect to be in the low-risk category during any given year?

EXAMPLE 4 **Employee Evaluation** A company rates every employee as below average, average, or above average. Past performance indicates that each year 10% of the below-average employees will raise their rating to average and 25% of the average employees will raise their rating to above average. On the other hand, 15% of the average employees will lower their rating to below average, and 15% of the above-average employees will lower their rating to average. Company policy prohibits rating changes from below average to above average, or conversely, in a single year. Over the long run, what percentage of employees will receive below-average ratings? Average ratings? Above-average ratings?

SOLUTION First, we find the transition matrix:

$$\text{This year} \begin{matrix} & \begin{matrix} & \text{Next year} & \\ A^- & A & A^+ \end{matrix} \\ \begin{matrix} A^- \\ A \\ A^+ \end{matrix} & \begin{bmatrix} .9 & .1 & 0 \\ .15 & .6 & .25 \\ 0 & .15 & .85 \end{bmatrix} \end{matrix} \quad \begin{matrix} A^- = \text{below average} \\ A = \text{average} \\ A^+ = \text{above average} \end{matrix}$$

To determine what happens over the long run, we find the stationary matrix by solving the following system:

$$[s_1 \quad s_2 \quad s_3] \begin{bmatrix} .9 & .1 & 0 \\ .15 & .6 & .25 \\ 0 & .15 & .85 \end{bmatrix} = [s_1 \quad s_2 \quad s_3] \quad \text{and} \quad s_1 + s_2 + s_3 = 1$$

which is equivalent to

$$\begin{aligned}
.9s_1 + .15s_2 \qquad\quad &= s_1 \qquad \text{or} \qquad -.1s_1 + .15s_2 \qquad\qquad = 0 \\
.1s_1 + .6s_2 + .15s_3 &= s_2 \qquad\qquad\qquad .1s_1 - .4s_2 + .15s_3 = 0 \\
.25s_2 + .85s_3 &= s_3 \qquad\qquad\qquad\qquad\quad .25s_2 - .15s_3 = 0 \\
s_1 + s_2 + s_3 &= 1 \qquad\qquad\qquad\quad s_1 + s_2 + s_3 = 1
\end{aligned}$$

Using Gauss–Jordan elimination to solve this system of four equations with three variables, we obtain

$$s_1 = .36 \qquad s_2 = .24 \qquad s_3 = .4$$

Thus, in the long run, 36% of the employees will be rated as below average, 24% as average, and 40% as above average. ▰

MATCHED PROBLEM 4 A mail-order company classifies its customers as preferred, standard, or infrequent, depending on the number of orders placed in a year. Past records indicate that each year 5% of the preferred customers are reclassified as standard and 12% as infrequent; 5% of the standard customers are reclassified as preferred and 5% as infrequent; and 9% of the infrequent customers are reclassified as preferred and 10% as standard. Assuming that these percentages remain valid, what percentage of customers can the company expect to have in each category in the long run?

▨ Graphing Calculator Approximations

If P is the transition matrix for a regular Markov chain, the powers of P approach the limiting matrix $\overline{P}$, where each row of $\overline{P}$ is equal to the stationary matrix S (Theorem 1C). We can use this result to approximate S by computing P^k for sufficiently large values of k. The next example illustrates this approach on a graphing calculator.

EXAMPLE 5

Approximating the Stationary Matrix Compute powers of the transition matrix P to approximate $\overline{P}$ and S to four decimal places. Check the approximation in the equation $SP = S$.

$$P = \begin{bmatrix} .5 & .2 & .3 \\ .7 & .1 & .2 \\ .4 & .1 & .5 \end{bmatrix}$$

SOLUTION To approximate $\overline{P}$ to four decimal places, we enter P in a graphing calculator (Fig. 1A), set the decimal display to four places, and compute powers of P until all three rows of P^k are identical. Examining the output in Figure 1B, we conclude that

$$\overline{P} = \begin{bmatrix} .4943 & .1494 & .3563 \\ .4943 & .1494 & .3563 \\ .4943 & .1494 & .3563 \end{bmatrix} \quad \text{and} \quad S = [.4943 \quad .1494 \quad .3563]$$

Entering S in the graphing calculator and computing SP shows that these matrices are correct to four decimal places (see Fig. 1C).

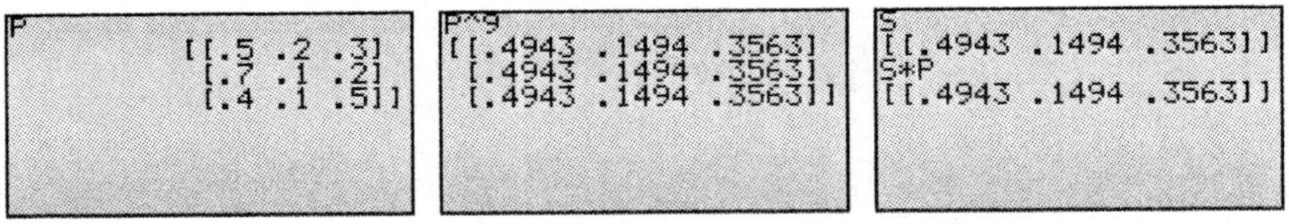

```
P
          [[.5 .2 .3]
           [.7 .1 .2]
           [.4 .1 .5]]
```

```
P^9
    [[.4943 .1494 .3563]
     [.4943 .1494 .3563]
     [.4943 .1494 .3563]]
```

```
S
  [[.4943 .1494 .3563]]
S*P
  [[.4943 .1494 .3563]]
```

(A) *P*   (B) *P⁹*   (C) Check: *SP = S*

FIGURE 1

MATCHED PROBLEM 5

Repeat Example 5 for $P = \begin{bmatrix} .3 & .6 & .1 \\ .2 & .3 & .5 \\ .1 & .2 & .7 \end{bmatrix}$.

INSIGHT

```
P
          [[1  0 ]
           [.7 .3]]
P^100
 [[1.0000 0.0000    ]
  [1.0000 5.1538E-53]]
```

FIGURE 2

1. We used a relatively small value of k to approximate $\overline{P}$ in Example 5. Many graphing calculators will compute P^k for large values of k almost as rapidly as for small values. However, round-off errors can occur in these calculations. A safe procedure is to start with a relatively small value of k, such as $k = 8$, and then keep doubling k until the rows of P^k are identical to the specified number of decimal places.

2. If any of the entries of P^k are approaching 0, the graphing calculator may use scientific notation to display these entries as very small numbers. Figure 2 shows the 100th power of a transition matrix P. The entry in row 2 and column 2 of P^{100} is approaching 0, but the graphing calculator displays it as 5.1538×10^{-53}. If this occurs, simply change this value to 0 in the corresponding entry in $\overline{P}$. Thus, from the output in Figure 2 we conclude that

$$P^k = \begin{bmatrix} 1 & 0 \\ .7 & .3 \end{bmatrix}^k \qquad \text{approaches} \qquad \overline{P} = \begin{bmatrix} 1 & 0 \\ 1 & 0 \end{bmatrix}$$

Answers to Matched Problems

1. (A) Regular   (B) Not regular   (C) Regular

2. $S = [.2 \quad .8]$; $\overline{P} = \begin{bmatrix} .2 & .8 \\ .2 & .8 \end{bmatrix}$

3. 97.5%

4. 28% preferred, 43% standard, 29% infrequent

5. $\overline{P} = \begin{bmatrix} .1618 & .2941 & .5441 \\ .1618 & .2941 & .5441 \\ .1618 & .2941 & .5441 \end{bmatrix}$; $S = [.1618 \quad .2941 \quad .5441]$

Exercise 9-2

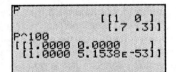

A *In Problems 1–14, could the given matrix be the transition matrix of a regular Markov chain?*

1. $\begin{bmatrix} .6 & .4 \\ .4 & .6 \end{bmatrix}$

2. $\begin{bmatrix} .3 & .7 \\ .2 & .6 \end{bmatrix}$

3. $\begin{bmatrix} .1 & .9 \\ .5 & .4 \end{bmatrix}$

4. $\begin{bmatrix} .5 & .5 \\ .8 & .2 \end{bmatrix}$

5. $\begin{bmatrix} .4 & .6 \\ 0 & 1 \end{bmatrix}$

6. $\begin{bmatrix} .4 & .6 \\ 1 & 0 \end{bmatrix}$

7. $\begin{bmatrix} 0 & 1 \\ .8 & .2 \end{bmatrix}$

8. $\begin{bmatrix} .3 & .7 \\ .2 & .6 \end{bmatrix}$

9. $\begin{bmatrix} .6 & .4 \\ .1 & .9 \\ .3 & .7 \end{bmatrix}$

10. $\begin{bmatrix} .2 & .5 & .3 \\ .6 & .3 & .1 \end{bmatrix}$

11. $\begin{bmatrix} 0 & 1 & 0 \\ 0 & 0 & 1 \\ .5 & .5 & 0 \end{bmatrix}$

12. $\begin{bmatrix} .2 & 0 & .8 \\ 0 & 0 & 1 \\ .7 & 0 & .3 \end{bmatrix}$

13. $\begin{bmatrix} .1 & .3 & .6 \\ .8 & .1 & .1 \\ 0 & 0 & 1 \end{bmatrix}$ **14.** $\begin{bmatrix} 0 & 0 & 1 \\ .9 & 0 & .1 \\ 0 & 1 & 0 \end{bmatrix}$

B *For each transition matrix P in Problems 15–22, solve the equation SP = S to find the stationary matrix S and the limiting matrix $\overline{P}$.*

15. $P = \begin{bmatrix} .1 & .9 \\ .6 & .4 \end{bmatrix}$ **16.** $P = \begin{bmatrix} .8 & .2 \\ .3 & .7 \end{bmatrix}$

17. $P = \begin{bmatrix} .5 & .5 \\ .3 & .7 \end{bmatrix}$ **18.** $P = \begin{bmatrix} .9 & .1 \\ .7 & .3 \end{bmatrix}$

19. $P = \begin{bmatrix} .5 & .1 & .4 \\ .3 & .7 & 0 \\ 0 & .6 & .4 \end{bmatrix}$ **20.** $P = \begin{bmatrix} .4 & .1 & .5 \\ .2 & .8 & 0 \\ 0 & .5 & .5 \end{bmatrix}$

21. $P = \begin{bmatrix} .8 & .2 & 0 \\ .5 & .1 & .4 \\ 0 & .6 & .4 \end{bmatrix}$ **22.** $P = \begin{bmatrix} .2 & .8 & 0 \\ .6 & .1 & .3 \\ 0 & .9 & .1 \end{bmatrix}$

In Problems 23 and 24, discuss the validity of each statement. If the statement is always true, explain why. If not, give a counterexample.

23. (A) If two entries of a 2×2 transition matrix P are 0, then P is not regular.

(B) If three entries of a 3×3 transition matrix P are 0, then P is not regular.

24. (A) If P is an $n \times n$ transition matrix for a Markov chain and S is a $1 \times n$ matrix such that $SP = S$, then S is a stationary matrix.

(B) If a transition matrix P for a Markov chain has a stationary matrix S, then P is regular.

In Problems 25–28, approximate the stationary matrix S for each transition matrix P by computing powers of the transition matrix P. Round matrix entries to four decimal places.

25. $P = \begin{bmatrix} .51 & .49 \\ .27 & .73 \end{bmatrix}$ **26.** $P = \begin{bmatrix} .68 & .32 \\ .19 & .81 \end{bmatrix}$

27. $P = \begin{bmatrix} .5 & .5 & 0 \\ 0 & .5 & .5 \\ .8 & .1 & .1 \end{bmatrix}$ **28.** $P = \begin{bmatrix} .2 & .2 & .6 \\ .5 & 0 & .5 \\ .5 & 0 & .5 \end{bmatrix}$

C

29. A red urn contains 2 red marbles and 3 blue marbles, and a blue urn contains 1 red marble and 4 blue marbles. A marble is selected from an urn, the color is noted, and the marble is returned to the urn from which it was drawn. The next marble is drawn from the urn whose color is the same as the marble just drawn. Thus, this is a Markov process with two states: draw from the red urn or draw from the blue urn.

(A) Draw a transition diagram for this process.

(B) Write the transition matrix.

(C) Find the stationary matrix and describe the long-run behavior of this process.

30. Repeat Problem 29 if the red urn contains 5 red and 3 blue marbles, and the blue urn contains 1 red and 3 blue marbles.

31. Given the transition matrix

$$P = \begin{bmatrix} 0 & 1 \\ 1 & 0 \end{bmatrix}$$

(A) Discuss the behavior of the state matrices $S_1, S_2, S_3, \ldots$ for the initial-state matrix $S_0 = [.2 \quad .8]$.

(B) Repeat part (A) for $S_0 = [.5 \quad .5]$.

(C) Discuss the behavior of $P^k, k = 2, 3, 4, \ldots$.

(D) Which of the conclusions of Theorem 1 are not valid for this matrix? Why is this not a contradiction?

32. Given the transition matrix

$$P = \begin{bmatrix} 0 & 1 & 0 \\ 0 & 0 & 1 \\ 1 & 0 & 0 \end{bmatrix}$$

(A) Discuss the behavior of the state matrices $S_1, S_2, S_3, \ldots$ for the initial-state matrix $S_0 = [.2 \quad .3 \quad .5]$.

(B) Repeat part (A) for $S_0 = \begin{bmatrix} \frac{1}{3} & \frac{1}{3} & \frac{1}{3} \end{bmatrix}$.

(C) Discuss the behavior of $P^k, k = 2, 3, 4, \ldots$.

(D) Which of the conclusions of Theorem 1 are not valid for this matrix? Why is this not a contradiction?

33. The transition matrix for a Markov chain is

$$P = \begin{bmatrix} 1 & 0 & 0 \\ .2 & .2 & .6 \\ 0 & 0 & 1 \end{bmatrix}$$

(A) Show that $R = [1 \quad 0 \quad 0]$ and $S = [0 \quad 0 \quad 1]$ are both stationary matrices for P. Explain why this does not contradict Theorem 1A.

(B) Find another stationary matrix for P. [*Hint:* Consider $T = aR + (1 - a)S$, where $0 < a < 1$.]

(C) How many different stationary matrices does P have?

34. The transition matrix for a Markov chain is

$$P = \begin{bmatrix} .7 & 0 & .3 \\ 0 & 1 & 0 \\ .2 & 0 & .8 \end{bmatrix}$$

(A) Show that $R = [.4 \quad 0 \quad .6]$ and $S = [0 \quad 1 \quad 0]$ are both stationary matrices for P. Explain why this does not contradict Theorem 1A.

(B) Find another stationary matrix for P. [*Hint:* Consider $T = aR + (1 - a)S$, where $0 < a < 1$.]

(C) How many different stationary matrices does P have?

Problems 35 and 36 require the use of a graphing calculator.

35. Refer to the transition matrix P in Problem 33. What matrix $\overline{P}$ do the powers of P appear to be approaching? Are the rows of $\overline{P}$ stationary matrices for P?

36. Refer to the transition matrix P in Problem 34. What matrix $\overline{P}$ do the powers of P appear to be approaching? Are the rows of $\overline{P}$ stationary matrices for P?

37. The transition matrix for a Markov chain is

$$P = \begin{bmatrix} .1 & .5 & .4 \\ .3 & .2 & .5 \\ .7 & .1 & .2 \end{bmatrix}$$

Let M_k denote the maximum entry in the second column of P^k. Note that $M_1 = .5$.

(A) Find M_2, M_3, M_4, and M_5 to three decimal places.

(B) Explain why $M_k \geq M_{k+1}$ for all positive integers k.

38. The transition matrix for a Markov chain is

$$P = \begin{bmatrix} 0 & .2 & .8 \\ .3 & .3 & .4 \\ .6 & .1 & .3 \end{bmatrix}$$

Let m_k denote the minimum entry in the third column of P^k. Note that $m_1 = .3$.

(A) Find m_2, m_3, m_4, and m_5 to three decimal places.

(B) Explain why $m_k \leq m_{k+1}$ for all positive integers k.

Applications

39. *Transportation.* Most railroad cars are owned by individual railroad companies. When a car leaves its home railroad's trackage, it becomes part of a national pool of cars and can be used by other railroads. The rules governing the use of these pooled cars are designed to eventually return the car to the home trackage. A particular railroad found that each month 11% of its boxcars on the home trackage left to join the national pool and 29% of its boxcars in the national pool were returned to the home trackage. If these percentages remain valid for a long period of time, what percentage of its boxcars can this railroad expect to have on its home trackage in the long run?

40. *Transportation.* The railroad in Problem 39 also has a fleet of tank cars. If 14% of the tank cars on the home trackage enter the national pool each month and 26% of the tank cars in the national pool are returned to the home trackage each month, what percentage of its tank cars can the railroad expect to have on its home trackage in the long run?

41. *Labor force.* Table 1 gives the percentage of the female population of the United States who were members of the civilian labor force in the years indicated.

TABLE 1

Year	Percent
1970	43.3
1980	51.5
1990	57.5
2000	59.8

The following transition matrix P is proposed as a model for the data, where L represents females who are in the labor force and L' represents females who are not in the labor force:

Next decade

$$\begin{array}{c} \\ \text{Current} \\ \text{decade} \end{array} \begin{array}{c} L \\ L' \end{array} \begin{bmatrix} L & L' \\ .92 & .08 \\ .2 & .8 \end{bmatrix} = P$$

(A) Let $S_0 = [.433 \quad .567]$, and find S_1, S_2, and S_3. (Compute the matrices exactly and then round entries to three decimal places.)

(B) Construct a new table comparing the results from part (A) with the data in Table 1.

(C) According to this transition matrix, what percentage of the female population will be in the labor force in the long run?

42. *Home ownership.* The U.S. Census Bureau published the home ownership rates given in Table 2.

TABLE 2

Year	Percent
1996	65.4
2000	67.4
2004	69.0

The following transition matrix P is proposed as a model for the data, where H represents the households that own their home.

Four years later

$$\begin{array}{c} \\ \text{Current} \\ \text{year} \end{array} \begin{array}{c} H \\ H' \end{array} \begin{bmatrix} H & H' \\ .95 & .05 \\ .15 & .85 \end{bmatrix} = P$$

(A) Let $S_0 = [.654 \quad .346]$, and find S_1 and S_2. (Compute both matrices exactly and then round entries to three decimal places.)

(B) Construct a new table comparing the results from part (A) with the data in Table 2.

(C) According to this transition matrix, what percentage of households will own their home in the long run?

43. *Market share.* Consumers in a certain state can choose between three long-distance telephone services: GTT, NCJ, and Dash. Aggressive marketing by all three companies results in a continual shift of customers among the three services. Each year, GTT loses 5% of its customers to NCJ and 20% to Dash, NCJ loses 15% of its customers to GTT and 10% to Dash, and Dash loses 5% of its customers to GTT and 10% to NCJ. Assuming that these percentages remain valid over a long period of time, what is each company's expected market share in the long run?

44. *Market share.* Consumers in a certain area can choose between three package delivery services: APS, GX, and WWP. Each week, APS loses 10% of its customers to GX and 20% to WWP, GX loses 15% of its customers to APS and 10% to WWP, and WWP loses 5% of its customers to

APS and 5% to GX. Assuming that these percentages remain valid over a long period of time, what is each company's expected market share in the long run?

45. *Insurance.* An auto insurance company classifies its customers in three categories: poor, satisfactory, and preferred. Each year, 40% of those in the poor category are moved to satisfactory, and 20% of those in the satisfactory category are moved to preferred. Also, 20% in the preferred category are moved to the satisfactory category, and 20% in the satisfactory category are moved to the poor category. Customers are never moved from poor to preferred, or conversely, in a single year. Assuming that these percentages remain valid over a long period of time, how many customers can the company expect to have in each category in the long run?

46. *Insurance.* Repeat Problem 45 if 40% of the preferred customers are moved to the satisfactory category each year and all other information remains the same.

Problems 47 and 48 require the use of a graphing calculator.

47. *Market share.* Acme Soap Company markets one brand of soap, called Standard Acme (*SA*), and Best Soap Company markets two brands, Standard Best (*SB*) and Deluxe Best (*DB*). Currently, Acme has 40% of the market, and the remainder is equally divided between the two Best brands. Acme is considering the introduction of a second brand to get a larger share of the market. A proposed new brand, called brand *X*, was test-marketed in several large cities, producing the following transition matrix for the consumers' weekly buying habits:

$$
P = \begin{array}{c}
\\
SB \\
DB \\
SA \\
X
\end{array}
\begin{array}{c}
\begin{array}{cccc}
SB & DB & SA & X
\end{array} \\
\left[\begin{array}{cccc}
.4 & .1 & .3 & .2 \\
.3 & .2 & .2 & .3 \\
.1 & .2 & .2 & .5 \\
.3 & .3 & .1 & .3
\end{array}\right]
\end{array}
$$

Assuming that *P* represents the consumers' buying habits over a long period of time, use this transition matrix and the initial-state matrix $S_0 = [.3 \quad .3 \quad .4 \quad 0]$ to compute successive state matrices in order to approximate the elements in the stationary matrix correct to two decimal places. If Acme decides to market this new soap, what is the long-run expected total market share for their two soaps?

48. *Market share.* Refer to Problem 47. The chemists at Acme Soap Company have developed a second new soap, called brand *Y*. Test-marketing this soap against the three established brands produces the following transition matrix:

$$
P = \begin{array}{c}
\\
SB \\
DB \\
SA \\
Y
\end{array}
\begin{array}{c}
\begin{array}{cccc}
SB & DB & SA & Y
\end{array} \\
\left[\begin{array}{cccc}
.3 & .2 & .2 & .3 \\
.2 & .2 & .2 & .4 \\
.2 & .2 & .4 & .2 \\
.1 & .2 & .3 & .4
\end{array}\right]
\end{array}
$$

Proceed as in Problem 47 to approximate the elements in the stationary matrix correct to two decimal places. If Acme decides to market brand *Y*, what is the long-run expected total market share for Standard Acme and brand *Y*? Should Acme market brand *X* or brand *Y*?

49. *Genetics.* A given plant species has red, pink, or white flowers according to the genotypes RR, RW, and WW, respectively. If each of these genotypes is crossed with a pink-flowering plant (genotype RW), the transition matrix is

$$
\begin{array}{c}
\\
\text{This} \\
\text{generation}
\end{array}
\begin{array}{c}
\text{Next generation} \\
\begin{array}{c}
 \\
\text{Red} \\
\text{Pink} \\
\text{White}
\end{array}
\begin{array}{c}
\begin{array}{ccc}
\text{Red} & \text{Pink} & \text{White}
\end{array} \\
\left[\begin{array}{ccc}
.5 & .5 & 0 \\
.25 & .5 & .25 \\
0 & .5 & .5
\end{array}\right]
\end{array}
\end{array}
$$

Assuming that the plants of each generation are crossed only with pink plants to produce the next generation, show that regardless of the makeup of the first generation, the genotype composition will eventually stabilize at 25% red, 50% pink, and 25% white. (Find the stationary matrix.)

50. *Gene mutation.* Suppose a gene in a chromosome is of type *A* or type *B*. Assume that the probability that a gene of type *A* will mutate to type *B* in one generation is 10^{-4} and that a gene of type *B* will mutate to type *A* is 10^{-6}.

(A) What is the transition matrix?

(B) After many generations, what is the probability that the gene will be of type *A*? Of type *B*? (Find the stationary matrix.)

51. *Rapid transit.* A new rapid transit system has just started operating. In the first month of operation, it is found that 25% of the commuters are using the system, while 75% still travel by automobile. The following transition matrix was determined from records of other rapid transit systems:

$$
\begin{array}{c}
\\
\text{Current} \\
\text{month}
\end{array}
\begin{array}{c}
\text{Next month} \\
\begin{array}{c}
 \\
 \\
\text{Rapid transit} \\
\text{Automobile}
\end{array}
\begin{array}{c}
\begin{array}{cc}
\text{Rapid} & \\
\text{transit} & \text{Automobile}
\end{array} \\
\left[\begin{array}{cc}
.8 & .2 \\
.3 & .7
\end{array}\right]
\end{array}
\end{array}
$$

(A) What is the initial-state matrix?

(B) What percentage of the commuters will be using the new system after 1 month? After 2 months?

(C) Find the percentage of commuters using each type of transportation after it has been in service for a long time.

52. *Politics: filibuster.* The Senate is in the middle of a floor debate and a filibuster is threatened. Senator Hanks, who is still vacillating, has a probability of .1 of changing his mind during the next 5 minutes. If this pattern continues for each 5 minutes that the debate continues, and if a 24-hour filibuster takes place before a vote is taken, what is the probability that Senator Hanks will cast a yes vote? A no vote?

(A) First, complete the following transition matrix:

Next 5 minutes

$$\begin{array}{c} \text{Current} \\ \text{5 minutes} \end{array} \begin{array}{c} \text{Yes} \\ \text{No} \end{array} \begin{bmatrix} \text{Yes} & \text{No} \\ .9 & .1 \\ & \end{bmatrix}$$

(B) Find the stationary matrix and answer the two questions.

(C) What is the stationary matrix if the probability of Senator Hanks changing his mind (.1) is replaced with an arbitrary probability p?

The center of population of the 48 contiguous states of the United States is the point where a flat, rigid map of the contiguous states would balance if the location of each person was represented on the map by a weight of equal measure. In 1790 the population center was 23 miles east of Baltimore, Maryland. By 1990, the center had shifted about 800 miles west and 100 miles south to a point in southeast Missouri. To study this shifting population, the U.S. Bureau of the Census divides the states into the four regions shown in the figure. Problems 53 and 54 deal with population shifts among some of these regions.

Figure for 53 and 54:
Regions of the United States and the center of population

53. *Population shifts.* Table 3 gives the percentage of the U.S. population living in the south region of the United States in the years indicated.

TABLE 3	
Year	**Percent**
1970	30.9
1980	33.3
1990	34.4
2000	35.6

The following transition matrix P is proposed as a model for the data, where S represents the population that lives in the south region:

Next decade

$$\begin{array}{c} \text{Current} \\ \text{decade} \end{array} \begin{array}{c} S \\ S' \end{array} \begin{bmatrix} S & S' \\ .61 & .39 \\ .21 & .79 \end{bmatrix} = P$$

(A) Let $S_0 = [.309 \quad .691]$, and find S_1, S_2, and S_3. (Compute the matrices exactly and then round entries to three decimal places.)

(B) Construct a new table comparing the results from part (A) with the data in Table 3.

(C) According to this transition matrix, what percentage of the population will live in the south region in the long run?

54. *Population shifts.* Table 4 gives the percentage of the U.S. population living in the northeast region of the United States in the years indicated.

TABLE 4	
Year	**Percent**
1970	24.1
1980	21.7
1990	20.4
2000	19.0

The following transition matrix P is proposed as a model for the data, where N represents the population that lives in the northeast region:

Next decade

$$\begin{array}{c} \text{Current} \\ \text{decade} \end{array} \begin{array}{c} N \\ N' \end{array} \begin{bmatrix} N & N' \\ .61 & .39 \\ .09 & .91 \end{bmatrix} = P$$

(A) Let $S_0 = [.241 \quad .759]$, and find S_1, S_2, and S_3. (Compute the matrices exactly and then round entries to three decimal places.)

(B) Construct a new table comparing the results from part (A) with the data in Table 4.

(C) According to this transition matrix, what percentage of the population will live in the northeast region in the long run?

Section 9-3 ABSORBING MARKOV CHAINS

- Absorbing States and Absorbing Chains
- Standard Form
- Limiting Matrix
- Graphing Calculator Approximations

In Section 9-2 we saw that the powers of a regular transition matrix always approach a limiting matrix. Not all transition matrices have this property. In this section we discuss another type of Markov chain, called an *absorbing Markov chain*. Although regular and absorbing Markov chains have some differences, they have one important similarity: the powers of the transition matrix for an absorbing Markov chain also approach a limiting matrix. After introducing basic concepts, we develop methods for finding the limiting matrix and discuss the relationship between the states in the Markov chain and the entries in the limiting matrix.

▨ Absorbing States and Absorbing Chains

A state in a Markov chain is called an **absorbing state** if once the state is entered, it is impossible to leave.

EXAMPLE 1   **Recognizing Absorbing States**   Identify any absorbing states for the following transition matrices:

$$(A) \quad P = \begin{matrix} & A & B & C \\ A & \begin{bmatrix} 1 & 0 & 0 \\ B & .5 & .5 & 0 \\ C & 0 & .5 & .5 \end{bmatrix} \end{matrix} \qquad (B) \quad P = \begin{matrix} & A & B & C \\ A & \begin{bmatrix} 0 & 0 & 1 \\ B & 0 & 1 & 0 \\ C & 1 & 0 & 0 \end{bmatrix} \end{matrix}$$

SOLUTION   (A) The probability of going from state A to state A is 1, and the probability of going from state A to either state B or state C is 0. Thus, once state A is entered, it is impossible to leave; hence, A is an absorbing state. Since the probability of going from state B to state A is nonzero, it is possible to leave B, and B is not an absorbing state. Similarly, the probability of going from state C to state B is nonzero, so C is not an absorbing state.

(B) Reasoning as before, the 1 in row 2 and column 2 indicates that state B is an absorbing state. The probability of going from state A to state C and the probability of going from state C to state A are both nonzero. Hence, A and C are not absorbing states.   ▬

MATCHED PROBLEM 1   Identify any absorbing states for the following transition matrices:

$$(A) \quad P = \begin{matrix} & A & B & C \\ A & \begin{bmatrix} .5 & 0 & .5 \\ B & 0 & 1 & 0 \\ C & 0 & .5 & .5 \end{bmatrix} \end{matrix} \qquad (B) \quad P = \begin{matrix} & A & B & C \\ A & \begin{bmatrix} 0 & 1 & 0 \\ B & 1 & 0 & 0 \\ C & 0 & 0 & 1 \end{bmatrix} \end{matrix}$$

The reasoning used in Example 1 to identify absorbing states is generalized in Theorem 1.

THEOREM 1   **ABSORBING STATES AND TRANSITION MATRICES**
A state in a Markov chain is **absorbing** if and only if the row of the transition matrix corresponding to the state has a 1 on the main diagonal and 0's elsewhere.

The presence of an absorbing state in a transition matrix does not guarantee that the powers of the matrix approach a limiting matrix nor that the state matrices in the corresponding Markov chain approach a stationary matrix. For example, if we square the matrix P from Example 1B, we obtain

$$P^2 = \begin{bmatrix} 0 & 0 & 1 \\ 0 & 1 & 0 \\ 1 & 0 & 0 \end{bmatrix} \begin{bmatrix} 0 & 0 & 1 \\ 0 & 1 & 0 \\ 1 & 0 & 0 \end{bmatrix} = \begin{bmatrix} 1 & 0 & 0 \\ 0 & 1 & 0 \\ 0 & 0 & 1 \end{bmatrix} = I$$

Since $P^2 = I$, the 3×3 identity matrix, it follows that

$$P^3 = PP^2 = PI = P \quad \text{Since } P^2 = I$$
$$P^4 = PP^3 = PP = I \quad \text{Since } P^3 = P \text{ and } PP = P^2 = I$$

In general, the powers of this transition matrix P oscillate between P and I and do not approach a limiting matrix.

Explore & Discuss **1**
(A) For the initial-state matrix $S_0 = [a \quad b \quad c]$, find the first four state matrices, S_1, S_2, S_3, and S_4, in the Markov chain with transition matrix

$$P = \begin{bmatrix} 0 & 0 & 1 \\ 0 & 1 & 0 \\ 1 & 0 & 0 \end{bmatrix}$$

(B) Do the state matrices appear to be approaching a stationary matrix? Discuss.

To ensure that transition matrices for Markov chains with one or more absorbing states have limiting matrices, it is necessary to require the chain to satisfy one additional condition, as stated in the following definition.

DEFINITION **Absorbing Markov Chains**

A Markov chain is an **absorbing chain** if

1. There is at least one absorbing state.
2. It is possible to go from each nonabsorbing state to at least one absorbing state in a finite number of steps.

As we saw earlier, absorbing states are easily identified by examining the rows of a transition matrix. It is also possible to use a transition matrix to determine whether a Markov chain is an absorbing chain, but this can be a difficult task, especially if the matrix is large. A transition diagram is often a more appropriate tool for determining whether a Markov chain is absorbing. The next example illustrates this approach for the two matrices discussed in Example 1.

EXAMPLE 2 **Recognizing Absorbing Markov Chains** Use a transition diagram to determine whether P is the transition matrix for an absorbing Markov chain.

$$\text{(A) } P = \begin{matrix} & A & B & C \\ A & \begin{bmatrix} 1 & 0 & 0 \\ B & .5 & .5 & 0 \\ C & 0 & .5 & .5 \end{bmatrix} \end{matrix} \qquad \text{(B) } P = \begin{matrix} & A & B & C \\ A & \begin{bmatrix} 0 & 0 & 1 \\ B & 0 & 1 & 0 \\ C & 1 & 0 & 0 \end{bmatrix} \end{matrix}$$

SOLUTION
(A) From Example 1A, we know that A is the only absorbing state. The second condition in the definition of an absorbing Markov chain is satisfied if we can show that it is possible to go from the nonabsorbing states B and C to the absorbing state A in a finite number of steps. This is easily determined by drawing a transition diagram. Examining the diagram in the margin, we see that it is possible to go from state B to the absorbing state A in one step and from state C to the absorbing state A in two steps. Thus, P is the transition matrix for an absorbing Markov chain.

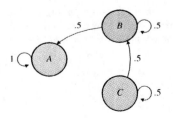

(B) Again, we draw the transition diagram for P, as shown on page 000. From this diagram it is clear that it is impossible to go from either state A or state C to the absorbing state *B*. Hence, *P* is not the transition matrix for an absorbing Markov chain.

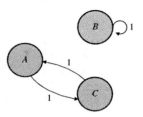

MATCHED PROBLEM 2 Use a transition diagram to determine whether *P* is the transition matrix for an absorbing Markov chain.

$$\text{(B) } P = \begin{array}{c} \\ A \\ B \\ C \end{array} \begin{array}{ccc} A & B & C \\ \left[\begin{array}{ccc} .5 & 0 & .5 \\ 0 & 1 & 0 \\ 0 & .5 & .5 \end{array} \right] \end{array} \qquad \text{(B) } P = \begin{array}{c} \\ A \\ B \\ C \end{array} \begin{array}{ccc} A & B & C \\ \left[\begin{array}{ccc} 0 & 1 & 0 \\ 1 & 0 & 0 \\ 0 & 0 & 1 \end{array} \right] \end{array}$$

Explore & Discuss **2** Determine whether each statement is true or false. Use examples and verbal arguments to support your conclusions.

(A) A Markov chain with two states, one nonabsorbing and one absorbing, is always an absorbing chain.

(B) A Markov chain with two states, both of which are absorbing, is always an absorbing chain.

(C) A Markov chain with three states, one nonabsorbing and two absorbing, is always an absorbing chain.

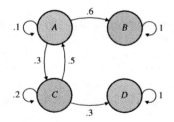

FIGURE 1

▦ Standard Form

The transition matrix for a Markov chain is not unique. Consider the transition diagram in Figure 1. Since there are 4! = 24 different ways to arrange the four states in this diagram, there are 24 different ways to write a transition matrix. (Some of these matrices may have identical entries, but all are different when the row and column labels are taken into account.) For example, matrices *M*, *N*, and *P* shown below are three different transition matrices for this diagram.

$$M = \begin{array}{c} \\ A \\ B \\ C \\ D \end{array} \begin{array}{cccc} A & B & C & D \\ \left[\begin{array}{cccc} .1 & .6 & .3 & 0 \\ 0 & 1 & 0 & 0 \\ .5 & 0 & .2 & .3 \\ 0 & 0 & 0 & 1 \end{array} \right] \end{array} \quad N = \begin{array}{c} \\ D \\ B \\ C \\ A \end{array} \begin{array}{cccc} D & B & C & A \\ \left[\begin{array}{cccc} 1 & 0 & 0 & 0 \\ 0 & 1 & 0 & 0 \\ .3 & 0 & .2 & .5 \\ 0 & .6 & .3 & .1 \end{array} \right] \end{array} \quad P = \begin{array}{c} \\ B \\ D \\ A \\ C \end{array} \begin{array}{cccc} B & D & A & C \\ \left[\begin{array}{cccc} 1 & 0 & 0 & 0 \\ 0 & 1 & 0 & 0 \\ .6 & 0 & .1 & .3 \\ 0 & .3 & .5 & .2 \end{array} \right] \end{array} \quad (1)$$

In matrices *N* and *P*, notice that all the absorbing states precede all the nonabsorbing states. A transition matrix written in this form is said to be a *standard form*. We will find standard forms very useful in determining limiting matrices for absorbing Markov chains. The general definition of standard form is given in the next box.

DEFINITION   **Standard Forms for Absorbing Markov Chains**

A transition matrix for an absorbing Markov chain is a **standard form** if the rows and columns are labeled so that all the absorbing states precede all the nonabsorbing states. (There may be more than one standard form.) Any standard form can always be partitioned into four submatrices:

$$
\begin{array}{c} \\ A \\ N \end{array}
\begin{array}{cc} A & N \end{array}
\left[\begin{array}{c|c} I & 0 \\ \hline R & Q \end{array}\right]
\begin{array}{l} A = \text{all absorbing states} \\ N = \text{all nonabsorbing states} \end{array}
$$

where I is an identity matrix and 0 is a zero matrix.

Referring to the matrix P in (1), we see that the submatrices in this standard form are

$$
I = \begin{bmatrix} 1 & 0 \\ 0 & 1 \end{bmatrix} \qquad 0 = \begin{bmatrix} 0 & 0 \\ 0 & 0 \end{bmatrix}
$$

$$
R = \begin{bmatrix} .6 & 0 \\ 0 & .3 \end{bmatrix} \qquad Q = \begin{bmatrix} .1 & .3 \\ .5 & .2 \end{bmatrix}
$$

$$
P = \begin{array}{c} \\ B \\ D \\ A \\ C \end{array}
\begin{array}{cccc} B & D & A & C \end{array}
\left[\begin{array}{cc|cc} 1 & 0 & 0 & 0 \\ 0 & 1 & 0 & 0 \\ \hline .6 & 0 & .1 & .3 \\ 0 & .3 & .5 & .2 \end{array}\right]
$$

Explore & Discuss 3 We used the diagram in Figure 1 to find the transition matrices M, N, and P in equations (1). Devise a procedure for transforming matrix M into standard forms N and P by interchanging rows and columns in M without reference to the transition diagram. Discuss the relative merits of using transition diagrams versus using row and column rearrangements to find standard forms.

■ Limiting Matrix

We are now ready to discuss the long-run behavior of absorbing Markov chains. We begin with an application.

EXAMPLE 3 **Real Estate Development** Two competing real estate companies are trying to buy all the farms in a particular area for future housing development. Each year, 20% of the farmers decide to sell to company A, 30% decide to sell to company B, and the rest continue to farm their land. Neither company ever sells any of the farms they purchase.

(A) Draw a transition diagram for this Markov process and determine whether the associated Markov chain is absorbing.

(B) Write a transition matrix that is in standard form.

(C) If neither company owns any farms at the beginning of this competitive buying process, estimate the percentage of farms that each company will purchase in the long run.

(D) If company A buys 50% of the farms before company B enters this competitive buying process, estimate the percentage of farms that each company will purchase in the long run.

SOLUTION (A)

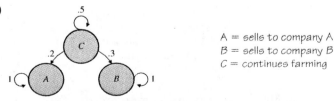

A = sells to company A
B = sells to company B
C = continues farming

The associated Markov chain is absorbing, since there are two absorbing states, A and B, and it is possible to go from the nonabsorbing state C to either A or B in one step.

(B) We use the transition diagram to write a transition matrix that is in standard form:

$$P = \begin{array}{c} \\ A \\ B \\ C \end{array} \begin{array}{ccc} A & B & C \\ \left[\begin{array}{ccc} 1 & 0 & 0 \\ 0 & 1 & 0 \\ .2 & .3 & .5 \end{array} \right] \end{array} \quad \text{Standard form}$$

(C) At the beginning of the competitive buying process all the farmers are in state C (own a farm). Thus, $S_0 = [0 \quad 0 \quad 1]$. The successive state matrices are (multiplication details omitted):

$$S_1 = S_0P = [.2 \quad .3 \quad .5]$$
$$S_2 = S_1P = [.3 \quad .45 \quad .25]$$
$$S_3 = S_2P = [.35 \quad .525 \quad .125]$$
$$S_4 = S_3P = [.375 \quad .5625 \quad .0625]$$
$$S_5 = S_4P = [.3875 \quad .58125 \quad .03125]$$
$$S_6 = S_5P = [.39375 \quad .590625 \quad .015625]$$
$$S_7 = S_6P = [.396875 \quad .5953125 \quad .0078125]$$
$$S_8 = S_7P = [.3984375 \quad .59765625 \quad .00390625]$$
$$S_9 = S_8P = [.39921875 \quad .598828125 \quad .001953125]$$

It appears that these state matrices are approaching the matrix

$$\begin{array}{ccc} A & B & C \end{array}$$
$$S = [.4 \quad .6 \quad 0]$$

This indicates that in the long run, company A will acquire approximately 40% of the farms and company B will acquire the remaining 60%.

(D) This time, at the beginning of the competitive buying process 50% of the farmers are already in state A and the rest are in state C. Thus, $S_0 = [.5 \quad 0 \quad .5]$. The successive state matrices are (multiplication details omitted):

$$S_1 = S_0P = [.6 \quad .15 \quad .25]$$
$$S_2 = S_1P = [.65 \quad .225 \quad .125]$$
$$S_3 = S_2P = [.675 \quad .2625 \quad .0625]$$
$$S_4 = S_3P = [.6875 \quad .28125 \quad .03125]$$
$$S_5 = S_4P = [.69375 \quad .290625 \quad .015625]$$
$$S_6 = S_5P = [.696875 \quad .2953125 \quad .0078125]$$
$$S_7 = S_6P = [.6984375 \quad .29765625 \quad .00390625]$$
$$S_8 = S_7P = [.69921875 \quad .298828125 \quad .001953125]$$

These state matrices approach a matrix different from the one in part (C):

$$\begin{array}{ccc} A & B & C \end{array}$$
$$S' = [.7 \quad .3 \quad 0]$$

Because of its head start, company A will now acquire approximately 70% of the farms and company B will acquire the remaining 30%. ▬▬

MATCHED PROBLEM 3 Repeat Example 3 if 10% of the farmers sell to company A each year, 40% sell to company B, and the remainder continue farming.

Recall from Theorem 1 in Section 9-2 that the successive state matrices of a regular Markov chain always approach a stationary matrix. Furthermore, this stationary matrix is unique. That is, changing the initial-state matrix does not change the stationary matrix. The successive state matrices for an absorbing Markov chain also approach a stationary matrix, but this matrix is not unique. To confirm this, consider the transition matrix P and the state matrices S and S' from Example 3:

$$
P = \begin{array}{c} \\ A \\ B \\ C \end{array} \begin{array}{c} \begin{array}{ccc} A & B & C \end{array} \\ \begin{bmatrix} 1 & 0 & 0 \\ 0 & 1 & 0 \\ .2 & .3 & .5 \end{bmatrix} \end{array} \qquad \begin{array}{ccc} A & B & C \end{array} \\ S = [.4 \quad .6 \quad 0] \qquad \begin{array}{ccc} A & B & C \end{array} \\ S' = [.7 \quad .3 \quad 0]
$$

It turns out that S and S' are both stationary matrices, as the following multiplications verify:

$$
SP = [.4 \quad .6 \quad 0] \begin{bmatrix} 1 & 0 & 0 \\ 0 & 1 & 0 \\ .2 & .3 & .5 \end{bmatrix} = [.4 \quad .6 \quad 0] = S
$$

$$
S'P = [.7 \quad .3 \quad 0] \begin{bmatrix} 1 & 0 & 0 \\ 0 & 1 & 0 \\ .2 & .3 & .5 \end{bmatrix} = [.7 \quad .3 \quad 0] = S'
$$

In fact, this absorbing Markov chain has an infinite number of stationary matrices (see Problems 41 and 42, Exercise 9-3).

Thus, changing the initial-state matrix for an absorbing Markov chain can cause the successive state matrices to approach a different stationary matrix.

In Section 9-2 we used the unique stationary matrix for a regular Markov chain to find the limiting matrix $\overline{P}$. Since an absorbing Markov chain can have many different stationary matrices, we cannot expect this approach to work for absorbing chains. However, it turns out that transition matrices for absorbing chains do have limiting matrices, and they are not very difficult to find. Theorem 2 gives us the necessary tools. The proof of this theorem is left for more advanced courses.

THEOREM 2   **LIMITING MATRICES FOR ABSORBING MARKOV CHAINS**

If a standard form P for an absorbing Markov chain is partitioned as

$$
P = \left[\begin{array}{c|c} 1 & 0 \\ \hline R & Q \end{array} \right]
$$

then P^k approaches a limiting matrix $\overline{P}$ as k increases, where

$$
\overline{P} = \left[\begin{array}{c|c} I & 0 \\ \hline FR & 0 \end{array} \right]
$$

The matrix F is given by $F = (I - Q)^{-1}$ and is called the **fundamental matrix** for P. The identity matrix used to form the fundamental matrix F must be the same size as the matrix Q.

EXAMPLE 4   Finding the Limiting Matrix

(A) Find the limiting matrix $\overline{P}$ for the standard form P found in Example 3.

(B) Use $\overline{P}$ to find the limit of the successive state matrices for $S_0 = [0 \quad 0 \quad 1]$.

(C) Use $\overline{P}$ to find the limit of the successive state matrices for $S_0 = [.5 \quad 0 \quad .5]$.

SOLUTION   (A) From Example 3, we have

$$
P = \begin{bmatrix} 1 & 0 & | & 0 \\ 0 & 1 & | & 0 \\ \hline .2 & .3 & | & .5 \end{bmatrix} \qquad \left[\begin{array}{c|c} I & 0 \\ \hline R & Q \end{array} \right]
$$

where

$$I = \begin{bmatrix} 1 & 0 \\ 0 & 1 \end{bmatrix} \qquad 0 = \begin{bmatrix} 0 \\ 0 \end{bmatrix} \qquad R = [.2 \quad .3] \qquad Q = [.5]$$

If $I = [1]$ is the 1×1 identity matrix, then $I - Q$ is also a 1×1 matrix, and $F = (I - Q)^{-1}$ is simply the multiplicative inverse of the single entry in $I - Q$. Thus,

$$F = ([1] - [.5])^{-1} = [.5]^{-1} = [2]$$
$$FR = [2][.2 \quad .3] = [.4 \quad .6]$$

and the limiting matrix is

$$\overline{P} = \begin{array}{c} \\ A \\ B \\ C \end{array} \begin{array}{ccc} A & B & C \\ \begin{bmatrix} 1 & 0 & 0 \\ 0 & 1 & 0 \\ .4 & .6 & 0 \end{bmatrix} \end{array} \begin{bmatrix} I & | & 0 \\ \hline FR & | & 0 \end{bmatrix}$$

(B) Since the successive state matrices are given by $S_k = S_0 P^k$ (Theorem 1, Section 9-1) and P^k approaches $\overline{P}$, it follows that S_k approaches

$$S_0 \overline{P} = [0 \quad 0 \quad 1] \begin{bmatrix} 1 & 0 & 0 \\ 0 & 1 & 0 \\ .4 & .6 & 0 \end{bmatrix} = [.4 \quad .6 \quad 0]$$

which agrees with the results in part (C) of Example 3.

(C) This time, the successive state matrices approach

$$S_0 \overline{P} = [.5 \quad 0 \quad .5] \begin{bmatrix} 1 & 0 & 0 \\ 0 & 1 & 0 \\ .4 & .6 & 0 \end{bmatrix} = [.7 \quad .3 \quad 0]$$

which agrees with the results in part (D) of Example 3.

MATCHED PROBLEM 4   Repeat Example 4 for the standard form P found in Matched Problem 3.

Recall that the limiting matrix for a regular Markov chain contains the long-run probabilities of going from any state to any other state. This is also true for the limiting matrix of an absorbing Markov chain. Let's compare the transition matrix P and its limiting matrix $\overline{P}$ from Example 4:

$$P = \begin{array}{c} \\ A \\ B \\ C \end{array} \begin{array}{ccc} A & B & C \\ \begin{bmatrix} 1 & 0 & 0 \\ 0 & 1 & 0 \\ .2 & .3 & .5 \end{bmatrix} \end{array} \qquad \text{approaches} \qquad \overline{P} = \begin{array}{c} \\ A \\ B \\ C \end{array} \begin{array}{ccc} A & B & C \\ \begin{bmatrix} 1 & 0 & 0 \\ 0 & 1 & 0 \\ .4 & .6 & 0 \end{bmatrix} \end{array}$$

The rows of P and $\overline{P}$ corresponding to the absorbing states A and B are identical. That is, if the probability of going from state A to state A is 1 at the beginning of the chain, this probability will remain 1 for all trials in the chain and for the limiting matrix. The entries in the third row of $\overline{P}$ give the long-run probabilities of going from the nonabsorbing state C to states A, B, or C.

The fundamental matrix F provides some additional information about an absorbing chain. Recall from Example 4 that $F = [2]$. It can be shown that the entries in F determine the average number of trials it takes to go from a given nonabsorbing state to an absorbing state. In the case of Example 4, the single entry 2 in F indicates that it will take an average of 2 years for a farmer to go from state C (owns a farm) to one of the absorbing states (sells the farm). Some will reach an absorbing state in 1 year, some will take more than 2 years, but the average will be 2 years. These observations are summarized in Theorem 3, which we state without proof.

THEOREM 3   **PROPERTIES OF THE LIMITING MATRIX $\overline{P}$**

If P is a transition matrix in standard form for an absorbing Markov chain, F is the fundamental matrix, and $\overline{P}$ is the limiting matrix, then

(A) The entry in row i and column j of $\overline{P}$ is the long-run probability of going from state i to state j. For the nonabsorbing states, these probabilities are also the entries in the matrix FR used to form $\overline{P}$.

(B) The sum of the entries in each row of the fundamental matrix F is the average number of trials it will take to go from each nonabsorbing state to some absorbing state.

(Note that the rows of both F and FR correspond to the nonabsorbing states in the order given in the standard form P.)

INSIGHT

1. The zero matrix in the lower right corner of the limiting matrix $\overline{P}$ in Theorem 2 indicates that the long-run probability of going from any nonabsorbing state to any other nonabsorbing state is always 0. That is, in the long run, all elements in an absorbing Markov chain end up in one of the absorbing states.

2. If the transition matrix for an absorbing Markov chain is not a standard form, it is still possible to find a limiting matrix (see Problems 37 and 38, Exercise 9-3). However, it is customary to use a standard form when investigating the limiting behavior of an absorbing chain.

Now that we have developed the necessary tools for analyzing the long-run behavior of an absorbing Markov chain, we apply these tools to an application we considered earlier (see Example 4, Section 9-1).

EXAMPLE 5   **University Enrollment**   The transition diagram for part-time students enrolled in an MBA program in a university is shown below:

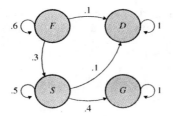

F = first-year students
S = second-year students
D = dropouts
G = graduates

(A) In the long run, what percentage of first-year students will graduate? What percentage of second-year students will not graduate?

(B) What is the average number of years a first-year student will remain in this program? A second-year student?

SOLUTION   (A) First, notice that this is an absorbing Markov chain with two absorbing states, state D and state G. A standard form for this absorbing chain is

$$
P = \begin{array}{c} \\ D \\ G \\ F \\ S \end{array}
\begin{array}{cc} \begin{array}{cccc} D & G & F & S \end{array} \\
\left[\begin{array}{cc|cc}
1 & 0 & 0 & 0 \\
0 & 1 & 0 & 0 \\
\hline
.1 & 0 & .6 & .3 \\
.1 & .4 & 0 & .5
\end{array} \right] \end{array}
\quad \left[\begin{array}{c|c} I & O \\ \hline R & Q \end{array} \right]
$$

The submatrices in this partition are

$$I = \begin{bmatrix} 1 & 0 \\ 0 & 1 \end{bmatrix} \quad O = \begin{bmatrix} 0 & 0 \\ 0 & 0 \end{bmatrix} \quad R = \begin{bmatrix} .1 & 0 \\ .1 & .4 \end{bmatrix} \quad Q = \begin{bmatrix} .6 & .3 \\ 0 & .5 \end{bmatrix}$$

Thus,

$$F = (I - Q)^{-1} = \left(\begin{bmatrix} 1 & 0 \\ 0 & 1 \end{bmatrix} - \begin{bmatrix} .6 & .3 \\ 0 & .5 \end{bmatrix} \right)^{-1}$$

$$= \begin{bmatrix} .4 & -.3 \\ 0 & .5 \end{bmatrix}^{-1} \quad \text{Use row operations to find this matrix inverse.}$$

$$= \begin{bmatrix} 2.5 & 1.5 \\ 0 & 2 \end{bmatrix}$$

and

$$FR = \begin{bmatrix} 2.5 & 1.5 \\ 0 & 2 \end{bmatrix} \begin{bmatrix} .1 & 0 \\ .1 & .4 \end{bmatrix} = \begin{bmatrix} .4 & .6 \\ .2 & .8 \end{bmatrix}$$

The limiting matrix is

$$\overline{P} = \begin{array}{c} \\ D \\ G \\ F \\ S \end{array} \begin{array}{c} \begin{array}{cccc} D & G & F & S \end{array} \\ \begin{bmatrix} 1 & 0 & 0 & 0 \\ 0 & 1 & 0 & 0 \\ .4 & .6 & 0 & 0 \\ .2 & .8 & 0 & 0 \end{bmatrix} \end{array} \quad \begin{bmatrix} I & | & O \\ \hline FR & | & O \end{bmatrix}$$

From this limiting form, we see that in the long run 60% of the first-year students will graduate and 20% of the second-year students will not graduate.

(B) The sum of the entries in the first row of the fundamental matrix F is $2.5 + 1.5 = 4$. According to Theorem 3, this indicates that a first-year student will spend an average of 4 years in the transient states F and S before reaching one of the absorbing states, D or G. The sum of the entries in the second row of F is $0 + 2 = 2$. Thus, a second-year student spends an average of 2 years in the program before either graduating or dropping out. ▬▬

MATCHED PROBLEM 5

Repeat Example 5 for the following transition diagram:

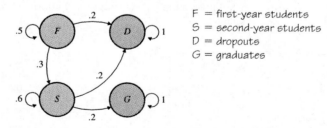

F = first-year students
S = second-year students
D = dropouts
G = graduates

▓ Graphing Calculator Approximations

Just as was the case for regular Markov chains, the limiting matrix $\overline{P}$ for an absorbing Markov chain with transition matrix P can be approximated by computing P^k on a graphing calculator for sufficiently large values of k. For example, computing P^{50} for the standard form P in Example 5 produces the following results:

$$P^{50} = \begin{bmatrix} 1 & 0 & 0 & 0 \\ 0 & 1 & 0 & 0 \\ .1 & 0 & .6 & .3 \\ .1 & .4 & 0 & .5 \end{bmatrix}^{50} = \begin{bmatrix} 1 & 0 & 0 & 0 \\ 0 & 1 & 0 & 0 \\ .4 & .6 & 0 & 0 \\ .2 & .8 & 0 & 0 \end{bmatrix} = \overline{P}$$

where once again we have replaced very small numbers displayed in scientific notation with 0 (see Insight 2 on page 000 in Section 9-2).

 CAUTION Before you use P^k to approximate $\overline{P}$, be certain to determine that $\overline{P}$ does in fact exist. If you attempt to approximate a limiting matrix when none exists, the results can be misleading. For example, consider the transition matrix

$$P = \begin{bmatrix} 1 & 0 & 0 & 0 & 0 \\ .2 & .2 & 0 & .3 & .3 \\ 0 & 0 & 0 & .5 & .5 \\ 0 & 0 & 1 & 0 & 0 \\ 0 & 0 & 1 & 0 & 0 \end{bmatrix}$$

Computing P^{50} on a graphing calculator produces the following matrix:

$$P^{50} = \begin{bmatrix} 1 & 0 & 0 & 0 & 0 \\ .25 & 0 & .625 & .0625 & .0625 \\ 0 & 0 & 1 & 0 & 0 \\ 0 & 0 & 0 & .5 & .5 \\ 0 & 0 & 0 & .5 & .5 \end{bmatrix} \quad (2)$$

It is tempting to stop at this point and conclude that the matrix in (2) must be a good approximation for $\overline{P}$. But to do so would be incorrect! If P^{50} approximates a limiting matrix $\overline{P}$, then P^{51} should also approximate the same matrix. However, computing P^{51} produces quite a different matrix:

$$P^{51} = \begin{bmatrix} 1 & 0 & 0 & 0 & 0 \\ .25 & 0 & .125 & .3125 & .3125 \\ 0 & 0 & 0 & .5 & .5 \\ 0 & 0 & 1 & 0 & 0 \\ 0 & 0 & 1 & 0 & 0 \end{bmatrix} \quad (3)$$

Computing additional powers of P shows that the even powers of P approach matrix (2) while the odd powers approach matrix (3). Thus, the transition matrix P does not have a limiting matrix.

A graphing calculator also can be used to perform the matrix calculations necessary to find $\overline{P}$ exactly, as illustrated in Figure 2 for the transition matrix P from Example 5. This approach has the advantage of producing the fundamental matrix F whose row sums provide additional information about the long-run behavior of the chain.

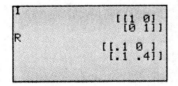

(A) Store I and R in the graphing calculator memory

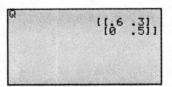

(B) Store Q in the graphing calculator memory

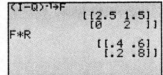

(C) Compute F and FR

FIGURE 2 Matrix calculations

Answers to Matched Problems   **1.** (A) State B is absorbing.

(B) State C is absorbing.

2. (A) Absorbing Markov chain

(B) Not an absorbing Markov chain

3. (A)

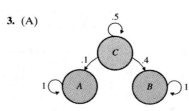

$$(B) \quad P = \begin{array}{c} \\ A \\ B \\ C \end{array} \begin{array}{ccc} A & B & C \\ \left[\begin{array}{ccc} 1 & 0 & 0 \\ 0 & 1 & 0 \\ .1 & .4 & .5 \end{array}\right] \end{array}$$

(C) Company *A* will purchase 20% of the farms and company *B* will purchase 80%.

(D) Company *A* will purchase 60% of the farms and company *B* will purchase 40%.

4. (A) $\overline{P} = \begin{array}{c} \\ A \\ B \\ C \end{array} \begin{array}{ccc} A & B & C \\ \left[\begin{array}{ccc} 1 & 0 & 0 \\ 0 & 1 & 0 \\ .2 & .8 & 0 \end{array}\right] \end{array}$ **(B)** [.2 .8 0] **(C)** [.6 .4 0]

5. (A) 30% of the first-year students will graduate; 50% of the second-year students will not graduate.

(B) A first-year student will spend an average of 3.5 years in the program; a second-year student will spend an average of 2.5 years in the program.

Exercise 9-3

A *In Problems 1–6, identify the absorbing states in the indicated transition matrix.*

1. $P = \begin{array}{c} \\ A \\ B \\ C \end{array} \begin{array}{ccc} A & B & C \\ \left[\begin{array}{ccc} .6 & .3 & .1 \\ 0 & 1 & 0 \\ 0 & 0 & 1 \end{array}\right] \end{array}$

2. $P = \begin{array}{c} \\ A \\ B \\ C \end{array} \begin{array}{ccc} A & B & C \\ \left[\begin{array}{ccc} 0 & 1 & 0 \\ .3 & .2 & .5 \\ 0 & 0 & 1 \end{array}\right] \end{array}$

3. $P = \begin{array}{c} \\ A \\ B \\ C \end{array} \begin{array}{ccc} A & B & C \\ \left[\begin{array}{ccc} 0 & 0 & 1 \\ 1 & 0 & 0 \\ 0 & 1 & 0 \end{array}\right] \end{array}$

4. $P = \begin{array}{c} \\ A \\ B \\ C \end{array} \begin{array}{ccc} A & B & C \\ \left[\begin{array}{ccc} 1 & 0 & 0 \\ .3 & .4 & .3 \\ 0 & 0 & 1 \end{array}\right] \end{array}$

5. $P = \begin{array}{c} \\ A \\ B \\ C \\ D \end{array} \begin{array}{cccc} A & B & C & D \\ \left[\begin{array}{cccc} 1 & 0 & 0 & 0 \\ 0 & 0 & 1 & 0 \\ .1 & .1 & .5 & .3 \\ 0 & 0 & 0 & 1 \end{array}\right] \end{array}$

6. $P = \begin{array}{c} \\ A \\ B \\ C \\ D \end{array} \begin{array}{cccc} A & B & C & D \\ \left[\begin{array}{cccc} 0 & 1 & 0 & 0 \\ 1 & 0 & 0 & 0 \\ .1 & .2 & .3 & .4 \\ .7 & .1 & .1 & .1 \end{array}\right] \end{array}$

In Problems 7–10, identify the absorbing states for each transition diagram, and determine whether the diagram represents an absorbing Markov chain.

7.

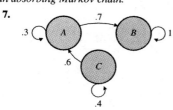

8.

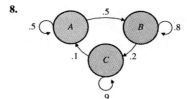

9.

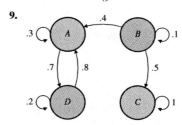

10.

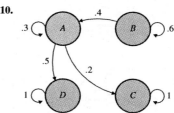

In Problems 11–20, could the given matrix be the transition matrix of an absorbing Markov chain?

11. $\begin{bmatrix} 0 & 1 \\ 1 & 0 \end{bmatrix}$

12. $\begin{bmatrix} 1 & 0 \\ 0 & 1 \end{bmatrix}$

13. $\begin{bmatrix} .3 & .7 \\ 0 & 1 \end{bmatrix}$

14. $\begin{bmatrix} .6 & .4 \\ 1 & 0 \end{bmatrix}$

15. $\begin{bmatrix} 1 & 0 & 0 \\ 0 & 1 & 0 \\ 0 & 0 & 1 \end{bmatrix}$

16. $\begin{bmatrix} 0 & 1 & 0 \\ 0 & 0 & 1 \\ 1 & 0 & 0 \end{bmatrix}$

17. $\begin{bmatrix} .9 & .1 & 0 \\ .1 & .9 & 0 \\ 0 & 0 & 1 \end{bmatrix}$

18. $\begin{bmatrix} .5 & .5 & 0 \\ .4 & .3 & .3 \\ 0 & 0 & 1 \end{bmatrix}$

19. $\begin{bmatrix} .9 & 0 & .1 \\ 0 & 1 & 0 \\ 0 & .2 & .8 \end{bmatrix}$

20. $\begin{bmatrix} 1 & 0 & 0 \\ 0 & 0 & 1 \\ 0 & .7 & .3 \end{bmatrix}$

B   *In Problems 21–24, find a standard form for the absorbing Markov chain with the indicated transition diagram.*

21.

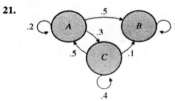

22.

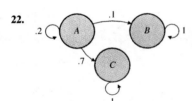

23.

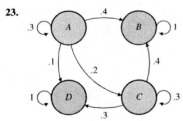

24.

In Problems 25–28, find a standard form for the absorbing Markov chain with the indicated transition matrix.

25. $P = \begin{array}{c} \\ A \\ B \\ C \end{array} \begin{array}{c} \begin{matrix} A & B & C \end{matrix} \\ \begin{bmatrix} .2 & .3 & .5 \\ 1 & 0 & 0 \\ 0 & 0 & 1 \end{bmatrix} \end{array}$

26. $P = \begin{array}{c} \\ A \\ B \\ C \end{array} \begin{array}{c} \begin{matrix} A & B & C \end{matrix} \\ \begin{bmatrix} 0 & 0 & 1 \\ 0 & 1 & 0 \\ .7 & .2 & .1 \end{bmatrix} \end{array}$

27. $P = \begin{array}{c} \\ A \\ B \\ C \\ D \end{array} \begin{array}{c} \begin{matrix} A & B & C & D \end{matrix} \\ \begin{bmatrix} .1 & .2 & .3 & .4 \\ 0 & 1 & 0 & 0 \\ .5 & .2 & .2 & .1 \\ 0 & 0 & 0 & 1 \end{bmatrix} \end{array}$

28. $P = \begin{array}{c} \\ A \\ B \\ C \\ D \end{array} \begin{array}{c} \begin{matrix} A & B & C & D \end{matrix} \\ \begin{bmatrix} 0 & .3 & .3 & .4 \\ 0 & 1 & 0 & 0 \\ 0 & 0 & 1 & 0 \\ .8 & .1 & .1 & 0 \end{bmatrix} \end{array}$

In Problems 29–34, find the limiting matrix for the indicated standard form. Find the long-run probability of going from each nonabsorbing state to each absorbing state and the average number of trials needed to go from each nonabsorbing state to an absorbing state.

29. $P = \begin{array}{c} \\ A \\ B \\ C \end{array} \begin{array}{c} \begin{matrix} A & B & C \end{matrix} \\ \begin{bmatrix} 1 & 0 & 0 \\ 0 & 1 & 0 \\ .1 & .4 & .5 \end{bmatrix} \end{array}$

30. $P = \begin{array}{c} \\ A \\ B \\ C \end{array} \begin{array}{c} \begin{matrix} A & B & C \end{matrix} \\ \begin{bmatrix} 1 & 0 & 0 \\ 0 & 1 & 0 \\ .3 & .2 & .5 \end{bmatrix} \end{array}$

31. $P = \begin{array}{c} \\ A \\ B \\ C \end{array} \begin{array}{c} \begin{matrix} A & B & C \end{matrix} \\ \begin{bmatrix} 1 & 0 & 0 \\ .2 & .6 & .2 \\ .4 & .2 & .4 \end{bmatrix} \end{array}$

32. $P = \begin{array}{c} \\ A \\ B \\ C \end{array} \begin{array}{c} \begin{matrix} A & B & C \end{matrix} \\ \begin{bmatrix} 1 & 0 & 0 \\ .1 & .6 & .3 \\ .2 & .2 & .6 \end{bmatrix} \end{array}$

33. $P = \begin{array}{c} \\ A \\ B \\ C \\ D \end{array} \begin{array}{c} \begin{matrix} A & B & C & D \end{matrix} \\ \begin{bmatrix} 1 & 0 & 0 & 0 \\ 0 & 1 & 0 & 0 \\ .1 & .2 & .6 & .1 \\ .2 & .2 & .3 & .3 \end{bmatrix} \end{array}$

34. $P = \begin{array}{c} \\ A \\ B \\ C \\ D \end{array} \begin{array}{c} \begin{matrix} A & B & C & D \end{matrix} \\ \begin{bmatrix} 1 & 0 & 0 & 0 \\ 0 & 1 & 0 & 0 \\ .1 & .1 & .7 & .1 \\ .3 & .1 & .4 & .2 \end{bmatrix} \end{array}$

Problems 35–40 refer to the matrices in Problems 29–34, as indicated. Use the limiting matrix $\overline{P}$ found for each transition matrix P in Problems 29–34 to determine the long-run behavior of the successive state matrices for the indicated initial-state matrices.

35. For matrix P from Problem 29 with

   (A) $S_0 = [0 \quad 0 \quad 1]$ (B) $S_0 = [.2 \quad .5 \quad .3]$

36. For matrix P from Problem 30 with

   (A) $S_0 = [0 \quad 0 \quad 1]$ (B) $S_0 = [.2 \quad .5 \quad .3]$

37. For matrix P from Problem 31 with

   (A) $S_0 = [0 \quad 0 \quad 1]$ (B) $S_0 = [.2 \quad .5 \quad .3]$

38. For matrix P from Problem 32 with

   (A) $S_0 = [0 \quad 0 \quad 1]$ (B) $S_0 = [.2 \quad .5 \quad .3]$

39. For matrix P from Problem 33 with

   (A) $S_0 = [0 \quad 0 \quad 0 \quad 1]$

   (B) $S_0 = [0 \quad 0 \quad 1 \quad 0]$

   (C) $S_0 = [0 \quad 0 \quad .4 \quad .6]$

   (D) $S_0 = [.1 \quad .2 \quad .3 \quad .4]$

40. For matrix P from Problem 34 with

   (A) $S_0 = [0 \quad 0 \quad 0 \quad 1]$

   (B) $S_0 = [0 \quad 0 \quad 1 \quad 0]$

   (C) $S_0 = [0 \quad 0 \quad .4 \quad .6]$

   (D) $S_0 = [.1 \quad .2 \quad .3 \quad .4]$

In Problems 41 and 42, discuss the validity of each statement. If the statement is always true, explain why. If not, give a counterexample.

41. (A) If every state of a Markov chain is absorbing, it is an absorbing chain.

   (B) If a Markov chain has absorbing states, it is an absorbing chain.

42. (A) In an absorbing Markov chain, if a nonabsorbing state is exited, it can never be entered again.

   (B) An absorbing Markov chain can have an infinite number of stationary matrices.

In Problems 43–46, use a graphing calculator to approximate the limiting matrix for the indicated standard form.

43.
$$P = \begin{array}{c} \\ A \\ B \\ C \\ D \end{array} \begin{array}{c} \begin{array}{cccc} A & B & C & D \end{array} \\ \begin{bmatrix} 1 & 0 & 0 & 0 \\ 0 & 1 & 0 & 0 \\ .5 & .3 & .1 & .1 \\ .6 & .2 & .1 & .1 \end{bmatrix} \end{array}$$

44.
$$P = \begin{array}{c} \\ A \\ B \\ C \\ D \end{array} \begin{array}{c} \begin{array}{cccc} A & B & C & D \end{array} \\ \begin{bmatrix} 1 & 0 & 0 & 0 \\ 0 & 1 & 0 & 0 \\ .1 & .1 & .5 & .3 \\ 0 & .2 & .3 & .5 \end{bmatrix} \end{array}$$

45.
$$P = \begin{array}{c} \\ A \\ B \\ C \\ D \\ E \end{array} \begin{array}{c} \begin{array}{ccccc} A & B & C & D & E \end{array} \\ \begin{bmatrix} 1 & 0 & 0 & 0 & 0 \\ 0 & 1 & 0 & 0 & 0 \\ 0 & .4 & .5 & 0 & .1 \\ 0 & .4 & 0 & .3 & .3 \\ .4 & .4 & 0 & .2 & 0 \end{bmatrix} \end{array}$$

46.
$$P = \begin{array}{c} \\ A \\ B \\ C \\ D \\ E \end{array} \begin{array}{c} \begin{array}{ccccc} A & B & C & D & E \end{array} \\ \begin{bmatrix} 1 & 0 & 0 & 0 & 0 \\ 0 & 1 & 0 & 0 & 0 \\ .5 & 0 & 0 & 0 & .5 \\ 0 & .4 & 0 & .2 & .4 \\ 0 & 0 & .1 & .7 & .2 \end{bmatrix} \end{array}$$

47. The following matrix P is a nonstandard transition matrix for an absorbing Markov chain:

$$P = \begin{array}{c} \\ A \\ B \\ C \\ D \end{array} \begin{array}{c} \begin{array}{cccc} A & B & C & D \end{array} \\ \begin{bmatrix} .2 & .2 & .6 & 0 \\ 0 & 1 & 0 & 0 \\ .5 & .1 & 0 & .4 \\ 0 & 0 & 0 & 1 \end{bmatrix} \end{array}$$

To find a limiting matrix for P, follow the steps outlined below.

   Step 1. Using a transition diagram as an aid, rearrange the columns and rows of P to produce a standard form for this chain.

   Step 2. Find the limiting matrix for this standard form.

   Step 3. Using a transition diagram as an aid, reverse the process used in step 1 to produce a limiting matrix for the original matrix P.

48. Repeat Problem 47 for

$$P = \begin{array}{c} \\ A \\ B \\ C \\ D \end{array} \begin{array}{c} \begin{array}{cccc} A & B & C & D \end{array} \\ \begin{bmatrix} 1 & 0 & 0 & 0 \\ .3 & .6 & 0 & .1 \\ .2 & .3 & .5 & 0 \\ 0 & 0 & 0 & 1 \end{bmatrix} \end{array}$$

49. Verify the results in Problem 47 by computing P^k on a graphing calculator for large values of k.

50. Verify the results in Problem 48 by computing P^k on a graphing calculator for large values of k.

51. Show that $S = [x \quad 1 - x \quad 0], 0 \le x \le 1$, is a stationary matrix for the transition matrix

$$P = \begin{array}{c} \\ A \\ B \\ C \end{array} \begin{array}{c} \begin{array}{ccc} A & B & C \end{array} \\ \begin{bmatrix} 1 & 0 & 0 \\ 0 & 1 & 0 \\ .1 & .5 & .4 \end{bmatrix} \end{array}$$

Discuss the generalization of this result to any absorbing Markov chain with two absorbing states and one nonabsorbing state.

52. Show that $S = [x \quad 1 - x \quad 0 \quad 0], 0 \le x \le 1$, is a stationary matrix for the transition matrix

$$P = \begin{array}{c} \\ A \\ B \\ C \\ D \end{array} \begin{array}{c} \begin{array}{cccc} A & B & C & D \end{array} \\ \begin{bmatrix} 1 & 0 & 0 & 0 \\ 0 & 1 & 0 & 0 \\ .1 & .2 & .3 & .4 \\ .6 & .2 & .1 & .1 \end{bmatrix} \end{array}$$

Discuss the generalization of this result to any absorbing Markov chain with two absorbing states and two nonabsorbing states.

53. An absorbing Markov chain has the following matrix P as a standard form:

$$P = \begin{array}{c} \\ A \\ B \\ C \\ D \end{array} \begin{array}{cccc} A & B & C & D \\ \left[\begin{array}{cccc} 1 & 0 & 0 & 0 \\ .2 & .3 & .1 & .4 \\ 0 & .5 & .3 & .2 \\ 0 & .1 & .6 & .3 \end{array} \right] \end{array} \left[\begin{array}{c|c} I & O \\ \hline R & Q \end{array} \right]$$

Let w_k denote the maximum entry in Q^k. Note that $w_1 = .6$

(A) Find w_2, w_4, w_8, w_{16}, and w_{32} to three decimal places.

(B) Describe Q^k when k is large.

 54. Refer to the matrices P and Q of Problem 53. For k a positive integer, let $T_k = I + Q + Q^2 + \cdots + Q^k$.

(A) Explain why $T_{k+1} = T_k Q + I$.

(B) Using a graphing calculator and part (A) to quickly compute the matrices T_k, discover and describe the connection between $(I - Q)^{-1}$ and T_k when k is large.

Applications

55. *Loans.* A credit union classifies automobile loans into one of four categories: the loan has been paid in full (F), the account is in good standing (G) with all payments up to date, the account is in arrears (A) with one or more missing payments, or the account has been classified as a bad debt (B) and sold to a collection agency. Past records indicate that each month 10% of the accounts in good standing pay the loan in full, 80% remain in good standing, and 10% become in arrears. Furthermore, 10% of the accounts in arrears are paid in full, 40% become accounts in good standing, 40% remain in arrears, and 10% are classified as bad debts.

(A) In the long run, what percentage of the accounts in arrears will pay their loan in full?

(B) In the long run, what percentage of the accounts in good standing will become bad debts?

(C) What is the average number of months an account in arrears will remain in this system before it is either paid in full or classified as a bad debt?

56. *Employee training.* A national chain of automobile muffler and brake repair shops maintains a training program for its mechanics. All new mechanics begin training in muffler repairs. Every 3 months the performance of each mechanic is reviewed. Past records indicate that after each quarterly review, 30% of the muffler repair trainees are rated as qualified to repair mufflers and begin training in brake repairs, 20% are terminated for unsatisfactory performance, and the remainder continue as muffler repair trainees. Also, 30% of the brake repair trainees are rated as fully qualified mechanics requiring no further training, 10% are terminated for unsatisfactory performance, and the remainder continue as brake repair trainees.

(A) In the long run, what percentage of the muffler repair trainees will become fully qualified mechanics?

(B) In the long run, what percentage of the brake repair trainees will be terminated?

(C) What is the average number of quarters a muffler repair trainee will remain in the training program before being either terminated or promoted to fully qualified mechanic?

57. *Marketing.* Three electronics firms are aggressively marketing their graphing calculators to high school and college mathematics departments by offering volume discounts, complimentary display equipment, and assistance with curriculum development. Due to the amount of equipment involved and the necessary curriculum changes, once a department decides to use a particular calculator in their courses, they never switch to another brand or stop using calculators. Each year, 6% of the departments decide to use calculators from company A, 3% decide to use calculators from company B, 11% decide to use calculators from company C, and the remainder decide not to use any calculators in their courses.

(A) In the long run, what is the market share of each company?

(B) On the average, how many years will it take a department to decide to use calculators from one of these companies in their courses?

58. *Pensions.* Once a year employees at a company are given the opportunity to join one of three pension plans, A, B, or C. Once an employee decides to join one of these plans, the employee cannot drop the plan or switch to another plan. Past records indicate that each year 4% of the employees elect to join plan A, 14% elect to join plan B, 7% elect to join plan C, and the remainder do not join any plan.

(A) In the long run, what percentage of the employees will elect to join plan A? Plan B? Plan C?

(B) On the average, how many years will it take an employee to decide to join a plan?

59. *Medicine.* After bypass surgery, patients are placed in an intensive care unit (ICU) until their condition stabilizes. Then they are transferred to a cardiac care ward (CCW) where they remain until they are released from the hospital. In a particular metropolitan area, a study of hospital records produced the following data: each day 2% of the patients in the ICU died, 52% were transferred to the CCW, and the remainder stayed in the ICU. Furthermore, each day 4% of the patients in the CCW developed complications and were returned to the ICU, 1% died while in the CCW, 22% were released from the hospital, and the remainder stayed in the CCW.

(A) In the long run, what percentage of the patients in the ICU are released from the hospital?

(B) In the long run, what percentage of the patients in the CCW die without ever being released from the hospital?

(C) What is the average number of days a patient in the ICU will stay in the hospital?

60. *Medicine.* The study discussed in Problem 59 also produced the following data for patients who underwent aortic valve replacements: each day 2% of the patients in the ICU died, 60% were transferred to the CCW, and the remainder stayed in the ICU. Furthermore, each day 5% of the patients in the CCW developed complications and were returned to the ICU, 1% died while in the CCW, 19% were released from the hospital, and the remainder stayed in the CCW.

(A) In the long run, what percentage of the patients in the CCW are released from the hospital?

(B) In the long run, what percentage of the patients in the ICU die without ever being released from the hospital?

(C) What is the average number of days a patient in the CCW will stay in the hospital?

61. *Psychology.* A rat is placed in room *F* or room *B* of the maze shown in the figure. The rat wanders from room to room until it enters one of the rooms containing food, *L* or *R*.

Assume that the rat chooses an exit from a room at random and that once it enters a room with food it never leaves.

(A) What is the long-run probability that a rat placed in room *B* ends up in room *R*?

(B) What is the average number of exits a rat placed in room *B* will choose until it finds food?

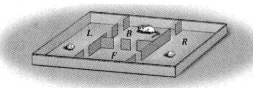

Figure for 61 and 62

62. *Psychology.* Repeat Problem 61 if the exit from room *B* to room *R* is blocked.

CHAPTER 9 REVIEW

Important Terms, Symbols, and Concepts

9-1 Properties of Markov Chains

Examples

- The progression of a system through a sequence of states is called a **stochastic process** if chance elements are involved in the transition from one state to the next.
- A **transition diagram** or **transition probability matrix** can be used to represent the probabilities of moving from one state to another. If those probabilities do not change with time, the stochastic process is called a **Markov chain.**
- If a Markov chain has *n* states, then the entry S_{ki} of the **kth-state matrix**

$$S_k = [S_{k1} \quad S_{k2} \cdots \quad S_{kn}]$$

gives the probability of being in state *i* after the *k*th trial. The sum of the entries in S_k is 1.

- The entry $p_{i,j}$ of the $n \times n$ **transition matrix** *P* gives the probability of moving from state *i* to state *j* on the next trial. The sum of the entries in each row of *P* is 1. — Ex. 1, p. 458
- If S_0 is an initial-state matrix for a Markov chain, then $S_k = S_0P^k$ (Theorem 1, page 459). — Ex. 2, p. 460 / Ex. 3, p. 460 / Ex. 4, p. 460

9-2 Regular Markov Chains

- A transition matrix *P* is **regular** is some power of *P* has only positive entries. — Ex. 1, p. 468
- A Markov chain is a **regular Markov chain** if its transition matrix is regular.
- A state matrix *S* is **stationary** if $SP = S$. — Ex. 2, p. 469
- The state matrices for a regular Markov chain approach a unique stationary matrix (Theorem 1, page 468). — Ex. 3, p. 470 / Ex. 4, p. 470 / Ex. 5, p. 471

9-3 Absorbing Markov Chains

- A state in a Markov chain is an **absorbing state** if once the state is entered it is impossible to leave. A state is absorbing if and only if its row in the transition matrix has a 1 on the main diagonal and 0's elsewhere. — Ex. 1, p. 477
- A Markov chain is an **absorbing Markov chain** if there is at least one absorbing state and it is possible to go from each nonabsorbing state to at least one absorbing state in a finite number of steps. — Ex. 2, p. 478
- A transition matrix for an absorbing Markov chain is a **standard form** if the rows and columns are labeled so that all the absorbing states precede all the nonabsorbing states.

- If a standard form P for an absorbing Markov chain is partitioned as

$$P = \left[\begin{array}{c|c} I & 0 \\ \hline R & Q \end{array}\right]$$

Ex. 3, p. 480
Ex. 4, p. 482

then P^k approaches a limiting matrix $\overline{P}$ as k increases, where

$$\overline{P} = \left[\begin{array}{c|c} I & 0 \\ \hline FR & 0 \end{array}\right]$$

The matrix $F = (I - Q)^{-1}$, where I is the identity matrix of the same size as Q, is called the **fundamental matrix** for P (Theorem 2, page 482).

- The entry in row i and column j of $\overline{P}$ is the long-run probability of going from state i to state j. The sum of the entries in each row of F is the average number of trials it will take to go from each nonabsorbing state to some absorbing state (Theorem 3, page 484).

Ex. 5, p. 484

REVIEW EXERCISE

Work through all the problems in this chapter review and check your answers in the back of the book. Answers to all review problems are there along with section numbers in italics to indicate where each type of problem is discussed. Where weaknesses show up, review appropriate sections in the text.

A

1. Given the transition matrix P and initial-state matrix S_0 shown below, find S_1 and S_2 and explain what each represents:

$$P = \begin{array}{c} \\ A \\ B \end{array}\begin{array}{cc} A & B \\ \left[\begin{array}{cc} .6 & .4 \\ .2 & .8 \end{array}\right] \end{array} \qquad S_0 = [.3 \quad .7]$$

In Problems 2–6, P is a transition matrix for a Markov chain. Identify any absorbing states and classify the chain as regular, absorbing, or neither.

2. $P = \begin{array}{c} A \\ B \end{array}\begin{array}{c} \overset{A \quad B}{\left[\begin{array}{cc} 1 & 0 \\ .7 & .3 \end{array}\right]} \end{array}$

3. $P = \begin{array}{c} A \\ B \end{array}\begin{array}{c} \overset{A \quad B}{\left[\begin{array}{cc} 0 & 1 \\ .7 & .3 \end{array}\right]} \end{array}$

4. $P = \begin{array}{c} A \\ B \end{array}\begin{array}{c} \overset{A \quad B}{\left[\begin{array}{cc} 0 & 1 \\ 1 & 0 \end{array}\right]} \end{array}$

5. $P = \begin{array}{c} A \\ B \\ C \end{array}\begin{array}{c} \overset{A \quad B \quad C}{\left[\begin{array}{ccc} .8 & 0 & .2 \\ 0 & 1 & 0 \\ 0 & 0 & 1 \end{array}\right]} \end{array}$

6. $P = \begin{array}{c} A \\ B \\ C \\ D \end{array}\begin{array}{c} \overset{A \quad B \quad C \quad D}{\left[\begin{array}{cccc} 1 & 0 & 0 & 0 \\ 0 & 1 & 0 & 0 \\ 0 & 0 & .3 & .7 \\ 0 & 0 & .6 & .4 \end{array}\right]} \end{array}$

In Problems 7–10, write a transition matrix for the transition diagram indicated, identify any absorbing states, and classify each Markov chain as regular, absorbing, or neither.

7.

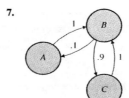

8.

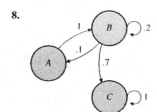

9.

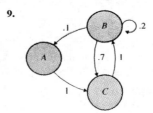

10.

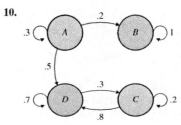

B

11. A Markov chain has three states, A, B, and C. The probability of going from state A to state B in one trial is .2, the probability of going from state A to state C in one trial is .5, the probability of going from state B to state A in one trial is .8, the probability of going from state B to state C in one trial is .2, the probability of going from state C to state A in one trial is .1, and the probability of going from state C to state B in one trial is .3. Draw a transition diagram and write a transition matrix for this chain.

12. Given the transition matrix

$$P = \begin{matrix} & A & B \\ A & \\ B \end{matrix}\begin{bmatrix} .4 & .6 \\ .9 & .1 \end{bmatrix}$$

find the probability of
(A) Going from state A to state B in two trials
(B) Going from state B to state A in three trials

In Problems 13 and 14, solve the equation $SP = S$ to find the stationary matrix S and the limiting matrix $\overline{P}$.

13. $P = \begin{matrix} & A & B \\ A \\ B \end{matrix}\begin{bmatrix} .4 & .6 \\ .2 & .8 \end{bmatrix}$

14. $P = \begin{matrix} & A & B & C \\ A \\ B \\ C \end{matrix}\begin{bmatrix} .4 & .6 & 0 \\ .5 & .3 & .2 \\ 0 & .8 & .2 \end{bmatrix}$

In Problems 15 and 16, find the limiting matrix for the indicated standard form. Find the long-run probability of going from each nonabsorbing state to each absorbing state and the average number of trials needed to go from each nonabsorbing state to an absorbing state.

15. $P = \begin{matrix} & A & B & C \\ A \\ B \\ C \end{matrix}\begin{bmatrix} 1 & 0 & 0 \\ 0 & 1 & 0 \\ .3 & .1 & .6 \end{bmatrix}$

16. $P = \begin{matrix} & A & B & C & D \\ A \\ B \\ C \\ D \end{matrix}\begin{bmatrix} 1 & 0 & 0 & 0 \\ 0 & 1 & 0 & 0 \\ .1 & .5 & .2 & .2 \\ .1 & .1 & .4 & .4 \end{bmatrix}$

In Problems 17–20, use a graphing calculator to approximate the limiting matrix for the indicated transition matrix.

17. Matrix P from Problem 13
18. Matrix P from Problem 14
19. Matrix P from Problem 15
20. Matrix P from Problem 16
21. Find a standard form for the absorbing Markov chain with transition matrix

$$P = \begin{matrix} & A & B & C & D \\ A \\ B \\ C \\ D \end{matrix}\begin{bmatrix} .6 & .1 & .2 & .1 \\ 0 & 1 & 0 & 0 \\ .3 & .2 & .3 & .2 \\ 0 & 0 & 0 & 1 \end{bmatrix}$$

In Problems 22 and 23, determine the long-run behavior of the successive state matrices for the indicated transition matrix and initial-state matrices.

22. $P = \begin{matrix} & A & B & C \\ A \\ B \\ C \end{matrix}\begin{bmatrix} 0 & 1 & 0 \\ 0 & 0 & 1 \\ .2 & .6 & .2 \end{bmatrix}$
(A) $S_0 = [0 \quad 0 \quad 1]$
(B) $S_0 = [.5 \quad .3 \quad .2]$

23. $P = \begin{matrix} & A & B & C \\ A \\ B \\ C \end{matrix}\begin{bmatrix} 1 & 0 & 0 \\ 0 & 1 & 0 \\ .2 & .6 & .2 \end{bmatrix}$
(A) $S_0 = [0 \quad 0 \quad 1]$
(B) $S_0 = [.5 \quad .3 \quad .2]$

24. Let P be a 2×2 transition matrix for a Markov chain. Can P be regular if two of its entries are 0? Explain.

25. Let P be a 3×3 transition matrix for a Markov chain. Can P be regular if three of its entries are 0? If four of its entries are 0? Explain.

C

26. A red urn contains 2 red marbles, 1 blue marble, and 1 green marble. A blue urn contains 1 red marble, 3 blue marbles, and 1 green marble. A green urn contains 6 red marbles, 3 blue marbles, and 1 green marble. A marble is selected from an urn, the color is noted, and the marble is returned to the urn from which it was drawn. The next marble is drawn from the urn whose color is the same as the marble just drawn. Thus, this is a Markov process with three states: draw from the red urn, draw from the blue urn, or draw from the green urn.
(A) Draw a transition diagram for this process.
(B) Write the transition matrix P.
(C) Determine whether this chain is regular, absorbing, or neither.
(D) Find the limiting matrix $\overline{P}$, if it exists, and describe the long-run behavior of this process.

27. Repeat Problem 26 if the blue and green marbles are removed from the red urn.

28. Show that $S = [x \quad y \quad z \quad 0]$, where $0 \leq x \leq 1$, $0 \leq y \leq 1, 0 \leq z \leq 1$, and $x + y + z = 1$, is a stationary matrix for the transition matrix

$$P = \begin{matrix} & A & B & C & D \\ A \\ B \\ C \\ D \end{matrix}\begin{bmatrix} 1 & 0 & 0 & 0 \\ 0 & 1 & 0 & 0 \\ 0 & 0 & 1 & 0 \\ .1 & .3 & .4 & .2 \end{bmatrix}$$

Discuss the generalization of this result to any absorbing chain with three absorbing states and one nonabsorbing state.

In Problems 29–35, either give an example of a Markov chain with the indicated properties or explain why no such chain can exist.

29. A regular Markov chain with an absorbing state.

An absorbing Markov chain that is regular.

A regular Markov chain with two different stationary matrices.

An absorbing Markov chain with two different stationary matrices.

A Markov chain with no limiting matrix.

A regular Markov chain with no limiting matrix.

An absorbing Markov chain with no limiting matrix.

 In Problems 36 and 37, use a graphing calculator to approximate the entries (to three decimal places) of the limiting matrix, if it exists, of the indicated transition matrix.

36. $P = \begin{array}{c} \\ A \\ B \\ C \\ D \end{array} \begin{array}{cccc} A & B & C & D \\ \left[\begin{array}{cccc} .2 & .3 & .1 & .4 \\ 0 & 0 & 1 & 0 \\ 0 & .8 & 0 & .2 \\ 0 & 0 & 1 & 0 \end{array} \right] \end{array}$

37. $P = \begin{array}{c} \\ A \\ B \\ C \\ D \end{array} \begin{array}{cccc} A & B & C & D \\ \left[\begin{array}{cccc} .1 & 0 & .3 & .6 \\ .2 & .4 & .1 & .3 \\ .3 & .5 & 0 & .2 \\ .9 & .1 & 0 & 0 \end{array} \right] \end{array}$

APPLICATIONS

Product switching. A company's brand (X) has 20% of the market. A market research firm finds that if a person uses brand X, the probability is .7 that he or she will buy it next time. On the other hand, if a person does not use brand X (represented by X'), the probability is .5 that he or she will switch to brand X the next time.

(A) Draw a transition diagram.

(B) Write a transition matrix.

(C) Write the initial-state matrix.

(D) Find the first-state matrix and explain what it represents.

(E) Find the stationary matrix.

(F) What percentage of the market will brand X have in the long run if the transition matrix does not change?

Marketing. Recent technological advances have led to the development of three new milling machines, brand A, brand B, and brand C. Due to the extensive retooling and startup costs, once a company converts its machine shop to one of these new machines, it never switches to another brand. Each year 6% of the machine shops convert to brand A machines, 8% convert to brand B machines, 11% convert to brand C machines, and the remainder continue to use their old machines.

(A) In the long run, what is the market share of each brand?

(B) What is the average number of years a company waits before converting to one of the new milling machines?

Internet. Table 1 gives the percentage of U.S. adults who at least occasionally used the Internet in the given year.

TABLE 1

Year	Percent
1995	14
2000	49
2005	68

Source: Pew Internet & American Life Project Surveys

The following transition matrix P is proposed as a model for the data, where I represents the population of Internet users.

$$\begin{array}{cc} & \text{Five years later} \\ & \begin{array}{cc} I & I' \end{array} \\ \begin{array}{c} \text{Current} \ \ I \\ \text{Year} \ \ I' \end{array} & \left[\begin{array}{cc} .95 & .05 \\ .40 & .60 \end{array} \right] = P \end{array}$$

(A) Let $S_0 = [.14 \ \ .86]$, and find S_1 and S_2. (Compute both matrices exactly and then round entries to two decimal places.)

(B) Construct a new table comparing the results from part (A) with the data in Table 1.

(C) According to this transition matrix, what percentage of the adult U.S. population will be online in the long run?

41. *Employee training.* In order to become a Fellow of the Society of Actuaries, a person must pass a series of ten examinations given by the society. Passage of the first two preliminary exams is a prerequisite for employment as a trainee in the actuarial department of a large insurance company. Each year 15% of the trainees complete the next three exams in the program and become associates of the Society of Actuaries, 5% leave the company, never to return, and the remainder continue as trainees. Furthermore, each year 17% of the associates complete the remaining five exams and become fellows of the Society of Actuaries, 3% leave the company, never to return, and the remainder continue as associates.

(A) In the long run, what percentage of the trainees will become fellows?

(B) In the long run, what percentage of the associates will leave the company?

(C) What is the average number of years a trainee remains in this program before either becoming a fellow or being discharged?

42. *Genetics.* A given plant species has red, pink, or white flowers according to the genotypes RR, RW, and WW, respectively. If each of these genotypes is crossed with a red-flowering plant, the transition matrix is

Next generation

$$\begin{array}{c}\text{This}\\\text{generation}\end{array}\begin{array}{c}Red\\Pink\\White\end{array}\begin{array}{ccc}Red & Pink & White\\\begin{bmatrix}1 & 0 & 0\\.5 & .5 & 0\\0 & 1 & 0\end{bmatrix}\end{array}$$

If each generation of the plant is crossed only with red plants to produce the next generation, show that eventually all the flowers produced by the plants will be red. (Find the limiting matrix.)

43. *Smoking.* Table 2 gives the percentage of U.S. adults who were smokers in the given year.

TABLE 2

Year	Percent
1985	30.1
1995	24.7
2005	20.9

Source: American Lung Association

The following transition matrix P is proposed as a model for the data, where S represents the population of smokers.

Five years later

$$\begin{array}{c}\text{Current}\\\text{year}\end{array}\begin{array}{c}S\\S'\end{array}\begin{array}{cc}S & S'\\\begin{bmatrix}.74 & .26\\.03 & .97\end{bmatrix}\end{array} = P$$

(A) Let $S_0 = [.301 \quad .699]$, and find S_1 and S_2. (Compute the matrices exactly and then round entries to three decimal places.)

(B) Construct a new table comparing the results from part (A) with the data in Table 2.

(C) According to this transition matrix, what percentage of the adult U.S. population will be smokers in the long run?

ANSWERS

CHAPTER 9
Exercise 9-1

1. $S_1 = \begin{matrix} A & B \\ [.8 & .2] \end{matrix}$; the probability of being in state A after one trial is .8, and the probability of being in state B after one trial is .2.

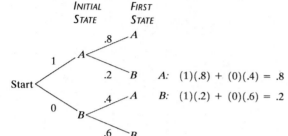

INITIAL STATE   FIRST STATE

A: $(1)(.8) + (0)(.4) = .8$
B: $(1)(.2) + (0)(.6) = .2$

3. $S_1 = \begin{matrix} A & B \\ [.6 & .4] \end{matrix}$; the probability of being in state A after one trial is .6, and the probability of being in state B after one trial is .4.

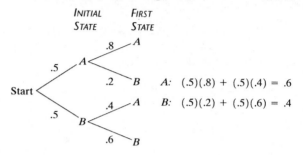

INITIAL STATE   FIRST STATE

A: $(.5)(.8) + (.5)(.4) = .6$
B: $(.5)(.2) + (.5)(.6) = .4$

5. $S_2 = \begin{matrix} A & B \\ [.72 & .28] \end{matrix}$; the probability of being in state A after two trials is .72, and the probability of being in state B after two trials is .28.

7. $S_2 = \begin{matrix} A & B \\ [.64 & .36] \end{matrix}$; the probability of being in state A after two trials is .64, and the probability of being in state B after two trials is .36.

9. Yes   11. No   13. No   15. Yes

17. 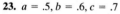 $\begin{matrix} & A & B \\ A & [.4 & .6 \\ B & .7 & .3] \end{matrix}$

19. No   21. $\begin{matrix} & A & B & C \\ A & [.1 & .4 & .5 \\ B & .5 & .2 & .3 \\ C & .7 & .2 & .1] \end{matrix}$

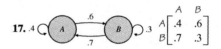

23. $a = .5, b = .6, c = .7$ 25. $a = .7, b = 1, c = .2$ 27. No

29. 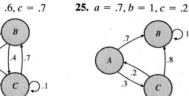 $\begin{matrix} & A & B \\ A & [.3 & .7 \\ B & .9 & .1] \end{matrix}$

31. 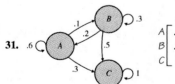 $\begin{matrix} & A & B & C \\ A & [.6 & .1 & .3 \\ B & .2 & .3 & .5 \\ C & 0 & 0 & 1] \end{matrix}$

33. .35   35. .212

37. $S_2 = \begin{matrix} A & B & C \\ [.43 & .35 & .22] \end{matrix}$; the probabilities of going from state A to states $A, B,$ and C in two trials

39. $S_3 = \begin{matrix} A & B & C \\ [.212 & .298 & .49] \end{matrix}$; the probabilities of going from state C to states $A, B,$ and C in three trials

41. $n = 9$ 43. $P^4 = \begin{matrix} & A & B \\ A & [.4375 & .5625 \\ B & .375 & .625] \end{matrix}$; $S_4 = \begin{matrix} A & B \\ [.425 & .575] \end{matrix}$

45. $P^4 = \begin{matrix} & A & B & C \\ A & [.36 & .16 & .48 \\ B & .6 & 0 & .4 \\ C & .4 & .24 & .36] \end{matrix}$; $S_4 = \begin{matrix} A & B & C \\ [.452 & .152 & .396] \end{matrix}$

49. (A) $\begin{matrix} & A & B & C & D \\ A & [.0154 & .3534 & .0153 & .6159 \\ B & 0 & 1 & 0 & 0 \\ C & .0102 & .2962 & .0103 & .6833 \\ D & 0 & 0 & 0 & 1] \end{matrix}$ (B) .6159   (C) .2962   (D) 0

53. (A) [.25 .75]   (B) [.25 .75]
(C) [.25 .75]   (D) [.25 .75]
(E) All the state matrices appear to approach the same matrix, $S = [.25 \quad .75]$, regardless of the values in the initial-state matrix.

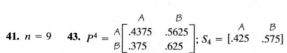

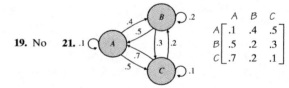

55. $Q = \begin{bmatrix} .25 & .75 \\ .25 & .75 \end{bmatrix}$; the rows of Q are the same as the matrix S from Problem 53

57. (A) R = rain, R' = no rain

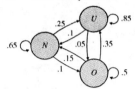

(B) $\begin{array}{cc} & R \quad R' \end{array}$
$\begin{array}{c} R \\ R' \end{array} \begin{bmatrix} .4 & .6 \\ .06 & .94 \end{bmatrix}$

(C) Saturday: .196; Sunday: .12664

59. (A)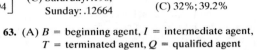

(B) $\begin{array}{cc} & X \quad X' \end{array}$
$\begin{array}{c} X \\ X' \end{array} \begin{bmatrix} .8 & .2 \\ .2 & .8 \end{bmatrix}$

(C) 32%; 39.2%

61. (A) N = National Property, U = United Family, O = other companies

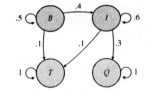

(B) $\begin{array}{ccc} & N & U & O \end{array}$
$\begin{array}{c} N \\ U \\ O \end{array} \begin{bmatrix} .65 & .25 & .1 \\ .1 & .85 & .05 \\ .15 & .35 & .5 \end{bmatrix}$

(C) 38.5%; 32% (D) 45%; 53.65%

63. (A) B = beginning agent, I = intermediate agent, T = terminated agent, Q = qualified agent

(B) $\begin{array}{ccccc} & B & I & T & Q \end{array}$
$\begin{array}{c} B \\ I \\ T \\ Q \end{array} \begin{bmatrix} .5 & .4 & .1 & 0 \\ 0 & .6 & .1 & .3 \\ 0 & 0 & 1 & 0 \\ 0 & 0 & 0 & 1 \end{bmatrix}$

(C) .12; .3612

65. (A) $\begin{array}{cccc} & HMO & PPO & FFS \end{array}$
$\begin{array}{c} HMO \\ PPO \\ FFS \end{array} \begin{bmatrix} .8 & .15 & .05 \\ .2 & .7 & .1 \\ .25 & .3 & .45 \end{bmatrix}$

(B) HMO: 34.75%; PPO: 37%; FFS: 28.25%

(C) HMO: 42.2625%; PPO: 39.5875%; FFS: 18.15%

67. (A) $\begin{array}{cc} & H \quad R \end{array}$
$\begin{array}{c} H \\ R \end{array} \begin{bmatrix} .924 & .076 \\ .108 & .892 \end{bmatrix}$ (B) 40.5% (C) 43.8%

Exercise 9-2

1. Yes **3.** No **5.** No **7.** Yes **9.** No **11.** Yes **13.** No

15. $S = [.4 \quad .6]; \overline{P} = \begin{bmatrix} .4 & .6 \\ .4 & .6 \end{bmatrix}$ **17.** $S = [.375 \quad .625]; \overline{P} = \begin{bmatrix} .375 & .625 \\ .375 & .625 \end{bmatrix}$ **19.** $S = [.3 \quad .5 \quad .2]; \overline{P} = \begin{bmatrix} .3 & .5 & .2 \\ .3 & .5 & .2 \\ .3 & .5 & .2 \end{bmatrix}$

21. $S = [.6 \quad .24 \quad .16]; \overline{P} = \begin{bmatrix} .6 & .24 & .16 \\ .6 & .24 & .16 \\ .6 & .24 & .16 \end{bmatrix}$ **23.** (A) True (B) False **25.** $S = [.3553 \quad .6447]$ **27.** $S = [.3636 \quad .4091 \quad .2273]$

29. (A) [diagram: Red, Blue] (B) $\begin{array}{cc} & Red \quad Blue \end{array}$
$\begin{array}{c} Red \\ Blue \end{array} \begin{bmatrix} .4 & .6 \\ .2 & .8 \end{bmatrix}$ (C) [.25 \quad .75]; in the long run, the red urn will be selected 25% of the time and the blue urn 75% of the time.

31. (A) The state matrices alternate between [.2 \quad .8] and [.8 \quad .2]; hence, they do not approach any one matrix.
(B) The state matrices are all equal to S_0; hence, S_0 is a stationary matrix.
(C) The powers of P alternate between P and I, the 2×2 identity; hence, they do not approach a limiting matrix.
(D) Parts (B) and (C) of Theorem 1 are not valid for this matrix. Since P is not regular, this is not a contradiction.

33. (A) Since P is not regular, it may have more than one stationary matrix. (B) [.5 \quad 0 \quad .5] is another stationary matrix.
(C) P has an infinite number of stationary matrices.

35. $\overline{P} = \begin{bmatrix} 1 & 0 & 0 \\ .25 & 0 & .75 \\ 0 & 0 & 1 \end{bmatrix}$; each row of $\overline{P}$ is a stationary matrix for P.

39. 72.5%

41. (A) $S_1 = [.512 \quad .488]$; $S_2 = [.568 \quad .432]$; $S_3 = [.609 \quad .391]$

(B)
Year	Data (%)	Model (%)
1970	43.3	43.3
1980	51.5	51.2
1990	57.5	56.8
2000	59.8	60.9

(C) 71.4%

53. (A) $S_1 = [.334 \quad .666]$; $S_2 = [.343 \quad .657]$; $S_3 = [.347 \quad .653]$

(B)
Year	Data (%)	Model (%)
1970	30.9	30.9
1980	33.3	33.4
1990	34.4	34.3
2000	35.6	34.7

(C) 35%

37. (A) .39; .3; .284; .277

(B) Each entry of the second column of P^{k+1} is the product of a row of P and the second column of P^k. Each entry of the latter is $\leq M_k$, so the product is $\leq M_k$.

43. GTT: 25%; NCJ: 25%; Dash: 50%

45. Poor: 20%; satisfactory: 40%; preferred: 40%   **47.** 51%

49. Stationary matrix = $[.25 \quad .50 \quad .25]$

51. (A) $[.25 \; .75]$ (B) 42.5%; 51.25%

(C) 60% rapid transit; 40% automobile

Exercise 9-3

1. B, C **3.** No absorbing states   **5.** A, D **7.** B is an absorbing state; absorbing chain

9. C is an absorbing state; not an absorbing chain   **11.** No   **13.** Yes   **15.** Yes   **17.** No   **19.** Yes

21. $\begin{array}{c} \\ B \\ A \\ C \end{array}\begin{array}{ccc} B & A & C \\ \begin{bmatrix} 1 & 0 & 0 \\ .5 & .2 & .3 \\ .1 & .5 & .4 \end{bmatrix} \end{array}$

23. $\begin{array}{c} \\ B \\ D \\ A \\ C \end{array}\begin{array}{cccc} B & D & A & C \\ \begin{bmatrix} 1 & 0 & 0 & 0 \\ 0 & 1 & 0 & 0 \\ .4 & .1 & .3 & .2 \\ .4 & .3 & 0 & .3 \end{bmatrix} \end{array}$

25. $\begin{array}{c} \\ C \\ A \\ B \end{array}\begin{array}{ccc} C & A & B \\ \begin{bmatrix} 1 & 0 & 0 \\ .5 & .2 & .3 \\ 0 & 1 & 0 \end{bmatrix} \end{array}$

27. $\begin{array}{c} \\ B \\ D \\ A \\ C \end{array}\begin{array}{cccc} B & D & A & C \\ \begin{bmatrix} 1 & 0 & 0 & 0 \\ 0 & 1 & 0 & 0 \\ .2 & .4 & .1 & .3 \\ .2 & .1 & .5 & .2 \end{bmatrix} \end{array}$

29. $\overline{P} = \begin{array}{c} A \\ B \\ C \end{array}\begin{array}{ccc} A & B & C \\ \begin{bmatrix} 1 & 0 & 0 \\ 0 & 1 & 0 \\ .2 & .8 & 0 \end{bmatrix} \end{array}$; $P(C \text{ to } A) = .2$; $P(C \text{ to } B) = .8$. It will take an average of 2 trials to go from C to either A or B.

31. $\overline{P} = \begin{array}{c} A \\ B \\ C \end{array}\begin{array}{ccc} A & B & C \\ \begin{bmatrix} 1 & 0 & 0 \\ 1 & 0 & 0 \\ 1 & 0 & 0 \end{bmatrix} \end{array}$; $P(B \text{ to } A) = 1$; $P(C \text{ to } A) = 1$.   It will take an average of 4 trials to go from B to A and an average of 3 trials to go from C to A.

33. $\overline{P} = \begin{array}{c} A \\ B \\ C \\ D \end{array}\begin{array}{cccc} A & B & C & D \\ \begin{bmatrix} 1 & 0 & 0 & 0 \\ 0 & 1 & 0 & 0 \\ .36 & .64 & 0 & 0 \\ .44 & .56 & 0 & 0 \end{bmatrix} \end{array}$; $P(C \text{ to } A) = .36$; $P(C \text{ to } B) = .64$; $P(D \text{ to } A) = .44$; $P(D \text{ to } B) = .56$. It will take an average of 3.2 trials to go from C to either A or B and an average of 2.8 trials to go from D to either A or B.

35. (A) $[.2 \quad .8 \quad 0]$ (B) $[.26 \quad .74 \quad 0]$ **37.** (A) $[1 \quad 0 \quad 0]$ (B) $[1 \quad 0 \quad 0]$

39. (A) $[.44 \quad .56 \quad 0 \quad 0]$ (B) $[.36 \quad .64 \quad 0 \quad 0]$ (C) $[.408 \quad .592 \quad 0 \quad 0]$ (D) $[.384 \quad .616 \quad 0 \quad 0]$ **41.** (A) True (B) False

43. $\begin{array}{c} A \\ B \\ C \\ D \end{array}\begin{array}{cccc} A & B & C & D \\ \begin{bmatrix} 1 & 0 & 0 & 0 \\ 0 & 1 & 0 & 0 \\ .6375 & .3625 & 0 & 0 \\ .7375 & .2625 & 0 & 0 \end{bmatrix} \end{array}$

45. $\begin{array}{c} A \\ B \\ C \\ D \\ E \end{array}\begin{array}{ccccc} A & B & C & D & E \\ \begin{bmatrix} 1 & 0 & 0 & 0 & 0 \\ 0 & 1 & 0 & 0 & 0 \\ .0875 & .9125 & 0 & 0 & 0 \\ .1875 & .8125 & 0 & 0 & 0 \\ .4375 & .5625 & 0 & 0 & 0 \end{bmatrix} \end{array}$

47. $\begin{array}{c} A \\ B \\ C \\ D \end{array}\begin{array}{cccc} A & B & C & D \\ \begin{bmatrix} 0 & .52 & 0 & .48 \\ 0 & 1 & 0 & 0 \\ 0 & .36 & 0 & .64 \\ 0 & 0 & 0 & 1 \end{bmatrix} \end{array}$

53. (A) .370; .297; .227; .132; .045   (B) For large k, all entries of Q^k are close to 0.

55. (A) 75%   (B) 12.5%   (C) 7.5 months   **57.** (A) Company A: 30%, company B: 15%, company C: 55%   (B) 5 yr

59. (A) 91.52%   (B) 4.96%   (C) 6.32 days   **61.** (A) .375   (B) 1.75 exits

Chapter 9 Review Exercise

1. $S_1 = \begin{matrix} A & B \\ [.32 & .68] \end{matrix}$; $S_2 = \begin{matrix} A & B \\ [.325 & .672] \end{matrix}$. The probability of being in state A after one trial is .32 and after two trials is .328; the probability of being in state B after one trial is .68 and after two trials is .672. *(9-1)*

2. State A is absorbing; chain is absorbing. *(9-2, 9-3)*   3. No absorbing states; chain is regular. *(9-2, 9-3)*

4. No absorbing states; chain is neither. *(9-2, 9-3)*   5. States B and C are absorbing; chain is absorbing. *(9-2, 9-3)*

6. States A and B are absorbing; chain is neither. *(9-2, 9-3)*

7. $\begin{matrix} & A & B & C \\ A & \begin{bmatrix} 0 & 1 & 0 \\ B & .1 & 0 & .9 \\ C & 0 & 1 & 0 \end{bmatrix} \end{matrix}$; no absorbing states; chain is neither. *(9-1, 9-2, 9-3)*

8. $\begin{matrix} & A & B & C \\ A & \begin{bmatrix} 0 & 1 & 0 \\ B & .1 & .2 & .7 \\ C & 0 & 0 & 1 \end{bmatrix} \end{matrix}$; C is absorbing; chain is absorbing. *(9-1, 9-2, 9-3)*

9. $\begin{matrix} & A & B & C \\ A & \begin{bmatrix} 0 & 0 & 1 \\ B & .1 & .2 & .7 \\ C & 0 & 1 & 0 \end{bmatrix} \end{matrix}$; no absorbing states; chain is regular. *(9-1, 9-2, 9-3)*

10. $\begin{matrix} & A & B & C & D \\ A & \begin{bmatrix} .3 & .2 & 0 & .5 \\ B & 0 & 1 & 0 & 0 \\ C & 0 & 0 & .2 & .8 \\ D & 0 & 0 & .3 & .7 \end{bmatrix} \end{matrix}$; B is absorbing; chain is neither. *(9-1, 9-2, 9-3)*

11.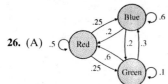
$\begin{matrix} & A & B & C \\ A & \begin{bmatrix} .3 & .2 & .5 \\ B & .8 & 0 & .2 \\ C & .1 & .3 & .6 \end{bmatrix} \end{matrix}$ *(9-1)*

12. (A) .3 (B) .675 *(9-1)*

13. $S = \begin{matrix} A & B \\ [.25 & .75] \end{matrix}$; $\overline{P} = \begin{matrix} & A & B \\ A & \begin{bmatrix} .25 & .75 \\ B & .25 & .75 \end{bmatrix} \end{matrix}$ *(9-2)*

14. $S = \begin{matrix} A & B & C \\ [.4 & .48 & .12] \end{matrix}$; $\overline{P} = \begin{matrix} & A & B & C \\ A & \begin{bmatrix} .4 & .48 & .12 \\ B & .4 & .48 & .12 \\ C & .4 & .48 & .12 \end{bmatrix} \end{matrix}$ *(9-2)*

15. $\begin{matrix} & A & B & C \\ A & \begin{bmatrix} 1 & 0 & 0 \\ B & 0 & 1 & 0 \\ C & .75 & .25 & 0 \end{bmatrix} \end{matrix}$; $P(C \text{ to } A) = .75$; $P(C \text{ to } B) = .25$. It takes an average of 2.5 trials to go from C to an absorbing state. *(9-3)*

16. $\begin{matrix} & A & B & C & D \\ A & \begin{bmatrix} 1 & 0 & 0 & 0 \\ B & 0 & 1 & 0 & 0 \\ C & .2 & .8 & 0 & 0 \\ D & .3 & .7 & 0 & 0 \end{bmatrix} \end{matrix}$; $P(C \text{ to } A) = .2$; $P(C \text{ to } B) = .8$; $P(D \text{ to } A) = .3$; $P(D \text{ to } B) = .7$. It takes an average of 2 trials to go from C to an absorbing state and an average of 3 trials to go from D to an absorbing state. *(9-3)*

21. $\begin{matrix} & B & D & A & C \\ B & \begin{bmatrix} 1 & 0 & 0 & 0 \\ D & 0 & 1 & 0 & 0 \\ A & .1 & .1 & .6 & .2 \\ C & .2 & .2 & .3 & .3 \end{bmatrix} \end{matrix}$ *(9-3)*

22. (A) $\begin{matrix} A & B & C \\ [.1 & .4 & .5] \end{matrix}$ (B) $\begin{matrix} A & B & C \\ [.1 & .4 & .5] \end{matrix}$ *(9-3)*   23. (A) $\begin{matrix} A & B & C \\ [.25 & .75 & 0] \end{matrix}$ (B) $\begin{matrix} A & B & C \\ [.55 & .45 & 0] \end{matrix}$ *(9-3)*

24. No. Each row of P would contain a 0 and a 1, but none of the four matrices with this property is regular. *(10-2)*

25. Yes; for example, $P = \begin{bmatrix} 0 & 0 & 1 \\ 0 & 0 & 1 \\ .2 & .3 & .5 \end{bmatrix}$ is regular. *(9-2)*

26. (A)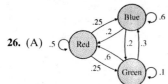
(B) $\begin{matrix} & R & B & G \\ R & \begin{bmatrix} .5 & .25 & .25 \\ B & .2 & .6 & .2 \\ G & .6 & .3 & .1 \end{bmatrix} \end{matrix}$
(C) Regular
(D) $\begin{matrix} & R & B & G \\ R & \begin{bmatrix} .4 & .4 & .2 \\ B & .4 & .4 & .2 \\ G & .4 & .4 & .2 \end{bmatrix} \end{matrix}$ In the long run, the red urn will be selected 40% of the time, the blue urn 40% of the time, and the green urn 20% of the time. *(9-2)*

27. (A)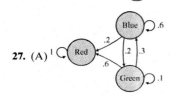
(B) $\begin{matrix} & R & B & G \\ R & \begin{bmatrix} 1 & 0 & 0 \\ B & .2 & .6 & .2 \\ G & .6 & .3 & .1 \end{bmatrix} \end{matrix}$
(C) Absorbing
(D) $\begin{matrix} & R & B & G \\ R & \begin{bmatrix} 1 & 0 & 0 \\ B & 1 & 0 & 0 \\ G & 1 & 0 & 0 \end{bmatrix} \end{matrix}$ Once the red urn is selected, the blue and green urns will never be selected again. It will take an average of 3.67 trials to reach the red urn from the blue urn and an average of 2.33 trials to reach the red urn from the green urn. *(9-3)*

29. No such chain exists. *(9-2, 9-3)*   **30.** No such chain exists. *(9-2, 9-3)*   **31.** No such chain exists. *(9-2)*

32. $S = [1 \quad 0 \quad 0]$ and $S' = [0 \quad 1 \quad 0]$ are both stationary matrices for $P = \begin{matrix} & \begin{matrix} A & B & C \end{matrix} \\ \begin{matrix} A \\ B \\ C \end{matrix} & \begin{bmatrix} 1 & 0 & 0 \\ 0 & 1 & 0 \\ .6 & .3 & .1 \end{bmatrix} \end{matrix}$ *(9-3)*   **33.** $P = \begin{matrix} & \begin{matrix} A & B \end{matrix} \\ \begin{matrix} A \\ B \end{matrix} & \begin{bmatrix} 0 & 1 \\ 1 & 0 \end{bmatrix} \end{matrix}$ *(9-2, 9-3)*

34. No such chain exists. *(9-2)*   **35.** No such chain exists. *(9-3)*   **36.** No limiting matrix *(9-2, 9-3)*

37. $P = \begin{matrix} & \begin{matrix} A & B & C & D \end{matrix} \\ \begin{matrix} A \\ B \\ C \\ D \end{matrix} & \begin{bmatrix} .392 & .163 & .134 & .311 \\ .392 & .163 & .134 & .311 \\ .392 & .163 & .134 & .311 \\ .392 & .163 & .134 & .311 \end{bmatrix} \end{matrix}$ *(9-2)*

38. (A)

(B) $\begin{matrix} & \begin{matrix} X & X' \end{matrix} \\ \begin{matrix} X \\ X' \end{matrix} & \begin{bmatrix} .7 & .3 \\ .5 & .5 \end{bmatrix} \end{matrix}$ (C) $\begin{matrix} \begin{matrix} X & X' \end{matrix} \\ [.2 \quad .8] \end{matrix}$

(D) $\begin{matrix} \begin{matrix} X & X' \end{matrix} \\ [.54 \quad .46] \end{matrix}$; 54% of the consumers will purchase brand X on the next purchase.

(E) $\begin{matrix} \begin{matrix} X & X' \end{matrix} \\ [.625 \quad .375] \end{matrix}$ (F) 62.5% *(9-2)*

39. (A) Brand A: 24%, brand B: 32%, brand C: 44%   (B) 4 yr *(9-3)*

40. (A) $S_1 = [.48 \quad .52]$; $S_2 = [.66 \quad .34]$

(B)

Year	Data (%)	Model (%)
1995	14	14
2000	49	48
2005	68	66

(C) 89% *(9-2)*

41. (A) 63.75%

(B) 15%

(C) 8.75 yr *(9-3)*

42. $\overline{P} = \begin{matrix} & \begin{matrix} Red & Pink & White \end{matrix} \\ \begin{matrix} Red \\ Pink \\ White \end{matrix} & \begin{bmatrix} 1 & 0 & 0 \\ 1 & 0 & 0 \\ 1 & 0 & 0 \end{bmatrix} \end{matrix}$ *(9-3)*

43. (A) $S_1 = [.244 \quad .756]$; $S_2 = [.203 \quad .797]$

(B)

Year	Data (%)	Model (%)
1985	30.1	30.1
1995	24.7	24.4
2005	20.9	20.3

(C) 10.3% *(9-2)*